JEPPESEN®
Sanderson Training Products

AIRCRAFT
GAS TURBINE
POWERPLANTS

Charles E. Otis
Peter A. Vosbury

MAINTEN
Master

Library of Congress Cataloging-in Publication Number 91-14478

3312648-005

Table of Contents

Preface vii
Introduction...xix

Chapter I   History of Turbine Development..1-1
    Hero's Aeolipile 1-1
    Chinese Rocket 1-1
    Branca's Turbine Device 1-1
    Newton's Horseless Carriage..1-2
    Moss Turbosupercharger 1-2
    Sir Frank Whittle, British Development..1-2
    German and Italian Developments 1-5
    Early American Gas Turbine Development..1-6
    Commercial Aircraft Development 1-6
    Commuter and Business Jets 1-8
    Other Developments 1-8

Chapter II   Jet Propulsion Theory...2-1
    Four Types of Jet Engines 2-1
    Powerplant Selection 2-2
    Turbine Engine Types 2-6
    Physics 2-10
    Potential and Kinetic Energy..2-14
    Bernoulli's Theorem 2-14
    The Brayton Cycle 2-18
    Newton's Laws and the Gas Turbine..2-19
    Thrust and SHP Calculations...2-21
    Gas Turbine Engine Performance Curves 2-29
    RPM Limits Imposed on Turbine Engines 2-36
    Why The Turbofan is Replacing the Turbojet..2-37

Chapter III   Turbine Engine Design and Construction 3-1
    Turbine Engine Entrance Ducts..3-1
    Accessory Section...3-8
    Compressor Section 3-10
    Compressor-Diffuser Section 3-29
    Combustion Section..3-30
    Turbine Section...3-35
    Exhaust Section 3-45
    Thrust Reversers 3-51
    Noise Suppression 3-56
    Engine Compartment Ventilation and Cooling...3-59
    Engine Mounts 3-60
    Bearings 3-62
    Construction Materials..3-62
    Engine Stations 3-64
    Directional References..3-67

Chapter IV   Engine Familiarization 4-1
    Familiarization With the Pratt and Whitney, USA, JT8D Turbofan Engine.......4-1
    Familiarization With the Allison-250 Turboshaft Engine 4-17
    Familiarization With The Pratt & Whitney, Canada, PT6 Turboprop Engine 4-34

Familiarization With The GE/Snecma CFM56 Turbofan Engine 4-46
Engine Data Sheets 4-60

Chapter V   Inspection and Maintenance 5-1

Line Maintenance 5-1
Shop Maintenance (Heavy) 5-8
Cold Section and Hot Section Inspection and Repairs 5-8
Main Bearings and Seals 5-33
Modular Maintenance 5-41
Torque Wrench Use 5-41
Locking Methods 5-44
Test Cell Maintenance 5-45
Time Between Overhaul (TBO) and Component Expected Service Life.............................5-50
Troubleshooting Ground and Flight Data..5-53
Inspection and Troubleshooting Terms...5-56
Technical Data Identification System (ATA)...5-59

Chapter VI   Lubrication Systems 6-1

Principles of Engine Lubrication 6-1
Requirements of Turbine Engine Lubricants...6-1
Oil Sampling 6-2
Synthetic Lubricants 6-4
Servicing 6-5
Dry Sump Systems 6-8
Small Engine Full Flow Lubrication System –General Electric CJ610 Turbojet.................6-22
Small Engine Pressure Relief Valve Lubrication System – Pratt & Whitney PT6 Turboprop.........6-29
Large Engine Pressure Relief Valve Lubrication System – Pratt and Whitney JT8D Turbofan 6-30
Large Engine Full Flow Lubrication System – CFM56-7B Turbofan 6-33
Hot Tank Vs. Cold Tank Systems...6-36
Troubleshooting Procedure...6-37

Chapter VII   Fuel Systems...7-1

Principles of Fuel Systems 7-1
Fuel Controls 7-5
Water Injection Thrust Augmentation 7-39
FAA Engine Power Ratings 7-43
Fuel System Components and Accessories 7-43
Example of Corporate Engine Fuel System (Pratt & Whitney JT-12)..................................7-56
Example of Commercial Engine Fuel System (Pratt & Whitney JT8D) 7-58
Example of Commercial Engine Fuel System (G.E./Snecma CFM56).................................7-62

Chapter VIII   Compressor Anti-Stall Systems..8-1

Variable Angle Compressor Vane System (Large Engine)..8-1
Variable Angle Inlet Guide Vane System (Small Engine)...8-4
Troubleshooting the Variable Vane System 8-5
Compressor Anti-Stall Bleed Systems..8-5
Troubleshooting Compressor Bleed Systems..8-12

Chapter IX   Anti-Icing Systems 9-1

System Operation..9-2
Regulator Valve 9-3
Cockpit Controls and Anti-Ice Valve Operation 9-3

Chapter X   Starter Systems 10-1

Electric Starters...10-3
Starter-Generator 10-4
Pneumatic (Air Turbine) Starter 10-4
Other Starting Systems..10-12

Chapter XI   Ignition Systems 11-1
    Main Ignition System 11-1
    Special Handling..11-3
    Joule Ratings...11-3
    Types of Ignition Systems 11-3
    Igniter Plug Types..11-8
    Complete Engine Ignition System – GE/Snecma CFM56.................................11-14
    Troubleshooting Ignition System..11-17

Chapter XII   Engine Instrument Systems 12-1
    Exhaust Temperature Indicating Systems..12-2
    Tachometer Percent RPM Indicating System..12-13
    Engine Pressure Ratio System...12-15
    Torque Indicating System..12-20
    Fuel Flow Indicating System...12-25
    Oil System Indicators 12-27
    Marking of Powerplant Instruments..12-32

Chapter XIII   Fire/Overheat Detection and Extinguishing
                    Systems for Turbine Engines...13-1
    Single-Wire Thermal Switch 13-1
    Two-Wire Thermal Switch 13-1
    Continuous Loop System..13-2
    Pneumatic System...13-3
    Other Fire Detection Systems...13-6
    Fire Extinguishing 13-6
    Typical Twin Engine Commercial Airplane System 13-8

Chapter XIV   Engine Operation...14-1
    Safety Precautions 14-1
    Engine Run-Up of Turbojet and Turbofan Engines 14-1
    Engine Runup of Turboprop Engines (Fixed Turbine Engine)............................14-2
    PT6 Engine Operation (Free Turbine)...14-3
    FAA Engine Power Ratings 14-6
    Typical Operating Cautions for All Turbine Powered Aircraft, Ground and Flight 14-6

Appendix 1   Type Certificate Data Sheet No. E1GL..A1-1

Appendix 2   Type Certificate Data Sheet No.E23EA A2-1

Appendix 3   Decimal Equivalents, Drill Sizes/Decimal Equivalents,
                    Temperature Conversions, Conversion Factors..A3-1

Appendix 4   Gas Turbine Powered Aircraft Familiarization A4-1

Appendix 5   Common Hand Signals..A5-1

Appendix 6   Local Speed of Sound (Cs) Chart...A6-1

Appendix 7   U.S. Standard Atmosphere, 1962 (Geopotential Altitude)........................A7-1

Appendix 8   Other Useful Formulas and Standard Information......................................A8-1

Appendix 9   Pressure Correction Factors, Temperature Correction Factors A9-1

Appendix 10   Ground Vs. Flight Performance Data...A10-1

Glossary G-1

Answers to Study Questions...Q-1

Index I-1

PREFACE

This textbook covers the historical development, theory and a wide range of technical aspects concerning the Aircraft Gas Turbine Engine. It is one of several classroom and self-study texts prepared by this publisher for people in aviation interested in this subject. Jeppesen Sanderson Inc. is one of the largest suppliers of technical training materials in the world. Its training manuals are part of a continuing effort to improve the quality of education for aviation maintenance and flight personnel as well as other interested individuals throughout the world.

The purpose of each training series is to provide basic information on the operation and principles of the various aircraft systems and their components.

Specific information on exact application procedures of a product should be obtained from the manufacturer through his appropriate maintenance manuals and followed in detail for best results.

This particular manual on Aircraft Gas Turbine Powerplants includes a series of carefully prepared questions and answers to emphasize key elements of the study, and to encourage you to continually test yourself for accuracy and retention as you use this book.

Author Profiles:
    Charles E. Otis is a Professor Emeritus at Embry-Riddle Aeronautical University, Daytona Beach, Florida.

    Peter A. Vosbury is a Professor at Embry-Riddle Aeronautical University, Daytona Beach, Florida.

We want to extend special thanks to:
    Bendix Corp.
    Boeing Corp.

Fenwall Corp.
General Electric Aircraft Engine Co.
Honeywell Aerospace (Garrett) Corp.
Honeywell Aerospace (Lycoming) Corp.
Kidde Corp.
Pratt & Whitney Corp., Canada
Pratt & Whitney Corp., USA
Rolls-Royce Corp., USA
Rolls-Royce Ltd, G.B.
Sunstrand Corp.
Unison Corp.
U.S Airforce Training
U.S. Navy Training

For product, service, or sales information, call 1-800-621-JEPP, 303-799-9090, or FAX 303-328-4153. If you have comments, questions, or need explanations about any Maintenance Training System, we are prepared to offer assistance at any time. If your dealer does not have a Jeppesen catalog, please request one and we will promptly send it to you. Just call the above telephone number, or write:

Marketing Manager, Training Products
Jeppesen Sanderson, Inc
55 Inverness Drive East
Englewood, CO 80112-5498

Please direct inquiries from Europe, Africa, and Middle East to:

Jeppesen & Co., GmbH
P.O. Box 70-05-51
Walter-Kolb-Strasse 13`
60594 Frankfurt
GERMANY
Tel: 011-49-69-961240
Fax: 011-49-69-96124898

Introduction

History relates that the first indication of the jet propulsion principle occurred when a steam-driven toy was demonstrated in Egypt during the pre-Christian era. After that, the idea evolved very slowly for nearly twenty centuries. It wasn't until the 1920's that Sir Frank Whittle, an English inventor, first described in a school notebook, the possibility of a gas turbine device as a means of jet propulsion for aircraft. From this idea, the use of jet aircraft has grown into a multi-billion dollar industry. It is interesting to note that Sir Frank Whittle, the "Father of the modern gas turbine engine", while in his 70's, still continued to contribute to the state-of-the-art of gas turbine engine design. He died at the age of 89 in 1996.

As the increasing complexity of gas turbine engine design for increased power and new applications is achieved by research and development, the technical tasks required to maintain the integrity and safety of gas turbine engines become more and more demanding. It is no longer possible for the technician to perform as an expert based on native intelligence alone. When working on such systems, expert technical training is required. This textbook is designed to help provide a starting point for this training process. It is for both the completely uninitiated person just starting out, as well as technicians and flight personnel trying to gain in-service upgrading within the industry.

Whether one proceeds through this book in a formal classroom setting, or as an interested reader studying independently, this material will serve to provide a sound foundation of the principles of gas turbine engine theory, design, maintenance and troubleshooting.

Every technical educational endeavor is designed to provide the learner with an entry-level skill. The proven way to achieve this skill is to read the material carefully, answer the review questions, go back and research the text, and lastly reinforce this knowledge by gaining actual work experience.

Chapter I
History Of Turbine Engine Development

The terms jet engine and gas turbine engine, although sometimes used synonymously to describe aircraft engines, represent quite different engine designs. Therefore, these terms are defined very carefully in this book.

The jet engine family includes the rocket jet, ramjet, pulse-jet, and gas turbine powered jet. The gas turbine powered jet is further broken down into the turbojet, turbo-propeller, turboshaft, and turbofan types. These four types of engines are the ones most commonly found in today's aircraft.

All of these engines have evolved through history in their own way and for their own purposes. We will first explore this historical development and then, in later chapters, concentrate on the types of gas turbine power-plants utilized for aircraft propulsion.

A. Hero's Aeolipile

Today's modern turbine engine is based on the reaction principle, which was discovered centuries ago.

One of the earliest accounts of the use of the reaction principle describes an Egyptian mathematician and philosopher named Heron, sometimes referred to as Hero, who invented a device which converted steam pressure to mechanical power. Current historians date this between one to two hundred years BC. The designer of the sketch of Hero's invention, the Aeolipile, is not known and the actual device might have looked quite differently.

It is known that by heating water in a closed vessel and by supplying steam to opposing nozzles mounted on a rotating sphere, Hero was able to successfully demonstrate the reaction principle. Whether he was able to put his aeolipile to practical use is not historically clear.

B. Chinese Rocket

Another early application of the reaction principle can be seen in rocket development as early as 1200 AD. By utilizing black powder, a mixture of charcoal, sulfur, and saltpeter, the Chinese were able to perfect a solid-fuel rocket.

In records available today, one can see a reference to a battle about 1230 A.D. in which the Chinese chronicled the use of the rocket as a military weapon.

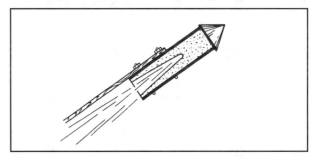
Fig. 1-2 — Chinese rocket.

C. Branca's Turbine Device

The first gas turbine device came into use in 1629 when the Italian engineer, Giovanni Branca, produced a steam-driven impulse turbine. Branca's design was a closed, water-filled vessel with one exhaust nozzle aimed at a turbine or impulse wheel. The vessel was heated by solid fuel, and the resulting steam was directed onto the impulse wheel. The wheel was thus rotated and used to drive a crude cogwheel reduction-gear system. This mechanism, now on display in the British Museum, is said to be the forerunner of the modern turbosupercharger used on reciprocating engines.

Fig. 1-1 — Hero's Aeolipile.

Fig. 1-3 — Branca's turbine.

D. Newton's Horseless Carriage

In 1687, Sir Isaac Newton, a British astronomer and physicist, recognized the principle of jet propulsion and published his third law of motion, every acting force has a reacting force equal in magnitude and opposite in direction. Later a British scientist, named Gravensade, designed and produced a model of a steam-powered vehicle based on Newton's third law. It is not historically clear whether he had an actual sketch made by Newton, but he nonetheless receives credit for constructing a jet powered vehicle based on Newton's principle. By mounting a watertight sphere on a four-wheeled carriage and heating the water to steam, he proposed to eject the hot exhaust rearward, propelling the vehicle forward. Although it is apparent that a thrust propelling force would be created in this manner, it is obvious that the vehicle would be grossly overweight and underpowered. There is no record of successful operation of this vehicle.

Fig. 1-4 — Newton's horseless carriage.

E. Moss Turbosupercharger

In 1900, Dr. Sanford A. Moss, while studying for an advanced engineering degree, published a thesis on the gas turbine engine. He used this early work in his future development of the first gas turbine device for aircraft application. In 1918, as a General Electric Company engineer, he supervised the production of the gas turbine driven turbosupercharger for reciprocating engines. This developmental work brought about many new low weight, high temperature, high strength materials needed for industrial gas turbine experimentation, which was concurrently on-going in Europe and the United States.

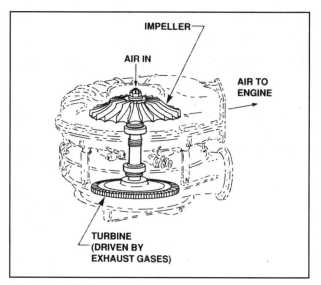

Fig. 1-5 — Turbosupercharger.

F. Sir Frank Whittle, British Development

Frank Whittle, while a cadet in the British Royal Air College, wrote a thesis advocating use of the gas turbine engine for aircraft propulsion. He was aware of developing industrial uses of ground installation type turbine engines and felt that, if an engine could be made light enough in weight, the ram effect of the incoming air in flight would provide sufficient power to make it an effective aircraft powerplant. In 1930, he patented the first turbojet aircraft engine, based on the ideas of his original thesis. His engine was to use a compressor impeller similar to that of Dr. Moss, driven by a turbine wheel.

During the early thirties, Whittle served as a regular officer in the Royal Air Force where he was a design engineer and test pilot of reciprocating engine powered aircraft. The reciprocating engine was in an accelerating developmental stage at that time, and Whittle was dissatisfied with what he referred to as their obvious limitations of altitude and top speed.

Between 1930 and 1935, Whittle exhausted every avenue of help but was unsuccessful in obtaining sufficient government or private support for constructing his turbojet engine.

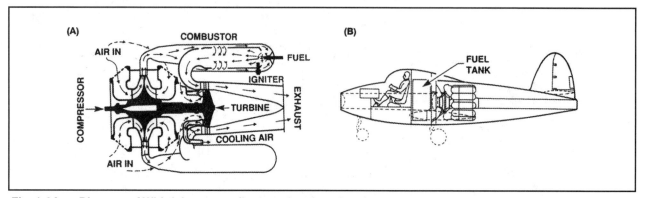

Fig. 1-6A — Diagram of Whittle's reverse-flow combustion chamber.
Fig. 1-6B — The first British jet aircraft to fly, the Gloster E28/39 experimental airplane.

Fig. 1-7 — W-IX, first experimental turbojet demonstrator engine run, April 12, 1937.

The idea prevailed that as a financial proposition his engine was as impractical for business as it was for flight. In discouragement, he put his idea aside, failing even to renew his patent. However, military buildup and political unrest in Europe in 1936 prompted some of Whittle's friends to approach him about forming a private company to start development of a prototype engine. This proposal led to the formation of Power Jets, Ltd., financed entirely by private funds.

The engine developed by Power Jets was a pure reaction turbojet. That is, its total thrust came from reaction to the hot gas stream emitted from a propelling nozzle. The engine featured an impeller-type compressor, a multiple-can combustion chamber, and a single stage turbine wheel. Today, the gas turbine engine receives its name from this design, wherein flowing gas drives the turbine wheel which is attached to, and drives, the compressor impeller.

On April 12, 1937, Whittle's prototype engine was the first flight gas turbine engine to successfully test run on a test stand. This engine eventually produced about 3,000 shaft horsepower on the test stand. (The Germans, who were concurrently developing a similar engine, had not reached Whittle's stage of development at that time.) In 1939, Power Jets, Ltd. was given an Air Ministry contract to produce a flight engine.

Whittle relates in his book, Jet - The Story of a Pioneer, published in 1953, that one of the biggest obstacles he had to overcome was obtaining the necessary high temperature strength metals for the combustion and turbine sections. The first combustor with flight integrity took Whittle three years of repeated testing to produce. It had ten separate combustion chambers.

In May, 1941, the Whittle W-1 was installed in the Gloster Aircraft Company's newly prepared Model

E28/39 aircraft. The aircraft, one of only three which were built, made its initial test flight at its design speed of 400 mph without complication. Its gas turbine power-plant is said to have produced approximately 1,000 pounds of thrust.

Fig. 1-8 — Whittle W-1 Turbojet engine.

Development was immediately started on the W-2, an engine of similar design but with more thrust, which in 1943 would power a twin engine aircraft called the Meteor. The Meteor later successfully engaged the

Fig. 1-9 — Gloster Meteor.

German V1 pulsejet powered buzz bomb in the only jet-versus-jet confrontation of World War II.

Fig. 1-10 — The Whittle W2/700 turbojet engine.

Fig. 1-11 — Frank Whittle (Born 1907, Died 1996) and the Whittle W-2/200 turbojet engine.

Whittle, while working on his production engine, also did experimental work on several other engine types. In 1936, he patented the first turbofan engine, wrote proposals for use of the gas turbine to drive a propeller, and developed a prototype supersonic flight engine with an axial compressor. He did not, however, have the funding or governmental support to proceed with these projects. They were all later developed as practical prime mover engines after Whittle had left the scene of active gas turbine engine development.

In 1945, Frank Whittle wrote the statements that would later show his profound understanding of the potential of the gas turbine engine. His statements are as follows:

1. The aircraft gas turbine has undoubtedly come to stay. In the space of a few years I expect to see it displace the reciprocating engine in all aircraft except possibly the light types. I make the reservation about light aircraft because at present it seems more difficult to design for lower powers than for much higher powers than we use at present, but it is possible that the gas turbine will invade the light aircraft field also.

2. For very high speeds and moderate range the turbojet is the appropriate application but for lower speeds and long range the gas turbine driving a propeller will be used. Personally I think there is a strong case for the use of a gas turbine driving a ducted fan for moderate speeds. Although no strong claims can be made for it on the basis of fuel consumption, it has important advantages in respect to noise reduction and absence of vibration when compared with a turbine-airscrew combination (turbo-prop). Further, for civil aircraft the elimination of visible 'whirling lumps' is not an inconsiderable psychological factor in its favour.

The speed possibilities inherent in gas turbines have been clearly shown by the establishment of the World's Air Speed Record at over 600 mph. Much higher speeds will undoubtedly be achieved in the fairly near future. There is no speed limit imposed by the powerplant. In fact, the higher the speed the greater the efficiency and power. The attainment of higher speeds therefore depends more upon the aircraft designer than on the turbine designer, though powerplant developments will naturally play their part. I do not think that we shall have to wait very long before aerodynamic developments make possible the attainment of supersonic speeds.

3. If long range is to be combined with high speed, flight at great heights will be necessary, and hence the development of the pressure cabin is of great importance. In the not very distant future I expect to see passenger aircraft covering long distances at speeds of approximately 500 mph at altitudes of the order of 40,000 ft., as a result of the parallel development of the gas turbine, the aircraft, the pressure cabin, and radio and radar aids to navigation.

The advent of the aircraft gas turbine makes necessary some important changes of outlook on the part of the designers. Hitherto it has been the practice to develop engines and aircraft virtually independently of each other, but this procedure will not do if we are to get the best out of gas turbine powered aircraft. The performance of the turbine is very dependent upon its installation in the aeroplane and the installation has a very large influence on aircraft drag characteristics. It follows that powerplant and airframe must each be 'tailor-made' to suit the other. The short development time required for gas turbines should make this procedure easy to follow, more especially as the nature of the engine is such that any successful basic design can be scaled up or down without introducing a host of fresh development troubles. This indeed is a very valuable characteristic.

We are as yet only at the beginning of this field of engineering and immense possibilities lie before us. The variations possible with a reciprocating engine are limited by the fact that the processes of compression, combustion and expansion take place in the same organ, the cylinder. In the gas turbine these processes take place in separate components. We can perform the compression process with axial flow compressors, centrifugal compressors, or combinations of these. The combustion chamber can take one of several forms, and there are a large number of variations possible in the turbine. There are many ways in which the major component units can be arranged in combination, and in addition there are the possibilities involved in the use of ducted fans, heat exchangers, after- burning, and other developments.

4. Up to the present two clear lines of development have been apparent in aircraft gas turbines, characterized by the use of either centrifugal compressor or the axial flow compressor. I am frequently asked whether one or the other will be ultimately dominant. My view is that there is a field for both, and that there will be many types in which both will be used in combination.

Much has been said about the high fuel consumption of turbojet units. It is true that they use a lot of fuel, but that is because they develop a lot of power. In fact, at speeds of the order of 600 mph, the fuel consumption in proportion to effective thrust horsepower is less than it would be for the piston engine and propeller combination at that speed. It is true, however, that at much lower speeds the turbo-jet unit compares very unfavourably with the conventional powerplant in respect of fuel consumption, but the gas turbine/propeller combination does not suffer from this disadvantage to anything like the same extent. In whatever form the gas turbine is used, the very low powerplant weight is an important compensating factor. Very low fuel consumption can be shown for complex engines, i.e., combinations of reciprocating engines and turbines. Though I have been amongst those who have proposed such schemes, I am doubtful whether the low fuel consumption is a sufficient compensation for the increased weight, complexity, long development time, and difficulty of installation, etc., except possibly for certain very specialized purposes.

Whittle did not enjoy the personal success and recognition in the gas turbine industry as did his engine. During the war years, 1939-1945, the government absorbed more and more control over his patents, allocating them to large manufacturers and diminishing Whittle's role. Before retiring as an Air Commodore in 1948, he was no longer working in the gas turbine engine field.

Soon after his retirement, some members of the government came to realize his contribution to the war effort and the future of aviation. He was knighted, becoming Sir Frank Whittle, and received a grant of 100,000 pounds sterling.

Sir Frank remained active through the years, as an author and as a private consultant to industry. He died at the age of 89 in 1996.

G. German And Italian Developments

While Whittle was struggling for governmental support, a German engineer named Hans Von Ohain, in 1936, had successfully demonstrated a model of the gas turbine engine to his government and was given practically unlimited funding for research and development. Working with the Heinkel Company, Von Ohain patented

and designed the powerplant for the single engine He-178 aircraft, which made the first purely jet propelled flight in history in August of 1939. Only one aircraft was built and it flew a total of three times.

Fig. 1-12 — The German Heinkle He-178, flown on August 27, 1939, was the first turbojet aircraft flight.

Fig. 1-13 — Hans von Ohain (Born 1911, Died 1998) stands by his original flight engine, the HeS 3b, which powered the worlds first turbojet powered plane.

The Heinkel He-178 was powered by a centrifugal flow turbojet engine, the HeS-3B, producing approximately 1,100 pounds of thrust. Von Ohain's engine was produced by completely independent development. History reveals that he used none of Whittle's early work in producing this first centrifugal compressor type engine. Von Ohain later went on to design the axial flow type engine, which has become the standard today for all large gas turbine engines.

After World War II, Mr. Von Ohain came to the United States to work as a scientist for the U.S. Air Force. He had a distinguished career, after which he retired from government service to become a university professor.

In 1942, the Germans flew the two-engine Me-262 aircraft with axial flow turbojet engines made by the Junker Company. The BMW Company later produced a similar engine for this aircraft. Both had a takeoff thrust of approximately 2,000 pounds and were capable of propelling this aircraft at speeds up to 500 mph.

Fig. 1-14 — The first operational jet fighter was the Messerschmidtt Me 262 Schwalbe (Swallow). It first flew on July 18, 1942. It was first introduced as a bomber intercepter.

Fig. 1-15 — The Me 262 was powered by two Junkers Jumo 004 turbojet engines.

The hot section (combustor and turbine) of these engines was not as highly developed as its British counterpart and had to be disassembled for inspection and replacement of parts every 10 to 15 flight hours.

The Italian Caproni Company and the designer, Secundo Campini, were heavily into producing a jet powered aircraft during the German and British developmental period. They were, however, designing along the lines of earlier experimenters who advocated driving the compressor with a liquid cooled reciprocating engine rather than by driving the compressor from a turbine wheel in the hot gas path, as described in Whittle's first patent. Their aircraft flew in late 1939 with a maximum speed of 205 mph. The limitations placed on the engine by the piston powerplant driving the compressor were the same as those Whittle described in his 1929 thesis and, consequently, this design died with the Caproni-Campini jet aircraft of that era.

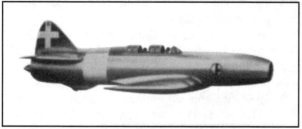

Fig. 1-16 — The Caproni-Campini "jet propelled" monoplane. It was powered by an Isotta Franschini radial piston engine, powering a ducted fan-type ramjet.

H. Early American Gas Turbine Development

While in England in 1941, General H.H. Hap Arnold was impressed by the progress being made with gas turbine powered aircraft as a tactical weapon. He procured a Whittle engine and was instrumental in securing an Air Force contract with the General Electric Company for research and development of this new concept in aviation. Between October 1, 1941, and April 2, 1942, General Electric had a redesigned engine running on a test cell.

Fig. 1-17 — The Bell "Airacomet" was a twin turbojet fighter, powered by two Whittle-type G.E. gas turbines.

General Electric was chosen because it had developed many of the necessary high temperature metals for its turbosupercharger production and also because some of its affiliate companies had been supporting Whittle's work in Britain. GE went on to develop the first American prototype turbojet, the GE- I-A.

The Bell Aircraft Company of Buffalo, New York, was chosen to construct the first jet airplane. The urgency to support the nation's war effort precipitated Bell's very rapid progress in designing an aircraft for General Electric's engine. In October, 1942, at Muroc Field, California, the Bell XP-59 was test flown, powered by two General Electric GE-I-A engines producing 1,250 pounds of thrust each. The Airacomet was never used in combat due to its limited flight time of 30 minutes. It did, however, become a valuable trainer for the later P-80 aircraft. A total of thirty XP-59A aircraft were built.

Although America did not use the jet airplane in World War II, it did go on to use the basic work of Whittle and General Electric for future military, commercial, and industrial gas turbine development.

I. Commercial Aircraft Development

The British tested the first turboprop powered passenger liner in 1948, the Vickers Viscount. This aircraft is still seen in service today. The British also tested the first turbojet powered airliner, the deHavilland Comet, in 1949. This four engine airliner, placed in service in 1952, experienced structural fatigue cracking, resulting in high altitude decompression. Catastrophic crashes occurred from this mysterious phenomenon of the time, and in 1954 the Comet was grounded for extensive testing.

During this period the Boeing Company of Seattle, Washington, made a pioneering move to bring America

Fig. 1-18A — Vickers Viscount, world's first commercial turboprop transport, in service 1950.
Fif. 1-18B — The worlds first commercial jet transport, the de Havilland DH 106 Comet 1, began passenger service in 1952.

Fig. 1-19 — The General Electric I-16 (J-31-GE-1 military designation)production model of the GE-1-A turbojet. It produced 1,650 lbs. of thrust at a rated 16,500 rpm.

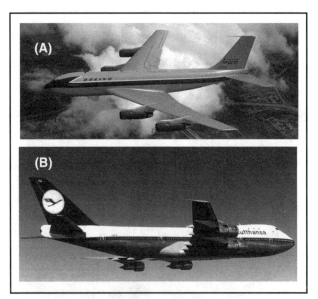

Fig. 1-20A — An early Boeing 707.
Fig. 1-20B — Boeing 747.

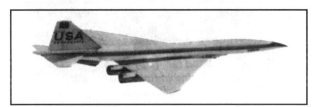

Fig. 1-21 — The American SST design, Boeing 2707-300.

into the commercial jet aircraft field. Utilizing Pratt & Whitney engines developed for the military, Boeing invested approximately one-fourth of their net worth in what was said to be one of the most notable business gambles ever taken in the aviation industry. The result was the world renowned Boeing 707, which, after years of testing, went into service in 1958. This company today produces many models of narrow-bodied airliners as well as the largest passenger liner flying today, the wide bodied B-747.

The Boeing Company tried to launch the United States into supersonic airline service with their Boeing 2707, a Mach 2.8 airspeed, 300 passenger aircraft, powered by four General Electric GE-4 68,000 pound thrust turbojet engines. Congress voted to stop funding for this program in the late sixties, primarily because of pressure from environmentalists, and in 1971 Boeing stopped work on the project. At that time, it was felt that high flight, in the 60,000 foot altitude range, would seriously affect the ozone layer.

EDITOR'S NOTE: Ozone provides a screening protection from the harmful ultraviolet rays bombarding the earth.

The British, in partnership with the French, built and placed into service in 1976 sixteen smaller supersonic jetliners named the Concorde. This aircraft is powered by Rolls-Royce Olympus turbojet engines and is a 100-passenger aircraft, capable of flying at speeds of 2.2 times the speed of sound. In actual service, its cruising speed has been closer to Mach 2.0. This was done to reduce the additional stresses on the airframe present at the higher airspeed.

Although still not completely clear at this writing, the Concorde and high flying military aircraft have been declared, by many researchers, to have a negligible impact on the ozone layer. Today, the feeling is that the atmosphere readily repairs itself in the presence of high flying aircraft. Current research seems to indicate that ozone depletion, in fact, occurs from industrial and agricultural pollution.

The aviation industry, however, must search for methods of complying with new and more stringent regula-

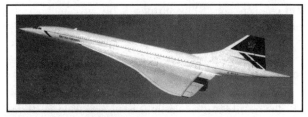

Fig. 1-22 — The British-French Concorde SST.

Fig. 1-23A — General Electric GE-36 unducted fan (UDF) demonstrator engine.
Fig. 1-23B — UDF installed on Boeing test aircraft. (Project cancelled 1995)

tions issued by the Environmental Protection Agency (EPA) and the Federal Aviation Administration (FAA) concerning noise and exhaust pollution. Only the future can tell the way in which the industry will solve these problems and take the next step forward in supersonic aviation. We can be sure, with history as a yardstick, that the aviation industry will find the necessary solutions.

J. Commuter And Business Jets

The use of the gas turbine engine in commuter aircraft, business jets, and even General Aviation aircraft, has been expanding greatly since the 70's and 80's. Now that we are into the 21st century, the trend continues.

The commuter airline industry, also known as regional carriers, was once dominated by the small turboprop airplane. Now that part of the industry is switching to turbofan powered airplanes, known as regional jets. Airplanes of 50 to 100 seat size, powered by high bypass fan engines, are selling in remarkably high numbers in order to meet the demand.

Business jets, also with high bypass fan engines, are continuing to increase in popularity. The business jet is no longer the sole domain of the Fortune 50, or Fortune 100 company. Many smaller companies are now enjoying the advantages of having a business jet at their disposal, often by way of a concept known as fractional ownership.

As of the writing of this book, there are companies hard at work trying to produce what is being billed as the affordable jet. This affordable jet would sell for less than 1 million dollars, have two small turbofan engines, seat 4 to 6 people, and be able to cruise at 450 to 500 Mph. The engines would produce between 500 and 1,000 pounds of thrust, and weigh between 70 and 100 pounds. It will be quite a milestone if such an aircraft can be produced for that price.

Pratt & Whitney, General Electric, Rolls Royce, Allied Signal (Garrett), Allison, and the Allied-Lycoming companies now produce the bulk of gas turbine engines used in fixed wing and rotary wing aircraft common to commuter and business aviation. These companies and others have all capitalized on earlier technological discoveries for military and commercial engines to produce a more reliable powerplant for the turbine powered aircraft of today. The turbine engine powered aircraft has become very popular, in part, because of its superior reliability and commercial airline type speed.

Much of the early technology base applied to the development of civil aviation was an outgrowth of work done for the military, sponsored with governmental funding. Today, throughout the world, research and development for new commercial and business aviation engines is done mostly with private funds.

K. Other Developments

Some other firsts in the evolution of the gas turbine engine in civil aviation are as follows:
1. First flight test of a commercial turboprop powered aircraft: The British Viscount, 1948.
2. First flight test of a commercial turbojet powered aircraft: The British Comet, 1949.
3. First flight test of a commercial turbofan powered aircraft: The British VC.10, 1959.
4. First flight test of a supersonic commercial turbojet powered airliner:
   (a) USSR TU-144, 1968;
   (b) The British/French Concorde, 1969.
5. First flight test of a commercial propfan engine in a Boeing 727 test aircraft: The GE-36, unducted fan engine (UDF), August 20, 1986.
6. First propfan in service, the Russian Antanov AN-70, first test flew in 1994.

QUESTIONS:
1. *What is the earliest indication, in history, of the presence of a jet propulsion device?*
2. *Whose first patent for a jet propulsion flight engine causes him to be recognized today as the father of the jet engine?*
3. *Which aircraft made the first purely jet propelled flight?*
4. *Name America's first gas turbine powered commercial airliner.*
5. *Name the western world's only supersonic transport.*

Chapter II
Jet Propulsion Theory

A. Four Types Of Jet Engines

Jet propulsion is defined as the reacting force produced by the acceleration of air, gas, or liquid through a nozzle. The four common types of jet engines, the rocket jet, the ramjet, the pulse-jet, and the turbine-type jet are all propelled forward by the emission of a gaseous fluid.

1. The rocket is a non-air breathing engine. This means it does not use atmospheric air to support combustion but carries its own oxidizer and fuel in a solid or liquid form. Combustion transforms solids or liquids of small volume into gases of large volume. The gases released by combustion of the fuel and oxidizer escape through an exhaust nozzle at an extremely high velocity. The thrust reaction from the exhaust gases drives the rocket at very high supersonic speeds and completely out of the earth's atmosphere (Figures 2-1, 2-2).

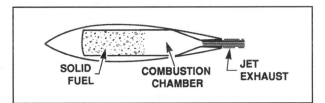

Fig. 2-1 — Solid fuel rocket.

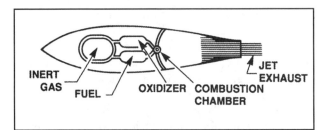

Fig. 2-2 — Liquid fuel rocket.

The German V-2 liquid fluid rocket of World War II is shown in Figure 2-3. It was propelled by combustion of a mixture of alcohol as the fuel and liquid oxygen as the oxidizer and produced 52,000 pounds of thrust.

The space shuttle's three main engines are supplied with liquid hydrogen fuel and each produces approximately 400,000 pounds of thrust. They are used during takeoff, together with solid fuel type rocket boosters. The boosters produce approximately three million pounds of thrust each and are jettisoned after takeoff. (Figure 2-4).

2. The athodyd (aero-thermodynamic duct) or ramjet, is the simplest of all power plants that use the atmosphere to support combustion. It is a duct with few component parts, designed to receive inlet air and change its velocity to static pressure. Fuel, typically of hydrocarbon base,

is added to the compressed air with the resultant combustion and expansion of gases. This combustion causes the mass airflow to quickly exit the engine. The change in velocity of entering and departing air results in reactive thrust. The ramjet is seen today in many military pilotless weapons delivery vehicles (Figure 2-5). There is also a proposed application for a future hypersonic (above Mach 6.0) engine, which would convert from a turbojet in initial lower speed flight to a type of ramjet in very high speed flight. Actually, this new type engine would be called a scram-jet because the airflow would be allowed to reach supersonic speeds during combustion, hence the term supersonic combustion-ramjet (scram-jet). This engine would have to use a more exotic fuel than kerosene, perhaps hydrogen, in order to support combustion at high airflow velocities. The scram-jet is stated as having the potential to power future high speed transports at velocities up to Mach 20.

3. The pulse-jet is similar to a ramjet except that the pulse-jet inlet is fitted with a system of air inlet flapper

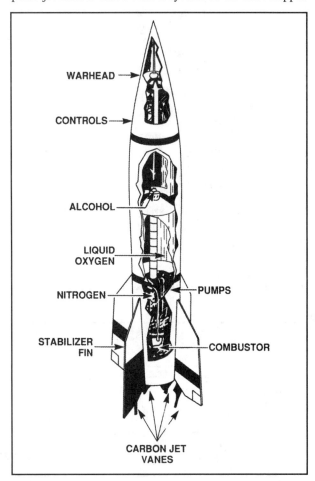

Fig. 2-3 —German V-2 rocket (Mach 3)

Aircraft Gas Turbine Powerplants

valves. These valves are closed during combustion and provide the device with a moderate static thrust that the ramjet does not have. However, this thrust is not sufficient to enable a pulse-jet to take off under its own power and, therefore, must be rocket boosted for initial flight. Major development of the pulse-jet seems to have ceased with the German V-1 rocket of World War II. The German V-1, buzz bomb, was powered by a rocket assisted pulse-jet engine which could propel the V-1 to approximately 400 mph.

This engine was fitted with inlet shutters (flapper-valves) which automatically blew open and closed approximately 40 times per second. Each time fuel (kerosene) pulsed into the combustion chamber, the back pressure created from combustion would force the shutters closed, then between combustion cycles ram inlet air pressure would reopen them. This intermittent combus-

tion was, in effect, a series of rapid backfires or pulses of force which created forward thrust of approximately 600 pounds. A single electrical spark igniter was used for initial starting. Subsequent ignition occurred from internal residual heat (Figure 2-7). Development of the pulse-jet ceased in the late 1940's due to the poor performance of this engine design.

4. The aircraft gas turbine is a heat engine using air as a working fluid. In its most basic form it consists of a compressor for compressing the air, a combustion chamber for burning the air/fuel mixture, and a turbine for extracting energy from the high velocity exhaust gases (Figure 2-8). Some of the energy in the highly heated gases is required to drive the compressor and accessories, the remainder being available to produce power or thrust. The turbine-type jet and, more specifically, the gas turbine engine is a name given to a family of engines based on the Whittle design, which include the turbojet, turboprop, turboshaft, and turbofan. These four gas turbines are discussed in detail throughout this chapter.

B. Powerplant Selection

Selection of a particular type of powerplant usually depends on the cruising speed requirements or specialized use of the aircraft.

1. Reciprocating Engine - Turboshaft Engine

Today's light aircraft, with a cruising speed of under 250 mph, would most likely utilize a reciprocating engine because of its low initial cost and low operating cost. On the other hand, a rotorcraft today would be more likely to use a turboshaft engine for its low weight-to-power ratio.

A turboshaft of comparable power would have an advantage of five to eight times less weight than that of the piston engine. Fuel consumption levels will, however, be about the same. The Honeywell (formerly Lycoming) T-55 Turboshaft engine used in the Chinook helicopter produces 4800 shaft horsepower with a weight of 832 pounds, giving a 5.7 to 1 power to weight ratio. This excellent ratio surpasses even the turboprop engine due to the absence of a bulky propeller reduction gearing system. In helicopters, the major portion of the reduction gearing occurs in the aircraft transmission.

Fig. 2-4 — Space shuttle and rocket booster

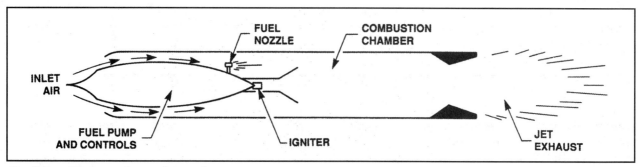

Fig. 2-5 — Diagram of a ramjet engine.

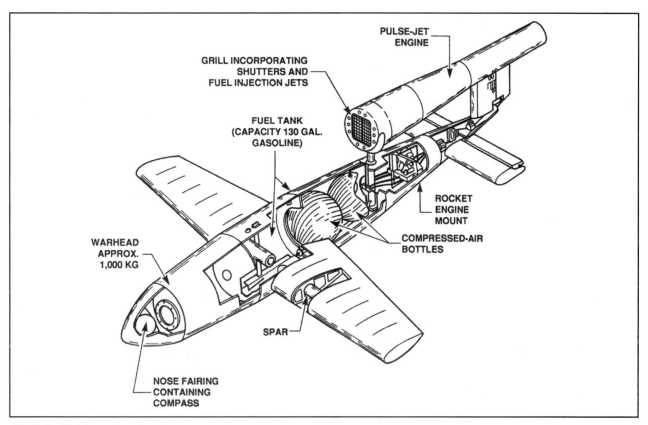

Fig.2-6— V-1 buzz bomb.

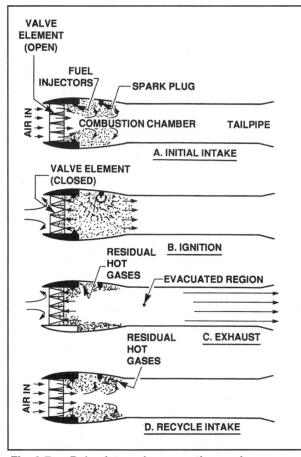

Fig. 2-7 — Pulse-jet engine operating cycle.

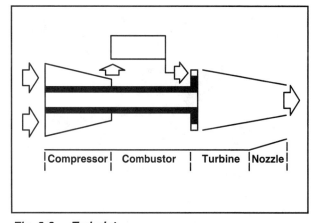

Fig. 2-8 — Turbojet.

2. Turboprop Engine

In the 250 to 450 mph range, turboprop engine performance and economy is best because, like the turboshaft, it produces more power per pound of weight than does the reciprocating engine. For example, one model developed by the Honeywell Company (formerly Garrett), the TPE 331 turboprop, weighs 360 pounds and produces 1,040 shp with a resultant power-to-weight ratio in excess of 2.8 to 1. The best reciprocating engine/propeller combination would have a power-to-weight ratio of slightly less than 1 to 1. However, the turboprop aircraft, like a piston engine aircraft, rapidly loses its power due to increased drag at higher airspeeds.

3. Turbojet-Turbofan (Figure 2-9)

From 450 mph on up, the turbofan or turbojet is most widely used. The turbofan is newer and has become the most popular powerplant for commercial and business jets because its design affords the most propulsive power at higher subsonic cruising speeds. The turbofan engine was developed in order to permit the use of higher turbine temperatures without a corresponding increase in jet velocity, because a high jet velocity is not efficient for subsonic flight. The turbojet engine is less efficient and has, for all practical purposes, been replaced by the turbofan.

Today some large turbojets remain in use in military aviation, and they are still used in the supersonic Concorde aircraft. All current military supersonic aircraft, like the B-1 bomber or F-22 advanced tactical fighter, are powered by low bypass turbofan engines.

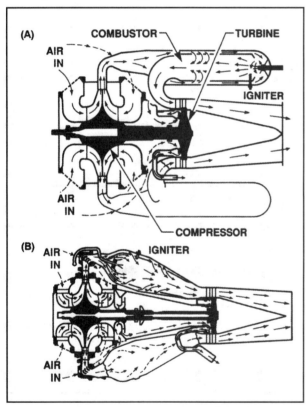

Fig. 2-9A — Early Whittle turbojet with reverse-flow combuster.
Fig. 2-9B — Whittle turbojet with flow-through combuster.

4. Rating The Power Output Of A Gas Turbine Engine

The gas turbine engine, being a reaction type of engine, produces power by the force of reaction. This thrust force is expressed in pounds, and the jet engine power output is rated in pounds of thrust. This rating is usually determined by the manufacturer, who operates the engine in a special test cell where the thrust output can be measured accurately.

Since a jet engine is rated in pounds of thrust, and a conventional reciprocating engine is rated in brake horsepower (bhp), no direct comparison can be made between the two. It should be noted, however, that the brake horsepower of a reciprocating engine is actually converted into thrust by the propeller. This being the case, a true comparison can be made of the two types of engines only by comparing the thrust from the jet engine with the thrust from the propeller of the reciprocating engine.

Figure 2-10 shows how four types of engines compare in thrust as airspeed is increased. Please bear in mind that this figure and the ones following it are for explanatory purposes only and are not for specific model engines.. The four types of engines are the reciprocating type driving a propeller, the jet engine driving a propeller (turboprop), the jet engine incorporating a fan (turbofan), and the turbojet engine. Comparison is made by plotting the performance curve for each engine, which shows how thrust varies with airspeed and by plotting the aircraft drag curve, which shows how maximum aircraft speed varies with the type of engine used. Since the graph is offered only as a means of comparison, the exact thrust, aircraft speed, and drag are not given a numerical value.

When we compare the four powerplants on the basis of thrust, certain things become evident. In the speed range shown to the left of Line A, the reciprocating engine (Curve P) outperforms the other three types. The turboprop (curve TP) outperforms the turbofan (curve TF) in the range to the left of line C. The turbofan engine outperforms the turbojet (curve TJ) in the range to the left of Line F. The turbofan engine outperforms the conventional engine to the right of Line B and the turboprop to the right of Line C. The turbojet outperforms the conventional engine to the right of Line D, the turboprop to the right of Line E, and the turbofan to the right of Line F.

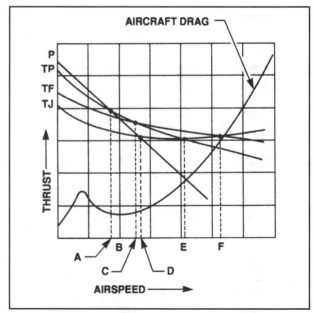

Fig. 2-10 — Comparison takeoff thrust to cruise thrust. Engine thrust vs. aircraft speed and drag.

The points where the aircraft drag curve intersects the thrust curves are the maximum aircraft speeds. If you draw a perpendicular line from each of the points to the base line of the graph, you can see that the turbojet aircraft can attain a higher maximum speed than aircraft equipped with the other types of engines. Aircraft equipped with the turbofan engine will attain a higher maximum speed than aircraft equipped with a turboprop or reciprocating engine.

5. Large Vs. Small Gas Turbine Engines

When comparing large and small gas turbine engines, it is apparent that an engine which is twice as large generates considerably more than twice as much thrust. This is due to the fact that engine mass airflow in the gas turbine engine is approximately proportional to the square of the engine diameter. For example, a 48,000 lb. thrust engine will not be 16 times larger in physical size than a 3,000 lb. thrust engine, it will only be four times larger. If the diameter of the engine with 3,000 lbs. of thrust is two feet, the diameter of the engine with 48,000 lbs. of thrust will be eight feet (4 times bigger in diameter, and 4 squared equals 16 times more mass air flow).

6. Turbine Vs. Piston (Figures 2-11, 2-12)

A comparison between different types or sizes of powerplants is sometimes made in terms of fuel consumed, because large turbine engines are known to consume large amounts of fuel while reciprocating engines appear to be more fuel conscious. But this is misleading. The ton/miles of useful payload, or passenger/miles per fuel consumed methods are more realistic ways of determining which powerplant to select under a given set of circumstances.

A jumbo jet, for instance, can move more payload than would be possible by the largest piston aircraft. If the B-747 could be somehow fitted with piston engines capable of providing the same aircraft performance, fuel consumption would be much higher. This increased fuel consumption would be a result of factors such as increased engine weight, size, drag and propeller efficiency losses.

The aircraft reciprocating engine today is relegated to light, low performance aircraft because of design limitations. For instance, the compression, combustion, and expansion processes all occur in one location, the cylinder. In the gas turbine engine, there is a separate location for each process and many variations of design are possible for flexibility of performance and application. While it appears the reciprocating engine cannot grow much further, the gas turbine seems to have no limit.

An interesting comparison can be made between one of the largest piston engines ever produced, the R-4360, a 28-cylinder radial, which developed 4,000 shp, and the JT9D engine powering the Boeing 747. If we use the generally accepted conversion of 2.5 pounds of thrust per shp, propeller static thrust of R-4360 would be approximately 10,000 pounds (neglecting propeller efficiency losses). The Boeing 747 would need 23 such engines to give the 230,000 lb. static thrust currently produced by its four JT9D turbofan engines.

A summary of advantages of turbine engines compared to reciprocating engines: Figures 2-11, 2-12.

a. Development time is drastically reduced. A turbine unit can be designed, built, and brought to the stage of practical operation in a quarter of the time usually necessary for a piston engine.

b. Production is simpler and speedier. A turbine unit has only about 1/4 the number of parts required for a comparable piston engine.

c. Because turbine components each perform one specific function, a proven turbine unit can be readily scaled up or down to meet power requirements.

d. In the turbine, power is produced continuously instead of intermittently. Consequently, working pressures are low and the structure, casings, and ducting are of light construction and weight.

e. By the exclusive use of rotating components, turbine engine vibration is virtually eliminated. Weight can therefore be saved on the airframe.

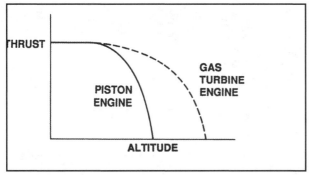

Fig. 2-11 — Thrust vs. altitude.

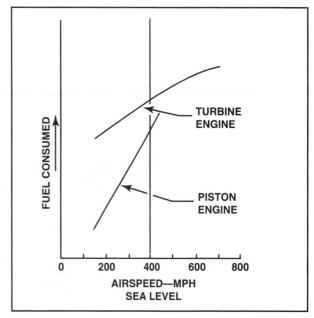

Fig. 2-12 — Fuel to airspeed comparing engines of the same power.

f. Absence of reciprocating parts enables higher operating speeds to be employed. Frontal area and space occupied are reduced, and power/weight ratio is improved. A turbine-jet unit is about 1/4 the weight of a comparable piston engine and is more compact, resulting in a significant weight reduction in the aircraft structure.

g. A turbine engine operates more efficiently at high altitude than at sea level. Therefore, it needs no complicated supercharging system to maintain power at altitude.

h. When compared to the piston engine, the higher the aircraft speed (ram), the more efficiently the turbine engine functions. This is due to the influence of ram pressure increasing its mass airflow and exhaust velocity.

C. Turbine Engine Types

Gas turbine engines are considered to be of two types: a. Thrust Producing Engines; b. Torque Producing Engines.

The two classifications of thrust producing turbine engines are: a. Turbojet; b. Turbofan.

The two classifications of torque producing turbine engines are: a. Turboprop; b. Turboshaft.

1. Turbojet Engines

The turbojet, as first patented by Sir Frank Whittle, had an impeller compressor, annular combustor, and a single stage turbine. Today it is possible to see many varieties of turbojet engine designs, but the basic components are still the compressor, combustor, and turbine.

The turbojet gets its propulsive power from reaction to the flow of hot gases. Air enters the inlet and its pressure is increased by the compressor. Fuel is added in the combustor and the expansion created by heat forces the turbine wheel to rotate. The turbine in turn drives the compressor. The energy remaining downstream of the turbine in the tailpipe accelerates into the atmosphere and creates the reaction we refer to as thrust. (Figure 2-9)

2. Turboshaft Engines

A gas turbine engine that delivers power through a shaft to operate something other than a propeller is referred to as a turboshaft. There is wide use of the turboshaft in other industries, but here we will concern ourselves with the turboshaft's aircraft application.

The early turboshaft engine's power output shaft was coupled directly to the gas generator turbine wheel. Today, the output shaft is driven by a separate turbine wheel. This latter design is referred to as the free power turbine. Figure 2-13 shows the free power turbine in both the front and rear power output shaft configurations. It also shows that turboshaft engines are thought of as having two major sections, the gas generator section and the power turbine section.

The gas generator's function is to produce the required energy to drive the power turbine system. The gas generator extracts about two-thirds of the combustion energy,

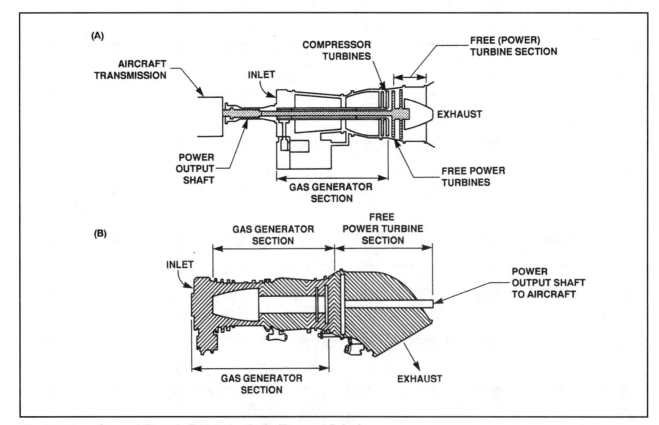

Fig. 2-13A — General Electric T-64 turboshaft. (Forward Drive)
Fig. 2-13 — General Electric T-58 turboshaft. (Rearward Drive)

leaving approximately one-third to drive the power turbine, which, in turn, drives the aircraft transmission. The transmission is in actuality a high ratio reduction gearbox. Occasionally, a turboshaft engine is designed to produce some hot exhaust thrust (up to 10%), while some are not. One consideration in this design is whether or not the rotor alone will produce the desired airspeed, while another is whether or not the helicopter can satisfactorily hover with constant forward thrust.

3. Turboprop Engines

The turboprop is similar in design to the turboshaft, except that the reduction gearbox is usually on the turboprop inlet. The turboprop is an application of the gas turbine engine with a propeller.

This propeller is driven by means of either a fixed or free turbine as shown in Figure 2-14. The fixed turbine is connected directly to the compressor, reduction gearbox, and propeller shaft. The free turbine is connected only to the gearbox and propeller shaft. This arrangement allows the free turbine to seek its optimum design speed while compressor speed is set at its design point (point of best compression).

Some of the advantages of the free turbine are:
1. The propeller can be held at very low rpm during taxiing, with low noise and low blade erosion.
2. The engine is easier to start, especially in cold weather.
3. The propeller and its gearbox do not directly transmit vibrations into the gas generator.
4. A rotor brake can be used to stop propeller movement during aircraft loading when engine shutdown is not desired.

Disadvantage: The engine does not have the instantaneous power of reciprocating engines.

One major difference between the turboprop engine and the basic gas turbine engine is that the turboprop will usually have more turbine stages. These additional stages are needed to drive the output reduction gearbox and the propeller. The total power of the turboprop is the sum of propeller thrust and exhaust nozzle thrust, with the exhaust thrust contributing from 5% to 25%, as seen in various engines in service today.

The exact amount of hot thrust is a function of best fuel economy at cruise speed. Unlike the turboshaft, the turboprop generally has some hot thrust because the higher flight speeds and ram compression add to the propulsive efficiency of the engine. Propulsive efficiency will be defined later in this chapter.

The physical dimensions of a turboprop engine equals only about two-thirds that of a turbojet of comparable thrust output because the mass airflow for thrust is handled by the propeller rather than the core portion of the engine.

The fuel consumption of the turboprop, however, will be slightly less. Again, this is due to its higher propulsive efficiency at lower airspeeds.

a. Ultra High Bypass Propfan/Unducted Fan (UDF) Engines (Figures 2-14D & 2-14E)

Some designers feel that recent developments in propeller blade aerodynamics will result in dramatically increased use of a new version of the turboprop in the near future. These developments provide for increased propulsive efficiency and decreased fuel consumption.

The conventional propeller is presently capable of attaining approximately 1.05 to 1 compression ratio, while the propfan is capable of a 1.2 to 1 ratio.

Contrarotating propellers may have even higher ratios and may be in popular use in the very near future. Because it is not axial flow energy, the swirl imparted to airflow by a propeller is a loss of energy. Contrarotation reduces the swirl losses by capturing the energy in the swirl of the first blade with the second blade and straightening it to a more nearly axial flow.

The propfan, also called ultra high bypass fan (UHB), will not look like a conventional turboprop. It will be fitted with a propeller of six to ten, highly loaded, sweptback and curved blades. This design was made possible by new material development in titanium, light-weight stainless steel, and composite materials. Conventional propeller designs of three or four blades of the same power would require larger diameter blades with a prohibitive resultant loading factor and tip-generated noises.

The powerplant itself is expected to be in the 10,000 to 15,000 horsepower class, which is two to three times the size of current turboprops. New engines, therefore, will have to be developed to accommodate the new propeller designs. The new propfan will power a 150-200 passenger size aircraft at current airliner speeds of Mach 0.8. Some designers propose placing the fan in front. Others will locate the fan in back of the engine. Additional designs include encasing the propfan in a conventional cowl-type inlet to achieve speeds of Mach 0.9. These engines will be known as "ducted UHB" engines.

It will be the most fuel conscious gas turbine in service, surpassing the high bypass turbofan in fuel efficiency by 15%-20%. Fuel economy will be high because hot combustion discharge gases are more efficient in performing mechanical work internally to drive a propeller shaft to create thrust than they are by discharging out of a tailpipe to create thrust.

Pure reactive thrust, by comparison, is less because some of the hot gas expands radially into the atmosphere, losing a good portion of its energy. Also, the higher comparative thrust at low speeds, associated with variable pitch propellers, will decrease climb-out time to cruise altitude and save even more fuel.

The propfan's required high bypass ratio (the ratio of air passing outside versus air passing through the engine) of 30 to 1 to a high of 100 to 1 will come from single or dual, 12 to 15 foot diameter propellers with higher tip speeds than propellers now in use. In order to propel an aircraft at Mach 0.8, the propeller tips may at times have

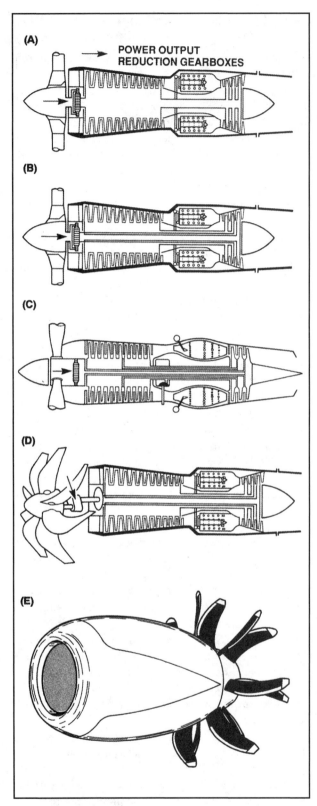

Fig. 2-14A — *Single axial flow compressor, direct drive turboprop.*

Fig. 2-14B — *Single axial flow compressor, free turbine drive.*

Fig. 2-14C — *Dual compressor three-shaft turboprop with free-turbine drive to propeller.*

Fig. 2-14D — *Front propfan.*

Fig. 2-14E — *Rear propfan counter-rotating blades.*

to travel at supersonic speeds. During take-off, this tip speed could be reduced to subsonic speed, but noise generated reportedly may still be in the 130 to 140 decibel range, which is 30 to 40 decibels higher than a turbofan of comparable size. Present development is aimed at reducing the negative aspects of high ground and cabin noise and to ultimately achieve a 30% savings in fuel consumption.

Airliners of the 400-passenger class will probably not convert to unducted UDF designs because the 60,000 pound thrust required would have to be achieved using a 25-foot diameter propfan, which does not seem practical at this time.

4. Turbofan Engines

The turbofan, in effect, is a ducted, multi-bladed propeller driven by a gas turbine engine. This fan produces a pressure ratio on the order of 2:1, or two atmospheres of compression. Generally, turbofans contain 20 to 40 fixed pitch blades. They were developed to provide a compromise between the best features of the turbojet and the turboprop. That is, with its ducted design, the turbofan has turbojet type cruise speed capability and yet retains some of the short field takeoff capability of the turboprop.

By comparison, the fan diameter of a turbofan engine is much less than that of the propeller on a turboprop engine, but it contains many more blades and moves the air with a greater velocity from its convergent exhaust nozzle.

There are several fan installation arrangements. These include: 1. Bolting the fan directly to the front compressor and traveling at the same speed (Figure 2-15A). 2. Connecting the fan by a reduction gearbox to the compressor, similar to the turboprop in Figure 2-14B. 3. Driving the fan by a separate turbine wheel to rotate independently of the compressor (Figure 2-15B). 4. Locating the fan in the turbine section as an extension of the turbine wheel blades (Figure 2-15C). 1, 2, and 3 are referred to as forward fans, while 4 is referred to as an aft-fan.

The aft-fan is not a popular design today. Very few will be seen because the fan does not contribute to compressor pressure ratio. The compressor of the aft-fan is also more susceptible to serious damage from ingested materials than the forward fan which tends to throw these materials outward and through the fan exhaust, with damage usually limited to the fan.

Turbofans in civil aircraft are generally divided into three classifications: Low bypass, medium bypass, and high bypass.

The low bypass classification indicates that the fan and the compressor sections are utilizing approximately the same mass airflow. They are described as having a bypass ratio of 1 to 1. The fan discharge may be slightly higher or slightly lower. Keep in mind that the bypass ratio concerns airflow mass. The fan discharge air is ducted along the entire length of the engine from what is

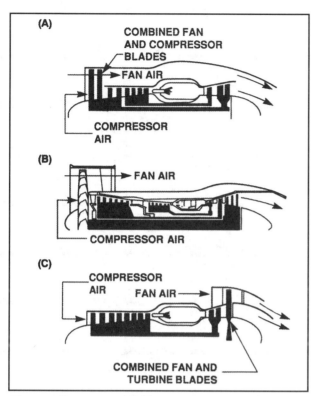

Fig. 2-15A — Dual axial flow compressor, forward fan engine with mixed exhaust.

Fig. 2-15B — Triple-spool front fan engine with unmixed exhaust.

Fig. 2-15C — Turbofan engine with an aft-fan and unmixed exhaust.

called a full fan duct. The end of the duct is configured with a converging discharge nozzle to produce a velocity increase and reactive thrust.

In the fully ducted fan engine shown (Figure 2-16), the hot and cold streams mix before being discharged to the atmosphere. This results in a reduction in aerodynamic drag associated with short ducted turbofans. Air passing over the core engine outer surfaces has much less skin friction if the air remains in the fan duct until it leaves the engine.

With the full duct, there is gain implied when drag is reduced. This design also has a noise attenuating quality as hot gas becomes diluted by fan air in the common exhaust duct.

The turbofan core engine air is compressed, ignited, and discharged in the same manner as a turbojet engine. The thrust of each gas stream of the fully ducted engine shown in the illustration is approximately equal, each delivering 8,000 to 10,000 pounds of thrust, depending on the model.

NOTE: Military fighter aircraft generally have a bypass ratio of less than 1 to 1 due to the narrow profile requirements imposed by supersonic flight.

The medium or intermediate bypass engines are considered to be in the range of 2 or 3 to 1 mass airflow ratio,

with a thrust ratio in approximate proportion to the bypass ratio. The fan will be slightly larger in diameter than a low bypass fan of comparable engine power, and its diameter will determine both the bypass ratio and thrust output of the fan versus the core of the engine.

It follows that the high bypass turbofan engine, with fan ratios of 4:1 and up, have even wider diameter fans in order to move more air. The illustration, Figure 2-17, shows the Pratt & Whitney PW-4000 engine, which represents one of the current state-of-the-art large engine designs for jumbo-jet aircraft.

High bypass engines boast the lowest fuel consumption of the various turbofan engines discussed. The PW-4000 is a 5:1 bypass ratio engine with 80% of the thrust produced by the fan and 20% by the core engine. The thrust percentages vary from engine to engine and are determined by such considerations as fuel economy at altitude, cruise speed, and propulsive efficiency for a particular aircraft design. Current high bypass turbofan engines range from a 75% to 85% bypass of the core by the air mass.

Very few high bypass turbofans are fully ducted. The thrust and low drag advantage mentioned above for low bypass engines equally applies here. But the weight penalty involved in wide diameter fully ducted engines presents design problems that are yet to be completely overcome.

The high bypass fan engine today has become the most widely used engine type for medium to large airliners because it offers the best fuel economy. This occurs when the total mass airflow is increased and the hot

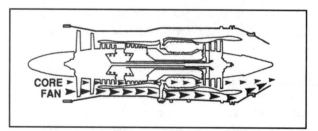

Fig. 2-16 — Fully ducted low and medium bypass turbofan design.

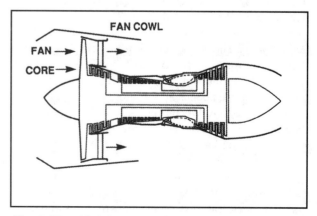

Fig. 2-17 — High bypass ratio turbofan.

exhaust wake velocity is decreased. This conservation of energy keeps more power within the engine to drive the fan and leads to a considerable increase in propulsive and thermal efficiency.

In fact, the aviation industry today has, for the most part, turned to the various fan engines and away from turbojet engines for high performance business, commercial, and military aircraft.

Chapter III will include many more construction features of the various engine types.

a. Ultra High Bypass Turbofan Engines (Ducted)

Another development in turbofans is the variable pitch (variable-bypass ratio) model now being tested for certification. This model is predicted to have the lowest fuel consumption rate per thrust ratio of any turbofan currently in service. It will also have much of the same flexibility of operation that the turboprops enjoy and, yet, will still be capable of the high subsonic cruising speeds that elude the conventional turboprop.

Its bypass ratio will fall somewhere between the high bypass turbofan and the propfan and will likely be fitted with a variable exhaust nozzle to accomodate the varying mass flow conditions. (Figure 2-18)

D. Physics

For a clear understanding of jet propulsion principles it is necessary to understand the applicable principles of physics. These are the physical principles which govern the action of mass or matter. The physics described here, however, are not intended to be complete in this regard but rather to present the basic ideas necessary for an understanding of the physical relationships of gases and the turbo-machinery within a gas turbine engine.

The mass-flow of gases referred to is atmospheric air which is compressed and accelerated in the gas turbine engine to create useful work at the turbine wheel and, ultimately, thrust. The thrust is created from either pure reaction to the flowing gases or from a propeller or fan driven by a turbine.

Some of the most important physical properties that apply to the gas turbine engine are: Weight, Density, Temperature, Pressure, and Mass. These properties are useful when applied to formulas such as: Force, Work, Acceleration, Thrust, and others which measure certain valuable performance factors. These properties will be described by formula in "English Units" throughout this text, for example pounds versus kilograms.

In Figure 2-19A, Weight can be seen as one-directional, toward the center of the earth regardless of the type of material. Weight has direction and quantity and is measured in pounds of force.

Figure 2-19B describes Density as the amount of material per unit volume and illustrates that two containers with identical type contents will have different weights if the contents are packed closer together. The

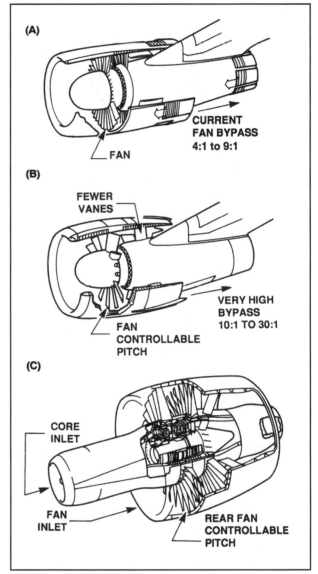

Fig. 2-18A — *Current technology engine.*
Fig. 2-18B — *Variable pitch front propfan engine.*
Fig. 2-18C — *Variable pitch rear propfan engine.*

compressor of a Gas Turbine Engine uses this principle and packs more and more molecules of air into a given space. This is to increase the density and weight of the airflow to create thrust.

For example, at Standard Day Condition the weight of air is 0.076475 lb./cubic foot. In an engine with a compressor pressure ratio of 30 to 1, the weight of air per cubic foot will be 30 times 0.076475, or 2.295 pounds/cubic foot.

Figure 2-19C describes Temperature as molecular energy of motion due to heat. At low temperature, molecular motion is low, and, at higher temperature, molecular motion increases. In the compressor of a gas turbine engine, this is a problem because it requires more and more work in terms of compressor speed and fuel consumption to increase density if the temperature of air is increased.

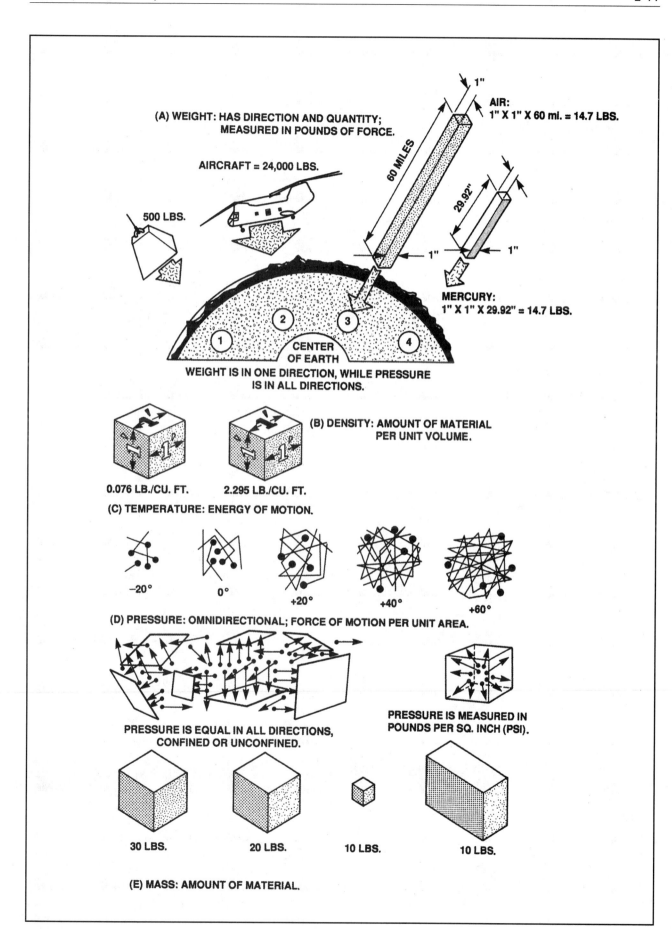

Fig. 2-19A, B, C, D, E — Some important physical properties of matter.

Figure 2-19D describes Pressure as an omnidirectional force of motion per unit area, in terms of the fact that air molecules are rebounding off the inner walls of the container with such great rapidity that an essentially even pressure is exerted over all of the inner surfaces. If a pressure gauge were inserted into the closed container, it would produce a steady reading in pounds per square inch.

Figure 2-19E describes Mass as the amount of material a body contains. In this respect, it is similar to the description of density. Within a gas turbine engine, the denser the air per unit volume, the more weight it has and the more mass.

1. Force

Force is defined as the capacity to do work, or the tendency to produce work. It is also a vector quantity that tends to produce acceleration of a body in the direction of its application. It can be measured in units of pounds.

The formula for force is:

Force = Pressure x Area, or $F = P \times A$

Where: F = Force in pounds
        P = Pressure in pounds per square inch (psi)
        A = Area in square inches

EXAMPLE: The pressure across the opening of a jet tailpipe (exhaust nozzle) is 6 psi above ambient and the opening is 300 square inches. What is the force present in pounds?

$F = P \times A$
$F = 6 \times 300$
$F = 1,800$ pounds

The force mentioned here is present in addition to reactive thrust in most gas turbine engine designs. This "pressure thrust" will be discussed later in this chapter.

2. Work

Mechanical work is present when a force acting on a body causes it to move through a distance. Work is described as useful motion. A force can act on an object vertically (opposite the effect of gravity), horizontally (90 degrees to the effect of gravity), or somewhere in between. A force can also act on an object in a downward direction, in which case it would be assisted by gravity. The typical units for work are "inch pounds" and "foot pounds".

The formula for work is:

Work = Force x Distance, or $W = F \times D$

Where: W = Work in foot pounds
        F = Force in pounds
        D = Distance in feet

EXAMPLE: How much work, in foot-pounds, is performed by a device which lifts a 2,500 pound engine a height of 9 feet?

$W = F \times D$
$W = 2,500 \times 9$
$W = 22,500$ foot pounds

Because the engine is being lifted vertically, the force applied must be equal to the force of gravity, which is what causes the engine to weigh 2,500 pounds. If the same engine were in a transport cart and moved 9 feet horizontally along a hangar floor, it would not involve nearly as much work. Moving the engine horizontally only requires that a certain amount of friction be overcome.

3. Power

The definition of work makes no mention of time. Whether it takes five seconds to move an object or five hours, the same amount of work would be accomplished. Power, by comparison, does take the time into account. To lift a ten pound object 15 feet off the floor in five seconds requires significantly more power than to lift it in five hours. Work performed per unit of time is power. Power is measured in units of foot pounds per second, foot pounds per minute, or mile pounds per hour.

The formula for power is:

$$\text{Power} = \frac{\text{Force} \times \text{Distance}}{\text{time}} \quad \text{or} \quad P = \frac{F \times D}{t}$$

Where: P = Power in foot pounds per minute
        D = Distance in feet
        t = Time in minutes

EXAMPLE: A 2,500 pound engine is to be hoisted a height of 9 feet in two minutes. How much power is required?

$$P = \frac{F \times D}{t}$$

$$P = \frac{2,500 \times 9}{2}$$

$P = 11,250$ ft. lbs./min.

4. Horsepower (Figures 2-20 & 2-21)

Horsepower is a more common and useful measure of electrical power. Years ago using the multiplier of 1.5 times a strong horse's ability to do useful work, it was determined that 33,000 pounds of weight lifted one foot in one minute would be the standard in the English system. If power is in foot pounds/minute, it can be divided by 33,000 to convert to horsepower. Mathematically, the units of foot pounds per minute will cancel each other out, leaving only the number. Horsepower does not have units, since horsepower is the unit. If power is being dealt with in units of foot pounds per second, 550 is the conversion number. If power is in mile pounds per hour, 375 is the conversion number.

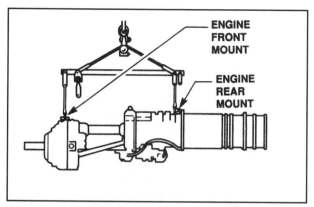

Fig. 2-20 — Hoisting engine during maintenance.

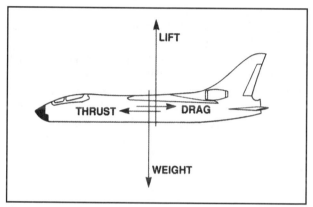

Fig. 2-21 — Horsepower is required to drive the engine. Force left over drives the aircraft.

The formula for converting to horsepower is:

$$Hp = \frac{Power\ (in\ ft.\ lbs./min.)}{33,000}$$

EXAMPLE: How much horsepower is required to hoist a 2,500 pound engine a height of 9 feet in two minutes (the previous example which required 11,250 ft. lbs./min of power)?

$$Hp = \frac{Power}{33,000}$$

$$Hp = \frac{11,250}{33,000}$$

$$Hp = 0.34\ or\ approximately\ 1/3\ Hp$$

5. Velocity

Velocity deals with how far an object moves, what direction it moves, and how long it took it to move that far. Velocity is expressed in the same units as speed, typically feet per second (fps) or miles per hour (mph). The difference is that speed does not have a particular direction associated with it. Velocity is identified as being a vector quantity, while speed is a scalar quantity.

The formula for velocity is:

Velocity = Distance ÷ time, or V = D ÷ t

EXAMPLE: Gas flows through a gas turbine engine tailpipe a distance of 5 feet in 0.003 seconds. What is its velocity in feet per second?

V = D ÷ t
V = 5 ÷ 0.003
V = 1,667 feet per second

To convert the velocity in feet per second to a value in miles per hour, the feet per second value is divided by 1.467. This conversion factor is the number of feet in a mile, 5280, divided by the number of seconds in an hour, 3600.

Velocity in fps ÷ 1.467 = mph
1,667 fps ÷ 1.467 = 1,136.3 mph

6. Acceleration (Figures 2-22 & 2-23)

In physics, acceleration is defined as a change in velocity with respect to time. Observe that distance traveled is not considered, only loss or gain of velocity with time. The typical units for acceleration are feet per second/second (fps/s) and miles per hour/second (mph/s). Feet per second/second are sometimes referred to as feet per second squared (fps^2).

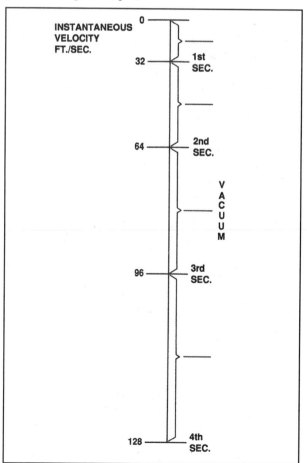

Fig. 2-22 — Effect of gravity on velocity.

Fig. 2-23 — Galileo's experiment with gravity.

The formula for calculating acceleration is:

$$\text{Acceleration} = \frac{\text{Velocity Final - Velocity Initial}}{\text{time}}$$

$$A = \frac{V2 - V1}{t}$$

EXAMPLE 1: For the Concorde SST in flight, the air enters the engine with a velocity of 500 feet per second. It exits the engine one second later with a velocity of 2,200 feet per second. What is the acceleration rate for the air?

$$A = \frac{V2 - V1}{t}$$

$$A = \frac{2,200 \text{ fps} - 500 \text{ fps}}{1 \text{ second}}$$

$$A = 1,700 \text{ feet per second/second}$$

EXAMPLE 2: A military fighter going 300 mph goes into full afterburner, and after ten seconds has accelerated to 1200 mph. What is the airplane's average acceleration in Mph/second and in fps/second?

$$A = \frac{1,200 \text{ mph} - 300 \text{ mph}}{10 \text{ seconds}}$$

$$A = 90 \text{ mph/second} \times 1.467 = 132 \text{ fps/sec.}$$

The acceleration rate due to gravity, when an object is in free fall with no drag, is 32.2 feet per second/second. When an object accelerates at this rate, it is experiencing what is known as a force of 1 "g". If we divided the acceleration rate for the example fighter airplane by 32.2, we would discover how many "g" forces it is experiencing (132 ÷ 32.2 = 4.1 g's).

E. Potential And Kinetic Energy

Energy is used to perform useful work. In the gas turbine engine this means producing motion and heat. The two forms of energy which best describe the propulsive power of the jet engine are potential and kinetic.

Figure 2-24A illustrates that pressure is equal in all parts of the sprinkler head and no motive power is present. In this manner potential or stored energy is said to be present. Figure 2-24B demonstrates how kinetic energy is formed. An opening or jet nozzle is placed in each sprinkler head, arranged 180 degrees apart.

If a constant fluid supply is present, a useful condition exists. At the points of exit, there is a reduced pressure as the fluid escapes from the nozzle. This creates a relatively higher pressure on the inside wall directly opposite the opening. The sprinkler head will now rotate on its axis as a result of this motive power.

Rotation created by potential energy being converted to kinetic energy is clearly the result of a force within the device and not the force of the fluid pushing on the atmosphere. In fact, the rotation would surely be quicker if the sprinkler were placed in a vacuum where no atmospheric back pressure on the nozzle were present. Later, we will discuss how thrust is similarly created within the gas turbine engine.

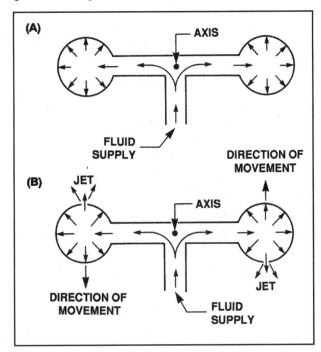

Fig. 2-24A — Potential energy.
Fig. 2-24B — Kinetic energy.

F. Bernoulli's Theorem

Bernoulli's principle deals with pressure of gases. Pressure can be changed in the gas turbine engine by adding or removing heat, changing the number of molecules present, or changing the volume in which the gas is contained.

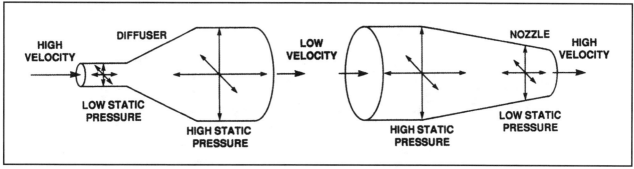

Fig. 2-25 — Ducts used to change static pressure and velocity.

The change in volume idea is of immediate importance to the understanding of the gas cycle of the turbine engine because it is the basis of Bernoulli's principle (Figure 2-25).

Bernoulli discovered that air acts as an incompressible fluid would act when flowing at subsonic flow rates. The principle is stated as follows: When a fluid or gas is supplied at a constant flow rate through a duct, the sum of pressure (potential) energy and velocity (kinetic) energy is constant. In other words, when static pressure increases, velocity (ram) pressure decreases. Or if static pressure decreases, velocity (ram) pressure increases, meaning that velocity pressure will change in relation to any change in static pressure.

To better understand this occurrence consider that air flowing through a duct has both internal (molecular motion) energy and kinetic energy. It can also be thought of as static pressure energy and kinetic (ram) pressure energy. If air is flowing through a straight section of ducting which then changes to a divergent shape, its kinetic energy in the axial direction will decrease as the air spreads out radially, and, as the total energy at constant flow rate of the air is unchanged, the potential energy must increase in relation to the kinetic energy decrease.

Now at a gauge opening in the divergent portion of the duct the molecules of air are more numerous than at a similar opening in the straight portion. This occurs because of the increased time available for the molecules to bounce or expand into the opening. The molecular force within the gauge is read as pressure in pounds per square inch. Conversely, if the duct shape converges, an air stream at constant flow rate must speed up. That is, the air stream's kinetic energy is said to increase as its potential (static pressure) energy proportionally decreases.

At a gauge opening in the convergent portion of the duct, the molecules finding their way into the gauge from the air stream's potential energy will be fewer because of the shorter time available in the faster moving air stream. As a result, a gauge will read out as a lower static pressure.

For a further understanding of the concept of static pressure, consider that internal (molecular) energy is present whether the gas is flowing or not and is quite separate from the kinetic energy of flow. Static pressure occurs, then, when molecules in great numbers inside a gauge mechanism are rebounding off walls of the container so repeatedly that it appears as if they are exerting a steady push or pressure.

Total Pressure is the sum of static pressure plus ram pressure and is often described as the pressure required from the opposite direction to stop the flow.

In Figure 2-26, we must assume the flow rate in pounds/second is constant through the duct at points "A", "B", and "C". Since "B" is smaller, it follows that the flowing gas will have to speed up with respect to "A". The static pressure at "B" will be lower than at "A".

This occurs because at the given gauge opening, with respect to time, fewer air molecules are present in duct "B" as the air stream velocity is increased. "C" will have a higher static pressure than "B" as the gas seeks the shape of its larger container by expanding outward and slowing down. The duct at A-B is described as a converging duct and at B-C as a diverging duct.

The diagram also illustrates that total pressure remains constant throughout the duct. Through the use of a specially shaped probe, both static and ram pressure components of total pressure can be measured. The total pressure can then be compared to the static pressure at the same point in the duct.

NOTE: *To calculate Ram Pressure and Total Pressure if Velocity and Density are known, use Formulas 14 and 15 in Appendix 8. See example, Chapter III, "Ram Recovery".*

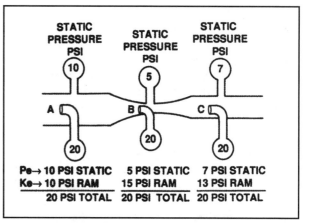

Fig. 2-26 — Application of Bernoulli's theorem.

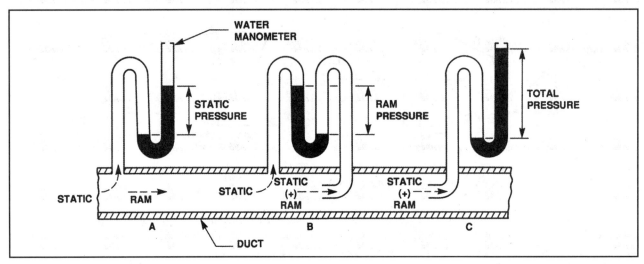

Fig. 2-27 — Measuring air pressure.

1. Measuring Static Pressure (Figure 2-27)

Static pressure is the pressure of the air or fluid, exerted in a direction at right angles to the plane of the duct and of the air stream.

To make this clearer, suppose that an air stream is flowing through a duct as indicated, and a U-type water manometer is connected to the duct as shown at "A". The pressure on the gauge tube connected to the duct in this manner will read the static pressure of the air inside the duct, indicated in inches of water.

If atmospheric air were not pressing on the water column in the right-hand leg of the gauge tube with a (normal) weight of 14.7 lb. per square inch, the water would be forced out of the gauge tube. So, we say that the difference between the two levels in the water manometer is the pressure difference between atmospheric pressure and the pressure of the air motion inside the duct.

This difference is the measurement of static pressure inside the duct (expressed in inches of water) above atmospheric pressure.

2. Measuring Total Pressure (Figure 2-27)

Total pressure is the force exerted by an air stream moving perpendicular to the plane of the duct. To measure this motion, a water gauge is connected to the duct as shown at "C". The gauge tube penetrates to the center of the duct, and the open end is then bent in at an angle of 90° into the air stream.

The height to which the water column climbs is then higher than with the arrangement shown at "A", due to the greater pressure that the airflow exerts on the water column.

3. Measuring Ram Pressure (Figure 2-27)

At "A", we are measuring static pressure only; at "C", we are measuring the total pressure. We further must be able to measure the other force which determines the speed of air motion. It is called ram pressure. Ram pressure is the total pressure less the static pressure.

At "B", notice that both ends of the water gauge are connected to the duct. The left end of the gauge at "B" is connected the same as the left end of the gauge at "A", measuring static pressure. The right end of the gauge at "B" is connected in the same way as shown for the left end at "C".

In arrangement "B", we call the left leg of the gauge the static tube and the other leg the impact tube. Thus, both forces, static and ram, act on the water column, and the difference between the fluid levels in the gauge tube in inches is the measurement of the ram pressure.

It is important to note that when using an arrangement such as that used at "B", in which both ends of the gauge tube are placed in the duct and neither has access to atmospheric pressure, the distance between the water levels in the two columns represents ram pressure.

4. Pressure-Velocity Through The Engine

Referring to Figure 2-28A, one can observe the function of Bernoulli's principle in an open duct by comparison of the pressure and velocity curves at points A, B, and C. Note that pressure is going up as velocity is going down. C to D indicates pressure increasing rapidly under the influence of work done by the compressor. Velocity is also increasing slightly in the convergent duct formed by the compressor and its outer case. Point D-D shows a slight pressure rise/velocity decrease effect of air passing through the divergent shaped diffuser.

Combustion occurs between D and E with pressure drop controlled as stated in the Brayton cycle graph. Pressure is rapidly changing to velocity to drive the turbine wheel at E to F. Also, at E to F, pressure and velocity stabilize as the gas moves between the rotor and stator; then, both pressure and velocity drop across the turbine wheel. Velocity drops here because the gas is losing axial velocity as the wheel throws the gas in a tangential direction. Velocity again rises axially, F to G, but not to the same value as at the turbine nozzle.

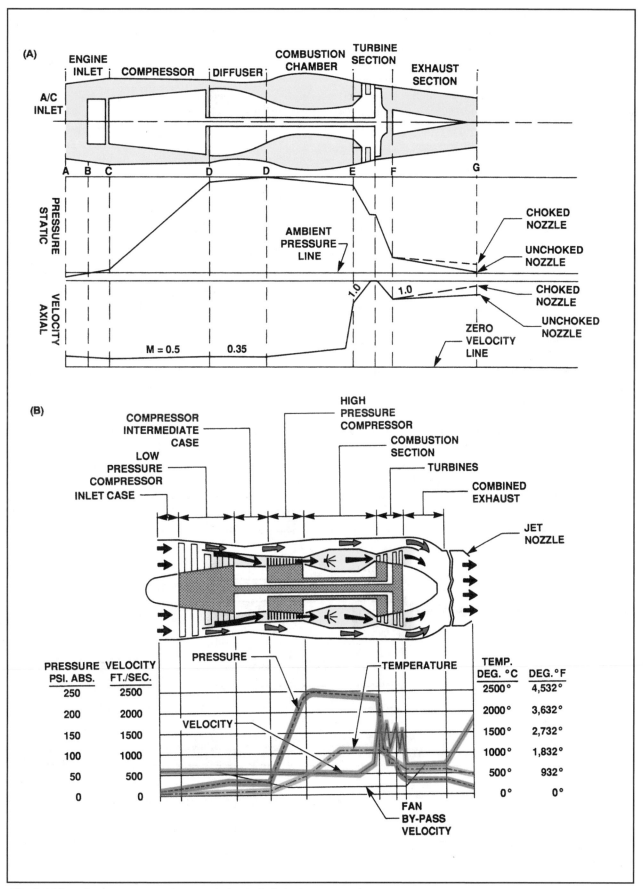

Fig. 2-28A — Pressure, velocity, graph (turbojet) during ground run-up.
Fig. 2-28B — Pressure, velocity, temperature graph (turbofan) during ground run-up.

The temperature difference, with both velocities being choked (gas in motion at the speed of sound) causes the exhaust velocity to be lower than the velocity at the turbine nozzle because, at the turbine nozzle, temperature is higher and therefore the speed of sound is also higher.

Finally, pressure drops to a value slightly above ambient if the nozzle is choked or to ambient if it is not choked.

NOTE: The speed of sound symbol (M=1) represents gas flowing at Mach one.

The internal temperature graph (Figure 2-29B) can be interpreted as follows:

During ground run-up, the temperature will drop slightly at points A, B and C, due to the chilling effect of fast moving air. C to D shows the temperature rise due to compression of air. In very large engines this rise can be on the order of 1,000°F. Points D-D show a slight rise in temperature to correspond with a slight pressure rise. Points D-E show combustor temperature peaking, then dropping off as cooling air enters the rear section of the combustor. The temperature continues to drop through sections F and G as the volume (flow area within the engine) increases. Finally, the gas leaves the engine at a temperature much higher than ambient.

G. The Brayton Cycle

Before the turn of this century, George Brayton, a Boston engineer, scientifically described the continuous combustion cycle. This name, the Brayton cycle, has been given to the continuous thermodynamic cycle of the gas turbine engine.

The Brayton cycle is also widely known as a "constant pressure cycle". The reason for this is that in the gas turbine engine, pressure is fairly constant across the combustion section as volume increases and gas velocities increase.

The four continuous events shown on the pressure-volume graph (Figure 2-29A) are: Intake, compression, expansion (power), and exhaust.

Referring to the graph, A to B indicates air entering the engine at below ambient pressure due to suction and increasing volume due to the divergent shape of the duct in the direction of flow. B to C shows air pressure returning to ambient and volume decreasing.

C to D shows compression occurring as volume is decreasing. D to E indicates a slight drop in pressure, approximately 3%, through the combustion section and an increasing volume. This pressure drop occurs as a result of combustion heat added and is controlled by the carefully sized exhaust nozzle opening. Recall that there is a basic gas law which states that gas will tend to flow from a point of high pressure to a point of low pressure.

The pressure drop in the combustor ensures the correct direction of gas flow through the engine from compressor to combustor. The air rushing in also cools and protects the metal by centering the flame.

E to F shows a pressure drop resulting from increasing velocity as the gas is accelerated through the turbine section.

F to G shows the volume (expansion) increase which causes this acceleration. G completes the cycle as gas pressure returns to ambient, or higher than ambient at the nozzle if it is choked.

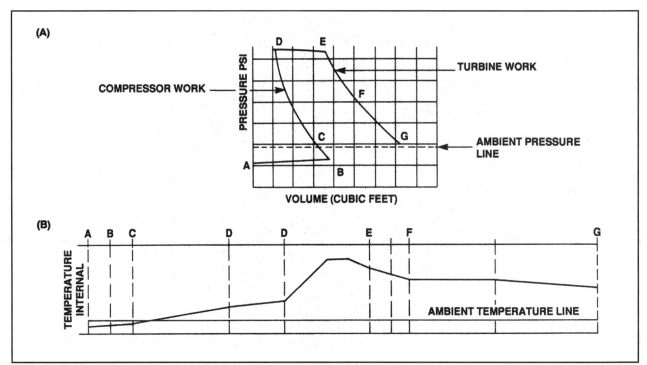

Fig. 2-29A — Pressure-volume continuous combustion (Brayton cycle).
Fig. 2-29B — Temperature graph.

Figure 2-28B shows essentially the same plots as seen in Figure 2-28A, except that this graph details the pressure, temperature, and velocity of a dual compressor turbofan engine. This figure also includes a velocity curve of the fan bypass airflow. Notice that fan air branches off from inlet airflow and decreases in value as it expands through the bypass duct. In this duct, pressure would typically increase 1.5 or even 2.0 times the ambient pressure. The velocity curve rises sharply in the area of the exhaust as bypass air is expanded from its exhaust nozzle to mix with the core engine exhaust gases.

For the purpose of this discussion, the velocities we are dealing with are Mach 1 or less, which one would normally find throughout the typical gas turbine engine. Supersonic velocities, as experienced in supersonic aircraft inlets, will be discussed later in Chapter III.

For a more in-depth understanding of the internal cycle of events of the gas turbine, one can consult texts in the field of thermodynamics and aerodynamic design of gas turbine engines.

H. Newton's Laws And The Gas Turbine

One principle of operation of the turbojet engine is based on Newton's first law of motion, "A body at rest tends to remain at rest, and a body in motion tends to remain in motion". This law states that a force is required to accelerate a mass; therefore, if an engine accelerates a mass of air, it will apply a force on the aircraft (a body in motion tends to stay in motion).

In this respect, the propeller and the turbojet are closely related. The propeller generates thrust by a relatively small acceleration to a large amount of air. The turbojet and turbofan achieve thrust by imparting a greater acceleration to a smaller quantity of air. (Figure 2-30)

1. Newton's Second Law

Newton's second law states that force is proportional to the product of mass and acceleration. As a formula, Newton's second law would be shown as:

Force = Mass x Acceleration, or F = M x A

Where: F = Force in pounds
        M = Mass in lbs./ft./sec.^{2}
        A = Acceleration in ft./sec.^{2}

Mass units are difficult to use mathematically, so let us consider that mass and weight are similar quantities when an object is in the field of gravity of the earth. Weight exists because of the force of gravity acting on a unit of mass, or mathematically stated:

Weight = Mass x Gravity

This formula can be transposed to solve for mass, and would look like:

$$Mass = \frac{Weight}{Gravity}$$

By utilizing the formula for acceleration learned earlier in this chapter, and the formula for mass shown above, the formula for Newton's second law would look like:

$$Force = \frac{Weight}{gravity} \times \frac{Velocity\ Final\ -\ Velocity\ Initial}{time}$$

$$F = \frac{W}{g} \times \frac{V2 - V1}{t}$$

Where: F = Force in pounds
        W = Weight in pounds
        g = Acceleration due to gravity in ft/sec^2
        V2 = Exit velocity in fps
        V1 = Entry velocity in fps
        t = Time in seconds

This formula forms the foundation for calculating the reactive thrust of a gas turbine engine, such as a turbojet or turbofan. The force in pounds would be the thrust, the weight would be the pounds of air going through the engine every second, V2 would be the velocity of the air leaving the engine, and V1 would be the velocity of the air as it enters the engine.

2. Comparison: Propeller To Turbojet Exhaust Thrust

Referring to Figure 2-30, a mathematical comparison can now be made between the thrust of the two propulsion systems shown using the expanded F = M x A formula. Here we will use Newton's Second Law rather than Bernoulli's Principle to explain propeller thrust, both methods being valid.

Figure 2-30 shows an airplane powered by a piston engine and propeller moving 976 pounds of air a second, and imparting to it an acceleration of 200 ft./sec./sec. The turbojet powered airplane is moving 122 pounds of air a second, and imparting to it an acceleration of 1,600 ft./sec./sec. If the thrust for both was calculated, the solutions would be as follows:

Piston Engine/Prop

$$F = \frac{W}{g} \times \frac{V2 - V1}{t}$$

$$F = \frac{976}{32.2} \times \frac{200 - 0}{1}$$

F = 6,062 lbs.

Turbojet

$$F = \frac{W}{g} \times \frac{V2 - V1}{t}$$

$$F = \frac{122}{32.2} \times \frac{1,600 - 0}{1}$$

F = 6,062 lbs.

Conclusion: Different types of propulsion systems provide different mass air flows and flow velocities. It is possible to have quite different mass and acceleration values and still have the same thrust, whether the engine is a piston and propeller combination, a turbo-propeller, a turbojet, or a turbofan.

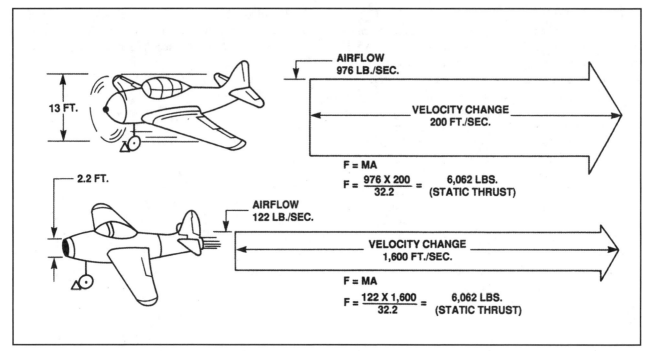

Fig. 2-30 — *Comparison of propeller and jet thrust*

3. Newton's Third Law

Newton's third law is the commonly stated theorem that "For every acting force there is an equal and opposite reacting force".

Figure 2-31 shows a balloon containing pressurized air and, as the air is released, the "acting force" creates an "equal and opposite reacting force" on the forward wall inside the balloon. The same idea applies for the "gun analogy". The air discharge and the bullet leaving the gun do not create reactive power by exerting a pushing force on the outside air. Rather, their acting forces create a reacting force within the device. In fact, if the air or bullet were to exit into a vacuum as rockets do in space, the exiting velocities would be greater and the resultant thrust would be greater.

To create the acting force within a turbine engine, a continuous flow cycle is utilized. Ambient air enters the inlet diffuser where it is subjected to changes in pressure, velocity, and temperature. It then passes through the compressor where pressure or potential energy is increased mechanically. The air continues at constant pressure to the combustion section where its temperature and volume are greatly increased by addition of fuel. Here, potential (stored) energy is converted to kinetic (motion) energy. The hot gases expand through an exhaust nozzle and create the necessary action to give the reacting thrust.

A further explanation of the creation of the "acting force" can be seen in Figure 2-32. The gas turbine engine operates on a principle of continuous combustion or one unit of mass airflow in and one unit of mass airflow out. Because the unit trying to exit has been increased in size (volume), it will have to accelerate greatly to leave the exhaust nozzle as the new unit enters the inlet.

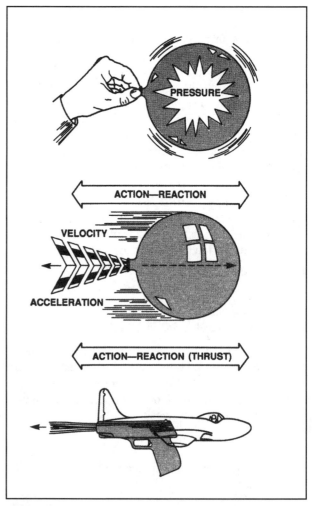

Fig. 2-31 — *Jet propulsion principle (Newton's Third Law).*

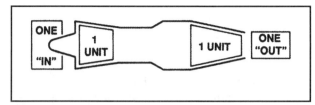

Fig. 2-32 — One-in, one-out theory.

I. Thrust And SHP Calculations

Thrust is transmitted to the aircraft through the engine mounts. All the points of thrust created within the engine are not easily identifiable, but variations in pressures within the engine exert forces all along its length, from the airframe inlet to the exhaust. A simple explanation of the operation of a gas turbine turbojet is that it is a device which increases potential energy and then converts it to kinetic energy. Some of this energy performs work at the turbine, while the remainder exits the engine in the form of thrust. These events are most simply explained in Newton's laws. Newton's third law describes how thrust is created but does not allow for a mathematical solution. However, his first and second laws provide the mathematical formulas to measure the reaction mentioned in the third law.

The $F = M \times A$ formula can be further expanded from the calculations in previous paragraphs to its final useful form for calculating thrust, as follows:

1. Gross Thrust (Static)

Gross thrust (Fg) is computed when the airplane is at rest. The acceleration of the gas within the engine (V2-V1) is the difference in velocities between a unit of air entering the engine and a unit of air exiting at the exhaust nozzle. When the engine is at rest, the value of V1 will be zero, because the air has no initial velocity before the engine starts working on it. The value of V1 will be greater than zero when the engine (aircraft) is moving. Using the symbol "Ms" for mass or weight of airflow per second through an engine, the formula for gross thrust would be:

$$Fg = \frac{Ms(V2 - V1)}{g}$$

Where: Fg = Gross thrust, in lbs.
Ms = Weight of airflow in lbs./sec.
V2 = Exhaust velocity, in ft./sec.
V1 = Inlet velocity, in ft./sec.
g = Gravity acceleration, 32.2 ft./sec.^{2}

From the formula above, it appears like the time factor in the acceleration formula has disappeared. It hasn't really, it is just included in the Ms value, which is pounds of airflow per second. Since the time frame is one second, there is no need to include its value in the calculation since dividing by one does not change the answer.

The mass of airflow through the engine every second can be thought about this way. Air enters what is essentially a round engine inlet, and is moving at a certain number of feet per second. If we imagine the air is moving at 200 feet per second, and the diameter of the engine inlet is 3 feet, then a column (cylinder) of air 200 feet long and 3 feet in diameter enters the engine every second. The question now becomes, how much does the air in that cylinder weigh? We can answer the question by finding out how many cubic feet of air the cylinder contains, and then multiplying by the weight of one cubic foot of air.

The way in which standard day weight of airflow in pounds per second is calculated is as follows:

The volume of a cylinder $(V) = \pi\,(\,r^2\,)\,(\,h\,)$

Where: V = Cubic feet of space
π = 3.1416
r = The radius of the circle
h = The height of the cylinder

One cubic foot of air, under standard day conditions, weighs 0.07647 lbs./cu. ft. The volume of the cylinder, which is one second's worth of airflow, can be multiplied by this number to obtain the mass airflow in pounds per second.

EXAMPLE: The diameter of an engine's inlet is 2.25 feet and its flow velocity is 400 feet per second. What is its mass airflow in pounds per second at standard day conditions?

$$
\begin{aligned}
\text{Mass airflow (lbs./sec.)} &= \pi\,(r^2)(h)\,(\,0.07647\,)\\
&= 3.1416\,(1.125^2)\,(400)\,(0.07647)\\
&= 121.6 \text{ lbs./sec.}
\end{aligned}
$$

The mass airflow in the example above, 122 pounds per second if rounded off to a whole number, corresponds to the airflow shown for the turbojet airplane in Figure 2-30.

EXAMPLE: A twin engine turbojet powered business jet is at rest and preparing for takeoff.

Each engine mass airflow at takeoff power is 60 pounds per second, exhaust velocity is 1,300 feet per second. What gross thrust is being produced by each engine?

$$
\begin{aligned}
Fg &= \frac{Ms(V2 - V1)}{g}\\[4pt]
Fg &= \frac{60(1300 - 0)}{32.2}\\[4pt]
Fg &= 2{,}422.4 \text{ lbs.}
\end{aligned}
$$

Where: Fg = Static thrust in pounds
Ms = 60 lbs./sec
V2 = 1,300 ft./sec.
V1 = 0 ft./sec.
g = 32.2 ft./sec.^{2}

It is helpful to note that velocity of air within the inlet is not V1, which is defined as aircraft speed. The velocity of air in the inlet is, in actuality, the (h) in the $V = \pi (r^2)(h)$ formula, where $\pi (r^2)$ represents the effective flow area of the inlet and (h) represents the flow velocity in the inlet.

The mass airflow of 60 pounds per second in the previous example might have been calculated as follows: If the diameter of the inlet is 1.42 feet and the velocity of airflow within the inlet at takeoff rpm is 496 feet per second:

$$\text{Mass airflow (lbs./sec.)} = \pi (r^2)(h)(0.07647)$$
$$= 3.1416(0.71^2)(496)(0.07647)$$
$$= 60.0 \text{ lbs./sec.}$$

2. Net Thrust

When an aircraft is flying, consider that any unit of mass airflow has initial momentum at the engine inlet. Its velocity change across the engine will be greatly reduced as compared to an engine at rest. When an aircraft is in flight, the output of the engines is referred to as net thrust, versus gross or static thrust when the aircraft is stationary.

The aircraft speed effect is called ram drag, or inlet momentum drag. The net thrust of the engine is the difference between what the static thrust would be and the ram drag. Shown as a formula, it would be:

Fn = Fg - Fd

Where: Fn = Net thrust in pounds
        Fg = Gross thrust in pounds
        Fd = Ram drag in pounds

Thinking about the previous example of calculating gross thrust, we multiplied the mass airflow by the exhaust velocity, and then divided by gravity. We did not need to do anything with the inlet velocity value, because it was zero. So in simple terms, the formula would be:

$$Fg = \frac{Ms(V2)}{g}$$

The formula for ram drag would be:

$$Fd = \frac{Ms(V1)}{g}$$

When ram drag is subtracted from gross thrust, and the values combined, the formula becomes the same one that was developed for the earlier examples, or:

$$Fn = \frac{Ms(V2 - V1)}{g}$$

EXAMPLE: The same business jet as in the gross thrust example is now flying at 400 mph (587 fps) near sea level. What is its net thrust if we consider, for the time being, that the mass airflow is still 60 lbs./sec. and the exhaust velocity is still 1300 fps?

$$Fn = \frac{60(1300 - 587)}{32.2}$$

Fn = 1,328.6 lbs.

3. Thrust With A Choked Nozzle

Most gas turbine engines are fitted with a device called a choked exhaust nozzle, or "jet nozzle" (Figure 2-33). From cruise to takeoff power, pressure in the exhaust duct is pushing the gas with such force that the gas velocity reaches the speed of sound. Pressure at the nozzle opening does not return to ambient with a choked nozzle but stays somewhere in excess of ambient. This pressure across the exhaust nozzle opening creates additional thrust by the principle of F = P x A, or force equals pressure times area.

Referring back to Bernoulli's Principle, recall that total pressure is the sum of static pressure and pressure due to flow and that, if a gas is accelerated, its static pressure will decrease. If energy is added to accelerate the gas, it can only do so up to the speed of sound. So if the jet nozzle is choked, it can be stated that there are two types of energy in the tailpipe, energy of flow (rearward) and energy from internal pressure (in all directions).

As choking (gas flowing at the speed of sound) occurs, pressure starts to build in the tailpipe between the wall of flowing gases in the front section and the constricting exhaust nozzle opening at the rear. As pressure builds above ambient pressure across the opening, a forward push is said to be created. (See Figure 2-34.)

The total thrust of the engine is now the sum of what would be called the "reaction thrust" and the "pressure thrust". The formula for calculating this thrust would be:

$$Fn = \frac{Ms(V2 - V1)}{g} + [Aj(Pj - Pam)]$$

Where: Fn = Net thrust in lbs.
        Ms = Mass airflow in lbs./sec.
        V2 = Exhaust velocity in fps
        V1 = Inlet velocity in fps
        g   = Gravity acceleration in fps^2
        Aj = Area of jet nozzle in sq. in.
        Pj = Pressure at jet nozzle in psi
        Pam = Pressure ambient

NOTE: This discussion is repeated in Chapter III, section "g".

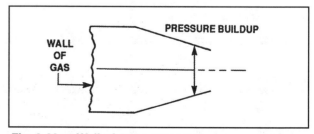

Fig. 2-33 — Wall of gas concept.

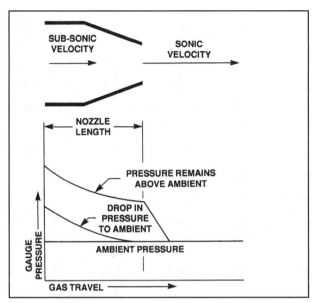

Fig. 2-34 — Choked-unchoked pressure curves.

By comparison, when the flow is unchoked, only the flow energy of the gas is creating thrust because pressure energy is decreasing in proportion to velocity increase, and has returned to ambient pressure at the jet nozzle opening.

EXAMPLE: The same aircraft as in the net thrust example now has a speed of 550 mph (807 fps), an Ms that is 50% of sea level value, and an exhaust velocity of 1,500 fps. The pressure at the exhaust nozzle is 11.5 psi, the area of the exhaust nozzle is 50 square inches, and the ambient pressure is 5.5 psi. What is the net thrust?

$$Fn = \frac{Ms(V2-V1)}{g} + [Aj(Pj-Pam)]$$

$$Fn = \frac{30(1500-807)}{32.2} + [50(11.5-5.5)]$$

$$Fn = 646 + 300$$

$$Fn = 946 \text{ lbs.}$$

4. Thrust Distribution

The rated thrust of an engine is calculated by finding the sum of forward forces within the engine and subtracting the sum of the rearward forces within the engine. The compressor, combustor, and exhaust cone exit areas exert forward forces; the turbine and tailpipe exit areas exert a rearward force.

When the outlet of a particular section exerts more force than is present at the inlet of that section, there is a forward pushing force. When the inlet of a section (in actuality the exit of the preceding section) exerts more force than is present at the exit, there is a rearward pushing force.

Figure 2-35 shows that the compressor section exerts a forward force. This occurs because the compressor discharge area has a much greater pressure force than the compressor inlet, which has zero force. A forward force or thrust is then exerted on the blades, vanes, and outer cases by internal gas pressure buildup at the compressor discharge area.

$$Fg = (A \times P) + \frac{Ms(V)}{g} - I$$

Mathematically this can be expressed as:

Where:
Fg	=	Section gross thrust in lbs.
A	=	Area in sq. in.
P	=	Pressure in psig
Ms	=	Mass airflow in lbs./sec.
V	=	Velocity in ft./sec.
I	=	Initial force in lbs.
g	=	32.2 ft./sec^2

The following hypothetical examples should help to explain thrust distribution within an engine.

a. At The Compressor Outlet:

The engine is a turbojet, with thrust related data as follows:

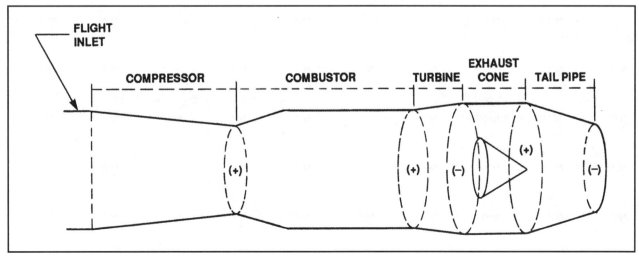

Fig. 2-35 — Thrust distribution.

Compressor outlet area: 60 sq. in.
Pressure at outlet: 55 psig
Mass airflow: 30 lbs./sec.
Velocity at outlet: 400 ft./sec.
Initial force at inlet: 0 lbs.
Gravity: 32.2 ft./sec^2

$$Fg = (A \times P) + \frac{Ms\,(V)}{g} - I$$

$$Fg = 60 \times 55 + \frac{30 \times 400 - 0}{32.2}$$

$$Fg = 3,300 + 373$$

$$Fg = 3,673 \text{ lbs. (forward thrust)}$$

The net forward thrust of 3,673 pounds occurs here because the compressor outlet is creating 3,673 pounds of thrust or force, and the inlet of the compressor is creating zero thrust.

You will notice the similarity in the above formula to the choked nozzle thrust formula; that is, thrust equals mass times acceleration, plus area times pressure. Its use here is possible because the pressure factor is always above ambient within the engine, just as it is when the jet nozzle is choked.

b. At The Combustor Outlet:

The force present at the combustor inlet is the same as the compressor outlet, 3,673 pounds. The thrust related data is:

Combustor outlet area: 157 sq. in.
Pressure at outlet: 53 psig
Mass airflow: 30 lbs./sec.
Velocity at outlet: 1,055 ft./sec.
Initial force at inlet: 3,673 lbs.
Gravity: 32.2 ft./sec^2

$$Fg = (157 \times 53) + \frac{30 \times 1,055}{32.2} - 3,673$$

$$Fg = 8,321 + 983 - 3,673$$

$$Fg = 5,631 \text{ lbs. (forward thrust)}$$

The net forward thrust of the combustor is 5,631 pounds because the combustor outlet is creating 9,304 pounds of thrust or force and the combustor inlet (same as the compressor outlet), is creating 3,673 pounds of force or thrust.

c. At The Turbine Outlet:

The force present at the turbine inlet is the same as the combustor outlet, 5,631 lbs. + 3,673 lbs., or a total of 9,304 lbs. of thrust. The thrust related data is:

Turbine outlet area: 170 sq. in.
Pressure at outlet: 11 psig
Mass airflow: 30 lbs./sec.
Velocity at outlet: 605.7 ft./sec.
Initial force at inlet: 9,304 lbs.
Gravity: 32.2 ft./sec^2

$$Fg = (A \times P) + \frac{Ms\,(V)}{g} - I$$

$$Fg = (170 \times 11) + \frac{30 \times 605.7}{32.2} - 9,304$$

$$Fg = 1,870 + 564.3 - 9,304$$

$$Fg = -6,869.7 \text{ lbs. (rearward thrust)}$$

The net rearward thrust of -6,869.7 pounds occurs here because the turbine outlet is creating only 2,434.3 pounds of thrust or force, and the combustor outlet is creating 9,304 pounds. This results from a change in direction of gas flow from axial to tangential (in the direction of the turbine blade rotation). Normally, we think of a pressure drop (53 dropping to 11) as creating a great velocity increase; but, as the gas accelerates at an angle, the effect of pressure drop to induce axial velocity change is lost. That is, a substantial pressure drop has actually resulted in an axial velocity decrease of 1,055 fps to 605.7 fps.

d. At The Exhaust Cone Outlet:

The force present at the inlet of the exhaust cone is the same as the turbine outlet, 2,434.3 lbs. The thrust related data is:

Exhaust cone outlet area: 202 sq. in.
Pressure at outlet: 12 psig
Mass airflow: 30 lbs./sec.
Velocity at outlet: 593.4 ft./sec.
Initial force at inlet: 2,434.3 lbs.
Gravity: 32.2 ft./sec^2

$$Fg = (A \times P) + \frac{Ms\,(V)}{g} - I$$

$$Fg = (202 \times 12) + \frac{30 \times 593.4}{32.2} - 2,434.3$$

$$Fg = 2,424 + 552.8 - 2,434.3$$

$$Fg = 542.5 \text{ lbs. (forward thrust)}$$

The net forward thrust of 542.5 pounds occurs here because the exhaust cone outlet area, in conjunction with the inner section (tailpipe), forms a divergent duct that has a thrust or force of 2,976.8 pounds. This is 542.5 pounds more than the exhaust cone inlet area (same as turbine outlet) of 2,434.3 pounds.

e. At The Tailpipe (With Its Jet Nozzle In A Choked Condition):

Note that the positive side of the formula here will in fact be the actual net thrust of the engine when the calculations are completed. The thrust related data is:

Jet nozzle outlet area: 105 sq. in.
Pressure at outlet: 5 psig
Mass airflow: 30 lbs./sec.
Velocity at outlet: 1,900 ft./sec.
Initial force at inlet: 2,976.8 lbs.
Gravity: 32.2 ft./sec^2

$$Fg = (A \times P) + \frac{Ms(V)}{g} - I$$

$$Fg = (105 \times 5) + \frac{30 \times 1,900}{32.2} - 2,976.8$$

$$Fg = 525 + 1,770.2 - 2,976.8$$

$$Fg = -681.6 \text{ lbs. (rearward thrust)}$$

The rearward thrust of -681.6 pounds occurs here because the tailpipe is creating velocity at the expense of pressure. The tailpipe outlet force or thrust is 2,295.2 pounds, but at the exhaust cone outlet (same as tailpipe inlet), the thrust is 2,976.8 pounds. This leaves -681.6 pounds of thrust or force. Note that the net thrust here (-681.6) is not the choked nozzle thrust, which is +525.

The sum of the rearward thrust or force values equals - 7,551.3 pounds, and the sum of the forward thrust values equals 9,846.5. The difference between the two leaves a forward thrust of 2,295.2 lbs.

By comparison of the thrust distribution formula to the conventional choked nozzle thrust formula, it becomes apparent that the final answer to a thrust calculation will be the same. The engine in the thrust distribution examples has a mass airflow of 30 pounds per second, a V2 of 1,900 feet per second, a V1 of zero feet per second, a pressure at the jet nozzle of 5 psig above ambient, and a jet nozzle area of 105 sq. in. If these numbers were punched into the choked nozzle thrust formula, the answer would solve to be 2, 295.2 lbs.

5. Fan Engine Thrust (unmixed exhaust)

Thrust calculation of a fan engine can be accomplished in the same way as the turbojet, except that the hot and cold stream nozzle thrust values are figured separately and then added together.

EXAMPLE: A business jet has turbofan engines with unmixed exhaust. The mass airflow of the engine's core and the fan are both 60 lbs./sec. The velocity of the fan discharge air is 800 fps and the core velocity is 1,000 fps. What is the total gross (static) thrust produced by the engine?

$$\text{Core Thrust } Fg = \frac{60(1000 - 0)}{32.2}$$

$$Fg = 1,863.4 \text{ lbs.}$$

$$\text{Fan Thrust } Fg = \frac{60(800 - 0)}{32.2}$$

$$Fg = 1,490.7 \text{ lbs.}$$

Total Thrust = 1,863.4 + 1,490.7 = 3,354.1 lbs.

Note that in the above examples no mention has been made of a humidity factor influencing thrust. The National Advisory Committee of Aeronautics (NACA) Standard Day conditions are 59°F (15°C), 14.7 psi (29.92 in. Hg), and zero percent humidity at 40° latitude.

However, an engine is seldom operated at zero percent humidity. The reason for not considering humidity in thrust calculations is that 65% to 75% of the mass airflow through a gas turbine engine is used for cooling the combustion mixture. The presence of moisture suspended in the atmosphere has a negligible effect on either the cooling process or the remaining 25% to 35% of mass airflow used for combustion. This situation concerning humidity holds true for all types of gas turbines.

6. Thrust Horsepower (THP) In Turbojet And Turbofan Engines.

Thrust producing engines such as turbojets and turbofans create sufficient power for very high speed flight. If one wanted to determine how much horsepower it would take to propel an aircraft at the same speeds using horsepower as a measurement instead of thrust, it is possible. Thrust horsepower also provides for comparison between gas turbine engines with reference to fuel consumption rates. In Chapter VII, an example is given comparing the fuel consumption per thrust horsepower of the Concorde Supersonic Aircraft with the DC-10 Subsonic Airliner.

To convert gas turbine engine thrust to thrust horsepower the following formula applies:

$$Thp = \frac{Fn \times \text{aircraft speed}}{375 \text{ mile lbs. per hour}}$$

The value 375 mile-pounds per hour is derived from the basic horsepower formula as follows:

1 Horsepower = 33,000 ft. lbs./min.

33,000 × 60 = 1,980,000 ft. lbs./hour

$$\frac{1,980,000 \text{ ft. lbs./hour}}{5,280 \text{ ft./mile}} = 375 \text{ mile lbs./hour}$$

If aircraft speed is expressed in feet per second, the following formula would apply:

$$Thp = \frac{Fn \times V1}{550}$$

Where: V1 = Aircraft speed in feet per second (fps)

As the formula indicates, thrust horsepower can only be calculated in flight, thus the use of the symbol Fn for thrust applies. The reasoning is that while the aircraft is stationary, no energy is expended for propulsion, and in the formula V1 (fps) is zero.

An observation can be made here that at very high aircraft speeds, the thrust horsepower of a gas turbine engine can be considerable.

EXAMPLE 1: The Concorde SST, if flying at 1,200 mph, will have a thrust horsepower factor of 1200 ÷ 375, or 3.2 times its net thrust output. On one model, thrust per engine at cruise is 10,000 lbs., so Thp = 3.2 x 10,000, or 32,000 thrust horsepower.

The graph (Figure 2-36) illustrates the relationship between thrust horsepower and aircraft speed (V1) for the Concorde engine.

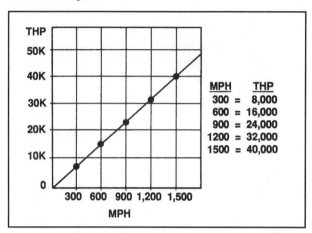

Fig. 2-36 — Thrust horsepower vs. airspeed for Concorde engine.

This aircraft would not actually fly at all cruise speeds plotted on the graph at rated cruise thrust, but rather, the graph indicates the faster the design speed for a given thrust, the greater the thrust horsepower. At 375 mph, one pound of thrust is equal to one horsepower. At 1,200 mph, one pound of thrust is equal to 3.2 horsepower.

From this, it can be seen that turbine engine development had to wait until faster aircraft could be designed in order to fulfill its role as an effective powerplant for high speed flight. If the Concorde, for instance, were speed limited to 750 mph, its per engine thrust horsepower in cruise would only be 20,000 (10,000 x 750 ÷ 375).

EXAMPLE 2: A gas turbine is producing 3,230 pounds of net thrust while the aircraft is flying at 500 mph. What thrust horsepower is being created?

$$Thp = \frac{Fn \times \text{aircraft speed}}{375 \text{ mile lbs. per hour}}$$

$$Thp = \frac{3,230 \times 500}{375}$$

$$Thp = 4,307$$

Note that thrust horsepower is not a means of measuring power of a turboshaft engine. Turboshaft engines are rated in shaft horsepower (shp), as are reciprocating engines, and this is measured directly at the output shaft by use of a dynamometer.

7. Propeller (Turboprop) Thrust

In the thrust horsepower formula in paragraph I.6, we arrived at a shaft horsepower value for a given thrust and speed of a turbojet and turbofan. By arranging this formula differently we can arrive at a net thrust (Fn) value for a turboprop engine in straight and level flight.

If:

$$Thp = \frac{Fn \times Mph}{375}$$

Then:

$$Fn = \frac{Thp \times 375}{Mph}$$

If we substitute shaft horsepower (Shp) for thrust horsepower (Thp) and use the conventional 80% efficiency factor for a propeller (Fp), the formula for the force (thrust) generated by a propeller becomes:

$$Fp = \frac{Shp \times 375 \times 0.80}{Mph}$$

If the propeller is 90% efficient, as compared to 80%, the top line of the formula would be multiplied by 0.90 instead of the 0.80. Theoretically, the propeller could be 100% efficient, if it had no friction or aerodynamic losses and converted all the power provided to it to thrust.

EXAMPLE: A turboprop engine produces 1,150 shp. How much propeller thrust does that equal if the aircraft is flying at 445 mph and the propeller efficiency is 100%?

$$Fp = \frac{Shp \times 375 \times 1.0}{Mph}$$

$$Fp = \frac{1,150 \times 375 \times 1.0}{445}$$

$$Fp = 969.1$$

If propeller thrust in a static condition is calculated (operating without moving forward), then a conversion factor of 2.5 is used. In a static condition, one shaft horsepower is equal to 2.5 pounds of thrust. For the engine in the example with 1,150 shaft horsepower, in a static condition this would be equal to 2,875 pounds of thrust. If a comparison is made between the above turboprop and a turbofan of similar size, it would be found that the turbofan would also be in the 2,500 to 3,000 lb. thrust range at sea level static.

Note that in the case of the turboprop, if total thrust were needed, the hot exhaust thrust (Fn) would have to be added to the propeller thrust (Fp).

The thrust of a turboprop can also be calculated by using Figure 2-37 if the shaft horsepower is known. The shaft horsepower of a turboprop will be indicated directly by a cockpit instrument or the shaft horsepower can be calculated by formula from a torque gauge in the cockpit. This torque system is discussed in detail in Chapter 7.

In the example plotted, at 275 mph and 80% propeller efficiency, the Fp to shaft horsepower ratio is 1.1 to 1. Recall that in a static condition it was 2.5 to 1.

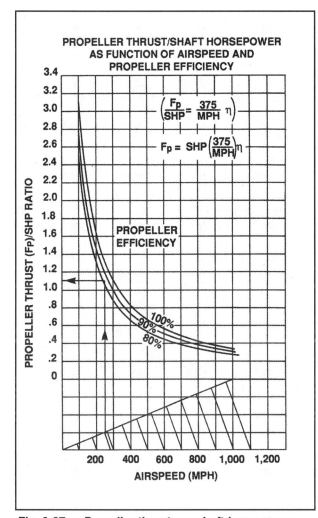

Fig. 2-37 — Propeller thrust per shaft horsepower.

EXAMPLE: According to the graph, what is the propeller thrust if, at 275 mph, 525 shaft horsepower is being produced and the prop is 80% efficient?

$$Fp = Shp \times \text{Conversion Factor}$$

The plot for 275 Mph and 80% intersects on the left of the chart at a ratio of 1.1.

$$Fp = 525 \times 1.1$$
$$Fp = 578 \text{ lbs.}$$

The 578 pounds of thrust calculation can be confirmed by formula as follows:

$$Fp = \frac{Shp \times 375 \times 0.80}{Mph}$$

$$Fp = \frac{525 \times 375 \times 0.80}{275}$$

$$Fp = 573$$

This answer is close to being the same as the previous answer of 578 lbs. The answer found by way of a math solution is the most accurate.

8. Equivalent Shaft Horsepower (Turboprop Ground Runup)

Another useful calculation, usually included in a discussion of gas turbine theory, is determination of the power of a turboprop. The exhaust thrust converted to shaft horsepower and the shaft horsepower obtained from a dynamometer check are added together. The sum is known as equivalent shaft horsepower (Eshp). Under static conditions, one shaft horsepower is equal to approximately 2.5 pounds of thrust. The formulas are as follows:

$$Hp \text{ (jet thrust)} = \frac{Jet\ Thrust\ (Fg)}{2.5}$$

$$Eshp = Shp \text{ (dynamometer)} + Hp \text{ (jet thrust)}$$

EXAMPLE: The Garrett turboprop model TPE-331 produces 187.5 pounds of jet thrust, with a rating of 680 shaft horsepower. What is its equivalent shaft horsepower rating?

$$Hp \text{ (jet thrust)} = \frac{Jet\ Thrust\ (Fg)}{2.5}$$

$$Hp \text{ (jet thrust)} = \frac{187.5}{2.5}$$

$$Hp \text{ (jet thrust)} = 75$$

$$Eshp = Shp \text{ (dynamometer)} + Hp \text{ (jet thrust)}$$
$$Eshp = 680 + 75$$
$$Eshp = 755$$

9. Equivalent Shaft Horsepower (Turboprop In Flight)

Equivalent shaft horsepower can also be calculated in flight if the variable hp (propeller efficiency) is introduced. If thrust horsepower represents the shaft horsepower a turbojet or turbofan has as useful power in flight, then shaft horsepower times ηp will equal the useful power available to a turboprop in flight.

The following formula will result:

$$Thp = \frac{Fn \times V1}{375}$$

$$Shp = Thp \div \eta p$$

$$Shp = \frac{Fn \times V1}{375} \div \eta p$$

Where: Fn = Net Thrust
          V1 = Aircraft Speed (Mph)
          375 = Conversion of Power to HP
          ηp = Efficiency (propeller)

Since equivalent shaft horsepower (Eshp) equals the engine's shaft horsepower, plus the shaft horsepower equivalent of the jet thrust, Eshp in flight would be calculated using the following formula:

$$\text{Eshp (flight)} = \text{Shp} + \frac{\text{Fn} \times \text{V1}}{\eta\text{p} \times 375}$$

EXAMPLE: A turboprop aircraft is operating in flight and the cockpit power gauge indicates 500 shaft horsepower. The aircraft speed is 275 mph, there is 200 pounds of exhaust hot thrust present, and the industry accepted propeller efficiency is 80 percent. What is the engine equivalent shaft horsepower?

$$\text{Eshp (flight)} = \text{Shp} + \frac{\text{Fn} \times \text{V1}}{\eta\text{p} \times 375}$$

$$\text{Eshp (flight)} = 500 + \frac{200 \times 275}{0.80 \times 375}$$

$$\text{Eshp (flight)} = 683$$

Conclusion: It would take 683 shp to produce the same airspeed as the present 500 shp and 200 pounds of thrust.

10. Horsepower Requirement To Drive The Compressor(s)

The turbine drives the compressor by extracting power from the flowing gas. The compression process demands that power be expended to produce a pressure rise. If the temperature rise above ambient across compression is known, and the engine mass airflow in pounds per second is known, the horsepower required to produce that temperature rise can be calculated by the following formula:

Hp (compressor) = Tr x Cp x Ms x 778 ÷ 550

Where: Tr = Temperature rise (°F)
　　　　Cp = 0.24 Btu/lb./°F
　　　　Ms = Mass airflow in lbs./sec.
　　　　778 = ft. lbs. in 1 Btu
　　　　550 = ft. lbs./sec. in 1 Hp

By using Cp, the specific heat ratio at constant pressure, the Btu (power) input per pound of air will result. Cp of 0.24 is the Btu value it takes to raise one pound of air 1°F, compared to water which takes 1.0 Btu/lb. to raise its temperature 1°F.

If there are 778 foot pounds of work in 1 Btu, multiplying Tr x Cp x Ms x 778 will give the power required to heat the air. Dividing power by the conversion factor of 550 foot pounds/second will then give horsepower.

EXAMPLE 1: If the engine in the thrust distribution example covered earlier in this chapter, has an inlet temperature of 60°F, a compressor discharge temperature of 270°F, and a mass airflow of 30 pounds/second, what horsepower is required to drive its compressor?

Hp(compressor) = Tr x Cp x Ms x 778 ÷ 550

Hp(compressor) = 210 x 0.24 x 30 x 778 ÷ 550

Hp(compressor) = 2,138.8 Hp extracted by turbine

On large and powerful engines, the horsepower extracted at the turbine is very high because both mass airflow (Ms) and temperature rise (Tr) are high due to high compression loads.

EXAMPLE 2: The Rolls-Royce Olympus 593 turbojet, in the Concorde aircraft, has a mass airflow of 415 pounds per second and a temperature rise across compression of 900°F above ambient. What horsepower is the turbine system extracting?

Hp(compressor) = Tr x Cp x Ms x 778 ÷ 550

Hp(compressor) = 900 x 0.24 x 415 x 778 ÷ 550

Hp(compressor) = 126,800

This represents only the power required to drive the compressor. The engine will also have to provide additional power to create thrust.

EXAMPLE 3: One model of the Pratt & Whitney JT8D dual spool turbofan is operating on a 59°F day and has the following operational parameters. What is the horsepower required to drive the compressor?

Fan Ms = 164 lbs./sec., fan discharge temp. = 214°F
N_1 Ms = 160 lbs./sec., N_1 discharge temp. = 380°F
N_2 Ms = 160 lbs./sec., N_2 discharge temp. = 820°F

These specifications can be found in Chapter IV, JT8D Engine Performance Data.

Hp = Tr x Cp x Ms x 778 ÷ 550

Hp(fan) = (214 − 59) x 0.24 x 164 x 778 ÷ 550

Hp(fan) = 8,630

Hp(N_1) = (380 − 59) x 0.24 x 160 x 778 ÷ 550

Hp(N_1) = 17,436

Hp(N_2) = (820 − 380) x 0.24 x 160 x 778 ÷ 550

Hp(N_2) = 23,900

11. Other Significant Horsepower Terms

a. Thermodynamic Horsepower:

This value represents the total available horsepower of a turboprop or turboshaft engine as measured on a dynamometer. Many engines are not used to their full potential (thermodynamic horsepower) because the aircraft does not require that amount of power. When this occurs, the engine is re-rated to a lower maximum horsepower and the new power rating is given as the shaft horsepower rating of the engine.

b. Isentropic Gas Horsepower:

This value represents the total potential work available in the exhaust gases leaving the gas generator portion of a free turbine type turboprop or turboshaft engine. The gases then enter the power turbine and expand to turn it, producing work. The shaft horsepower rating of such an engine is obtained by multiplying the isentropic horsepower by the percentage of power turbine efficiency.

c. Ram Shaft Horsepower:

This value represents the total equivalent shaft horsepower available to a turboprop engine at the point of takeoff. At this time, ram air compression in the engine inlet boosts the static rated takeoff equivalent shaft horsepower 1 to 2 percent.

J. Gas Turbine Engine Performance Curves

1. Propulsive Efficiency

In Figure 2-38, the curves depict graphically the way in which propulsive efficiency varies with aircraft speed. Herein lies an important difference between turbine and reciprocating engines. The thrust of the turbine is fairly constant, whereas the thrust of reciprocating engines drops off rapidly as speed increases. The turbine engine performs better than a reciprocating engine under high speed conditions because it makes use of the increased inlet air mass and air pressure (resulting from the ram effect) to maintain its thrust.

Propulsive efficiency is described as the external powerplant efficiency or a measure of the effectiveness with which kinetic energy in a powerplant is converted to useful work for propelling the aircraft. It can also be described as a comparison of the engine's propelling exhaust velocity (jet wake or prop wake) versus aircraft speed. The graph reveals how propeller-driven aircraft gain their efficiency first at low airspeeds because the controllable pitch propeller is capable of moving large mass airflows. The curves all peak out as soon as more fuel energy is introduced to create an exhaust velocity increase. Work then comes out in the form of increased aircraft speed.

The curves can be interpreted as follows:

a. The propeller aircraft (either piston or turbine driven) peaks out slightly above 85%, after which the propeller loses efficiency. That is, its exhaust wake velocity continues to increase from added fuel energy, but aircraft speed does not increase proportionally. Note that after reaching approximately 375 mph, propulsive efficiency starts to decrease. Aerodynamic drag and tip shock stall are involved here and by 500 mph efficiency decreases to 65%.

b. The ultra-high bypass turbofan curve peaks at approximately 560 mph (Mach 0.85), after which the fan suffers the same losses in drag and tip speed as the propeller. In order to go 700 mph (aircraft speed), the exhaust velocity will have to be increased to an uneconomical level.

c. The high bypass turbofan is the most widely used engine today in both large and small aircraft. Its propulsive efficiency curve peaks out slightly lower than the UHB engine but at approximately the same airspeed.

d. Subsonic aircraft with low and medium bypass turbofans all operate in the 500 to 600 mph range. Note that the curve shows a lower efficiency value than a high bypass engine in that range. Because of this, high bypass engines are rapidly replacing low and medium bypass engines in many aircraft.

e. The supersonic low bypass turbofan and turbojet have a theoretical propulsive efficiency peak limit in the 2,000 to 3,000 mph range. Their narrow, low-drag profile allows this range. Any additional energy added (in the form of fuel) to increase speed further would raise the internal engine temperatures to unacceptable levels. The graph (Figure 2-39) can be defined mathematically for engines with a single exhaust, as follows:

$$Peff = \frac{2}{1 + \dfrac{Vf}{Vi}}$$

Where: Peff = Propulsive efficiency
             Vf   = Exhaust velocity (final)
             Vi   = Aircraft speed (initial)

Derivation of the propulsive efficiency formula is arrived at by manipulating the familiar kinetic energy formula, $Ke = 1/2mV^2$. Consider that there is a great deal of energy wasted or energy left behind the engine in its prop

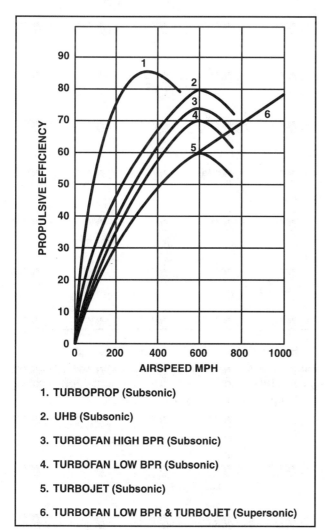

1. **TURBOPROP (Subsonic)**

2. **UHB (Subsonic)**

3. **TURBOFAN HIGH BPR (Subsonic)**

4. **TURBOFAN LOW BPR (Subsonic)**

5. **TURBOJET (Subsonic)**

6. **TURBOFAN LOW BPR & TURBOJET (Supersonic)**

Fig. 2-38 — Propulsive efficiency chart.

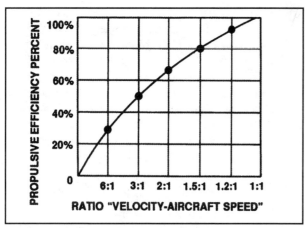

Fig. 2-39 — Comparison: Ratio exhaust velocity to aircraft speed vs propulsive efficiency.

wake or jet wake. If we calculate the energy wasted, we can find the operating conditions that waste the least energy. In doing so, we can also find the conditions of highest propulsive efficiency. In the kinetic energy formula "m" is airflow through the engine and "V" is the velocity change of that mass airflow as it moves through the engine.

NOTE: This same idea is further discussed in the last part of this chapter under the heading of, "Why the Turbofan is Replacing the Turbojet".

The propulsive efficiency formula, as shown in the text above, is relatively simple to use and apply. How it is derived, however, involves a fairly complex process. The method by which it is derived is shown in the box to the right, for those who are interested.

EXAMPLE 1: The propeller aircraft in the graph, Figure 2-38, which seems to have approximately 87% propulsive efficiency at 375 mph, would also have a prop wake (VF) of 490 mph as follows:

$$Peff = \frac{2}{1 + \frac{Vf}{Vi}}$$

$$Peff = \frac{2}{1 + \frac{490}{375}}$$

$$Peff = \frac{2}{2.3} = 0.87 = 87\%$$

EXAMPLE 2: A turbofan aircraft with a mixed exhaust is operating at cruise power. Its speed is 550 mph (807 fps). Velocity from the mixed exhaust is 1,348 fps. What is the propulsive efficiency at this time?

$$Peff = \frac{2}{1 + \frac{1,348}{807}}$$

$$= \frac{2}{2.67} = 0.75 = 75\%$$

NOTE: This calculation is made in fps, which works equally as well as calculations made in mph.

$$Peff = \frac{Thrust\ Power}{Thrust\ Power\ +\ Kinetic\ Energy\ Wasted}$$

$$Peff = \frac{Thrust \times Vi}{Thrust \times Vi + 1/2\ m\ V^2}$$

$$Peff = \frac{M(Vf - Vi)Vi}{M(Vf - Vi)Vi + 1/2M(Vf - Vi)^2}$$

$$Peff = \frac{MVfVi - MVi^2}{MVfVi - MVi^2 + [1/2M(Vf^2 + Vi^2 - 2VfVi)]}$$

$$Peff = \frac{M(VfVi - Vi^2)}{MVfVi - MVi^2 + \frac{MVf^2}{2} + \frac{MVi^2}{2} - MVfVi}$$

$$Peff = \frac{M(VfVi - Vi^2)}{M\left(\frac{Vi^2}{2} + \frac{Vf^2}{2} - Vi^2\right)}$$

$$Peff = \frac{VfVi - Vi^2}{\frac{Vi^2}{2} + \frac{Vf^2}{2} - \frac{Vi^2}{1}}$$

$$Peff = \frac{VfVi - Vi^2}{\frac{Vf^2 - Vi^2}{2}}$$

$$Peff = VfVi - Vi^2 \div \left(\frac{Vf^2 - Vi^2}{2}\right)$$

$$Peff = VfVi - Vi^2 \times \frac{2}{Vf^2 - Vi^2}$$

$$Peff = \frac{2VfVi - 2Vi^2}{Vf^2 - Vi^2}$$

$$Peff = \frac{2Vi(Vf - Vi)}{(Vf - Vi)(Vf + Vi)}$$

$$Peff = \frac{2Vi}{Vf + Vi} = 2 \div \frac{Vf + Vi}{Vi}$$

$$Peff = \frac{2}{\frac{Vf + Vi}{Vi}} = \frac{2}{\frac{Vi}{Vi} + \frac{Vf}{Vi}}$$

$$Peff = \frac{2}{1 + \frac{Vf}{Vi}}$$

EXAMPLE 3: The same aircraft in example 2 has just taken off and is climbing out. Its speed is 200 mph (293.4 fps) and the velocity of its exhaust is 1,650 fps. What is the propulsive efficiency at this time?

$$Peff = \frac{2}{1 + \frac{1,650}{293.4}}$$

$$= \frac{2}{6.62} = 0.30 = 30\%$$

NOTE: The low efficiency shown here results from high exhaust velocity relative to aircraft speed.

The propulsive efficiency formula for a turbofan engine with an unmixed exhaust, which is the case with most high bypass engines, is based on the kinetic energy being wasted by the hot stream gases and by the fan discharge gases. The complete formula, from which the simplified propulsive efficiency is derived, would be used. It would be necessary, however, to calculate for both gas streams.

EXAMPLE 4: A high bypass turbofan is at cruise altitude, with a flight speed of 532 mph (780 fps). Its fan exhaust velocity is 995 fps; core engine exhaust velocity is 1,450 fps; fan mass airflow is 550 lb./sec.; core engine mass airflow is 110 lb./sec. What is its propulsive efficiency? (See the calculation labeled "Formula A").

Conclusion: The closer the aircraft speed comes to exhaust velocity, the higher the propulsive efficiency. The ideal propulsive efficiency would appear to be reached by the aircraft traveling at the same speed as its prop wake or exhaust velocity; in other words, 100%. This, of course, is not possible in a practical sense because no momentum change would occur with regard to mass airflow and no reactive thrust would result.

2. Thermal Efficiency

Thermal efficiency, one of the prime factors in gas turbine performance, is the ratio of the net work produced by the engine to the fuel energy input. In the aircraft, thermal efficiency cannot be measured directly but could, if desired, be calculated by utilizing a cockpit fuel-flow indication.

$$\text{Thermal Efficiency} = \frac{\text{Hp output of engine}}{\text{Hp value of fuel consumed}}$$

EXAMPLE 1: A turboshaft engine produces 725 shaft horsepower. Its fuel consumption is 300 pounds/hour, and its fuel contains 18,730 Btu/pound. Each Btu can produce 778 ft. lbs. of work. What is the engine's thermal efficiency?

Fuel consumed per minute = 5 lbs.(300 ÷ 60)

Btu's in 5 lbs. of fuel   = 93,650 Btu's

Power in 5 lbs. of fuel   = 72,859,700 ft. lbs./min.

$$Hp = \frac{72,859,700 \text{ ft. lbs. min.}}{33,000 \text{ ft. lbs. min.}}$$

Hp = 2,208

$$\text{Thermal Efficiency} = \frac{725 \text{ engine Hp}}{2,208 \text{ fuel Hp}} = 32.8\%$$

Note that the other 67.2% is lost due to: 1) Friction of the rotors (approximately 17%); and, 2) Heat given up to the atmosphere (approximately 50%).

EXAMPLE 2: A turbofan engine produces 11,000 pounds of net thrust in flight at 561 mph. Its fuel consumption is 5,600 pounds per hour. Its fuel contains 18,730 Btu/pound, and each Btu equals 778 ft. lbs. of work. What is its thermal efficiency?

Fuel consumed per minute = 93.3 lbs.(5600 ÷ 60)

Btu's in 93.3 lbs. of fuel   = 1,748,130 Btu's

Power in 93.3 lbs. of fuel = 1,360,000,000 ft. lbs./min.

$$Hp = \frac{1,360,000,000 \text{ ft. lbs./min.}}{33,000 \text{ ft. lbs. min.}}$$

Hp = 41,214

Engine Thp   = 11,000 × 561 ÷ 375 = 16,456

$$\text{Thermal Efficiency} = \frac{16,456 \text{ engine Hp}}{41,214 \text{ fuel Hp}} = 40\%$$

3. Overall Efficiency

Selection of the exact designs of gas turbine engines for a particular aircraft is a process of numerous compromises and trade-offs. Physical features, such as weight, size, and shape are a few of the considerations. Discovering just the right performance factors also figures heavily into the final design of any engine.

FORMULA "A"

$$P_{eff} = \frac{M1Vi \ (V2f - Vi) + M2Vi \ (V2j - Vi)}{[M1Vi \ (V2f - Vi)] + [M2Vi \ (V2j - Vi)] + [1/2M1 \ (V2f - Vi)^2] + [1/2M2 \ (V2j - Vi)^2]}$$

Where :

M1 = Mass airflow of the fan

M2 = Mass airflow of the core engine

Vi   = Aircraft speed

V2f = Exhaust velocity of the fan

V2j = Exhaust velocity of the core

$$P_{eff} = \frac{550 \times 780 \ (995 - 780) + 110 \times 780 \ (1,450 - 780)}{[550 \times 780 \ (995 - 780)] + [110 \times 780 \ (1,450 - 780)] + [1/2 \times 550 \ (995 - 780)^2] + [1/2 \times 110 \ (1,450 - 780)^2]}$$

P_{eff} = 0.080 = 80%

The propulsive efficiency idea previously discussed is one measure of an engine's performance. Another, discussed in the paragraph above, concerns thermal efficiency. The engine designer carefully considers these two factors, called overall efficiency, in combination (see Figure 2-40).

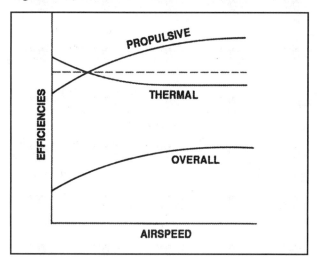

Fig. 2-40 — Efficiency curves.

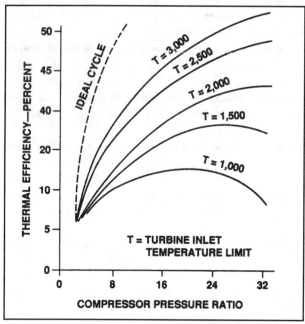

Fig. 2-41 — The effect of compression ratio on thermal efficiency.

Overall Efficiency = (Propulsive Efficiency %) (Thermal Efficiency %)

EXAMPLE: A turbofan engine has a propulsive efficiency of 80% and a thermal efficiency of 40%. What is its overall efficiency?
Overall Efficiency = 80% x 40% = 32%.

Figure 2-40 can be explained as follows:

a. Propulsive efficiency increases as airspeed approaches exhaust velocity values.

b. Thermal efficiency decreases due to added fuel needs at higher airspeeds.

c. Overall efficiency increases as airspeed increases because propulsive efficiency increases more than thermal efficiency decreases.

4. Thermal Efficiency Curves

The three most important factors affecting thermal efficiency are turbine inlet temperature (TIT), compression ratio, and component efficiencies of the compressor and turbine.

Figure 2-41 shows the effect that changing compression ratio has on thermal efficiency. The ideal cycle on the graph would result if compressor and turbine efficiencies were at 100% and all air turbulence within the engine could somehow be eliminated. The ideal curve would eventually peak out at approximately 70% and is of theoretical value only. The best thermal efficiency being realized by airliners today at cruise altitude is in the 45% to 50% range. This is seen in very large engines which have a 30 to 1 compression ratio, or higher, and

turbine inlet temperatures of 2,500 to 3,000°F. The most ideal situation on the graph in Figure 2-41 is 3,000°F, with a 32 to 1 compression ratio. This occurs because expansion in the combustion and turbine sections is greatest when high pressure and high heat are combined.

High TIT has been, and probably always will be, an indicator of high thermal efficiency. The idea here is that, if a particular engine is given higher heat-strength parts, the amount of cooling air required would naturally be less. In turn, the compressor could be scaled down and the turbine wheel set to extract a corresponding lower amount of energy. This in turn would increase the thermal efficiency because for a particular fuel flow, more gas energy would be present in the tailpipe for thrust or more energy would be available to drive a turbine connected to a fan or propeller.

In all turbine engines, heat energy (fuel) is added to accelerate the gases in the combustor. The designer tries to prevent the heated gas from directly touching the metal by providing a film of cooling air. At the turbine, this is not so easily done, and in older designs the heated gases did touch some of the metal and more cooling air had to be added to decrease turbine inlet temperatures. This leads to lower thermal efficiency.

The curve also shows that if a limit of only 1,000°F (TIT value) is set, the benefit of producing a high compression ratio is lost. That is, fuel consumption increases faster than horsepower production increases.

The most energy efficient condition of the compressor and turbine sections in a gas turbine engine occurs when compression temperatures are low. Low compressor temperatures are desirable because they allow greater temperature rise in the combustor and the greatest expansion (acceleration) of the gases.

Large sized, modern engines have efficiency percentages of the compressor and turbine in the mid- to high-eighties. Smaller engines will be slightly less due to scale effect, which means that small engines cannot withstand the same pressures and temperatures as larger ones. Also, when compared to larger engines, smaller ones require that rotor blade tip clearances be a larger percentage of the blade length, resulting in a relatively greater tip leakage and a loss in efficiency.

Figure 2-42 illustrates that with 80 to 90% compressor and turbine efficiencies, thermal efficiency rises with compression ratio.

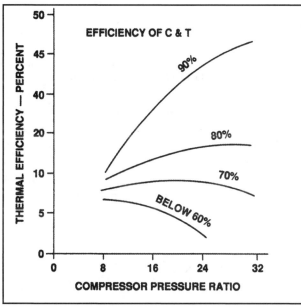

Fig. 2-42 — Turbine and compressor efficiency vs. thermal efficiency.

In other words, the ideal compressor efficiency (adiabatic compression) occurs when the compressor produces the maximum pressure with the least temperature rise, and the ideal turbine extracts the most work for the least fuel consumption.

As engines build service time, a loss of compressor and turbine efficiency occurs as follows:

a. As higher temperatures appear during compression, more energy is required to raise temperatures still further in combustion for the purpose of gas expansion and power. Therefore, the combustor will require more Btu's (fuel) per pound of air to raise air temperature when the warmer air is delivered to the combustor by the compressor. As a result, the overall thermal efficiency of the engine is adversely affected.

b. Ideal turbine efficiency exists when the turbine wheel performs the most work, by rotating at high speeds, with the least extraction of energy from the flowing gases. This, of course, is more attainable today than in the past because of newer lightweight materials, more advanced designs made possible by newer manufacturing methods, and closer production tolerances in manufacture.

Referring to the graph in Figure 2-42, it follows that below 60% efficiency, heat from compression is excessive, the compressor is dirty or damaged, or fuel flow is excessive because of damage to components in the turbine area.

5. Factors That Affect Thrust

There are several factors that affect inlet air density and thus affect gas turbine engine thrust: Ambient temperature, altitude, airspeed, and engine RPM.

Figure 2-43 reveals the way in which changing ambient temperature affects net thrust if altitude, RPM, and airspeed are held constant. This curve would equally apply to ground level (gross) thrust.

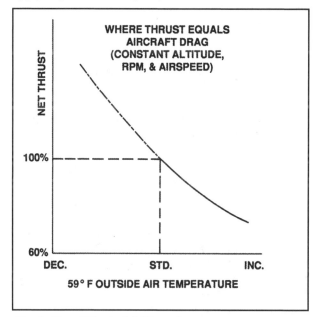

Fig. 2-43 — Effect of OAT on thrust output.

Observe that as the temperature falls below the outside air temperature (OAT) at which the engine is rated, net thrust available at the base line increases over the 100% line to the left. Although sometimes desirable, such as in an emergency, it could quickly cause excessively high internal engine temperatures to occur. For this reason, thrust above 100% rated power is rarely, if ever, used.

The pilot, in the interest of engine service life and fuel conservation, usually schedules power only to the minimum required for satisfactory operation of the aircraft.

The increased thrust seen on the graph due to low ambient temperatures is the result of two factors. First, the energy extracted at the turbine to drive the compressor(s) varies directly with air temperature. Cool air compresses more easily than warm air, and, thus, more energy is left in the engine to accelerate the airflow to create thrust. Second, cool air is more dense, which increases the mass airflow, which in turn increases thrust.

Increasing altitude has conflicting influences on thrust. Although the volume of flow into the engine for a given speed remains unchanged, mass airflow decreases.

The altitude effect on thrust can best be discussed as a result of ambient temperature change and density pressure change. In this case, an increase in altitude causes a decrease in both pressure and temperature. Since the temperature lapse rate is less than the pressure lapse rate, a net decrease in density will result as altitude is increased.

Figure 2-44 illustrates that, as an aircraft gains altitude to 36,000 feet, its thrust decreases at a lower rate than it does above 36,000 feet. This is a result of the combined effects of temperature and pressure lapse rates previously mentioned. However, at 36,000 feet and above, the ambient temperature remains constant (Consult Appendix 7 for Atmospheric Chart.), while the barometric pressure continues to drop. This atmospheric phenomenon results in the more pronounced rate of decrease in thrust, as can be seen on the curve above 36,000 feet.

Another way to think about thrust versus altitude is takeoff from runways which are above sea level. Figure 2-45 shows an engine with 15,500 pounds of thrust at 59°F at sea level. This drops to 9,500 pounds of thrust at 59°F and 14,000 feet elevation. If the pilot were to add fuel to make up for deteriorating thrust, internal temperatures within the engine would reach prohibitively high levels long before regaining 15,500 pounds of thrust.

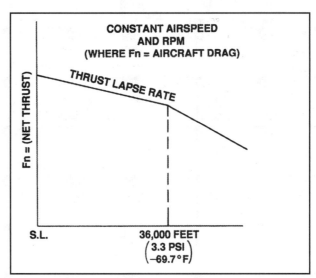

Fig. 2-44 — Effect of altitude on net thrust.

Also notice that starting at the 2000 ft. line, the curves drop off in steps. This is to accommodate aircraft needs for thrust, but at the expense of engine hot section life.

Note that on this graph the full rated thrust of 15,500 pounds can only be attained up to 84°F (28.9°C), after

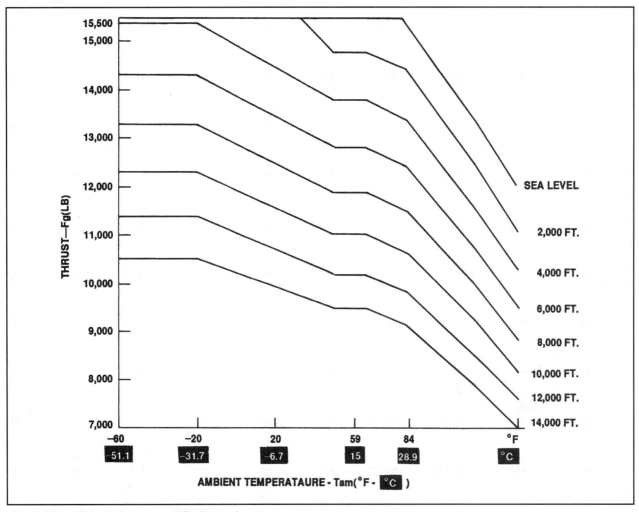

Fig. 2-45 — Effect of runway altitude on thrust.

which the pilot uses only the lesser corresponding thrust on the chart. The full rated thrust being available to a temperature higher than standard day is referred to as flat rating, a topic discussed in detail in chapter 7. The curve corresponds to the curve in Figure 2-43.

When engine power is increased to a higher constant value, the aircraft flies faster and thrust is affected as shown in Figure 2-46.

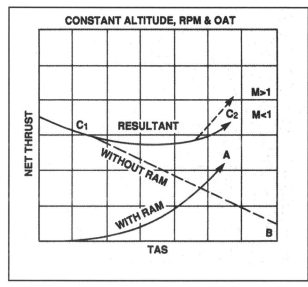

Fig. 2-46 — Effect of airspeed on net thrust.

Curve A indicates that net thrust will tend to increase, due to ram air compression in the engine inlet, as airspeed increases.

Curve B shows the reverse occurring and the net thrust tendency decreasing due to the reduced velocity change of mass airflow through the engine.

Curve C represents curves A and B combined and is seen as an initial decrease in net thrust (at point C). This can be interpreted as the effect of minimal help from ram compression, which occurs at low airspeed, at a time when thrust decreased from reduced velocity change within the engine is more immediate. The net result is an initially diminished thrust situation, a condition which eventually corrects itself as the aircraft approaches its design speed.

In actual figures, the point at which thrust in Curve C starts to recover in the average turbojet or turbofan engine is between 300 and 350 mph, and the point at which thrust is recovered completely is between 500 and 600 mph. This results from ram pressure in the inlet increasing thrust at a faster rate than aircraft speed is diminishing thrust.

Aircraft designed for subsonic cruise speeds, when moving from ground level to altitude, will eventually experience a decrease in net thrust due to altitude effect. With less drag on the aircraft at higher altitudes, the loss of thrust will not be as detrimental to the cruise capability of the aircraft.

In supersonic flight, one would see Curve C2 turn upward very sharply as ram compression greatly increases mass airflow into the engine inlet. During supersonic flight in some aircraft, inlet pressure, due to ram compression, can be as much as 30:1 and net thrust will increase as a result of the increased forward speed.

Figure 2-47 shows the general effect that RPM has on thrust. As RPM increases thrust also increases because more mass airflow and velocity changes occur within the engine.

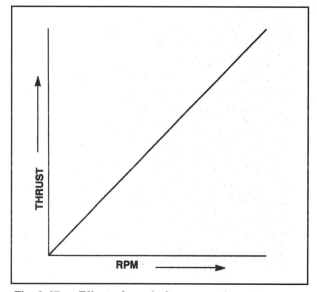

Fig. 2-47 — Effect of revolutions per minute on thrust.

Some early turbojet engines had a close enough relationship between compressor speed and engine thrust that the operator could set engine power output (Figure 2-48) by use of the throttle and the percent rpm cockpit indicator. The power available was dependent on outside air temperature as shown in Fig. 2-43.

Many modern turbofan engines also use fan speed (percent rpm) as a means of setting engine thrust in this same manner.

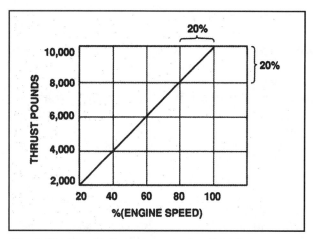

Fig. 2-48— Revolutions per minute effect "when a linear relationship exists".

The majority of dual-spool thrust producing engines, however, use the percent rpm indicator only as an engine condition gauge and not as an indication of engine power. This is required because of the non-linear relationship that exists between compressor speed and engine thrust, as shown in Figure 2-49. Most dual-spool engines utilize an Engine Pressure Ratio (EPR) indicating system to show engine power. EPR is discussed in detail in chapters 7 and 12.

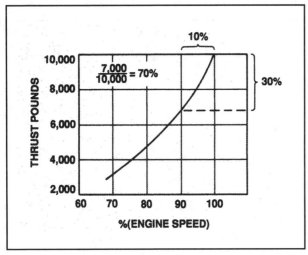

Fig. 2-49 — Revolutions per minute effect on thrust, dual-spool compressor.

K. RPM Limits Imposed On Turbine Engines

1. Axial Flow Compressor

From previous discussions, the reader may have gathered that by increasing RPM to higher and higher values, the effects of atmospheric changes on thrust could be negated or reversed. This is not the case, however, because there is a definite RPM limit present in the form of tip speed limitations. The speed at the tips of all rotating airfoils within the engine is carefully governed to keep the airflow over any part of the airfoils from creating shock waves. Until recently, compressor designs permitted airflow only at subsonic values, and compression values were much lower for a given number of stages of compression. Tip-flow limits today are much higher (in the low supersonic range), but definite limits are still imposed to prevent excessive shock stall and loss of component efficiency.

As a result, the diameter of the rotor itself is its own RPM limiting factor. A look at the operational parameters of any small diameter turbine engine would reveal that its rotational speed at full power is very high, perhaps as high as 50,000 revolutions per minute. Conversely, rotational speed of a large diameter engine would be much lower. For example, a Boeing 747 fan speed is only 3,000 revolutions per minute at full power.

Tip speed formulas:

$$\text{Tip Speed (Ts)} = \pi \times \text{diameter} \times \text{Rpm} \div 60$$

$$\text{Mach Number (M)} = \text{Ts} \div \text{local speed of sound (Cs)}$$

Where :

$$\pi = 3.1416$$

$$60 = \text{Conversion to Revolutions per second}$$

$$\text{Diameter} = \text{value in feet}$$

$$\text{Cs (fps)} = 49.022 \sqrt{\text{Degrees Rankine}}$$

$$°\text{Rankine} = °\text{Fahrenheit} + 460$$

EXAMPLE 1: Using the above formulas, calculate the tip speed in feet per second, and Mach number, of the first compressor stage. The compressor diameter, blade tip to blade tip, is 1.8 feet. Rated speed is 16,500 revolutions per minute and temperature is 59°F.

$$\text{Ts} = \pi \times \text{diameter} \times \text{Rpm} \div 60$$

$$\text{Ts} = 3.1416 \times 1.8 \times 16,500 \div 60$$

$$\text{Ts} = 1,555.1 \text{ fps}$$

$$\text{M} = \text{Ts} \div \text{(Cs)}$$

$$\text{M} = \frac{1,555.1}{1,116.8} = 1.39$$

Where :

$$\pi = 3.1416$$

$$\text{Rpm} = 16,500$$

$$\text{Dia.} = 1.8 \text{ feet}$$

$$\text{Cs} = 49.022 \sqrt{519} = 1,116.8 \text{ f.p.s.}$$

$$°\text{R} = 59 + 460 = 519°$$

In the rear stages of the compressor, the local speed of sound changes because of the change in temperature. As temperature increases, the speed of sound in air increases. Because the temperature in the rear stages of the compressor may be many hundreds of degrees higher than in the front stages, the same tip speed will be a substantially lower Mach number.

EXAMPLE 2: Calculate the tip speed of a 2.5-foot diameter turbine wheel rotating at 16,500 revolutions per minute when turbine gas temperature is 1,400°R.

$$\text{Ts} = 3.1416 \times 2.5 \times 16,500$$

$$\text{Ts} = 2,159.9 \text{ fps}$$

$$\text{M} = \frac{2,159.9}{1,834.2} = 1.18$$

$$\text{Cs} = 49.022 \sqrt{1,400} = 1,834.2 \text{ f.p.s.}$$

2. Centrifugal Flow Compressors

The centrifugal flow compressor also has RPM limitations. Tip speeds of centrifugal compressors are generally in the range of Mach 1.2 to Mach 1.3. The minor shock waves which result are controlled by the design of the compressor and diffuser to prevent loss of compressor aerodynamics. Centrifugal flow compressors are discussed in detail in Chapter III.

3. Speed Of Sound

It is interesting to note that the speed of sound in air is solely dependent on temperature change and not change in pressure. These are two changes that continually take place in airflow within the engine.

Air temperature influences Mach number because the local speed of sound in air is dependent on both elasticity and density changes that take place in air. Observe the formula:

$$Cs = \sqrt{\frac{\text{Elasticity of air}}{\text{Density of air}}}$$

It is a fact that as temperature goes up, density of the air goes down, but elasticity remains constant. So, from the Cs formula, we can see that a density decrease will cause a speed of sound increase.

It is also a fact that, as pressure goes up, density and elasticity both go up proportionally. When computing with the (Cs) speed of sound formula, no change in the speed of sound will occur.

So, the two basic components that govern the speed of sound are density and elasticity. To see how this situation occurs within a gas turbine engine, consider that during compression both pressure and temperature are increasing. But only the air temperature increase affects the local speed of sound. Mathematical units for the formula above are above the scope of this text, but can be found in any good, sound engineering manual.

L. Why The Turbofan Is Replacing The Turbojet (Figure 2-50)

The turbofan has replaced the turbojet in most airliners and is now doing the same in business jets, because the turbofan is as much as 30 to 40 percent more fuel efficient than turbojet engines.

If a turbojet and turbofan are of the same rated thrust, the turbofan will burn less fuel. The explanation is as follows:

a. The lower amount of kinetic energy wasted from its fan exhaust makes the turbofan more propulsively efficient. That is, its average fan/core exhaust velocity (V2) is closer to aircraft speed (V1).

b. The amount of kinetic energy left in the atmosphere after the aircraft has passed by is less with the turbofan versus the turbojet.

c. In terms of mathematics, consider the following example:

EXAMPLE: An aircraft turbine engine expels 10 mass units of air from its exhaust (322 lb. divided by gravity constant), and its exhaust velocity is 1,000 ft./sec faster than the aircraft speed. How much kinetic energy is being wasted?

Fig. 2-50A — Early turbojet powered airliner with narrow inlet and single exhaust.

Fig. 2-50B — Modern turbofan airliner showing wide inlet and dual (fan and core) exhaust.

$$\text{Kinetic Energy} = 1/2 \times M \times V^2$$

$$Ke = 1/2 \times 10 \times 1{,}000^2$$

$$Ke = 5{,}000{,}000 \text{ ft. lbs.}$$

Where:

M = 10 lbs./ft./sec.^{2}

V = 1,000 ft./sec.

NOTE: *Realizing that thrust equals mass time acceleration (F = M A), it at first appears that either "M" or "A" can be doubled to get the same resulting doubling of thrust. That is true, but in terms of energy wasted, it is inefficient to increase the amount of acceleration unless the aircraft is going to fly at a very high speed. It is more efficient to get more thrust by increasing the amount of mass airflow, and keeping the exhaust velocity as close as possible to the aircraft speed.*

In the previous example, if the mass airflow was increased to 20 unit, and the velocity increase reduced to 500 ft./sec., the engine thrust would still be the same. The engine, however, would be much more fuel efficient.

Conclusion: The maximum thrust for the least fuel flow can be obtained by giving the smallest acceleration to the largest possible mass airflow. The high bypass turbofan does just that. It also lends proof to the idea that high exhaust velocity at low aircraft speed is an inefficient operating condition.

QUESTIONS:

1. Which of the four types of gas turbine engines, the turbojet, turboshaft, turboprop, or turbofan, would most likely be installed in a late model business jet of the 500 mph class?

2. What type gas turbine engine is utilized in a helicopter?

3. The gas turbine developed by Whittle was designed with what type compressor unit?

4. Name another type of gas turbine most similar in design to the turboshaft engine.

5. Of the two forms of energy, potential and kinetic, which one is an energy of motion?

6. Considering the formulas for work, force, power, horsepower, velocity and acceleration, which three formulas are expressed in units with respect to time?

7. Which of Newton's laws states the principle of "action-reaction"?

8. What type of thermodynamic cycle of events is known as the Brayton cycle?

9. Bernoulli's principle describes the relationship between velocity pressure and static pressure of a fluid moving through a duct. Is this relationship direct or inverse?

10. Is thrust, calculated when an aircraft is in flight, referred to as gross thrust or net thrust?

11. Does a choked nozzle add additional supersonic velocity or additional thrust?

12. What are the three most important factors that will affect the thrust of a gas turbine engine during operation?

13. Would a turboprop engine be rated in thrust horsepower or equivalent shaft horsepower?

14. Which part of a compressor blade is speed limited and what occurs if this part of the blade exceeds the limiting speed by too high a value?

15. Thermal efficiency is a function of component efficiencies, turbine inlet temperature, and which other factor?

Chapter III
Turbine Engine Design And Construction

The design features of gas turbine engines are varied. It is common to see engines in the same power classification which seem to have little or no resemblance to each other. To search for an answer as to which design is best, or why an engine looks the way it does, may or may not prove successful for the following reasons:

1. Details of many designs are proprietary information and may not be explained by the manufacturer.
2. Many designs that do not appear to be the best, are in actuality best for that engine and the airplane on which it is intended to be installed. A compromise of designs for operation over a wide range of altitudes and power factors is common.
3. Many designs depend on the prior experience of the manufacturer. The company may stay with their proven developments rather than changing to newer ones.
4. What we see may be a design philosophy of the manufacturer, which he does not explain in technical terms but rather in terms of overall performance.

A. Turbine Engine Entrance Ducts

1. Principles Of Operations (Figure 3-1)

The air entrance or flight inlet duct is normally considered to be part of the airframe, not part of the engine. Nevertheless, it is usually identified as Engine Station Number One. Understanding the function of the inlet and its importance to engine performance makes it a necessary part of any discussion on gas turbine engine design and construction.

The turbine engine inlet must furnish a uniform supply of air to the compressor if the engine is to enjoy stall-free compressor performance. The inlet duct must also create as little drag as possible. It has been discovered that even a small discontinuity of airflow can cause significant efficiency loss, as well as many unexplainable engine performance problems. Therefore, it follows that, if the inlet duct is to retain its function of delivering air with minimum turbulence, it must be maintained in as close to new condition as possible. If repairs to this inlet become

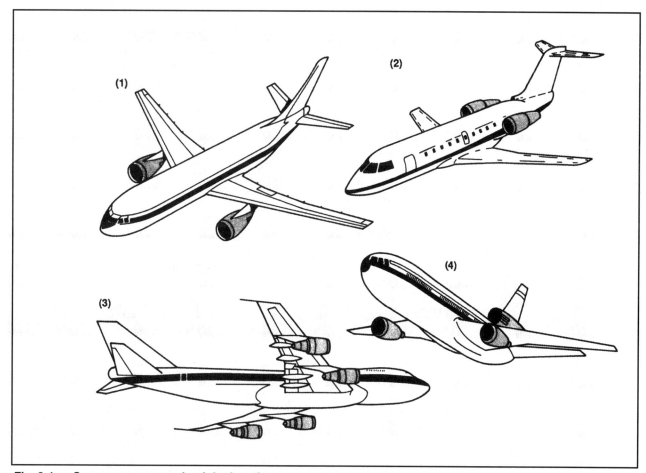

Fig. 3-1 — Some common engine inlet locations.

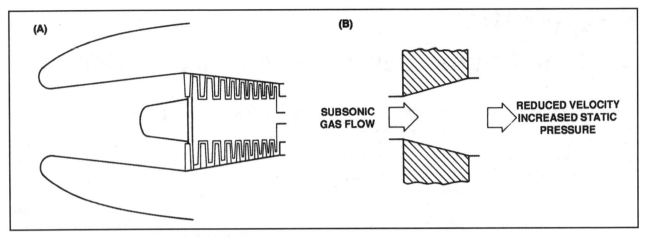

Fig. 3-2A — Divergent sub-sonic inlet duct.
Fig. 3-2B — Divergent duct effect on airflow.

necessary, expertly installed flush patches are mandatory to prevent drag. Moreover, the use of an inlet cover is recommended to promote cleanliness and to prevent corrosion and abrasion.

2. Subsonic Inlets

The inlet duct, such as those found on business and commercial jet aircraft, is of fixed geometry and has a divergent shape. A diverging duct progressively increases in diameter from front to back, as can be seen in Figure 3-2. This duct is sometimes referred to as an inlet diffuser because of its effect on pressure. Air enters the aerodynamically contoured inlet at ambient pressure and starts to diffuse, arriving at the compressor at a slightly increased static pressure. Usually, the air is allowed to diffuse (increase in static pressure) in the front portion of the duct and to progress at a fairly constant pressure past the engine inlet fairing, also called inlet center body, to the compressor. The engine, in this manner, receives its air with minimal turbulence and at a more uniform pressure.

Inlet pressure increases add significantly to the mass airflow as the aircraft reaches its desired cruising speed. It is here that the compressor reaches its aerodynamic design

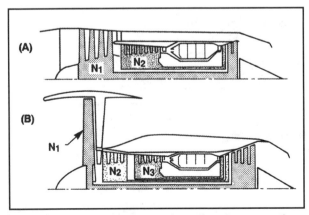

Fig. 3-3A — Turbofan low and medium bypass ratio.
Fig. 3-3B — Turbofan high bypass ratio.

point and produces its optimum compression and best fuel economy. At this point the flight inlet, compressor, combustor, turbine, and tailpipe are designed to be in match with each other. If any one section does not match the others, for whatever reason, damage, contamination, or ambient conditions, engine performance will be affected.

The turbofan inlet is similar in design to the turbojet except that it discharges only a portion of its air into the engine, with the remainder passing into the fan.

Figure 3-3 shows two common airflow arrangements. One, Figure 3-3A, is a full duct design utilized on low bypass and medium bypass engines, and the other, Figure 3-3B, is the short duct design of a high bypass turbofan. The long ducting configuration, seen in Figure 3-3A, reduces surface drag of the fan discharge air and enhances thrust. Many of the older, high bypass engines cannot take advantage of this drag reduction concept because of the weight penalty involved in the wide diameter of a long duct. New lightweight materials and designs are, however, changing this situation in new generation engines.

3. Ram Pressure Recovery

As previously mentioned in the theory chapter, a gas turbine engine, when operated in place on the ground, has a negative pressure within its inlet because of the high velocity airflow. As the aircraft moves forward, a condition known as ram pressure recovery takes place. This is the point at which pressure inside the inlet returns to ambient value. Ram (aerodynamic) compression is the result of ram velocity and diffusion of the airflow.

The aircraft inlet, while stationary, will not generally have 100 percent duct recovery. If ambient pressure (Ps) is 14.7 pounds per square inch absolute, pressure at the compressor inlet (Ps) will be slightly less than 14.7 psia. However, as the aircraft moves forward on the ground for takeoff, Ps will increase to 14.7 psia. This point is generally reached in the average inlet duct at an aircraft speed of Mach 0.1 to Mach 0.2 .

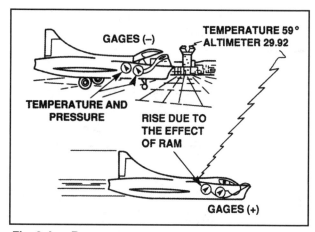

Fig. 3-4 — Ram pressure recovery.

In Figure 3-4, note the gauge readings changing from a negative to a positive value as the aircraft goes from ground static condition to flight condition. As the aircraft moves faster in flight, the inlet will produce more and more ram compression. The engine will take advantage of this condition by a corresponding increase in compressor pressure ratio, creating more thrust with less and less fuel expenditure.

To calculate ram compression (ram pressure ratio) at any flight mach number, the following formula can be used:

$$\frac{Pt}{Ps} = \left[1 + \left(\frac{\gamma - 1}{2} \times M^2 \right) \right]^{\frac{\gamma}{\gamma - 1}}$$

Where : γ (gamma) = 1.4 (specific heat)

M = Mach number

γ, 1, 2 = Constants

$$\frac{Pt}{Ps} = \frac{Pt_2}{Pam}$$

$$\frac{\gamma}{\gamma - 1} = \frac{Cp}{Cp - Cv} \quad \text{(See Appendix 8)}$$

EXAMPLE: A business jet is traveling at Mach 0.8 flight speed, at an altitude of 31,000 feet. What is the pressure ratio of engine inlet pressure to ambient pressure?

$$\frac{Pt}{Ps} = \left[1 + \left(\frac{1.4 - 1}{2} \times 0.8^2 \right) \right]^{\frac{1.4}{1.4 - 1}}$$

$$\frac{Pt}{Ps} = \left[1 + \left(0.2 \times 0.64 \right) \right]^{3.5}$$

$$\frac{Pt}{Ps} = 1.524$$

From this calculation, it is easy to see that very high speed aircraft create a great deal of inlet ram compres-

sion. The supersonic Concorde airliner, for instance, at a cruise speed of Mach 2.2, would produce a ram compression of 10.7 to 1.

The reasoning behind using the above Pt/Ps formula is as follows:

In actuality, the Pt/Ps formula represents Pt_2/P_{am}, which is pressure total at the engine face divided by pressure ambient, to give inlet compression ratio. The formula becomes applicable because Pt_2 is essentially the same value as Pt_1, pressure total at the lip of the flight inlet, which is given in the formula as (Pt).

As air moves down the inlet, assuming 100% efficiency, the total pressure at which the air entered does not change. The change is in the static pressure and ram pressure components of total pressure. In other words, static pressure has increased and ram pressure has decreased as the air moves down the inlet diffuser toward the engine, but total pressure has remained the same.

When density in pounds per cubic foot and velocity in feet per second are known, the total pressure in the inlet can be calculated as follows:

Total pressure = Ram pressure (Q) + Static pressure (p)

Pt = Q + p

Pt = 1/2 ρ V^2 (flow density) + p

Where:

Q = 1/2 ρ V^2 (flow density)

ρ = lbs./ft.^{3} / gravity constant

V = ft./sec. (in the inlet)

p = lbs./in.^{2} (static pressure)

EXAMPLE: An airplane is cruising at 550 miles per hour (806 feet per second). The static pressure in the flight inlet is 5.0 pounds per square inch and the density, from a standard altitude chart (Appendix 7), is .032 cubic foot per pound.

1. What is the total pressure (Pt) in the inlet?
2. What is the inlet compression ratio (Cr)?

Solution to #1

Q = 1/2 ρ V^2 (flow density)

$$Q = \frac{1}{2} \left(\frac{0.032 \text{ lbs./ft.}^3}{32.16 \text{ ft./sec.}^2} \right) \left(\frac{806 \text{ ft.}}{\text{sec.}} \right)^2$$

$$Q = \frac{1}{2} \frac{0.032 \text{ lbs.}}{\text{ft.}^3} \times \frac{\text{sec.}^2}{32.16 \text{ft.}} \times \frac{806^2 \text{ft.}^2}{\text{sec.}^2}$$

Q = 323.2 lbs./ft.^{2}

Q = 2.24 lbs./in.^{2}

Pt = Q + p

Pt = 2.24 + p

Pt = 7.24 lbs./in.^{2} (psi)

Solution to # 2

Cr   =   7.24 ÷ 5.0

Cr   =   1.45 to 1 (inlet compression ratio)

4. Supersonic Inlets

A convergent-divergent inlet duct (fixed or variable) is required on all supersonic aircraft. A supersonic transport, for example, is configured with an inlet that slows the airflow to subsonic speed at the face of the engine, regardless of aircraft speed. Subsonic airflow into the compressor is required if the rotating airfoils are to remain free of shock wave accumulation, which would be detrimental to the compression process.

In order to vary the geometry, or shape, of the inlet a movable restrictor is often employed to form a convergent-divergent (C-D) shape of variable proportion. The C-D shaped duct becomes necessary in reducing supersonic airflow to subsonic speeds. At this point, it is important to remember that at subsonic flow rates, air flowing in a duct acts as an incompressible liquid, but at supersonic flow rates air is compressed to the point of creating the familiar shock wave phenomenon.

Figure 3-5 depicts a fixed geometry (non-adjustable) C-D duct in which supersonic airflow is slowed by air compression and shock formation at its throat area. Once reduced to Mach-1, the airflow enters the subsonic diffuser section where velocity is further reduced and its pressure increased before entering the engine compressor. Some military aircraft, designed to fly as fast as Mach-2, utilize this type of inlet. There are several reasons, concerning operational flexibility, why the fixed geometry inlet is not always feasible. For further explanation of the effect a C-D inlet has on supersonic airflow, one should consult textbooks containing a discussion of the stagnation pressure effect of supersonic inlets.

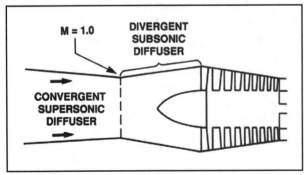

Fig. 3-5 — Supersonic convergent-divergent (C-D) inlet.

An inlet shock wave is very similar to shock waves common to aircraft wings and other airfoils. A shock wave is defined as an accumulation of sound wave energy, or pressure, developed when the wave, trying to move away from an object, is held in a stationary position by the oncoming flow of air. One useful aspect of a shock

wave is that airflow passing through the high pressure shock region slows down. (Figure 3-6)

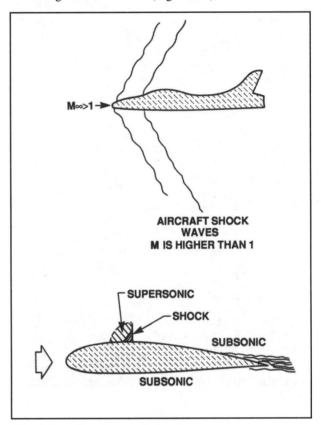

Fig. 3-6 — Shock wave formation.

The supersonic diffuser type of inlet, shown in Figure 3-7, provides a means of creating both a shock wave formation to reduce air velocity and a variable convergent-divergent shape to meet the various flight conditions from takeoff to cruise. Air velocity will drop to approximately Mach 0.8 in back of the final shock wave and then to Mach 0.5 by diffusion. Figure 3-7A shows a variable-geometry inlet in its high cruise shock wave condition and it also shows a movable spike which acts to create more C-D effect when in its forward position.

Figure 3-7B illustrates a movable wedge which provides a similar function of convergence, divergence, and shock wave formation. It also has a spill valve to dump unwanted ram air overboard at high speed. Many high performance aircraft have an excess of mass flow at cruising speeds.

Figure 3-7C shows another popular supersonic inlet, this time with a movable plug. In very high speed flight, especially, the inlet receives too much air due to ram effect. This inlet restricts airflow as well as controls shock formation by slowing the airflow to subsonic speed before it enters the engine.

5. Bellmouth Compressor Inlets

Bellmouth inlets are converging in shape, found primarily on helicopters, and provide an inlet with very thin

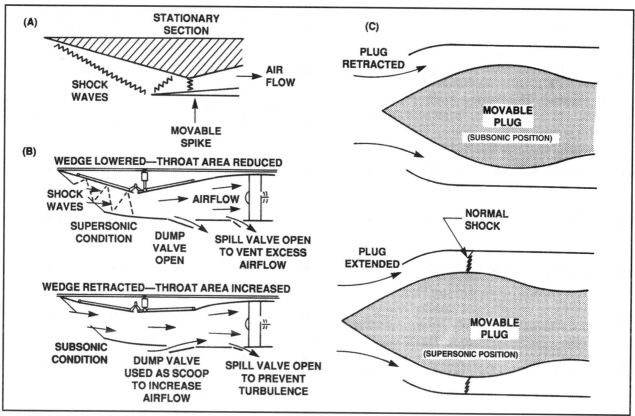

Fig. 3-7A — Movable spike inlet.
Fig. 3-7B — Movable wedge inlet.
Fig. 3-7C — Movable plug inlet.

boundary layers and corresponding low pressure losses. This type of inlet produces a large drag factor, but its low speed drag is outweighed by the high degree of aerodynamic efficiency it provides.

During calibration, engines on ground test stands also utilize a bellmouth, sometimes fitted with an anti-ingestion screen. Duct loss is so slight in this design that it is considered to be zero. Engine performance data, such as engine trimming for rated thrust are obtained while using a bellmouth compressor inlet (Figure 3-8).

Aerodynamic efficiency and duct loss are illustrated in Figure 3-9A. Notice that a rounded leading edge allows the airstream to make use of the total inlet cross section while the effective diameter of the sharp-edge orifice is greatly reduced (Figure 3-9B).

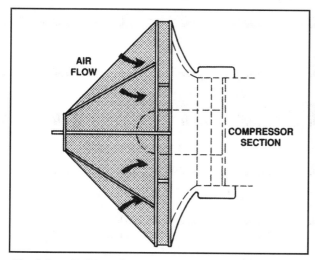

Fig. 3-8 — Bellmouth compressor inlet (with screen).

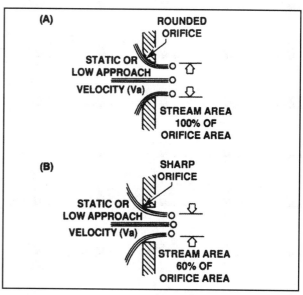

Fig. 3-9A — Low velocity entry flow through round edge orifice.
Fig. 3-9B — Low velocity entry flow through sharp edge orifice.

6. Compressor Inlet Screens, Sand, And Ice Separators

The use of compressor inlet screens is usually limited to rotorcraft, turboprops, and ground turbine installations. This may appear peculiar to the casual observer who realizes the appetite of all gas turbines for debris such as nuts, bolts, stones, etc. Screens have been tried in high subsonic flight engines in the past, but icing and screen fatigue failure caused so many maintenance problems that the use of inlet screens has for the most part been avoided.

When aircraft are fitted with inlet screens for protection against foreign object ingestion, they may be located internally or externally at either the inlet duct or the engine compressor inlet. Refer to Figure 3-10A and B. Often these separators are removable at the discretion of the operator. In the sand separator (Figure 3-10B), inlet suction causes particles of sand and other small debris to be directed by centrifugal loading into the sediment trap.

In the other illustration of the sand and ice separator (Figure 3-10C), a movable vane can be extended into the inlet airstream. This causes a sudden turn in the engine inlet air, and sand or ice particles continue out undeflected because of their greater momentum. The movable vane in this installation is operated by the pilot through a control handle in the cockpit.

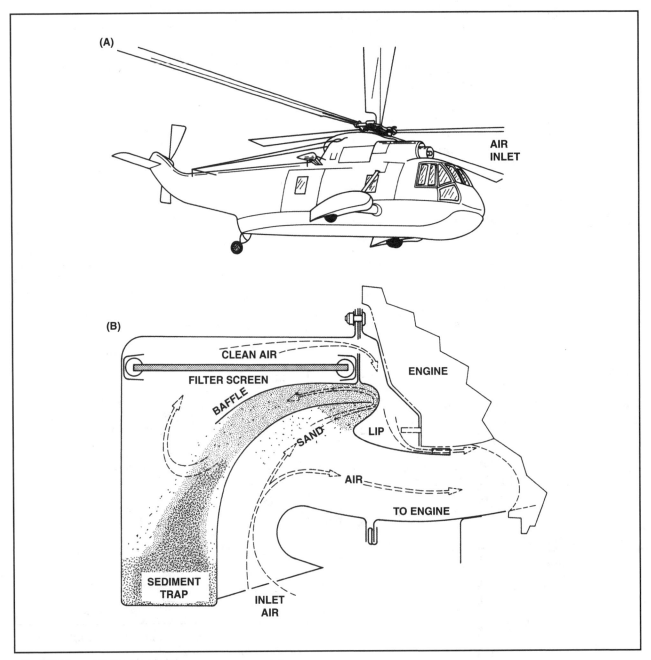

Fig. 3-10A — Helicopter inlet.
Fig. 3-10B — Sand and ice separator (centrifugal).

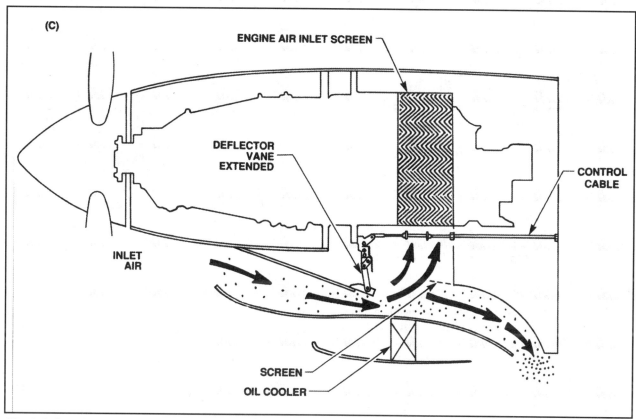

Fig. 3-10C — Sand and ice separator (inertial).

7. Engine Inlet Vortex Dissipator

Some gas turbine engine inlets have a tendency to form a vortex between the ground and the flight inlet. The suction creating the vortex is strong enough to lift water and debris such as sand, small stones, nuts, bolts, etc., from the ground and direct it into the engine, causing serious compressor erosion or damage (see Figure 3-11). This is especially true on wing pod installed engines that are mounted with very low ground clearance, as seen on many of the newer high-bypass turbofan powered aircraft. To alleviate this problem a vortex dissipator (also known as a blow-away jet) is installed (see Figure 3-12).

To dissipate the vortex, a small jet of compressor discharge air is directed at the ground under the inlet from a discharge nozzle located in the lower part of the engine flight cowl. The system is generally activated by a landing gear switch which opens a valve in the line between the engine compressor bleed port and the dissipator nozzle whenever the engine is operating and weight is on the main landing gear.

Fig. 3-11 — Water vortex during test cell run-up.

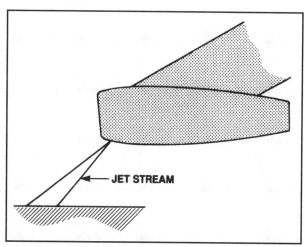

Fig. 3-12 — Vortex dissipator.

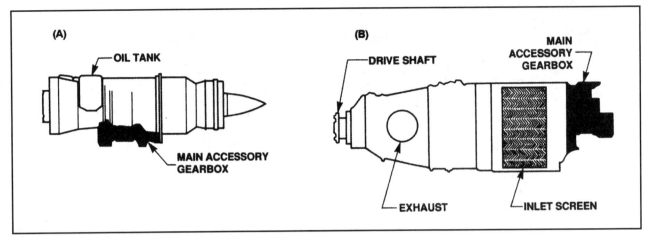

Fig. 3-13A — Accessory gearbox location—6 o'clock position.
Fig. 3-13B — Accessory gearbox location—rear.

B. Accessory Section

The engine driven external gearbox is the main unit of the accessory section. Accessory units essential to the operation of the engine, such as the fuel pump, oil pump, fuel control, and starter, and components such as hydraulic pumps and generators are mounted on the main gearbox (Figure 3-13A and B).

The gearbox is often driven by a radial shaft that meshes with a bevel gear driven by the main rotor shaft. On some installations an auxiliary gearbox is employed to drive the main gearbox. This arrangement allows the gearbox to be placed so that the envelope size of the engine can be kept to a minimum (Figure 3-14A). Other main gearbox locations are the front or rear of the engine if the inlet or exhaust locations will permit it. This is a particularly desirable design because it appears to allow for the narrowest engine diameter and lowest drag configuration (Figure 3-13B). In a rare few instances, the main gearbox can be found at the top of the engine in the area of the compressor. Some models of the CFM56 turbofan engine have the gearbox mounted on the side.

Each individual accessory and component drive pad is designed to provide a gear reduction from compressor speed, as needed (Figures 3-14B and 3-15B). The RPM of each accessory and the direction it rotates, either clockwise or counterclockwise, is determined by the number of teeth on the gears and whether they mesh outside to outside or inside to outside. When a large gear drives a small gear, the small one turns faster and experiences a loss in force. If the teeth mesh outside to outside, the direction of rotation is reversed. In Figure 3-15B, for example, the compressor bevel gear with 47 teeth is driving the radial bevel gear with 35 teeth. The radial bevel gear turns faster, by a factor of 47/35, and it turns opposite in direction. The alternator gear shaft turns the same direction as the gear driving it, because it is meshing outside teeth to inside teeth. It also turns faster, by a factor of 67/28, because it has 28 teeth and the gear driving it has 67 teeth.

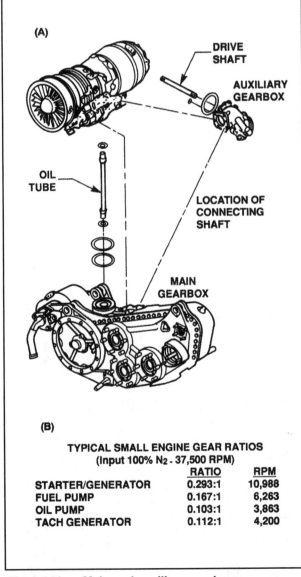

TYPICAL SMALL ENGINE GEAR RATIOS
(Input 100% N_2 - 37,500 RPM)

	RATIO	RPM
STARTER/GENERATOR	0.293:1	10,988
FUEL PUMP	0.167:1	6,263
OIL PUMP	0.103:1	3,863
TACH GENERATOR	0.112:1	4,200

Fig. 3-14A — Main and auxiliary gearbox arrangement.
Fig. 3-14B — Typical small engine gear ratios.

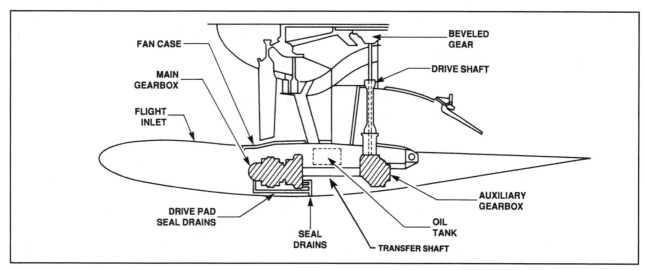

Fig. 3-15A — Main accessory gearbox location.

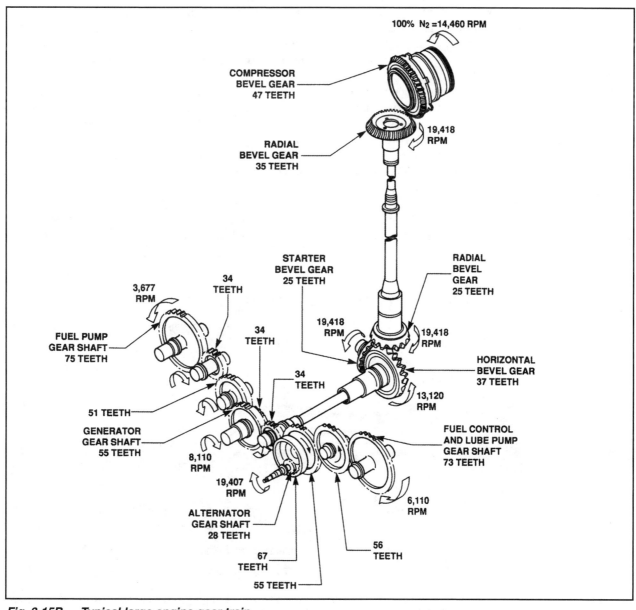

Fig. 3-15B — Typical large engine gear train.

Each individual drive pad is a point of potential oil leakage. Fluids such as fuel, from the fuel control or fuel pump; engine oil, from the main oil pump or scavenge oil pump; and hydraulic oil, from the hydraulic pump; may leak into, or from, the gearbox through the drive shaft seal. A system of seal drain tubes connects to each drive pad and is normally routed to the bottom of the engine cowling. The leakage is generally minute and presents little problem as it leaves the drain point into the atmosphere (Figure 3-15a).

The allowable leakage rate of the various fluids is listed in the manufacturer's maintenance instructions and is generally in the range of 5 to 20 drops per minute, depending on the source of the leak.

A secondary function of many main gearboxes is to provide a collection point for scavenged oil before being pumped back to the oil tank. This arrangement allows for splash-type lubrication of many internal gears and bearings inside the gearbox. However, it is not common today for the main oil supply to be kept in the accessory gearbox. Instead, a separate oil tank is normally utilized.

C. Compressor Section

The compressor section houses the compressor rotor and works to supply air in sufficient quantity to satisfy the needs of the combustor. Compression results when fuel energy of combustion and mechanical work of the compressor and turbine are converted into potential energy. Compressors operate on the principle of acceleration of a working fluid followed by diffusion to convert the acquired kinetic energy to a pressure rise. The primary purpose of the compressor is to increase the pressure of the mass of air entering the engine inlet and discharge it

to the diffuser and then to the combustor section at the correct velocity, temperature, and pressure.

The problems associated with these requirements can be realized if one considers that some compressors must flow air at a velocity of 400 to 500 feet per second and raise its static pressure perhaps 20 to 30 times in the space of only a few feet of engine length.

In early compressors which were less efficient than what we have today, a given amount of work input produced air at a lower pressure and at a higher temperature. To improve on laminar air flow over hundreds of small airfoils at high velocity and pressure, compressors have been undergoing constant development through the years to achieve optimum efficiency. Presently, this efficiency is said to be in the 85 to 90% range. As previously discussed in Chapter II, compressor efficiency is based on the principle of maximum compression with the least temperature rise. Laminar flow minimizes friction-induced heat in the air.

A secondary purpose of the compressor section is to supply Engine Service Bleed Air to cool hot section parts, to pressurize bearing seals, and to supply heated air for inlet anti-icing and fuel system heat for deicing. Another secondary purpose is to extract air for aircraft uses, and this is usually referred to as Customer Service Bleed Air. Common uses for this air include aircraft cabin pressurization, air conditioning systems, pneumatic starting, and various other incidental functions that require clean pressurized air (See Figures 3-16 and 3-17).

1. Centrifugal Flow Compressors

The centrifugal flow compressor, sometimes referred to as a radial out-flow compressor, is the oldest design

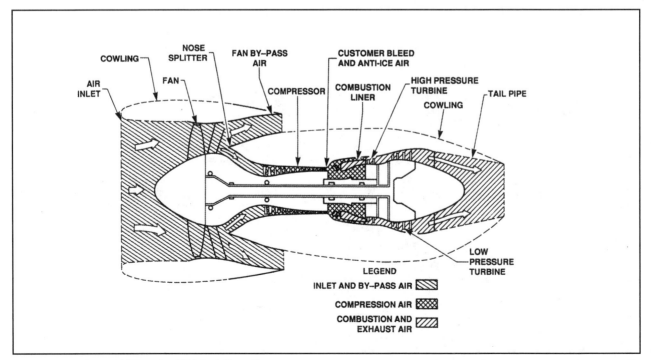

Fig. 3-16 — General Electric CF-34 airflow diagram.

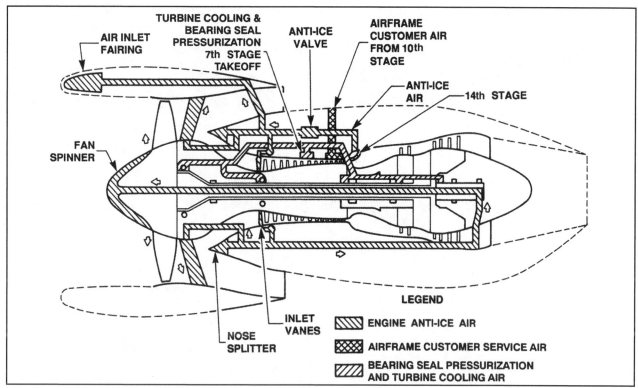

Fig. 3-17 — Bleed air distribution.

and is still in use today. Many smaller engines, as well as the majority of auxiliary gas turbine powerplants, use this design.

In a centrifugal flow engine, the compressor performs its duties by receiving its air at the center of the impeller in an axial direction and accelerating the air outward by centrifugal reaction to its rotational speed. The air is then allowed to expand into a divergent duct, called a diffuser, and according to Bernoulli's Principle, as the air spreads out its speed slows down and the static pressure builds (Figure 3-18).

Centrifugal flow compressor assemblies consist basically of an impeller rotor, a diffuser, and a manifold (Figure 3-19). The impeller is usually made from aluminum alloy or titanium alloy and can be either single or dual sided (Figure 3-20). The diffuser provides a divergent duct in which the air spreads out, slows down, and increases in static pressure. The compressor manifold distributes the air in a turbulence free condition to the combustion section.

The single sided impeller, Figure 3-20A, benefits from ram effect and less turbulent air entry. It is for this reason that this type of impeller is well suited to many aircraft installations.

The single stage dual-sided impeller design, Figure 3-20B, allows for a narrower overall engine diameter and high mass airflow. For this reason, it was favored in many flight engines in the past. This design does not, however, receive the full benefit from ram effect because the air has to turn radially inward from a plenum chamber into the center of the impellers.

Compression ratios attainable are about the same for both previously mentioned single stage types of impellers. However, as seen in Figure 3-21, more than two stages of single entry type are considered impractical. The energy loss to the airflow (slowing down) when making the turns from one impeller to the next, the added weight, and the drive shaft power extraction all seem to offset the benefit of additional compression with more than two stages.

The main consideration in the many design features one sees, such as types of impeller, shapes of inlets, shapes of outer casings, etc., usually lies in the fact that one design fits the needs of a particular aircraft better than another design.

The most commonly seen centrifugal compressor is the single sided type in either one or two stages. It is most often used in small engines, to include turboshaft, turboprop, and turbofan. It is not found in large gas turbine engines because it would impose a serious limitation on mass airflow.

A resurgence of the use of centrifugal compressors can be seen. Recent developments have produced compression ratios as high as 10:1 from a single centrifugal compressor. Formerly, only axial flow compressors could attain this level of compression. The centrifugal compressor is shorter in length than an axial compressor and that is its main advantage.

Tip speed of centrifugal impellers reaches approximately Mach 1.3. Radial airflow, however, remains subsonic. The pressure within the compressor casing is capable of preventing airflow separation at low supersonic

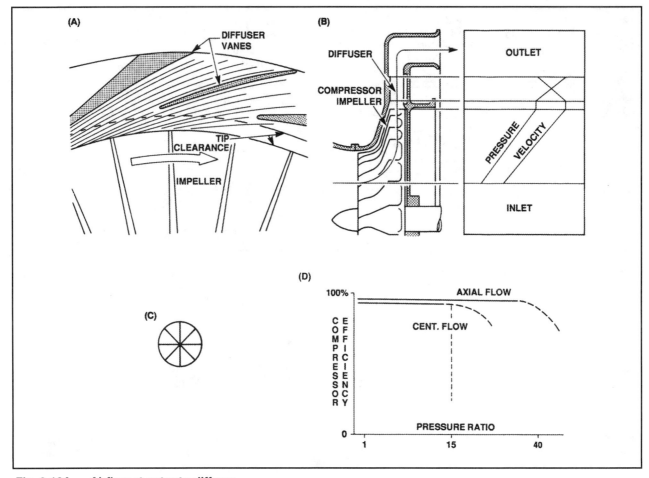

Fig. 3-18A — *Airflow at entry to diffuser.*
Fig. 3-18B — *Pressure and velocity changes through a centrifugal compressor.*
Fig. 3-18C — *Spoke theory of accelerating air.*
Fig. 3-18D — *Compressor pressure ratio vs. efficiency.*

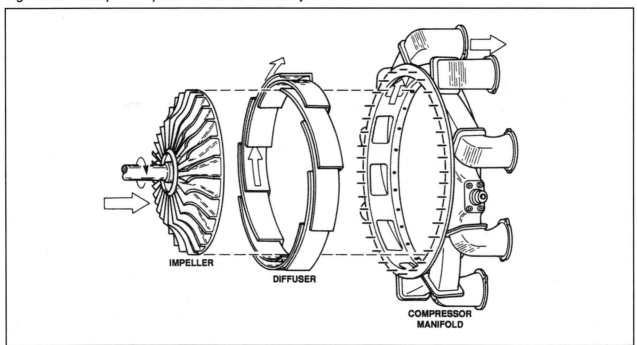

Fig. 3-19 — *Components of centrifugal flow compressor.*

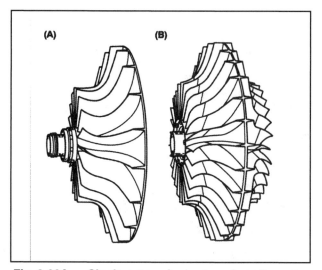

Fig. 3-20A — Single-entry, single stage impeller.
Fig. 3-20B — Dual-entry, single stage impeller.

rotor speeds and causing a high energy transfer to the air-flow.

The centrifugal compressor is commonly used in conjunction with the axial flow compressor (see Figure 3-33) but seems only to meet the needs of smaller flight engines. All larger engines today are of the axial flow type.

The advantages of the centrifugal compressor are as follows:

a. High pressure rise per stage: Up to 10:1 and 15:1 in a dual stage;

b. Good efficiency (compression) over a wide rotational speed range, idle to full power (approximately 1.3 Mach tip speed);

c. Simplicity of manufacture and low cost, compared to the axial compressor;

d. Low weight;

e. Low starting power requirements.

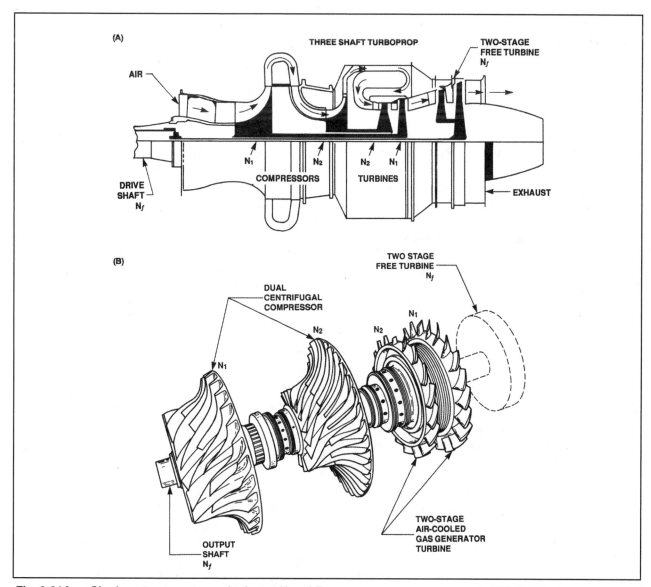

Fig. 3-21A — Single entry, two stage, dual centrifugal flow compressor arrangement—PW-120, Turboprop.
Fig. 3-21B — Compressor and turbines of PWA-120 turboprop.

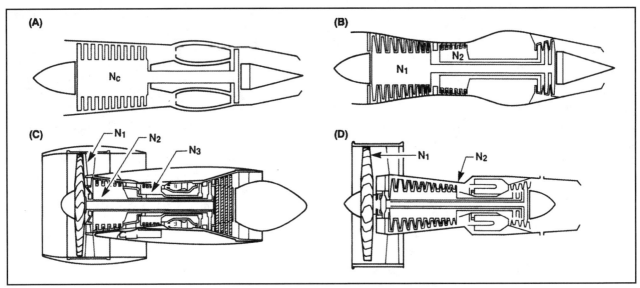

Fig. 3-22A — Single-spool compressor.
Fig. 3-22B — Dual-spool compressor.
Fig. 3-22C — Triple-spool rotor arrangement.
Fig. 3-22D — Dual-spool engine (Geared-fan).

Disadvantages are as follows:
a. Large frontal area for a given mass airflow;
b. More than two stages is not practical because of the energy losses between stages.

2. Axial Flow Compressors And Fans

a. Types

The axial compressor is so named because airflow and compression occur parallel to the rotational axis of the compressor. There are three types of axial flow compressors: Single-spool, dual-spool, and triple-spool. The single-spool was common in the past for small and large engines, but today it is typically found only in small turboshafts and turboprops. The dual-spool is the most common design currently being used in large turbofan and turboprop engines. The triple-spool, a more recent technological development, is used on some large and medium size turbofan engines. At one time, the word spool was only used when describing an axial flow compressor, but many manufacturers today also use the word spool when describing a centrifugal flow compressor. The Pratt and Whitney 100 series turboprop, for example, has two separately rotating centrifugal compressors plus a power turbine and is described as a three shaft, two spool engine.

Figure 3-22A illustrates a single-spool compressor. This design was the first type of axial compressor developed for the gas turbine engine and is seen in some aircraft today as current technology. It has only one rotating mass. The compressor, shaft, and turbine all rotate together as a single unit.

Figs. 3-22B, 3-22C, and 3-22D show how, in multi-spool engines, the turbine shafts attach to their compressors by fitting coaxially (one within the other).

In Figure 3-22B, the front compressor is referred to as the low pressure, or N_1 compressor. The rear compressor is referred to as the high pressure, or N_2 compressor.

In Figure 3-22C, the rotor arrangement is such that the fan is referred to as the N_1, or low pressure compressor, the compressor next in line is called the N_2, or intermediate compressor, and the innermost compressor, the N_3, or high pressure compressor.

Fig. 3-22D shows a geared, fan type, dual-spool engine. It was developed for smaller engines so that higher turbine speeds could be converted to torque to drive the fan. The geared fan does not need a separate turbine to have a different speed from the compressor. For example, the Garrett TFE-731 turbofan has a fan gearbox ratio of 0.496:1. When its turbine is turning at 10,000 RPM, the fan is only rotating at 4,960 RPM. Because the fan is not attached directly to the compressor, the compressor is not speed limited to fan speed.

In most turbofan engines, blade tip speeds of the fan are allowed to go over Mach 1 at high power settings. The pressure within the fan duct tends to retard airflow separation from the blades at speeds over Mach 1 so that there is a good energy transfer to the air, good compression ratio, and little aerodynamic disturbance from shock formation.

1) Reasons For Multi-spool Designs:
(Figure 3-23)

Dual and triple-spool axial compressors were developed for the operational flexibility they provide to the engine in the form of high compression ratios, quick acceleration, and better control of stall characteristics. This operational flexibility is not possible with single spool, axial flow engines.

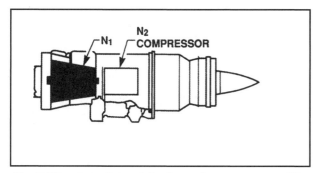

Fig. 3-23 — Location of dual-spool compressor within the engine.

For any given power lever setting, the high pressure compressor speed is held fairly constant by a fuel control governor. Assuming that a fairly constant energy level is available at the turbine, the low pressure compressor(s) will speed up and slow down with changes in aircraft inlet conditions resulting from atmospheric changes or flight maneuvers. The varying low pressure compressor output, therefore, provides the high pressure compressor with the best inlet condition within the limits of its design. That is, the N_1 compressor tries to supply the N_2 compressor with a fairly constant air pressure for a particular power setting.

To better understand when the low pressure compressor speeds up and slows down, consider that when ambient temperature increases, the air's molecular motion increases. In order to continue to collect air molecules at the same rate as temperature increases, the compressor would have to change either its blade angles, which it cannot do, or its speed, which it in fact does. Additionally, the speed of the low pressure compressor increases with altitude as the atmosphere rarefies from barometric pressure density loss. Conversely, as the aircraft descends, the speed of the low pressure compressor will decrease as the air becomes more dense and easier to compress (Figure 3-24).

Figure 3-25A shows that as ambient temperature increases N_2 speed increases. This is necessary in order to maintain compression ratio and mass airflow until RPM reaches a limit set by the fuel scheduling system.

Considering that the effect of ambient pressure change predominates over the effect of temperature change on density, Figure 3-25B shows that, as the altitude increases, N_1 will increase. This, in effect, is like supercharging the N_2 system and is a result of a reduction in drag on the N_1 compressor in the less dense air at altitude. With a fairly constant energy level, its turbine will rotate the N_1 system faster. In fact, the operator may, at some point, need to keep N_1 from exceeding its maximum speed by retarding the power lever.

In Figure 3-25C it can be seen that as N_2 rotor speed increases, N_1 increases, but not in direct proportion. While the rotors are not mechanically connected together, as has been previously stated, they are linked by an aerodynamic couple.

Figure 3-25D shows the way in which N_2 RPM is non-linear to engine thrust (Fg). For example, at 90 percent N_2 RPM, there will not necessarily be 90 percent thrust available. It is for this reason N_2% is not used as a power parameter indicator in the cockpit.

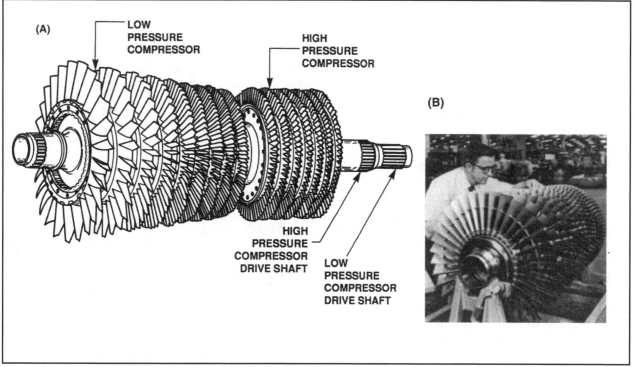

Fig. 3-24A — Dual-spool compressor.
Fig. 3-24B — Compressor rotor inspection.

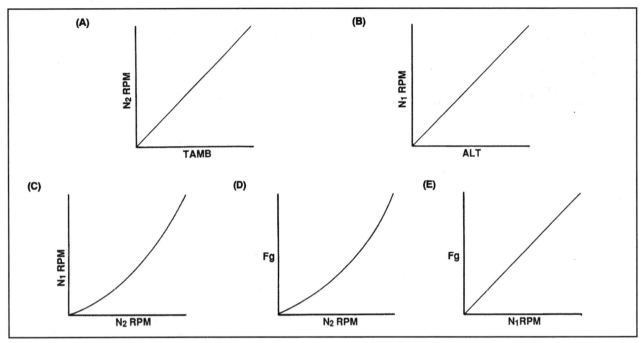

Fig. 3-25A — N$_2$ increase vs. ambient temperature increase.

Fig. 3-25B — N$_1$ increase vs. altitude increase.

Fig. 3-25C — N$_2$ increase vs. N$_1$ increase.

Fig. 3-25D — N$_2$ increase vs. thrust (Fg) increase.

Fig. 3-25E — N$_1$ increase vs. thrust (Fg) increase.

Figure 3-25E shows the way in which the N$_1$ compressor speed of a turbojet or N$_1$ fan speed of a turbofan engine is linear to thrust. As a result, the N$_1$ tachometer indicator in the cockpit is often used as an indication of thrust. This will be discussed again in the fuel system chapter.

Some dual or triple-spool compressors have a counter-rotating component. It is not common, but one spool can be made to rotate in the opposite direction of the other spool(s). This is generally not a design for aerodynamic reasons but rather for dampening gyroscopic effect and reducing engine vibration tendencies.

b. Blades And Vanes

An axial flow compressor has two main components, the rotor and the stator. A rotor and the following stator make up a stage, and several stages (depending on the design and the manufacturer) are combined to make up the complete compressor. Each rotor consists of a set of blades fitted into a disk, which move air rearward through each stage.

The speed of the rotor determines the velocity present in each stage and, with increased velocity, kinetic energy is transferred to the air. The stator vanes are placed to the rear of the rotor blades to receive the air at high velocity and act as a diffuser, changing kinetic energy to potential energy (pressure). The stators also have a secondary function of directing airflow to the next stage of compression at the desired angle.

Compressor blades are constructed with a varying angle of incidence, or twist, similar to that of a propeller. This design feature compensates for the effect on airflow caused by differences in airflow over the different stations of each blade from the base to the tip.

The blades also reduce in size from the first stage to the last to accommodate the converging or tapering shape (see Figure 3-26) of the compressor housing in which they are rotating. The need for a converging duct within the compressor is explained in a subsequent paragraph entitled "Compressor Taper Design".

There are several reasons for the shapes of compressor airfoils. The length, chord, thickness, and aspect ratio (ratio of length to width) are calculated to suit the performance factors required for a particular engine and aircraft combination.

Some design aspects common to both compressor and fan blades are:

1) A twist is present (called a stagger angle) from base to tip to maintain exit velocity of airflow at the same value along the blade length;

2) The base area has more camber than the tip area, again to increase axial velocity of airflow and maintain base to tip exit velocity;

3) The trailing edge is knife-edge thin to minimize turbulence and provide the best aerodynamic efficiency.

4) An advanced tip design can be seen in Figure 3-27B. It is called an "end bend" blade due to its radical stagger angle at the base and tip.

c. Tips And Roots

The axial compressor will normally have from 10 to 18 stages of compression. The blades of each stage are usually dovetail fitted into the disk and secured with a pin, lock tab, or lockwire as shown in Figure 3-26A.

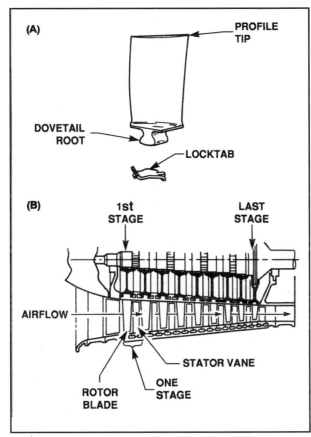

Fig. 3-26A — Blade attachment and retention.
Fig. 3-26B — Identification of one stage (rotor blade—followed by stator vane.)

As previously mentioned, the fan blade is considered the first stage of compression. The span-shroud, shown in Figure 3-27, is fitted to each blade. When all blades in the first stage are in place, their shrouds form a circular ring which supports the blades against the bending forces from the airstream. The shrouds however, cause a blockage to airflow and aerodynamic drag which tends to reduce efficiency. Newer and stronger composite materials are presently being developed and these shrouds are being removed.

The area, from approximately the span-shrouds to the root, serves as the core engine compressor blade section. The root of the blade is sometimes loosely fitted into the compressor disk for ease of blade assembly and the vibration damping effect it provides. As the compressor rotates, centrifugal loading locks the blade in its correct position, and the airstream over the airfoil provides a shock mounting or cushioning effect.

Some blades are cut off square at the tip and are referred to as flat-machine tips, while some blades have a reduced

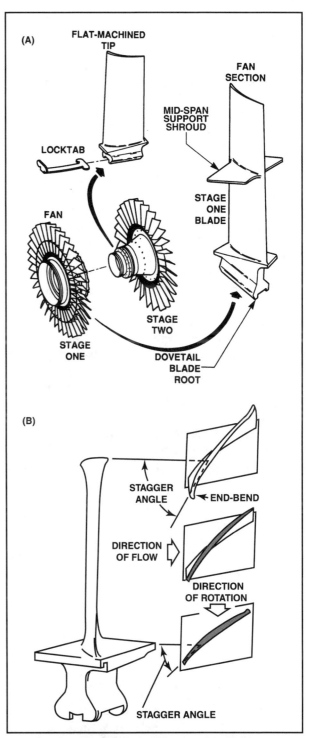

Fig. 3-27A — Compressor blade and fan blade.
Fig. 3-27B — End-bend blade.

thickness at the tips and are referred to as having a profile, or squeeler tip. Blade designers may have had several ideas in mind when designing a squeeler tip, such as:

1) All rotating machinery has a tendency to vibrate, and profiling is a means of increasing the natural frequency of blades, called frequency tuning. By raising the natural frequency of the blade beyond the frequency of rotation of the engine, the vibration tendency is

reduced. For blades without profiles, frequency tuning is done by other aerodynamic designs. Tip vibration of blades is closely controlled because it causes blade root galling and even fatigue fractures, problems that have always existed with rotating airfoils of all types including turbines blades and compressor blades.

2) The profile is also designed as a vortex tip. The thin trailing edge section causes a vortex which increases air velocity and insures minimum tip leakage and a smooth axial airflow.

3) On some newer engines the tips are designed with tight running clearances and rotate within a shroud strip of abradable material. This strip will wear away with no loss of blade length if contact loading takes place. The strip is later replaced at overhaul. This feature is the reason that profile blades are also referred to as a squeeler tip. Sometimes, during coastdown, a high pitched noise can be heard if the blade tip and shroud strip are touching.

4) Some high performance compressors need a means of controlling tip shock wave intensity. Profiling changes the aerodynamics at the tip to facilitate smooth axial airflow even though the tip is rotating at speeds beyond the speed of sound and flow separation is starting to occur.

A recent departure from the traditional blade base and tip is the end-bend design which employs a more radical twist (Fig. 3-27B). The aerodynamic effect of added twist and swirl conteracts the tendency for pile up of slow or stagnant airflow that occurs in boundary layers at the blade base and in the area of the tip clearance. This design provides minimal airflow separation from the blade surfaces under high swirl conditions and a higher compression per stage results.

d. Inlet Guide Vanes

Stator vanes can be either of two types, stationary or variable angle. Figure 3-28 shows the vane locations.

This illustration also shows the location of the inlet guide vanes which precede the first stage rotor blades. These vanes can also be of stationary or variable design. Their function is to direct airflow into the rotor at the most desirable angle. Similar vanes are placed at the compressor exit to remove the rotational moment imparted to the air during compression. A later chapter is devoted to variable guide vane systems.

e. Compressor Pressure Ratio

Compressor Pressure Ratio of a gas turbine engine is an extremely important design consideration. In general, the higher the compression, the more remarkable the advantage to the operating cycle in terms of greater thermal efficiency.

The compressor designer strives to achieve the highest possible compressor pressure ratio (Cr) and the lowest mass airflow (Ms) and yet obtain the desired engine power output. This will produce an engine with the least flow area, smallest physical size, and lowest weight for a given power output. The compressor designer has to

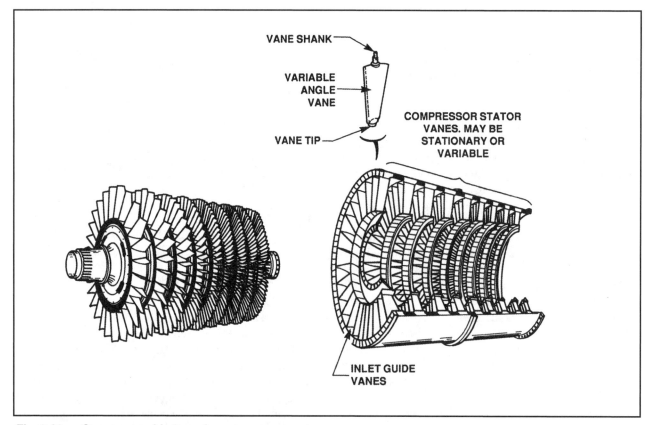

Fig. 3-28 — Compressor blade and vane arrangement.

make some trade-offs, however, when considering the optimum Cr and Ms relationship.

In actual practice, the greater the pressure ratio for a given mass airflow and thrust, the lower the engine fuel consumption. If both pressure ratio and mass increase, thrust will increase. But engine weight also goes up as strength of materials is increased.

Very high pressure ratios mean considerable expense will be incurred when manufacturing with exotic construction materials required to produce the desired compressor strength. Again, higher pressure ratio benefits the engine most when turbine inlet temperature is also high. This prompts an additional expense in the use of higher heat strength super alloys in the engine combustor and turbine areas.

In the modern compressor for business jets, a moderate compression pressure ratio and an implied lower manufacturing cost can be seen. Very high compression engines, which are very expensive, will be found in airliners, whose success depends on the lowest operating expense over many thousands of operating hours.

A gas turbine engine in a business jet has a compression ratio rating on the order of 6:1 in older models and up to 24:1 in newer designs. By comparison, the engine of a modern wide-body jumbo jet will compress the air up to 40 atmospheres, or 40:1. (Figure 3-29).

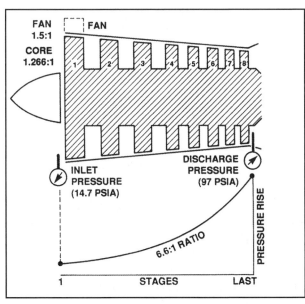

Fig. 3-29 — Compressor pressure ratio graph.

Compressor pressure ratio is determined by measuring the total pressure, after the last stage of compression, and dividing it by compressor inlet total pressure. Assuming no velocity change between the two points, static pressures could be used to calculate compressor pressure ratio.

If ambient pressure is 14.7 pounds absolute per square inch and the inlet has 100 percent duct recovery, compressor inlet pressure total (Pt) will also be 14.7 psia. Considering an inlet air velocity of 500 feet per second at sea level rated power, static pressure will be 12.63 psia and ram pressure

will be 2.07 psi, giving a total pressure of 14.7 psi. This calculation can be accomplished using Appendix 8, Formula 14, and the sea level density figure from Formula 7.

$$Pt = 1/2 \; \rho \; V^2 \; \text{(flow density)} + p$$

$$Pt = \left(1/2 \; \frac{0.076515}{32.16} \times 500^2\right) + p$$

$$Pt = 197 \; \text{lbs./ft.}^2 + p$$

$$Pt = 2.07 \; \text{lbs./in.}^2 + p$$

$$Pt = 2.07 + 12.63$$

$$Pt = 14.7 \; \text{psi}$$

$$\rho = \frac{\text{Specific weight of air}}{\text{Atmospheric standard for gravity}}$$

$$\rho = 0.076515 \; \text{lbs./cu.ft.} \div 32.16 \; \text{ft/sec.}^2$$

Observe that when compressor inlet total pressure is 14.7 psia and compressor discharge total pressure is 97.0 psia, the compressor pressure ratio is expressed as 97 divided by 14.7, or 6.6 to 1, as indicated in Figure 3-29. In this discussion about "compressor pressure ratio" the expression "compression ratio" is not used. This is because compression ratio, by definition, is a ratio of air density rather than air pressure.

1) Pressure Rise Per Stage

The compressor pressure ratio of a compressor is also described in terms of pressure ratio per stage. For example, a business jet may have a small turbofan with an overall compression ratio of 6.6:1 over eight stages. If we calculate the 8th root of 6.6 we would find it to be 1.266 or a 1.266:1 pressure ratio per stage. The fan, if it is a single stage, would probably have a compression ratio of between 1.5 and 1.7 to 1. Towards the hub where the fan blades become the first stage compressor blades, compression would be 1.266:1. The twist in the blades accomplishes this compression ratio change.

All scientific calculators today have the capability of performing power and root calculations. A number can be taken to a certain power by using the exponent key, typically labeled Y^X or X^Y. These same keys generally become a root key by hitting a shift or 2nd function key first. The typical input for the numbers in the previous example would be as follows:

To calculate $\sqrt[8]{6.6}$ = 1.266

Enter 6.6

Press the 2nd function or shift key

Press the Y^x key

Press 8, and then press = sign

This method does not work on all calculators, but is typical of many Casio and Texas Instruments units.

The pressure rise per stage throughout compression is an average. Compressors are not designed for constant pressure rise per stage but rather constant efficiency per stage. This can constitute using as many as 20 to 50 different blade designs within the same compressor. If we were to calculate compression at each stage, the Standard Day pressure rise would occur as follows:

Stage No.	P_1	Cr (stage)		Compression (psia)
1	14.70	1.266	=	18.61
2	18.61	1.266	=	23.56
3	23.56	1.266	=	29.83
4	29.83	1.266	=	37.76
5	37.76	1.266	=	47.81
6	47.81	1.266	=	60.53
7	60.53	1.266	=	76.63
8	76.63	1.266	=	97.01
		Total Cr	=	97 ÷ 14.7 or 6.6:1

For dual-spool engines, compressor pressure ratio is normally given for each compressor as follows in this typical example:

N_1 compressor, 4:1; N_2 compressor, 5:1; total compression, 20:1.

Note that the ratio of one compressor is multiplied by the other to give the total compressor pressure ratio. The N_2 compressor, because of its smaller diameter, is able to turn at a higher RPM and therefore generate more compression than the N_1. The N_2 compressor is also able to generate more pressure rise per stage than the N_1 because it is working with the higher pressures supplied to it by the N_1.

Therefore, a dual compressor of ten stages would have a higher compressor pressure ratio than a single compressor of ten stages. Therein lies one of the principle advantages of the dual-spool compressor. The ability of the N_1 compressor to increase speed in flight results in a higher compression ratio than could be attained by a single-spool compressor of the same size and weight.

2) Cycle Pressure Ratio

The cycle pressure ratio of a gas turbine engine is calculated using flight conditions at full aircraft speed. It is calculated by multiplying the compressor pressure ratio by the inlet compression due to ram. If the compressor pressure ratio happens to be 10:1 for a particular engine, and inlet conditions change from 14.7 lbs. per square inch to 16 lbs. per square inch as the aircraft flies faster, then the compressor discharge pressure will be 160 lbs. per square inch instead of the original 147.

An engine's compressor pressure ratio is essentially the same at all flight altitudes. The cycle pressure ratio is not the same at all flight altitudes because of the aerodynamic changes that occur in the engine inlet. If the engine shown in Figure 3-29 was in an airplane flying at Mach 0.8, with an inlet compression of 1.524 to 1, the cycle pressure ratio would be 10.06 to 1 (1.524 times 6.6).

Increasing inlet compression also affects mass airflow. If the mass airflow rating of an engine is 50 pound per second at sea level, with standard day conditions at full power, as the aircraft moves forward mass airflow will increase with an increase in compressor discharge pres-

sure. In fact, the mass airflow change which occurs after takeoff will cause the pilot to reduce power to keep from over boosting the engine.

At altitudes where ambient pressure is only about one-fourth that of sea level value, ram compression created in the engine inlet helps the diminishing mass airflow condition.

3) Fan Pressure Ratio

Fan compression ratios for single low bypass fans are approximately 1.5:1 and for high bypass fans as high as 1.7:1. Some high bypass engines (those with fan bypass ratios of 4:1 and above) are designed with high aspect ratio blades. That is, they are long and have a narrow chord (Figure 3-30).

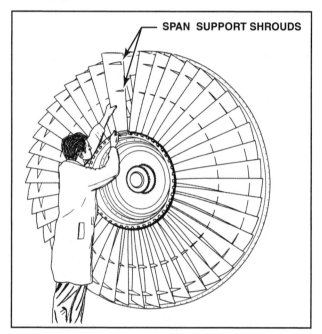

Fig. 3-30 — High bypass fan with high aspect ratio blades.

Low aspect ratio (wide chord) blades are coming into wider use today because of their tolerance to foreign objects, especially bird strike damage. In the past, low aspect ratio blades have not been the choice of most designers because of their high weight. Recently, hollow titanium blades with composite inner reinforcement materials have been developed. These blades have no stabilizing support shrouds and thus produce more mass airflow as a result of the greater flow area (Figure 3-31).

f. Fan Bypass Ratio

Fan bypass ratio is the ratio of the mass airflow which flows through the fan duct, divided by the mass airflow which flows through the core portion of the engine. Fan airflow passes over the outer part of the fan blade and then out of the fan exhaust and back to the atmosphere. Core engine airflow passes over the inner part of the fan blades and is then compressed, combusted, and exhausted from the hot exhaust duct.

Fig. 3-31 — High bypass fan with low aspect ratio blades.

Fig. 3-32 — Removal of the first stage fan from an axial flow compressor.

g. Advantages/Disadvantages Of Axial Flow Compressors

There are several advantages of the axial flow compressor. They are:
1) High peak efficiencies (i.e., compressor pressure ratios), created by its straight through design;
2) Higher peak efficiencies (pressure) attainable by the use of additional stages of compression;
3) Higher mass airflow for a given frontal area and a low drag coefficient.

The disadvantages of the axial flow compressor are:
1) Difficulty and high cost of manufacture;
2) Relatively high weight;
3) High starting power requirements;
4) Low pressure rise per stage (currently around 1.4 to 1, but as high as 1.5 to 1.6 to 1 in newer engines being developed);
5) Good compression in the cruise to takeoff power range only.

The low pressure rise per stage occurs in the axial blade design where inlet and exit velocities are held at about the same values. By comparison, the centrifugal compressor has a much higher airflow exit velocity as compared to its inlet velocity and can achieve much higher compression per stage.

3. Combination Compressors

To take advantage of the several good points of both the centrifugal and the axial flow compressor and to eliminate some of their disadvantages, the combination axial-centrifugal compressor was designed. This application is currently being used in many small turbine engines installed in business jets and helicopters. It produces a high mass airflow in its axial section for a small cross-sectional area, due to the high axial velocity present. The centrifugal section creates a good compression ratio over a wider operating range which is much better than would

Generally speaking, the higher the bypass ratio, the higher the propulsive efficiency the engine will have. But that only happens up to a bypass ratio of approximately 9 to 1 on aircraft designed to cruise at normal airliner, commuter, and business jet speeds of Mach 0.8 to Mach 0.85 (Figure 3-32).

To achieve high bypass ratios, wide diameter fans are needed. There is, however, a weight and drag penalty in this design. There is also a thrust decay which occurs in conventionally designed, fixed pitch rotating airfoils, at high flight speeds. This prevents bypass ratios of greater values from being used. For example, the General Electric GE-90 turbofan has a bypass ratio of 9 to 1 in the newer Boeing B-777 aircraft, whereas the older CF-6 turbofan for the DC-10 aircraft has a 6 to 1 bypass ratio.

The typical bypass ratios that can be seen most widely used are as follows:
1) Business jets, 2 to 1 in older aircraft and up to 5 to 1 in newer designs;
2) Commuter (regional jets), 4 or 5 to 1;
3) Older narrow body airliners with full fan ducts (DC-9 or 727), 1 or 2 to 1;
4) Wide body airliners, 5 to 1 up to 9 to 1.

New variable pitch airfoils in the ultrahigh bypass (UHB) propfan engines presently being developed, will greatly change the bypass condition as we know it now. Ducted propfans are predicted to be in the range of 15:1 to 20:1, and unducted propfans up to 100:1, with target cruising speeds remaining in the Mach 0.80 to 0.90 range.

be possible with an axial compressor by itself. The combination compressor is also especially well suited to engines with a reverse flow annular combustor. The engine is designed with a greater diameter to accommodate this type of combustor, so there is no disadvantage in the use of the centrifugal compressor, which is, by nature of its design, much wider than a comparable axial flow compressor. Figure 3-33 shows a six-stage axial, one stage centrifugal, combination compressor.

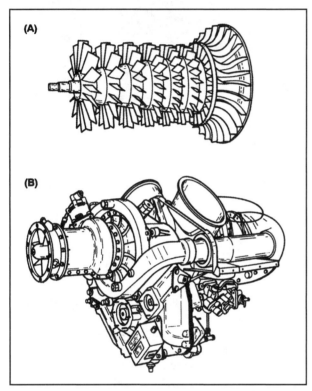

Fig. 3-33A — Combination axial-centrifugal flow compressor.
Fig. 3-33B — Turboshaft engine with combination compressor.

4. Comparison Of Axial To Centrifugal Compressors And Lift

After the previous discussion, the reader realizes that there are two common types of compressors in use today. Both sections compress air, i.e. raise air pressure. The centrifugal compressor raises air pressure by accelerating the air outward into a single diffuser shaped as a divergent duct, where, according to Bernoulli's principle, the air spreads out, slows down, and pressure rises. The idea here is that, if airflow is slower, more air molecules must be present in the duct at any given time.

The axial compressor raises air pressure by accelerating air rearward into many small diffusers, or divergent ducts, formed by the shape and positions of the stator vanes. In addition, the blade pair's trailing edges also form divergent ducts, which start the rise in air pressure prior to entry into the stators.

A further understanding of a gas turbine engine compressor can be realized by examining the traditional theory of lift and the airfoil.

A wing exerts a downward force on the air that supports it. This force creates a downward velocity in the air equal to the lift (upward force). The compressor airfoil in a similar manner exerts a rearward force on the air. This force creates a rearward velocity in air equal to the lift (forward force). The resultant pushing force aids in propelling the engine as well as producing pressure for combustion (Figure 3-34).

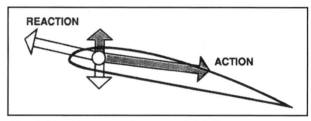

Fig. 3-34 —Forces acting on an airfoil.

5. Compressor Interstage Airflow

The compressor both compresses and pumps air from one stage to the next. In this process, the compressor airfoils experience an infinite variety of angles-of-attack (AOA) and air densities, which in turn create pressure and velocity changes. Controlling AOA is a design function of the inlet duct, the compressor and the fuel controlling system. Inlet ducts were discussed in the first part of this chapter and fuel controls will be discussed in Chapter 7.

The principles of rotating airfoil compression can be understood by analyzing the following steps in vectoring, and the narrative on inter-stage airflow that follows.

A vector represents force in a particular direction. Figure 3-35 shows that, if a force in the direction of Arrow 1 experiences a second force in the direction of Arrow 2, a new direction and force results, shown by Arrow 3.

Referring to Figure 3-36, note that rotation of the compressor blades causes the initial increase in air velocity near the engine entrance in the inlet duct. Airflow is drawn through the inlet guide vanes, which impart an angular change only. No velocity or pressure change in the airflow occurs due to the straight duct flow area formed by each pair of vanes.

The straight-in angle at which the inlet guide vanes receive air, and the vectored angle at which the air leaves the vanes is determined by the vane positioning and curvature. Note that the two arrows on the diagram are the same length indicating no change in velocity but a change in direction only. Previously, variable inlet guide vanes were mentioned. For the purposes of this discussion these vanes will remain fixed.

There are two vector forces acting on airflow. One vector is inlet effect, either ram or suction, which creates air velocity into the compressor. It is depicted by the

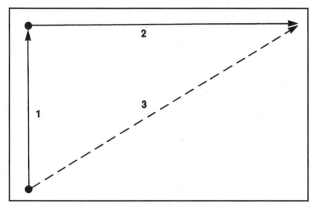

Fig. 3-35 — Steps in vectoring airflow.

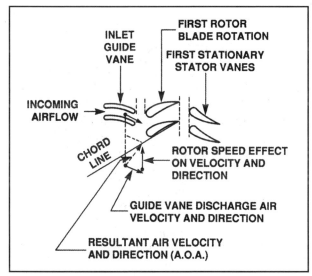

Fig. 3-36 — Vector diagram of interstage compressor airflow.

arrow labeled "guide vane discharge air velocity and direction". The other vector is created by the effect of the rotating blade. As it rotates in one direction, air is caused to flow over the airfoil in a direction opposite that of rotation. This vector is labeled "rotor speed effect on velocity and direction".

The two vector forces present here are inlet effect on velocity of flow and RPM effect on velocity of flow.

The resultant vector, if the two combined vector forces are in the proper proportion, will provide a suitable angle-of-attack of incoming air in relation to the blade chord line, and air will remain on the airfoil surfaces and produce minimal turbulence and friction. Airflow, after passing through the first stage of compression as shown on the diagram, will then proceed through each stage in this same manner. It is interesting to note that, if a particular molecule of air were followed through the compressor, it would probably rotate no more than 180 degrees, due to the straightening effect of the compressor stator vanes. Since the last compression stage is followed by a stationary vane set, called exit guide vanes, the airflow is turned

completely back to an axial direction on its way to the combustor.

Now that the angular direction of airflow has been discussed, let us look at the way in which the passage of air through the blades of the compressor creates pressure. Observe that the passageway, formed by the top (cambered side) of one blade and the bottom side of the blade next to it, is diverging. This diverging shape causes a slight rise in static pressure of the air as it passes through. At the same time, the blades are performing work on the air to increase its velocity.

When the air leaves the compressor blades, it flows into a row of stator vanes. The stator vanes also form diverging ducts which decrease the velocity of the air and increase the static pressure. The compressor blade and stator vane action continues through all the stages of the compressor. When the air leaves the compressor, it will have approximately the same velocity with which it started but a much greater static pressure.

If you look critically at the passageway formed by any of the pairs of blades or vanes you will realize that the shape is actually convergent at the leading edges and divergent toward the trailing edge, forming what is called a convergent-divergent duct or passageway. This does not create a sonic shock because airflow is subsonic in this area of the engine, and the net effect is that of a plain divergent duct. This is of course the same result that one would see in a convergent-divergent flight inlet at subsonic flight speeds. This idea was expanded upon in the first part of this chapter under Convergent-Divergent Inlet Ducts.

a. Cascade Effect

The axial compressor is described as containing sets of airfoils in cascade. This means that the airfoils are arranged in series which influences air under low pressure in the front stages to flow into an area of higher pressure. The ability of air to flow rearward against an ever increasing pressure is similar to forcing water to flow uphill. Pressure must be constantly applied to achieve the correct flow. The idea of the constantly applied pressure is explained in the following narrative and drawings. Figure 3-37 shows that if a slight positive angle of attack exists, a relatively high pressure is present on the bottom of the airfoil in relation to the pressure on the top of the airfoil. These high and low pressure zones apply to both the rotating airfoils (rotor blades) and to the stationary airfoils (stator vanes). These high and low pressure zones allow the air in one set of airfoils to come under the influence of the next set. This is the cascade effect.

Figure 3-38 depicts high pressure zone air of the first stage blade being pumped into the low pressure zone of its stator. Notice that the stator's leading edge faces in the opposite direction of the rotor blade's leading edge, thereby causing the pumping action to occur. The high pressure zone of the first stage stator vane then pumps into the low pressure zone of the second stage rotor blade. This

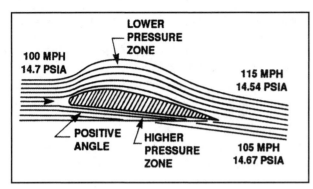

Fig. 3-37 — Pressure zones on an airfoil.

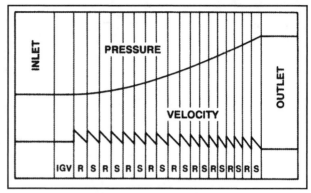

Fig. 3-39 — Pressure and velocity change through an axial compressor.

cascade progress continues through to the last stage of compression.

When observing Figure 3-38, it might appear that the rotor blade high and low pressure zones might cancel each other out as thcy blend together; but the overall effect of the divergent shape of the flow path results in a net decrease in velocity and an increase in static pressure.

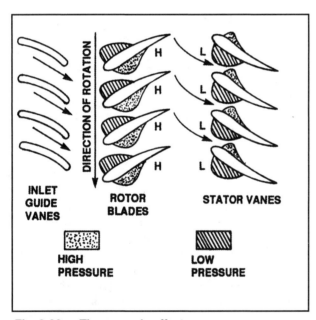

Fig. 3-38 — The cascade effect.

b. Compressor Taper Design

As pressure builds in the rear stages of the compressor, velocity tends to drop, in accordance with Bernoulli's Principle. This is not desirable because, in order to create thrust, the gas turbine engine operates on a principle of velocity change in airflow. Figure 3-39 shows velocity rising and falling through the successive stages of the compressor, but maintaining approximately the same inlet and outlet velocity. Even though the pressure is rising dramatically, the velocity is held relatively constant. In order to stabilize the velocity, the shape of the compressor gas path converges, reducing to approximately

25% of the inlet flow area. This tapered shape provides the proper amount of space for the compressed air to occupy.

Figure 3-40 illustrates the tapered annulus concept and also reiterates the one- in, one-out idea developed in Chapter II. That is, each unit of air passing through will have a certain physical size. If ideal compression in a particular engine is considered to be 12:1, and if airflow discontinuities in the compressor cause compression to drop to 10:1, the units will be larger in size and will try to accelerate in order to exit as the next unit enters. This acceleration creates an angle of attack change, the consequences of which are significant.

If the compressor pressure ratio is designed to be 12:1 at takeoff power, Illustration (b) depicts the size of a unit of air under normal compression as it moves from the compressor inlet to the compressor exit. The angle of attack (AOA) will be normal in this case.

If the air is not properly compressed as shown, as in Illustration (c), its exit velocity will be high, its angle of attack will be low, and this will affect the pressure zone as indicated in illustrations (e) and (g).

If compression is too high as seen in Illustration (d), it will cause a low velocity vector, a high AOA and too large a pressure zone. The results of high AOA can be seen in Illustrations (e) and (f). An explanation of the causes of high and low velocities affecting AOA follows.

c. Angle Of Attack And Compressor Stall

As Figure 3-41 shows, the angle of attack of the compressor blade is the result of inlet air velocity and the compressor RPM effect on airflow. The two forces combine to form a vector, which is the actual angle of attack of air approaching the airfoil. A compressor stall, a condition all gas turbine engines experience from time to time, can be described as an imbalance between the two vector quantities, inlet velocity and compressor RPM.

Compressor stalls cause air flowing through the compressor to slow down, to stagnate (stop), or to reverse direction, depending on the stall intensity. Stall conditions can usually be heard and range in audibility from an

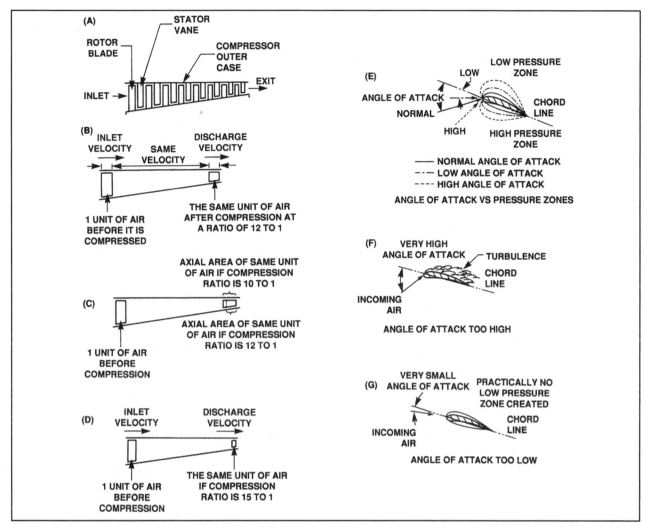

Fig. 3-40 — Compressor pressure ratio influence on angle of attack.

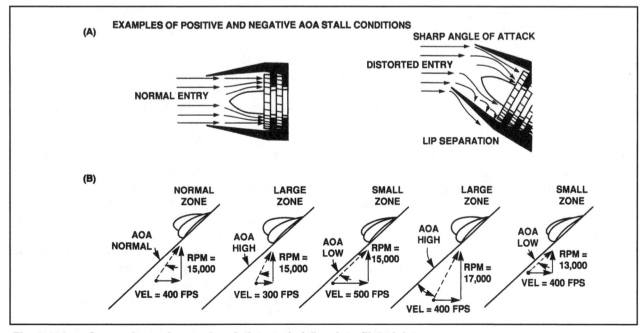

Fig. 3-41A — Comparison of normal and distorted airflow into flight inlet.
Fig. 3-41B — Vector analysis of compressor stall.

air pulsating, or fluttering type sound in their mildest form, to a louder pulsating type sound, to a sound of violent backfire or explosion. Quite often the cockpit gauges do not show a mild stall condition, called a transient stall. These stalls are not usually harmful to the engine and often correct themselves after one or two pulsations. Severe stalls, called hung stalls, can significantly decay engine performance, cause loss of power, or can even damage or cause the engine to fail. Stall conditions are generally cyclic and result from many causes, the most common of which are as follows:

1) Turbulent or disrupted airflow to the engine inlet (reduces the velocity vector);

2) Excessive fuel flow caused by abrupt engine acceleration (reduces the velocity vector by increasing combustor back pressure);

3) Excessively lean fuel mixture caused by abrupt engine deceleration, (increases the velocity vector by reducing combustor back pressure);

4) Contaminated or damaged compressor(s) (increases the velocity vector by reducing compression);

5) Damaged turbine components, causing loss of power to the compressor and low compression (increases the velocity vector by reducing compression);

6) Engine operation above or below designed RPM (increases or decreases the RPM vector).

For an example of disrupted airflow to the inlet, consider the situation of a business jet with two engines mounted on its rear fuselage. If this airplane goes into a sharp right hand turn, airflow to the left engine may be partially blocked by the aircraft fuselage. This sideslip could cause low inlet air velocity to result and a momentary increase in the effective angle of attack sufficient to create a compressor stall.

The pilot will know that an engine is experiencing compressor stall by an audible noise, by fluctuation in RPM, by an increase in Exhaust Gas Temperature, or by a combination of these three. His reaction will probably be to reduce power so the inlet air velocity and RPM will return back to their proper relationship.

In some instances of extremely severe compressor stall or surge, caused by fuel system malfunction or foreign object ingestion, a reversal of airflow occurs with such force that bending stresses on the rear of compressor blades can cause them to contact the stator vanes. At that point a series of material failures can result in total disintegration of the rotor system and complete engine failure.

d. Relationship Between Compression Ratio And Mass Airflow

When an engine is operating at designed-speed, the compressor blades are at a high angle-of-attack, which is very close to its stall angle but which gives the maximum pressure rise.

By referring to Figure 3-42, the relationship between compressor pressure ratio and mass airflow can be estab-

lished. Figure 3-42(a) shows that a mass airflow of 30 pounds per second, when flowing from an unrestricted nozzle, will build only a minimal amount of pressure. Entering the inlet at 15 pounds per square inch - absolute, under the influence of the compressor action and mass airflow, pressure builds to only 20 pounds per square inch - absolute, representing a compressor pressure ratio of 1.3:1.

In Figure 3-42(b), with a constricted discharge nozzle restricting the flow, pressure builds to 50 pounds per square inch-absolute at the same mass airflow of 30 pounds per second. The result now is a 3.3:1 compressor pressure ratio.

Figure 3-42(c) shows the final pressure rise, again under the influence of the same mass airflow of 30 pounds per second, to the designed compressor pressure ratio of 6.6 to 1. Note that here combustor back pressure and the restriction to flow created by the turbine system are added to the exhaust nozzle back pressure.

So it can be seen that, in order for the engine to function correctly, compressor pressure ratio and mass airflow must remain within the established relationship. This can only occur if inlet compression, compressor efficiency, fuel flow, turbine efficiency, and exhaust nozzle flow all remain within the designed operating parameters. If they do not, a compressor stall or surge may result.

e. Stall Or Surge Margin Graph

Another way to describe stall phenomena in a compressor is by way of a stall or surge margin curve. A stall is defined as a localized condition whereas a surge occurs across the whole compressor. Every compressor has a best operating point for a particular compression ratio (Cr), compressor speed (RPM), and mass airflow (Ms), which is commonly called the design point.

The surge-stall line is a series of connecting points on the graph that are plotted during the development stage of the compressor. This line represents the maximum Cr and Ms that the compressor is capable of maintaining at a particular RPM. When the three factors are proportionately matched, the engine operates comfortably on the normal operating line. This line is well below the surge-stall line to give a margin for changes which occur in the atmosphere, the aircraft's flight attitude, and the engine's fuel schedule during acceleration and deceleration. If for any reason Cr increases or decreases, the design point will shift up or down and out of sync with RPM. If Ms increases or decreases, the design point will move to the right or left and out of symmetry with RPM.

In Figure 3-43, the normal operating line indicates that the engine will perform without surge or stall at the various compressor pressure ratios, engine speeds, and mass airflows along the length of the line, the line falling well below the surge-stall zone. The design point is the point on this line at which the engine will operate during most of its service life, that is, cruise speed, at altitude.

From the graph it can be seen that at any given compressor speed (RPM), a band of compressor pressure

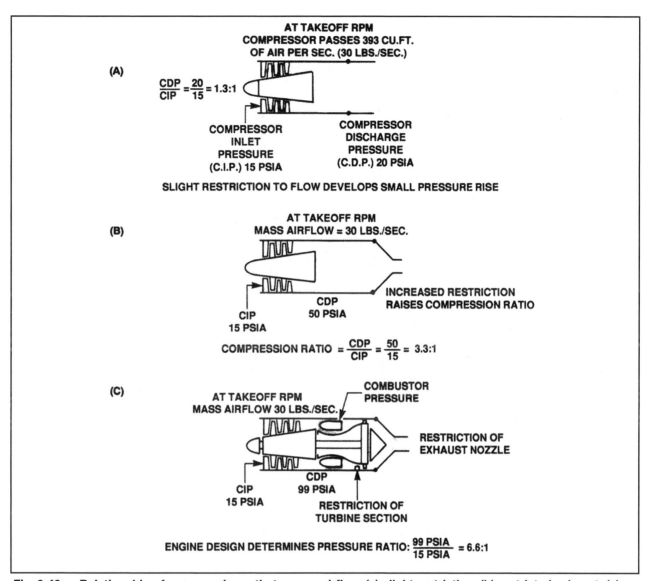

Fig. 3-42 — *Relationship of compression ratio to mass airflow. (a) slight-restriction; (b) restricted exhaust; (c) restricted exhaust with combustor and turbine back pressures factored in.*

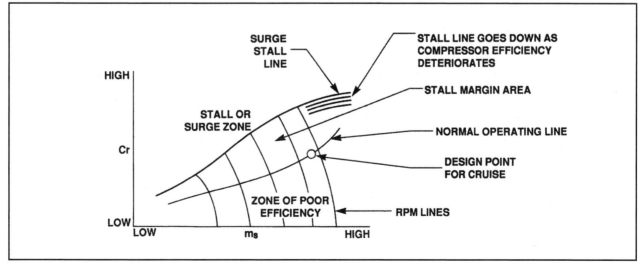

Fig. 3-43 — *Stall margin graph.*

ratios are acceptable for the engine to operate satisfactorily above the normal operating line and within the stall margin (the space between the normal operating line and the stall line).

The same is true for mass airflow. At any given RPM there exists a band of mass flows at which point the engine can operate satisfactorily above the normal operating line and within the stall margin.

For instance, assume the designed compression ratio is 12:1, as previously mentioned in the paragraph concerning Compressor Taper Design. The engine is operating at cruise RPM with mass airflow, RPM, and compression ratio plots all meeting at Point A on the stall map, Figure 3-44. This represents the compressor pressure ratio and mass airflow needs of the engine while operating at cruise RPM.

If the aircraft were to enter turbulent weather conditions at high altitude, and at the same time the engine compressor were dirty and operating at less than peak efficiency, then a compressor pressure ratio loss down to 10:1 could occur. This loss of compression to Point B could cause mass airflow to decrease to Point C, and beyond into the surge-stall zone. Note also that the normal stall line has shifted slightly downward because of the dirty compressor.

At this point, a mismatch of compressor and combustor also comes into play because the power lever has not yet been moved, fuel flow remains high, and combustor pressure is now greater than compressor discharge pressure. This causes AOA problems and hurts the compression process. The operator will have to react quickly by reducing power to allow Cr and Ms to come back into symmetry with RPM. After recovering from the stall, the operator will carefully accelerate the engine and try to avoid the adverse weather that caused the surge-stall problem.

A significant factor about the stall map and engine performance is that a compressor pressure ratio decrease causes a mass airflow decrease. But mass airflow drops in a much more pronounced way, bringing the engine to the stall line. Also, with the engine operating at the right end of the normal operating line, imagine the pilot placing the aircraft nose down, making no change in RPM, and see

that a compressor pressure ratio rise along with increased mass airflow could easily move the operating point above the stall line.

In flight, the fuel control will sense the parameters of Cr, Ms, and RPM, and under all but the most unusual circumstances keep all in fine adjustment and in proportion at all times. If, however, the limits of the fuel control scheduling system is exceeded, the operator will have to react by making a coarse adjustment with the power lever. The fuel system is further discussed in a later chapter.

f. Advances In Compressor Design And Compressor Stall

Compressor designers, with the aid of computer mapping, have recently made significant advances in the study of flow fields of mass airflow passing through the compression process, areas of importance being viscosity changes, shock wave formation, flow separation, and turbulence.

1) Blades

Newly designed fan blades have radically changed the traditional airfoil shape of turbine engine compressor blades. In the new blades, both leading and trailing edges may have an irregular waviness at certain points or even all along their length, base to tip. This new aerodynamic design gives a distinct stall margin at each blade station along the blade's length and allows the normal operating line to shift toward the surge-stall line. The result is a compressor with a higher pressure ratio for a given RPM, yet, a compressor which remains stall free.

The simple axial compressor allows for only subsonic axial airflow down the gas path and only subsonic airflow over all parts of its airfoil systems.

New materials and designs have brought about advanced compressor designs with high subsonic axial flow and transonic airfoil flow characteristics. This means that airflow over some parts of the blades, especially in the area of the blade tips, is allowed to exceed sonic velocity.

Transonic velocity is achieved simply by increasing compressor speed, which in turn creates higher axial air-

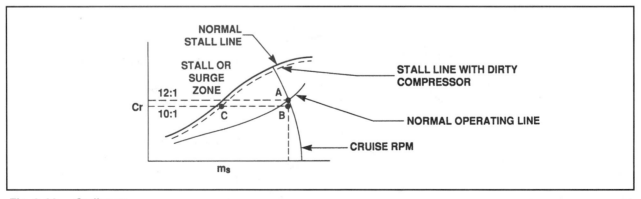

Fig. 3-44 — Stall map.

flow velocity. The significance of higher velocity is that mass airflow is equal to the flow area multiplied by the axial velocity and that mass airflow can be increased without increasing the diameter of the engine.

Because the transonic blade is designed to accommodate higher air velocity entry speeds, another benefit of transonic fan blades is that, in many engines, they eliminate the need for inlet guide vanes.

The discussion on compressor interstage airflow earlier in this chapter was based on the simple compressor design where both velocity over the airfoils and axial flow velocity were subsonic. In actuality, the more advanced compressor today will have supersonic blade tip flow of up to approximately Mach 1.3. This condition allows axial airflow down the gas path to come much closer to sonic speeds than was previously possible (Figure 3-45).

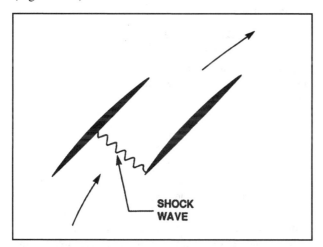

Fig. 3-45 — Transonic compressor blades

The 1.40:1 per stage pressure ratio achievable in the high performance compressor is accomplished by supersonic diffusion. Some compressors being installed in the newest engines, or being developed for future engines, are running pressure ratios as high as 1.5 to 1.6 per stage. Some new engines today are still using the high aspect ratio blades, but the highest performance is being obtained from wide chord blades with what is called 3D aerodynamic design. This is made possible by advances in metallurgy, new manufacturing processes, and a higher state-of-the-art of compressor aerodynamics.

These advances allow a supersonic airflow over airfoil sections which does not produce detrimental shock stalls and which keeps the airflow laminar to the surfaces for maximum compression. Illustrative or mathematical explanations of the supersonic airfoil is beyond the scope of this text but can be found in many textbooks which deal with compressor aerodynamics.

2) Active Clearance Control (Figure 3-69)

Another compression enhancing design that can be observed on newer engines is called "active clearance control". One such system introduces cooling air into tubing external to the engine. This cooling action in effect shrinks the outer compressor case to desired clearance from the compressor blade tips running within the case.

The active clearance control system schedules airflow in amounts necessary to provide the optimum compressor pressure ratio at varying power settings. In this way, engine efficiencies and, thus, lower fuel consumption results.

The Pratt & Whitney Company is presently developing another method called the Thermatic Compressor Rotor® as an offshoot of case active clearance control. The rotor will be thermally controlled, meaning heated from within, to cause it to expand. The expansion will tighten running clearances between the compressor blades and the outer compressor case.

This clearance control method has an advantage over the external case shrinking method in that it can control clearances in more areas. The reason for this is that the use of external tubing is restricted because of the many other engine systems located on the exterior of the engine.

3) Mixed Flow Compressors (Figure 3-46A)

Still another advanced technology design is seen in the Mixed-Flow compressor, which imparts both centrifugal and axial flow to compress air. The current mixed-flow design is an outgrowth of mixed-flow compressors that were built in the early 1950's. Production, however, was discontinued on these early compressors because of low efficiency. Although this compressor is not currently installed in flight engines, a resurgence in the use of centrifugal compressors in small engines due to recent advances in high pressure flow technology may likely bring about the re-use of the mixed-flow compressor.

4) Fan And Compressor Rotor Blisks

A blisk is a one piece blade and disk unit rather than an assembly of many separate blades fitted to the rim of a separate disk. Forged blisk technology is being applied to many smaller fans, compressor rotors and stators, and to some turbine components. Figure 3-46B shows a forging and a fan after machining of the unit to its final shape. A weight saving of 40% to 50% can be achieved by this method.

The engine used in the current F/A-18 Hornet airplane has a traditional 3 stage fan, with separate disks and blades. A new design for its engine, called the EDE (enhanced durability engine), has a two stage fan on the drawing board utilizing blisk technology.

D. Compressor-Diffuser Section

The engine section between the compressor and combustor sections is known as the compressor-diffuser because it provides additional space in which air coming from the compressor spreads out. It is a diverging duct and is usually a separate section that is bolted to the compressor case. The diffuser is known as the point of

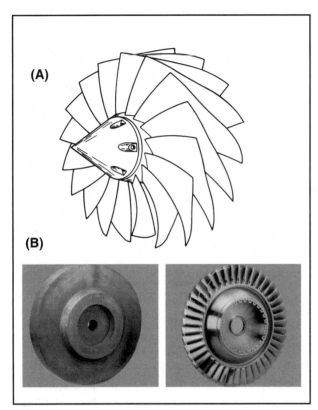

Fig. 3-46A — Mixed flow compressor.
Fig. 3-46B — Fan Blisk

highest pressure in the gas turbine engine. The high wall of pressure it provides, in effect, gives the combustion products something to push against (Figure 3-47).

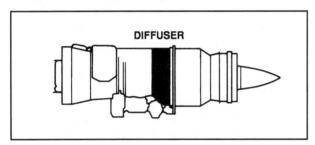

Fig. 3-47 — Location of compressor-deffuser section.

The point of highest pressure idea needs some interpretation in reference to pressure total (Pt) or pressure static (Ps). At the diffuser inlet, for example, if total pressure (Pt) is 200 pounds per square inch absolute, at the exit of the diffuser, Pt is also 200 pounds per square inch absolute. The diffusing action that takes place as air moves from the inlet to the exit of the diffuser section creates an increase in static pressure (Ps) at the expense of velocity.

Static pressure (measured as either absolute pressure or gauge pressure) will be higher at the diffuser exit, and this is the point of highest static pressure (Ps) in the engine.

If the now familiar (Pt/Ps) formula were used to calculate Ps at the diffuser inlet when airflow Mach = 0.5 (an average value engine to engine), Ps would be approximately 169 pounds per square inch - absolute. The remaining 31 psig would be in the form of ram pressure. At the diffuser outlet if airflow drops to Mach = 0.35 (another average value), Ps would be approximately 184 pounds per square inch absolute, leaving 16 pounds per square inch absolute as ram pressure. What is evident here is that the total pressure (Pt) of 200 does not change if mass flow does not change and that only static and ram pressure values change.

Low velocities are desirable at the combustor entrance, but if the Mach number is allowed to drop too low in a divergent duct, there enters a serious aerodynamic problem as airflow starts to separate from the walls creating turbulence. Therefore, Mach 0.35 is presently the mean low limit.

E. Combustion Section

The combustion section or burner, as it is called, consists basically of an outer casing, an inner perforated liner, a fuel injection system, and a starting ignition system. The function of this section is to add heat energy to the flowing gases, thereby expanding and accelerating the gases into the turbine section (Figure 3-48).

One way to think about combustion is that, when fuel heat is added, the volume of the gas is increased and, with flow area remaining the same, this causes an acceleration of gases to occur. A further explanation is that the expansion and acceleration is caused by combustion resulting from the interaction of oxygen molecules and molecules of fuel which are heated to ignition temperatures. At the high fuel flow and airflow present in large turbine engines, this combustion could result in heat energy equal to 4 to 8 hundred-million Btu/hr.

The most common combustor configuration is the "through-flow", or "straight-through" combustor, in which gases entering from compression are immediately ignited and then pass directly into the turbine sections. The multiple-can, annular, and can-annular combustors are generally through-flow combustors.

The other configuration is the reverse flow annular combustor in which gases exiting the compressor flow to the rear of the combustor and make a 180 degree turn to enter the flame zone. As the gases exit the combustor they make another 180 degree turn and enter the turbine section. The airflow ends up making an S-turn as it enters and exits the combustor. Illustrations of these combustor types will follow in succeeding paragraphs.

The various types of combustion chambers in use are:
1. Multiple-can;
2. Can-annular;
3. Annular-through flow;
4. Annular-reverse flow.

To function efficiently, the combustion chamber must provide a means for proper mixing of air and fuel. It must

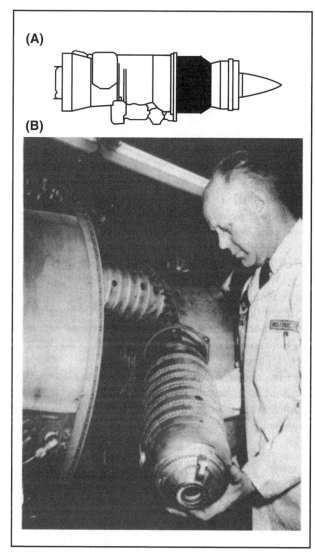

Fig. 3-48A — Location of combustor.
Fig. 3-48B — Removal of through-flow, can-annular liner, from Pratt & Whitney JT8D turbofan.

also cool the hot combustion products to a temperature which the turbine section components can withstand. To accomplish this, airflow through the combustor is divided into primary and secondary air paths. Primary air is routed to the fuel nozzle area to support combustion and secondary air is used for cooling.

In early gas turbine engines, primary air could be as low as 25% of the air leaving the compressor, with the other 75% being needed for cooling. In the more modern engines today, as much as 45% of the air leaving the compressor is used for combustion. Of the remaining compressor air, 35% would typically be used for cooling the combustor and 20% would be used for cooling the turbine. By using more air to support combustion, the thermal efficiency of the engine is improved and the size of the engine for a given thrust is reduced.

Approximately one half of primary air flows axially through swirl vanes in the combustion liner in the area of

the fuel nozzle openings, the remaining primary air enters radially through small holes in the first one-third of the liner. Both axial and radial airflows support combustion.

A portion of secondary air, the percent varying depending on the vintage of the engine, provides a cooling air blanket over inside and outside surfaces of the liner and centers the flame, preventing it from contacting the metal surfaces. The other portion of secondary air enters the liner at the rear and dilutes the mixture to a temperature acceptable for the good service life of the turbine components.

Developments in recent years have lead to what is called the smokeless or reduced smoke combustor. Early engines suffered from incomplete combustion, which left unburned fuel in the tailpipe to carbonize and enter the atmosphere as smoke. By shortening the flame pattern, increasing its heat intensity, and using new materials that can withstand higher operating temperatures, manufacturers have been able to almost completely eliminate smoke emissions from turbine engines.

An interesting facet of combustion chamber operation is the velocity of the air in the flame zone immediately in front of the fuel nozzles. Although secondary airflow in the chamber may be at a velocity of several hundred feet per second, primary airflow is metered and slowed by swirl vanes. These swirl vanes create radial motion and retard axial motion of the air to an almost stagnant 5 or 6 feet per second, in a vortex type flow. (See Figure 3-49 and 3-51B)

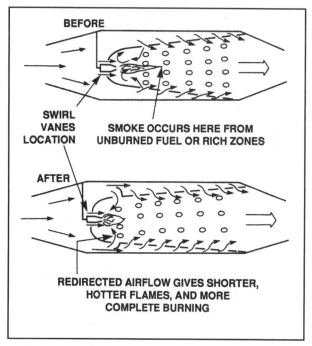

Fig. 3-49 — Development of reduced smoke combustors.

The vortex created in the flame area provides the required mixing time of air and fuel. One major design problem is that in an attempt to increase mixing time by

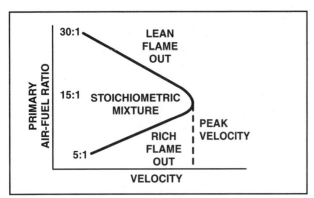

Fig. 3-50 — Range of burnable fuel-air ratios vs. combustor gas velocity.

creating vortex turbulence, combustor pressure drops and combustor efficiency decreases. Because of the slow flame propagation rate of jet fuels, if primary air flow velocity were too high, it would literally blow the flame out of the engine causing what is called a "flame-out".

As it is, the combustion process is completed in the first one third of the combustion liner. In the remaining two thirds of combustor length, the combusted and uncombusted gas is mixed to provide an even heat distribution at the turbine nozzle.

Although flame-out is uncommon in modern engines, it still occurs. Turbulent weather, high altitude, slow acceleration during maneuvers, and high speed maneuvers are four of the more typical conditions which set up combustor flame-out.

Flame-out (lean) — This condition usually occurs at low fuel pressures, at low engine speeds, or in high altitude flight. This sets up a weak mixture which can be easily blown out, even at normal airflows.

Flame-out (rich) — This condition usually occurs during very fast engine acceleration in which an over-rich mixture is present causing combustion pressure to increase until compressor airflow stagnates (slows or stops). The momentary interruption in airflow then causes flame extinction. Turbulent inlet conditions and violent flight maneuvers can also cause stalls which could result in compression stagnation and loss of combustion.

Combustor Instability — These can occur in a mild form from flight conditions. They are difficult to predict and sometimes allow formations of small gas pressure fluctuations in the combustor. These low pressure cycles, if left unattended, can generate greater and greater combustor instability until the pilot makes the necessary adjustment in flight conditions or to engine controls.

Correct velocity of airflow in the combustor depends on a correct matching of compression ratio, mass airflow, and engine speed. Figure 3-50 indicates that only at the stoichiometric mixture can velocity be at its peak. If the mixture is lean or rich, the velocity will be at a corresponding lower value and the thermal efficiency will suffer.

Efficiency — The combustor is efficient in the range of 99 to 100%. That is to say the combustor extracts heat

equal to 99-100% of the potential heat actually contained in the fuel.

Combustor design is often referred to as a "black art". That is, it is not always known why one combustor design works well and gives good service life and another type will not when installed in the same engine. Just as in Whittle's time, when obtaining good combustor performance took the bulk of the engine research and developmental time, the same situation exists today.

The tendency of manufacturers seems to be one of building on their known technological base for their new engines. Because of this we often see familiar combustor designs from one generation of engine to the next. The various types of combustors of proven performance for flight engines are as follows:

1. Multiple-Can Combustor (Through Flow)

This older type of combustion chamber is not commonly used today. It consists of multiple outer housings, each with its own perforated inner liner. Each of the multiple combustors (cans) is in effect a separate burner unit, all of which discharge into one open area at the turbine nozzle inlet. The individual combustors are interconnected with small interconnector tubes so that, as combustion occurs in the two combustors with igniter plugs, the flame can move to all of the remaining cans.

The Rolls Royce Dart, Figure 3-51, is a good example of an engine using this design. The cans are mounted on a slight angle to reduce the total engine length. The cutaway view shows the position of a can-type combustor's various components.

2. Can-Annular Combustor (Through Flow)

The can-annular combustor is more common to commercial aircraft powered by Pratt & Whitney engines. This design consists of an outer case containing multiple liners located radially about the axis of the engine. The liners take air in at the front and discharge it at the rear. Flame propagation tubes are utilized to connect the liners and provision is made for two igniter plugs in the lower cans.

In Figure 3-52, eight liners are used. Each liner has its own fuel nozzle cluster supporting the liner at the front end, and a device with eight apertures, called an outlet duct, supporting the liner at the back. An advantage of this combustor is that it is designed for ease of on-the-wing maintenance. The outer case is made to slide back to facilitate liner inspection.

3. Annular Combustor (Through Flow)

The annular combustor takes air in at the front and discharges it at the rear. It consists of an outer housing, containing only one liner. The perforated liner is often referred to as a basket. Multiple fuel spray nozzles protrude into the

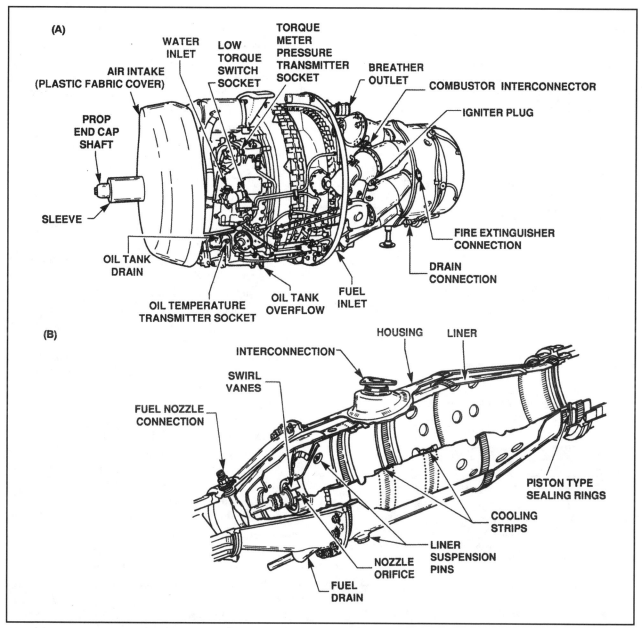

Fig. 3-51A — Rolls-Royce Dart turboprop engine with multiple-can combustor.
Fig. 3-51B — Combustion can and its liner.

basket. Primary and secondary air provide for combustion and cooling as in other combustor designs.

The annular combustor is commonly used today in all sizes of engines. It is said to be the most efficient design from the standpoint of thermal efficiency versus weight and for its shorter length than the other types. Its minimal surface area requires less cooling air. It appears to make the best use of the available space between the diffuser and turbine sections, especially on large engines where other combustor types would be much heavier for the mass airflow (Figure 3-53).

4. Annular Reverse-Flow Combustor

This design is common to the Pratt & Whitney JT-15D turbofan, PT-6 turboprop, the Avco Lycoming T-53/55, and

several other low mass flow engines installed in corporate aviation aircraft. The reverse-flow combustor has the same function as the through-flow combustor types. It only differs in the flow of air through the combustor. Instead of air entering the combustor from the front, it flows over the liner and enters from the rear, with the combustion gas flow being opposite in direction to the normal airflow through the engine. After combustion takes place, the gases flow into a deflector, which turns them 180 degrees, to exit the engine in the normal direction.

In Figure 3-54A, notice that the turbine wheels are inside the combustor area rather than in tandem with it as in the other previously mentioned types. This arrangement provides for shorter engine length and weight reduction and also allows for preheating of the compres-

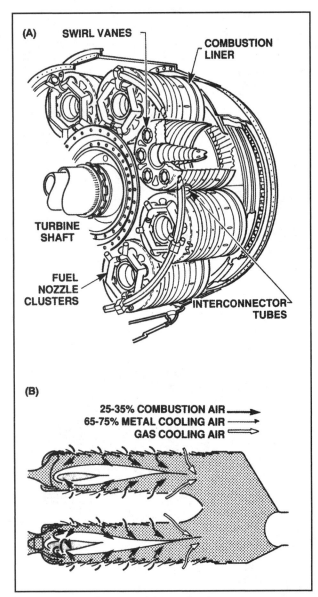

Fig. 3-52A — Can-annular combustor.
Fig. 3-52B — Liner showing primary and secondary airflow.

sor discharge air. These two factors make up for the loss of efficiency, which occurs when the gas makes the turns during combustion.

5. New Designs Of Combustors

One new combustor design that is coming into use in small engines is called the Precombustor Chamber. It is an annular combustor in which a portion of primary air comes first into a precombustor chamber where it mixes with fuel and ignites; the gas then goes into the main chamber where it meets a second fuel nozzle and the remainder of primary airflow. Manufacturers' claims for this more complex combustor are that it promotes ease of cold weather starting, low emissions, and high resistance to flameout (Figure 3-54C). The traditional Allison-250 combustion liner is shown in Figure 3-54B.

Another new type liner (Figure 3-54E) is the machined ring liner, constructed by welding together rings of heavy gauge metal. This technique is said to produce a liner of much higher mechanical strength than the traditional stamped sheet metal liner as shown in Figure 3-54D. This type of liner is now common in the larger fan engines with annular combustors.

6. Combustor Generated Emissions

The Gas Turbine Engine has a highly efficient combustion cycle and produces very little atmospheric pollution in comparison to many industrial fuel-burning processes.

Combustor efficiency is over 99 percent when the engine is operating at a high power setting, dropping to approximately 95 percent at idle. Most of the emissions from the hot exhaust are non-pollutants consisting of the following approximate values: Oxygen, 15%; inert gas and water vapor, 82%; and carbon dioxide, 4%. Actual pollutants by weight are only about 0.04% at full power and 0.13% at idle power.

Gas Turbine emissions classed as pollutants by the Environmental Protection Agency (EPA) are as follows:
a. Smoke (carbon particles);
b. Unburned hydrocarbons in fuel (HC);
c. Carbon Monoxide (CO);
d. Oxides of Nitrogen (NOx).

Pollutants are formed in two ways, by inefficiency in the combustion process, and by high flame temperature reaction to burning of hydrocarbon fuel in air. HC and CO result mainly from combustor inefficiencies and NOx results from high flame temperatures, which changes atmospheric ozone to nitric acid during combustion.

HC and CO are formed primarily at low power settings near the walls of the combustor liner where cooling air inhibits complete combustion at a time when atomization of fuel by the fuel nozzle is poor and combustor temperatures are low. NOx is the natural by-product of hydrocarbon fuel burned at the very high temperature necessary for good power production and fuel economy.

The "reduced smoke" combustor liner mentioned in the early part of the combustor section was designed to reduce HC, CO, and smoke, but it increased slightly the NOx emission by producing a shorter, hotter flame pattern. From these two examples, one can see some of the trade-offs between forms of pollution and economy of operation.

All gas turbine engines are tested by the EPA to ensure that federal standards are being met. Engine manufacturers consistently strive to improve their products by increasing engine performance and reducing fuel consumption and, at the same time, meet current EPA standards (Figure 3-55).

During one cycle of operation, which involves idle and taxi time, takeoff and climbout, and approach for landing, the current standards for pollutants are as follows:

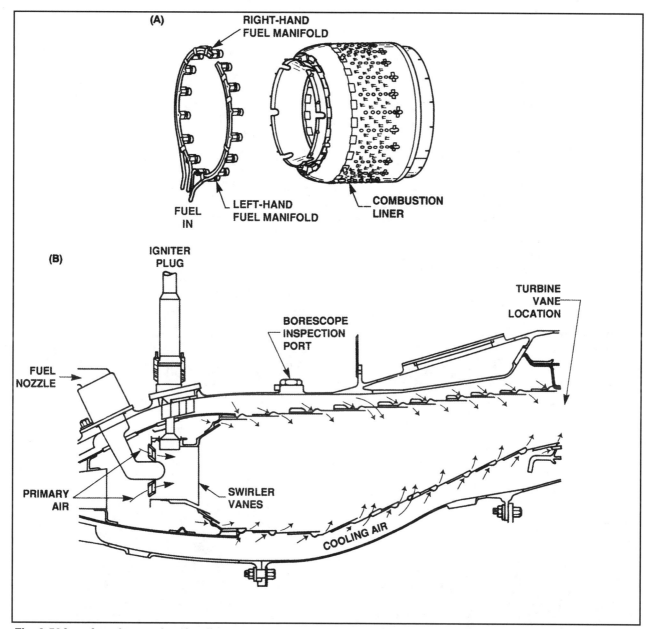

Fig. 3-53A — Annular combustion liner.
Fig. 3-53B — Cross-section of annular liner, General Electric CF6 turbofan engine.

- Hydrocarbons - no more than 0.19 lbs. per 1,000 pounds of thrust.
- Oxides of nitrogen - no more than 0.31 lbs. per 1,000 pounds of thrust.
- Carbon Monoxide - no more than 1.16 lbs. per 1,000 pounds of thrust.

F. Turbine Section

1. Turbine Rotor And Stator

a. Mechanical Work And The Turbine

The turbine section is bolted to the combustor and contains the turbine wheels and turbine stators. The turbine functions to transform a portion of the kinetic energy and heat energy in the exhaust gases into mechanical

work, thereby enabling the turbine to drive the compressor and accessories (Figure 3-56).

Recall that the compressor adds energy to air by increasing its pressure. The turbine extracts energy by reducing pressure of the flowing gases. This occurs as pressure is converted to velocity at the nozzles formed at the trailing edge of the turbine stator vanes and rotor blades. The velocity referred to is vectored in a tangential direction rather than axial. This slows the gas flow axially, reducing its reactive power, but adds shaft power to the rotor system.

The mass (weight) of airflow naturally does not change in the transfer of energy to the rotor system, but the velocity of mass flow being slowed axially is said to account for the energy-of-flow loss as the energy of shaft

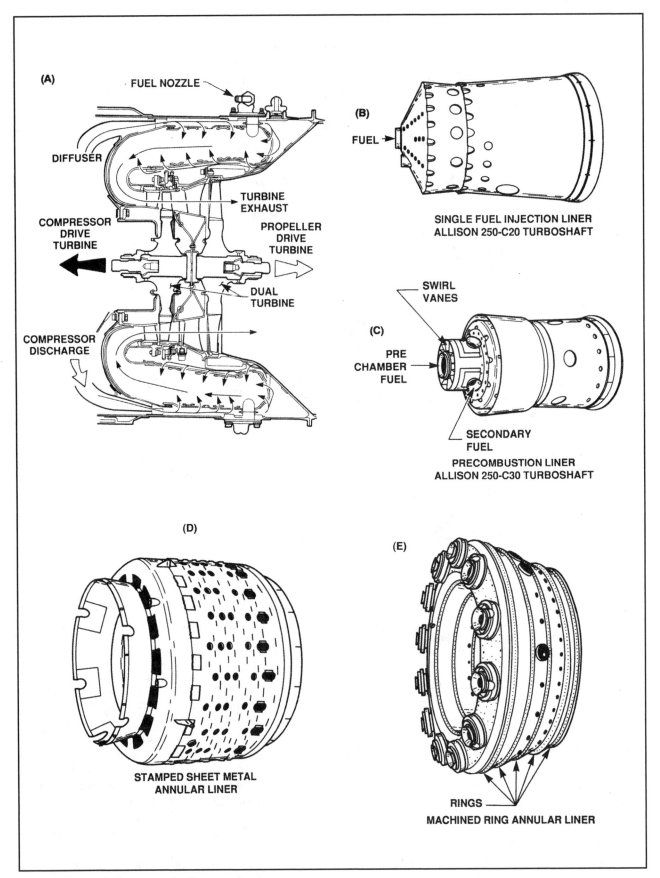

Fig. 3-54A — Annular reverse flow combustor.
Fig. 3-54B & C — Comparison of single and dual fuel injection type liners.
Fig. 3-54D & E — Comparison of early and new combustion liner for General Electric T-700 turboshaft engine.

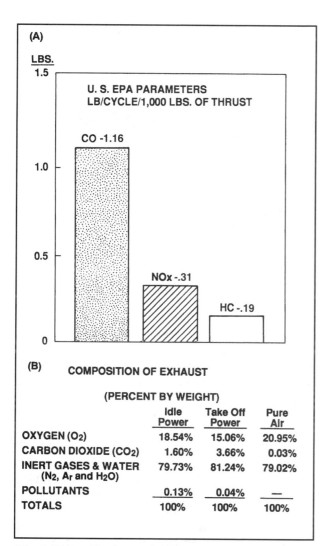

Fig. 3-55A — Engine emissions limits for turbofan engines: Pound of pollutants, per take-off and landing cycle, per 1000 pounds of rated thrust.
Fig. 3-55B — Typical composition of aircraft gas turbine engine emissions.

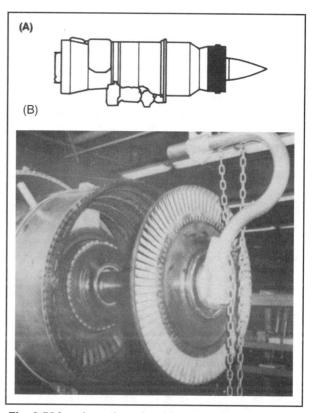

Fig. 3-56A — Location of turbine section.
Fig. 56B — Horizontal removal of turbine wheel – Pratt & Whitney JT8D Turbofan engine.

Fig. 3-57 — Removal of Turbine stator assembly.

power is increased. In other words, tangential velocity is essentially a loss of kinetic energy to the engine and this best explains the idea of how the turbine extracts energy from the flowing gasses.

As compared to a turbojet or turbofan, the turboprop and turboshaft have very little reactive thrust remaining in the tailpipe after the turbine extracts its required power.

This is done in various ways: By a larger deflection of mass flow from an axial to a tangential direction; by closing the openings down between vanes to increase the energy change from pressure to velocity; (figure 3-57) or, by increasing the number of vanes and blades. Another method is simply to add more turbine stages.

The most efficient turbine will perform a maximum of work for the least fuel consumption. This will happen if the turbine is operating at its design point for temperature and RPM, and the compressor is operating at its design point of compressor pressure ratio and mass airflow.

The type of turbine design used in almost all flight engines is the axial flow type, in which the products of combustion pass through the turbine vanes and blades, changing their angle momentarily, then returning to an axial direction.

As previously mentioned, the turbine absorbs most of the energy created in combustion. Consequently, this unit is the most highly stressed component in the engine. Stress can occur as high as 30,000 pound per square inch or more on turbine blades. The disk, generally a heavy forging, also suffers many thousands of G-forces. Turbine disks and blades, sometimes referred to as buckets, are made of super alloys, usually of a nickel-base variety. The properties of these alloys are: High thermal strength, resistance to corrosion, and a low co-efficient of expansion.

The G-Force experienced by a rotating turbine blade is a result of centrifugal force. The amount of centrifugal force, and the "G" force on the blade, can be calculated as follows:

$$\text{Centrifugal Force} = \frac{\text{Weight}}{\text{gravity}} \times \frac{\text{Velocity}^2}{\text{radius}}$$

$$\text{Where}: \quad \frac{\text{Weight}}{\text{Gravity}} = \text{Mass}$$

$$\text{Velocity} = \text{fps at blade C.G.}$$

$$\text{radius} = \text{radius (ft) of blade C.G.}$$

$$\text{C.G.} = \text{blade center of gravity}$$

$$\text{gravity} = 32.16 \text{ ft./sec.}^2$$

$$\text{"G" Force} = \text{Centrifugal Force} \div \text{Blade Weight}$$

EXAMPLE: If the distance between the center of gravity (CG) point of one turbine blade and its opposite blade CG is 2.0 feet (diameter), blade weight is 0.2 pounds, and the RPM is 9,980, what is the g-force on each blade?

$$\text{Velocity} = \pi \times \text{dia.} \times \text{Rpm} \div 60$$

$$V = 3.1416 \times 2 \times 9,980 \div 60$$

$$V = 1,045 \text{ fps}$$

$$\text{Centrifugal Force} = \frac{\text{Weight}}{\text{gravity}} \times \frac{\text{Velocity}^2}{\text{radius}}$$

$$\text{C.F.} = \frac{0.2 \text{ lbs } (1,045 \text{ ft./sec.})^2}{32.16 \text{ ft./sec.}^2 \times 1 \text{ ft.}}$$

$$\text{C.F.} = \frac{218,405}{32.16} \text{ lbs.}$$

$$\text{C.F.} = 6,791 \text{ lbs.}$$

$$\text{"G" Force} = 6,791 \div 0.2$$

$$\text{"G" Force} = 33,956$$

b. Function Of Turbine Stators

The turbine sections, like the compressor section, contain many blades and vanes; but, unlike the compressor, its stator vanes are located in front of the blades. Whereas the compressor stator vanes act as diffusers, decreasing velocity and increasing pressure, the turbine stator vanes act as nozzles, increasing velocity and decreasing pres-

sure. The turbine nozzle assembly is also known as the turbine nozzle, nozzle diaphragm, or the turbine nozzle guide vane assembly (Figure 3-58).

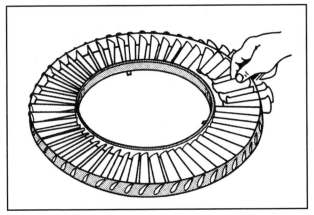

Fig 3-58 — Assembly of turbine nozzle guide vanes.

Most turbine nozzles operate in a choked condition (at Mach 1 gas velocity) while in the cruise to takeoff power range. This gives a predictable energy level to the turbine wheel at any point in the normal operating range. The velocity of gases is more dependent on temperature of the gas in relation to the local speed of sound than on back pressures within the rear sections of the engine.

This is because downstream pressure will have little effect on the choked turbine nozzle which creates its own back pressure. The pressure downstream also being much less than the head of pressure in front of the nozzle keeps flow constant to the turbine wheel.

A secondary purpose of the turbine stator is to direct the gases at the optimum angle into the turbine blades so that the wheel will turn with the maximum efficiency. The greater the tangential component of the gas flow to and from the turbine wheel, the greater the torque to drive the compressor.

The turbine stator is known as the point of highest velocity in the turbine engine. The velocity, in this case, is angular velocity rather than axial velocity. The velocity is controlled by the total area of the opening between the vanes. Vane sets have flow areas of certain sizes referred to as classes. The stator assembly can, in many cases, be built up with varying vane classes to provide an effective flow area according to the needs of a particular engine.

If, for instance, a new compressor is installed during overhaul, it sometimes can create more mass airflow than the engine can accommodate without stalling, due to back pressure at a restricted turbine nozzle. In this instance, the nozzle area can be reconstructed with a larger opening to relieve the back pressure and correct the stall problem.

c. Shrouds And Seals

The shroud ring shown in Figure 3-59A is present to minimize gas loss over the blade tips. Excessive air leakage over the blade tips creates air turbulence which can destroy the blade efficiency in the tip area. Air leakage also can be thought of as disrupted airflow bypassing the working portion of the engine. That is, in effect, an efficiency loss to the engine.

The air seals shown in Figure 3-59B are generally a rotating knife-edge type seal, sometimes called a rotating rim. This seal is made up of several thin sheet-metal rims which form seal dams, and at the same time act as metering orifices to control movement of gas path air to the inner areas of the engine. The source of this air is bleed air from the compressor.

The bleed air coming off the compressor is utilized to pressurize labyrinth and carbon oil seals and cool certain hot section areas. When the air has completed its cooling

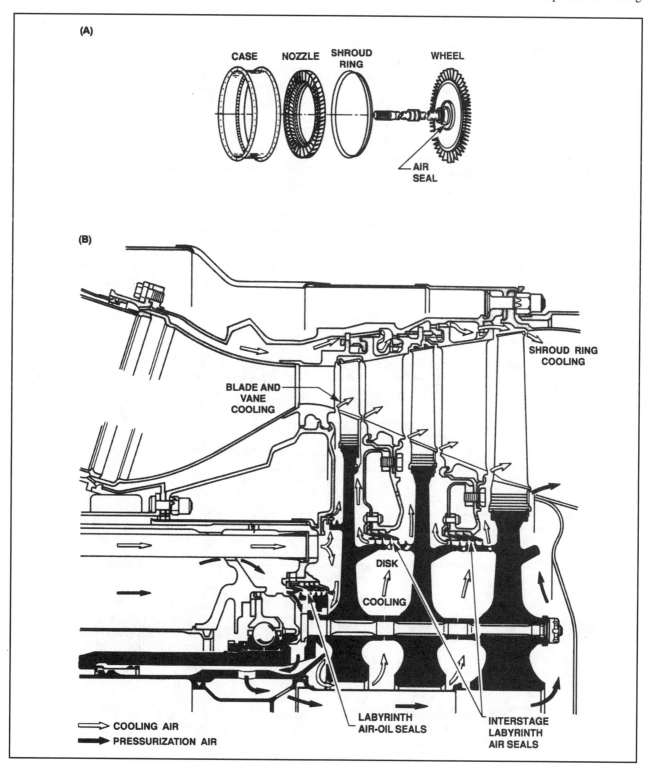

Fig. 3-59A — Turbine rotor assembly.
Fig. 3-59B — Turbine section airflow

functions, it will generally bleed back into the gas path through other seals similar to the ones shown in the illustration.

2. Impulse-Reaction Blades

The turbine disk is fitted with blades of compound curvature, referred to as an impulse-reaction design. The twist in the blade is used to distribute the workload evenly along the blade length by keeping the exit pressure and velocity uniform from the base to the tip. This is accomplished by extracting different amounts of kinetic energy at various blade stations. In flight engines, the design usually found to be the most efficient is 50% reaction and 50% impulse.

The graph in Figure 3-60 can be used to show that blade inlet pressure is lowest at the base. This occurs in relation to the high turbine stator vane exit velocity. Also, pressure is highest at the tip in relation to a lower turbine stator exit velocity. With this varying inlet pressure, the resultant blade exit pressure and exit velocity are made uniform along the blade length.

An explanation of the occurrence described in the preceding paragraph can be found in the following narrative and drawings (Figure 3-61).

The reaction position is at the blade tip. This portion of the blade exerts the greatest torque arm force by rotating with greater speed than the base. The tip area is therefore designed to absorb the least kinetic energy from the flowing gases. The straight duct design of the stator at this blade position keeps pressure relatively high as the blade tips receive the gas at Area A.

The converging duct formed at area B between the blade pairs accelerates the gas to counteract the tendency of high tip rotational speed to reduce the gas axial velocity. The turbine blade passageways (ducts) in this area are, in fact, rotating nozzles and the turbine wheel's rotational force at the blade tips is said to be in reaction to the axial acceleration of the gases.

This is a situation of action and reaction, as described in Newton's third law. The relatively high pressure available at the tip area has a secondary purpose of counteracting the tendency of centrifugal reaction attempting to throw more air outward than would be desirable.

Figure 3-62 illustrates the impulse position at the blade base. The base exerts the least torque arm force by rotating with less speed, relative to the tip. The tendency of the base to do less work is counteracted by supplying it with a larger share of the available kinetic energy.

Recalling that work equals force times distance, it can be seen that more force must be applied at the base of the blade where the distance to the axis is less. This allows the base to accomplish the same amount of work as the tip.

The cup-shaped base area receives the greatest amount of kinetic energy from a convergent stator vane section, and the gases force the blades around in a circular path.

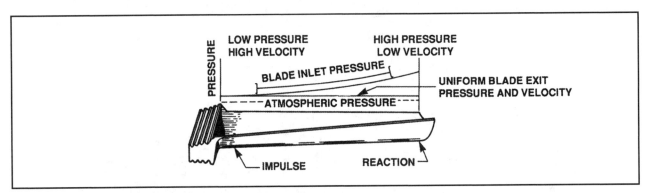

Fig. 3-60 — The combination impulse-reaction turbine blade.

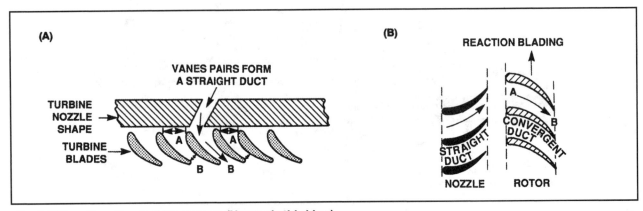

Fig. 3-61A — Reaction turbine system (Newton's third law).
Fig. 3-61B — Vane and blade flow areas at blade tip.

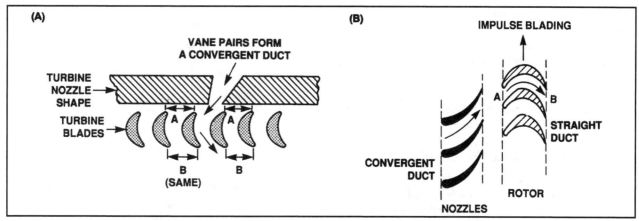

Fig. 3-62A — Impulse turbine system (Newton's second law).
Fig. 3-62B — Vane and blade flow area at blade base.

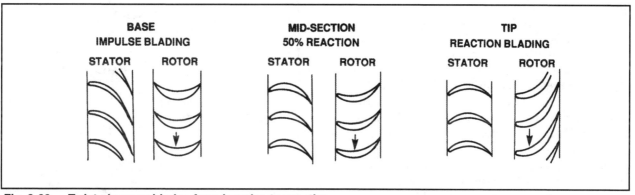

Fig. 3-63 — Twist changes blades from impulse to reaction.

This is a situation of unbalanced forces as described in Newton's second law.

To compare forces acting on the blade base versus forces acting on the blade tips, consider that the gases are guided onto the cup shaped portion of each blade with a high velocity in order to apply force to the blade and thus to the wheel. At the tip area, the gases are only guided into the blades at the best angle. The blades then squirt the air out at high velocity, creating a reacting force which forces the blade around (Figure 3-63).

The axial velocity and pressure drop which occurs at the turbine blade base is minimized by the straight duct formed by the turbine blade pairs and the slower rotational speed.

With the combination impulse-reaction design, the workload is now said to be evenly distributed along the length of the blade, and axial velocity and pressure drop across the blade, from base to tip, is considered uniform.

3. Axial Turbine Construction

a. Shafts:

Construction features of the turbine are shown in Figure 3-64. Observe that the N_2 shaft is bolted to the turbine disk at the aft end. The turbine shaft must have some means for attachment to the compressor and this is

accomplished by means of a spline cut on the forward end of the shaft. The spline fits into a coupling device which slips over turbine shaft splines. The N_2 compressor also has a splined shaft which fits into the coupling at the front end.

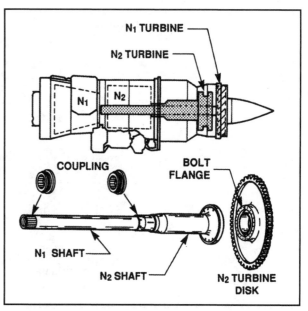

Fig. 3-64 — Turbine shaft locations.

This illustration also shows a dual coaxial turbine shaft arrangement. The long shaft mechanically couples the rear, low pressure (N_1) turbine to the front (N_1) compressor. The short shaft couples the front turbine to the rear (N_2) compressor.

The N_2 turbine is referred to as the high pressure turbine because it receives the highest gas pressure from combustion. The low pressure turbine receives its name because there is a pressure drop in the gas flow before it reaches the low pressure turbine.

b. Attachment And Retention Devices

There are various ways of attaching turbine blades, or buckets, as they are sometimes called, to the disk. The most commonly seen method for positive engagement under the high heat and high centrifugal loading conditions that turbine blades experience, is the fir tree design (Figure 3-65).

Turbine blades are retained in their grooves by a variety of methods. Some of the more common methods are rivets, locktabs, lockwires, and roll pins (Figure 3-65).

c. Shrouded Tips And Knife-Edge Seals

Turbine blades are either open at the tip or fitted with interlocking shrouds, as seen in Figures 3-65 and 3-66. It is common to see both types in one engine, with the high speed wheel containing open tip blades and the lower speed wheel shrouded tip blades. Tip loading from rotational forces often limits the use of shrouds to lower speed locations, such as low pressure turbines in turbofan engines. This is also true of LP turbines in turboshaft engines, where all the energy is designed to be absorbed by the turbine blades, and energy remaining in the tailpipe as a result of tip losses would be completely lost to the engine.

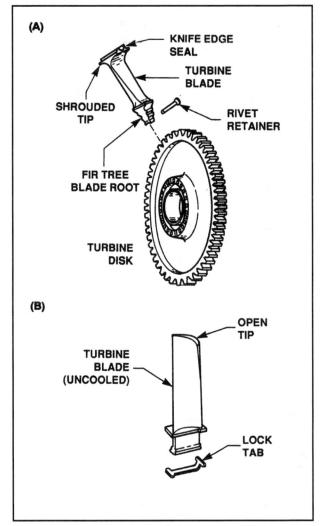

Fig. 3-65A — Turbine disk and shrouded tip blade.
Fig. 3-65B — Open tip blade.

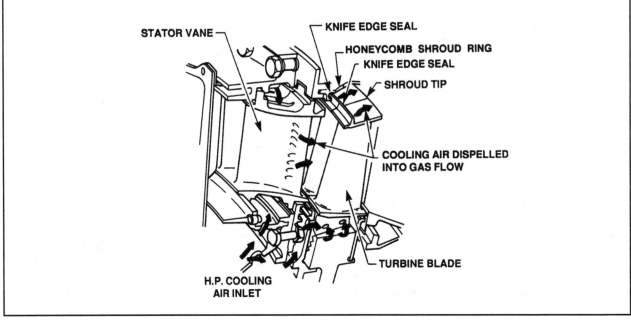

Fig. 3-66 — Shrouded air-cooled blade and air-cooled turbine stator vane.

Tip shrouds do several things to aid turbine wheel efficiency. They allow for lighter construction, that is, long thin blades. They prevent air loss at the tips and blade distortion or untwisting under heavy gas loading. They dampen vibration and also provide a mounting base for knife-edge type air seals.

The knife-edge seal also reduces air losses at the blade tips, and it keeps the airflow in an axial direction to maximize the impact force of the flowing gases onto the blading. The knife-edge seal fits in close tolerance to a shroud ring mounted in the outer turbine case. This shroud is often constructed of a honeycomb material or some other porous material (Figure 3-67).

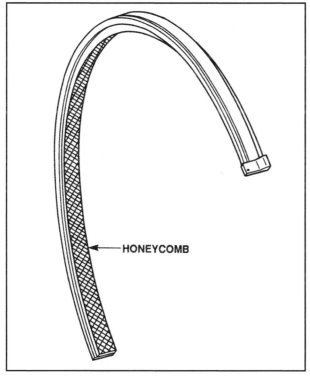

Fig. 3-67 —Honeycomb turbine shroud ring segment.

Occasionally, high G-forces from flight maneuvers or hard landings will cause contact as cases distort and the knife-edge seals cut into the honeycomb shroud ring. This occurs with minimal wear to the seal and shroud and at no loss of blade length.

d. Turbine Vane And Blade Cooling

Many modern engines today utilize air cooled stator vanes and rotor blades. This is more the case with high pressure turbines where the highest temperatures are experienced. Cooling allows the components to operate in a thermal environment 600 to 800°F above the temperature limits of the alloys used for vane and blade construction (Figure 3-68).

With cooled blades and vanes, maximum turbine inlet temperature (TIT) of an engine today is approximately 3,000°F. This figure has risen through the years as new

metals are developed and will no doubt continue to rise in the same way in the future (Figure 3-59 and 3-66). A disadvantage of cooling blades and vanes is that it increases the demand on the compressor, but it is generally felt that overall efficiency increases due to turbine inlet temperature (TIT) increases more than making up for the compressor airflow losses.

The cooling methods generally employed are:
1) Internal air flow cooling. Air flows through hollow blades and vanes referred to as convection cooling and heat is carried away directly by the cooling air.
2) Surface film cooling. Air flows from small exit ports in leading and/or trailing edges of the vanes or blades to form a heat barrier on the surfaces.
3) Combination convection and surface cooling.

Cooling air is extracted from the gas path at the compressor section and, after cooling is accomplished, the air is directed back into the gas path at the cooling location. At this point, some air may also cool the shroud seals and shroud rings.

e. Turbine Case Cooling (Figure 3-69)

A method of controlling the clearance between the tips of the turbine blades and the turbine case/shroud ring is active tip clearance control. The term active means that the tip clearance is controlled by varying the amount of cooling air, to vary the thermal expansion rate of the turbine outer case. This in turn keeps tip losses at a minimum at all power settings.

Active Clearance Control also applies to compressor cases in regards to Tip Clearance Control, but it is most common on the turbine cases. Both systems are operated at the command of an Electronic Engine Control (EEC), often as part of an engine FADEC system (full authority digital engine control).

f. Counter-Rotating Turbines

Some dual- and triple-shaft engines have counter-rotating turbine wheels. It is not common in large engines, but it is sometimes seen in smaller engines, especially turboshaft engines. This is generally not a design for aerodynamic reasons but rather for dampening gyroscopic effect and reducing engine vibratory tendencies.

4. Radial Inflow Turbine

Another type of turbine design is the radial inflow. Like the centrifugal compressor, it has advantages of low cost and simplicity of design. Its primary application is in auxiliary gas turbine engines. It derives its name from the fact that gases flow through a stator vane assembly located at the radius of the turbine. The gas then flows inward from the tip area and finally exits at the center. This design is used because it extracts up to 100 percent of the kinetic energy from the flowing gases.

The radial inflow turbine has high single stage turbine efficiency but has poor multistage efficiency. It also has the disadvantage of low axial velocity discharge and short

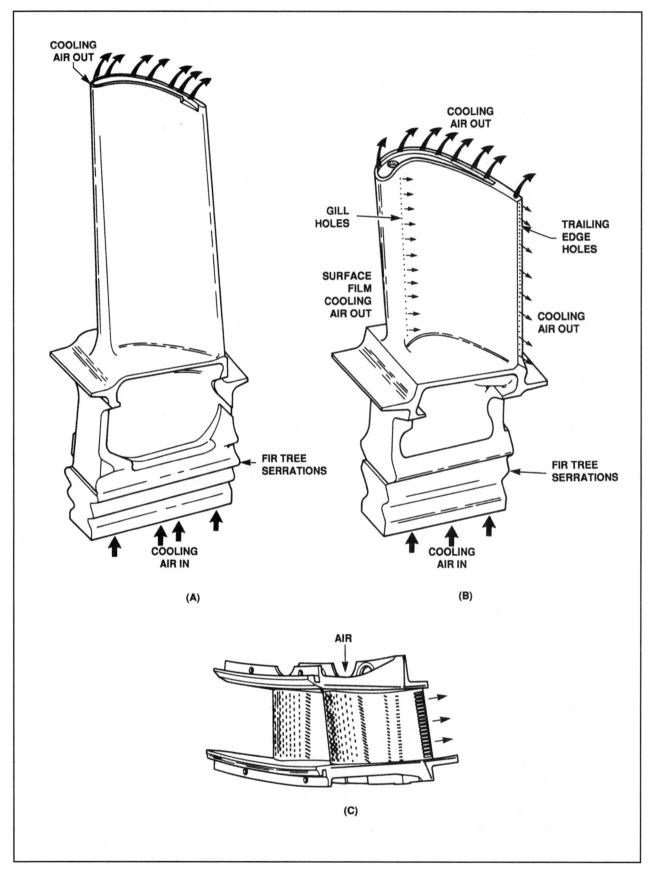

Fig. 3-68A — Internal blade cooling.
Fig. 3-68B — Internal and surface film cooling.
Fig. 3-68C — Pair of surface film cooled turbine vanes.

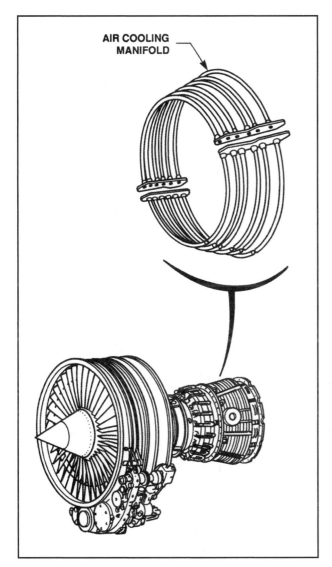

AIR COOLING MANIFOLD

Fig. 3-69 — Turbine case cooling. Active clearance control.

service life under high temperature loads due primarily to high centrifugal loads on the disk. To date, these problems have not been solved for use of the radial inflow turbine in flight engines (Figure 3-70).

G. Exhaust Section
1. Exhaust Cone, Tail Cone, And Tailpipe

The exhaust section is located directly behind the turbine section and consists in most cases of a convergent exhaust outer cone and an inner tail cone. The exhaust cone, sometimes referred to as the turbine exhaust collector, collects the exhaust gases discharged from turbine discharge and gradually converts them into a uniform wall of gases. This process is accomplished in conjunction with the tail cone, also called exhaust plug, and its radial support struts. The tail cone shape acts to form a

diffuser within the exhaust cone and the resulting pressure buildup reduces turbulence downstream of the turbine wheel. The struts act to return the airflow to an axial direction. The exhaust cone is the terminating component of many engines, as delivered by the engine manufacturer (Figure 3-71).

On some very early model engines, the tail cone was movable. In order to increase exhaust velocity and thrust, the tail cone was mechanically moved rearward decreasing the effective size of the jet nozzle (Figure 3-72). Today, smooth and rapid acceleration is accomplished on subsonic airliners and business jets by more sophisticated fuel scheduling techniques using a fixed tail cone within a fixed area tailpipe. Only on supersonic aircraft is a variable exhaust used.

The tailpipe is an airframe part, used to adapt an engine to a particular airplane installation. The tailpipe is in most cases a convergent duct. It is also referred to as the jet pipe or exhaust duct. Its convergent shape causes the gases to accelerate to the design speed necessary for producing the required thrust. This convergent tailpipe is for use on most subsonic aircraft. The shape is generally of fixed geometry; that is, its flow area cannot be changed during engine operation, although some tailpipes are manufactured in both standard and other sizes and can on occasion be used to regain lagging engine performance (Figure 3-73).

On some older model engines small tabs (inserts) could be fitted to the tailpipe to change the effective open area of the exhaust nozzle and recover some small amount of lost performance. These tabs are rarely seen today.

The convergent shaped exhaust ducts as described here can accelerate the exhaust gases to Mach 1 (the speed of sound) and no faster in terms of Mach number. The exhaust nozzle opening, being an orifice, forces the gas molecules to pile up as the mass airflow throughout the engine increases with airspeed. At Mach 1, the gas flow is said to be choked at the exhaust nozzle opening to the atmosphere.

a. Convergent "Choked" Nozzle Theory

When gas initially flows down a convergent duct, the shape accelerates the gas. As more and more mass of air flows down stream, the shape of the duct starts to constrict the flow. At the point of Mach 1 airflow, the walls of the duct are constricting with a force equal to the air's axial flow force. The flow, therefore, stabilizes at Mach 1.

The choked nozzle condition of exhaust ducts can be further explained here by again using the Pt/Ps formula from the Appendix.

If Pt/Ps is calculated when M = 1.0, it will be found that a minimum exhaust duct to ambient pressure ratio of 1.89 is required to achieve a choked condition. Consider here that Pt is the exhaust duct entrance pressure, which will drop to pressure ambient (equal to Ps) at the exhaust nozzle.

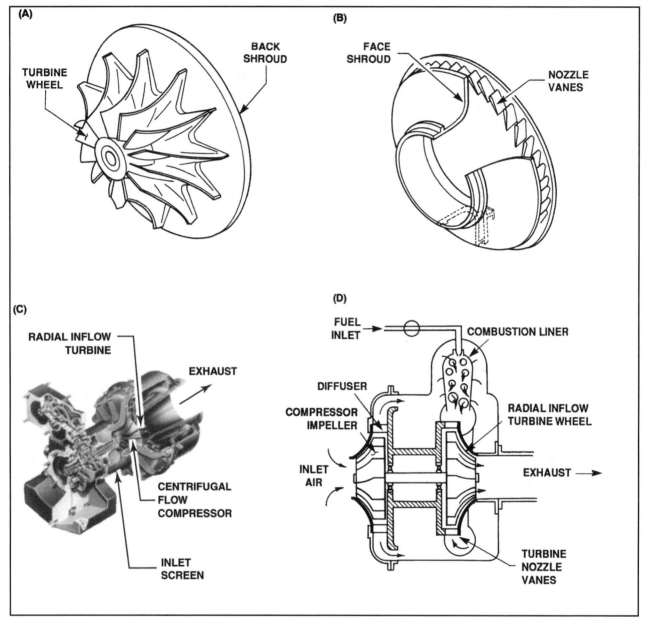

Fig. 3-70A — Radial inflow turbine rotor.
Fig. 3-70B — Radial inflow turbine stator ring.
Fig. 3-70C — Photo of a gas turbine APU.
Fig. 3-70D — Turbine rotor location in engine.

$$\frac{Pt}{Ps} = \left[1 + \left(\frac{\gamma - 1}{2} \times M^2\right)\right]^{\frac{\gamma}{\gamma - 1}}$$

Where :

γ (gamma) = 1.4 (specific heat)

M = Mach number

γ, 1, 2 = Constants

$$\frac{Pt}{Ps} = \left[1 + \left(\frac{1.4 - 1}{2} \times 1.0^2\right)\right]^{\frac{1.4}{1.4 - 1}}$$

$$\frac{Pt}{Ps} = [1 + (0.2 \times 1.0)]^{3.5}$$

$$\frac{Pt}{Ps} = 1.89$$

See Appendix 8, Formula 16.

This mathematical statement indicates that it takes a pressure ratio of 1.89 across the exhaust duct in order to achieve a choked condition.

1) In terms of engine power during ground runup, if (Pt) represents turbine discharge pressure and (Ps) represents compressor inlet pressure, it could then be deduced that, when the Engine Pressure Ratio (EPR) gauge in the cockpit is reading above 1.89, the exhaust nozzle is choked. Engine Pressure Ratio is discussed in detail in the Fuel Chapter and again in the Instrument Chapter.

2) This situation changes in flight at altitude/cruise, when the nozzle pressure ratio is approximately 4:1 when Engine Pressure Ratio is 1:89 in the cockpit. This occurs

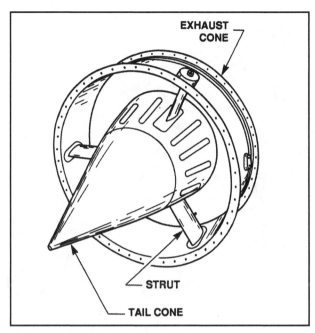

Fig. 3-71 — Exhaust cone, tail cone, and support struts.

because as ambient pressure (Ps) decreases at altitude, flight speed influence on inlet compression helps to boost engine compression ratio and, ultimately, turbine discharge pressure.

When the gas exits a choked orifice, it accelerates radially (spreads out) faster than it accelerates axially, the axial velocity being fixed at Mach 1. If more fuel is added after Mach 1 gas velocity is reached, engine speed, compression, and mass airflow would increase, and pressure (pile-up) in the tailpipe would increase.

The additional exhaust nozzle pressure will give a small increase in thrust, as we observed in the Chapter II thrust formula for choked exhaust nozzles, but this condition would soon be uneconomical in terms of fuel consumption. Also, temperatures within the engine would elevate significantly. When supersonic exhaust nozzle velocities are needed for supersonic flight, a convergent-divergent nozzle is required, rather than a simple convergent-type jet nozzle.

Another way to describe choking is in terms of a change in potential and kinetic energy, as seen in Figure 3-73.

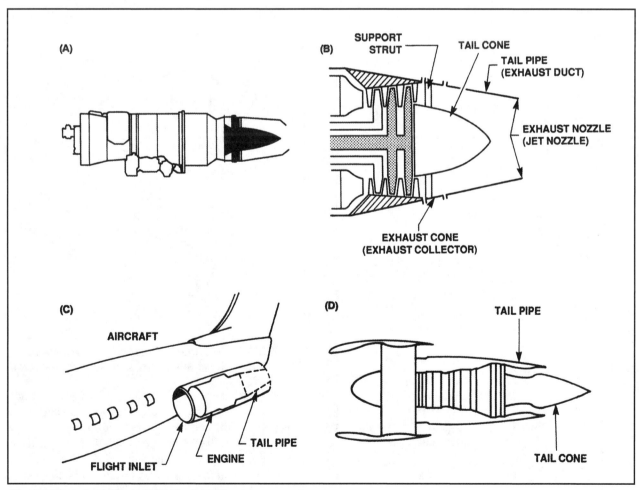

Fig. 3-72A — Location of exhaust section.
Fig. 3-72B — Conventional convergent exhaust duct.
Fig. 3-72C — Tailpipe, small and medium sized engines.
Fig. 3-72D — Tailpipe for large engines.

To answer the question of why velocity (kinetic energy) from a convergent duct cannot exceed Mach 1, first recall what Bernoulli stated about subsonic flow through a convergent duct. That is, when velocity is less than Mach 1, the potential energy (static pressure) is greater than the kinetic energy (ram pressure), and, therefore, velocity is forced to increase because of the squeezing-down action created by the shape of the duct.

In Figure 3-73, Illustration (A), as air at subsonic speed flows through a convergent duct, the velocity at point "W" is increasing and reaches its maximum at point "X". This occurs because the air molecules of potential

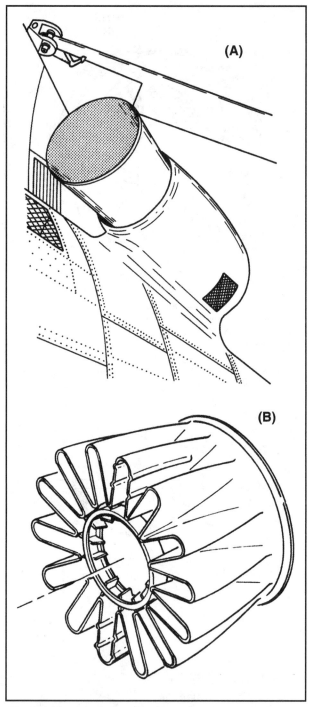

Fig. 3-74A — *Rotorcraft exhaust duct installation.*
Fig. 3-74B — *Noise suppressing mixer exhaust duct.*

energy, which were formerly pushing outward perpendicular to the direction of flow, are now moving in the direction of flow and being converted to kinetic energy. The velocity at the jet nozzle is still subsonic, and the pressure at the nozzle will be ambient.

In Illustration (B), gas enters the duct at high potential energy (Pe) and low kinetic energy (Ke), and, as it approaches the nozzle, kinetic energy increases as potential energy decreases. In the example, it can be seen that gas flow is still subsonic with a flow rate of M 0.7.

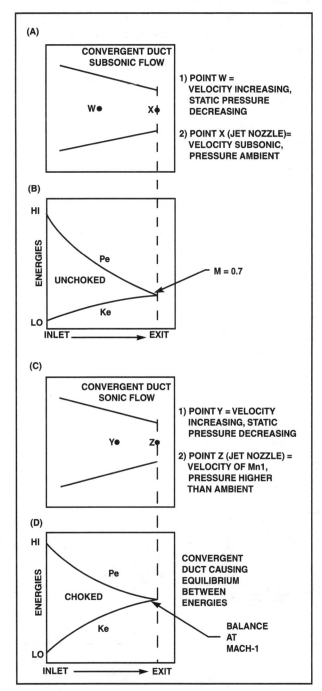

Fig. 3-73 — *Theory of choked nozzles.*

In Illustration (C), the velocity at point "Y" is subsonic and is increasing to its maximum at point "Z". In this case, the velocity at point "Z" has reached mach 1 and cannot go any faster. Any additional energy added to this duct will not cause an increase in the velocity of the air, but rather will exit the jet nozzle in the form of higher than ambient pressure.

In Illustration (D), when the kinetic energy of the gas molecules reach the speed of sound, Mach 1, the potential energy in the gas and the kinetic energy in the gas are in equilibrium. That is, airflow through a convergent duct, trying to move faster and faster, will move to a point of balance. This occurs when the squeezing-in action on airflow caused by the shape of the duct is counterbalanced by the pushing out action of potential energy.

In actual practice, the nozzle will choke, in accordance with Formula 16 in Appendix 8, at an inlet to outlet pressure ratio of 1.89. An interesting note concerning choked nozzle flow is that nozzle flow mach numbers can be less than the aircraft mach number. The reason for this is the fact that Mach number is influenced by the temperature of the gas. At higher temperatures, it takes a greater velocity to equal mach 1.

b. Convergent-Divergent Exhaust Ducts (For Subsonic Aircraft)

A recent development in exhaust nozzle technology is the use of convergent-divergent exhaust nozzles in subsonic aircraft. These C-D nozzles are of fixed geometry with a slight increase in final opening size. They are designed to maximize cruise thrust and reduce engine noise.

The C-D nozzle comes in the form of an exhaust mixer that is described in the noise suppression material in a later part of this chapter (Figure 3-88).

c. Divergent Exhaust Nozzles

The rotorcraft tailpipe is normally divergent in shape, rather than convergent. This shape nullifies thrust to enhance hover capabilities (Figure 3-74A). A newer design for helicopter exhaust utilizes a scalloped shape outer perimeter designed for noise suppression (Figure 3-74B).

2. Convergent-Divergent (C-D) Nozzle Theory (For Supersonic Aircraft)

Supersonic aircraft utilize the variable geometry C-D type of tailpipe, called an afterburner. The advantage of the convergent-divergent duct is greatest at high Mach numbers because of the high pressure ratio available across the tailpipe. That is, high supersonic inlet ram pressure results in high exhaust duct pressure.

To ensure that a constant weight of a gas will flow past any given point after sonic velocity is reached, the rear portion of the duct is enlarged. This in turn increases gas velocity after it emerges from the throat area to become supersonic.

Gas traveling at supersonic speeds has the property of expanding outward faster than it accelerates rearward

because, as the gas is compressed axially, it releases its energy radially (Figure 3-75). The C-D nozzle takes advantage of this principle to create the thrust necessary to propel the aircraft at supersonic speeds. The C-D tailpipe is in fact an afterburner, such as one would see on the Concorde-SST.

The forward, convergent section (Figure 3-75A and B) causes pressure to build as the throat area chokes, creating a back pressure. The aft, divergent section allows velocity to increase to the desired Mach number, depending on the force being applied by combustion. If shaped properly the C-D duct will effectively control gas expansion, capture the releasing energy, and produce the required thrust.

In a convergent-divergent exhaust, several events take place when the pressure ratio is higher than 1.89. In the converging section, the events are as follows:
- The air stream lines converge.
- The density of the air increases at the throat.
- The velocity of the air stabilizes at mach 1.
- The pressure at the throat is higher than ambient.
In the diverging section, the events are as follows:
- The density of the air decreases.
- The velocity increases to supersonic speed.
- The pressure decreases, reaching ambient at the nozzle opening.

The modern supersonic aircraft tailpipe (Figure 3-77) is such that the rearmost section has a slight divergence in normal mode (non-afterburning). In this mode, many

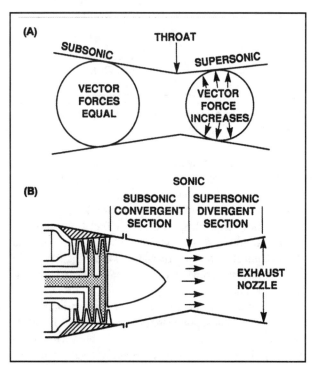

Fig. 3-75A — Energy released in a convergent—divergent duct.

Fig. 3-75B — Gas flow in a convergent-divergent tailpipe.

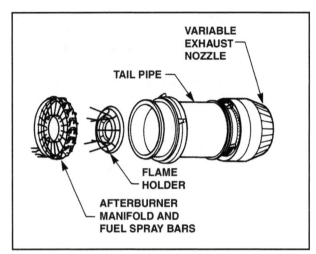

Fig. 3-76 — Afterburner assembly.

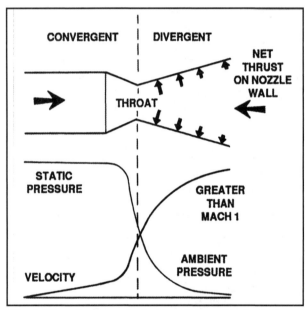

Fig. 3-77 — Pressure/velocity relationship in C-D tailpipe.

supersonic aircraft are capable of supersonic flight speeds. When afterburner mode is selected, the mechanism is designed so that the divergence of the exhaust nozzle increases to handle (properly accelerate) the new mass airflow created by afterburner fuel flow. In other words the divergent section functions as a variable area exhaust nozzle. In non-afterburner, the exhaust nozzle area is smallest, and when afterburner is selected the nozzle is scheduled to a more open position.

The addition of afterburner fuel and the expansion of gases it creates causes outward pressure forces on the walls of the afterburner rear duct, and the forces are vectored forward by the diverging shape. Scientific testing indicates that fully expanded supersonic flow results in the best thrust augmentation. That is, pressure across the exhaust duct returns to ambient value. In this case, no "pressure thrust" is available at the exhaust nozzle, but an increase in

thrust still occurs because exhaust velocity increases above Mach 1 in proportion to fuel energy supplied.

Supersonic flow causes the familiar shock wave phenomena to occur, but a properly designed afterburner will have no shock distortion to airflow within the duct, only shock rings which are visible in the jet exhaust stream.

3. Afterburning

Afterburning provides the maximum exhaust velocity and maximum engine thrust for a given engine frontal area, but at the expense of fuel flow. The addition of an afterburner to a gas turbine engine is made possible by the fact that the products of combustion in the tailpipe contain a large quantity of unburned oxygen. The portion of compressor discharge air used for combustor cooling mixes with combusted air at the turbine and then flows downstream to the tailpipe. A set of afterburner fuel nozzles called spray bars are fitted into the tailpipe entrance along with a suitable ignition system. When afterburner fuel and unburned oxygen mix and ignite, additional propulsive power is created as the gases are further accelerated by the additional heat energy applied.

Along with fuel and ignition components, another device, called a flameholder, is required for good combustion (Figure 3-76). It is a tubular grid or spoke-shaped obstruction placed downstream of the fuel nozzles. As gases impinge on the flameholder, turbulence is created which enhances fuel-air mixing. This promotes complete and stable combustion in a very fast moving airstream.

In effect, the afterburner is a form of ramjet attached to the rear of a gas turbine engine. The only types of gas turbines, however, that utilize afterburning are the turbojet and the turbofans with mixed exhausts. That is, turbofans in which the fan and core engine gases pre-mix and exit from one exhaust nozzle.

Older afterburners were two-position types. They formed a convergent nozzle in non-afterburning mode and a convergent-divergent (C-D) nozzle when open in afterburning mode. In newer aircraft, the afterburner nozzle is C-D shaped in both modes, changing both the throat flow area and the final nozzle size to their largest area and flow angles in full afterburner. Electronic sensors are utilized to match the flow area to the mass flow in afterburners of this type. Constant monitoring helps to combat the low thermal efficiency (high fuel flow) which is typical of engines operating in the afterburner mode.

Afterburning is used primarily for takeoff with heavy aircraft loading and for rapid climb-out speeds.

Afterburner fitted aircraft can have as much as 100% additional thrust in afterburning mode, with fuel flows increasing by three to five times. On the other hand, some modern aircraft have very powerful engines and require only limited thrust augmentation in the 15 to 20% range. In this case, the tendency today is to refer to the C-D tailpipe as a thrust augmenter rather than an afterburner.

An interesting aspect of afterburner thrust is that even a low boost to gross thrust can still bring about a significant boost to net thrust in flight. When an aircraft is operating in afterburner on the ground, gross and net thrust are the same value. If, at that time, the afterburner (A/B) boosts gross thrust by 25%, in flight the same A/B contribution to net thrust would be a much greater percentage; as much as 100%. This occurs because ram drag, which affects engine thrust, does not affect A/B thrust. In other words, ram drag is the same whether the engine is in A/B or not.

Consider the following statements about an aircraft operating on the ground versus its performance in flight:
Gross (static) thrust without afterburner = 16,000 lbs.
Gross (static) thrust with afterburner = 20,000 lbs.
(That represents an increase of 4,000, or 25%.)
Net (in flight) thrust without afterburner = 4,000 lbs.
Net (in flight) thrust with afterburner = 8,000 lbs.
(That represents an increase of 4,000, or 100%.)

NOTE: *RAM drag is defined as aircraft speed times mass airflow, and net thrust is defined as gross thrust minus RAM drag.*

Fig. 3-78 — Afterburner operation showing shock rings in exhaust.

4. Vectoring Afterburner Exhaust Nozzles

The most recent development in afterburners is the vectoring exhaust nozzle, currently being used only on military aircraft. It is capable of vectoring the exhaust up or down at the command of the pilot to enhance take-off or for low speed flight maneuverability of the aircraft. It is also capable of reversing the flow of exhaust gases throughout the flight envelope, including approach, and to aid in braking during landing (Figure 3-79A).

In the up position, the nose of the aircraft will be pushed up quickly for short field take-off or for low speed maneuvering. When the nozzle is pointed down, the nose of the aircraft will move down in forward flight without changing altitude. This is not possible with conventional fighter aircraft. Only V-STOL aircraft, such as the British Harrier fitted with lift-fan engines, have this capability.

5. Variable Area Exhaust Nozzles For Subsonic Aircraft Engines

One of the most recent exhaust nozzle developments is the variable area exhaust nozzle for use with subsonic airplanes. The unit shown in Figure 3-79B also contains a thrust reverser system, while others have only the variable

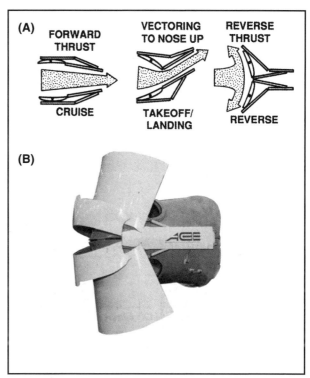

Fig. 3-79A — New type vectoring afterburner exhaust nozzle.
Fig. 3-79B — Variable area, reversing exhaust nozzle.

nozzle. The unit operates in a manner very similar to the variable exhaust used on the afterburners of supersonic airplanes. The unit shown can change the exhaust throat flow area by up to 15% to optimize a small turbofan engine's hot exhaust flow and performance during take-off, climb, and cruise operation.

H. Thrust Reversers (Figures 3-80 and 3-81)

Airliners powered by turbojets and turbofans, most commuter aircraft, and an increasing number of business jets are equipped with engine thrust reversers to:

1. Aid in braking and directional control during normal landing and to reduce brake maintenance.
2. Provide braking and directional control during emergency landings and rejected take-offs.
3. In some aircraft to act as speed brakes to increase the aircraft's rate of descent.
4. Back an aircraft out of a parking spot in what is called a "power back" operation.

The two types of thrust reversers in popular use are the aerodynamic blockage, sometimes referred to as cascade or egg crate reversers (Figures 3-81 and 3-82), and the mechanical blockage (Figure 3-80), often referred to as clamshell or target reversers. A common method for operating both types is a pneumatic actuating system powered by compressor discharge pressure. Other types are operated by hydraulic actuators.

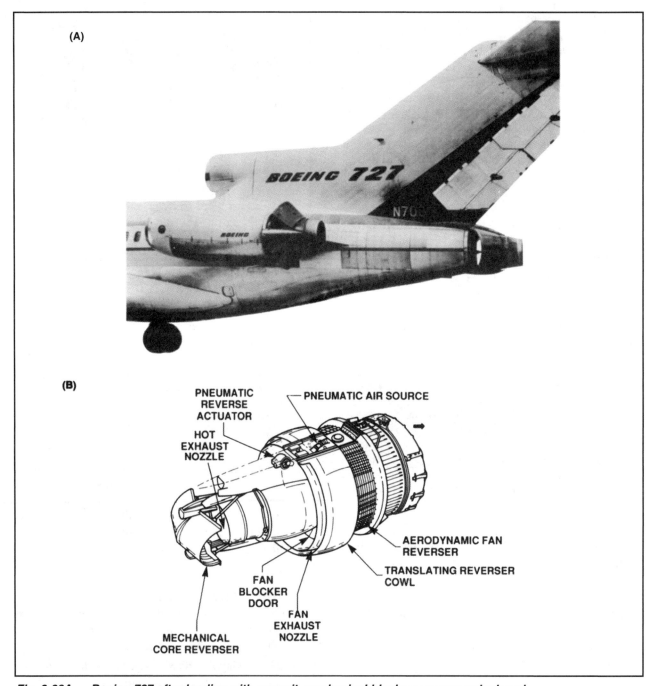

Fig. 3-80A — Boeing 727 after landing with pre-exit, mechanical blockage reverser deployed.
Fig. 3-80B — View of post-exit mechanical blockage type reverser deployed. Also deployed are the fan blocker doors and aerodynamic blockage reverser.

The aerodynamic type consists of a set of cascade turning vanes in a pre-exit position in either the fan exhaust or hot exhaust. The vanes turn the escaping gases to a forward direction which in turn causes a rearward thrust. The mechanical blockage type can be placed in either a pre-exit or post-exit position. This type reverser, when deployed, forms a solid blocking door in the jet exhaust path.

In reverse, exhaust gases hit the clamshell, or turning vanes, and are angled forward enough to give reverse thrust but not enough to allow gas re-ingestion into the engine inlet. Thrust reversers are controlled by a cockpit lever at the command of the pilot. After thrust reverse is selected, the pilot can move the reverse-throttle lever from idle select-position up to takeoff position, as required by landing conditions. Thrust reversers provide approximately 20% of the braking force under normal runway conditions. Reversers are capable of producing between 35 and 50% of rated thrust in the reverse direction (Fig. 3- 82).

Reversers are especially helpful when landing on wet or icy runways and provide approximately 50% assist in

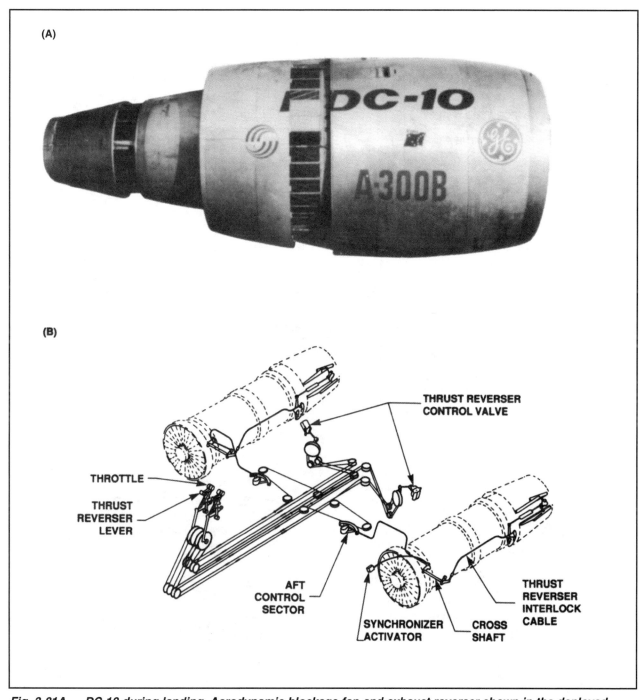

Fig. 3-81A — DC-10 during landing. Aerodynamic blockage fan and exhaust reverser shown in the deployed position.
Fig. 3-81B — Throttle and thrust reverse control system.

stopping the aircraft. The normal method of operation of this system is to apply reverse as soon as the aircraft is firmly on the runway and then to apply as much reverse power as is needed for existing conditions of wetness, ice, etc. Then as the aircraft slows to approximately 80 knots, power is reduced back to reverse-idle and then to forward thrust as soon as practical (Figure 3-83A).

Operating in reverse at low ground speeds can cause re-ingestion of hot gases and compressor stalls. It can also cause ingestion of fine sand and other runway debris that can abrade gas path components and even find its way through main bearing air-oil seals into oil sumps. The normal operating procedure for thrust reverse is to select reverse after touchdown at ground idle speed and re-apply power to approximately 75% N_2 speed (100% in emergencies).

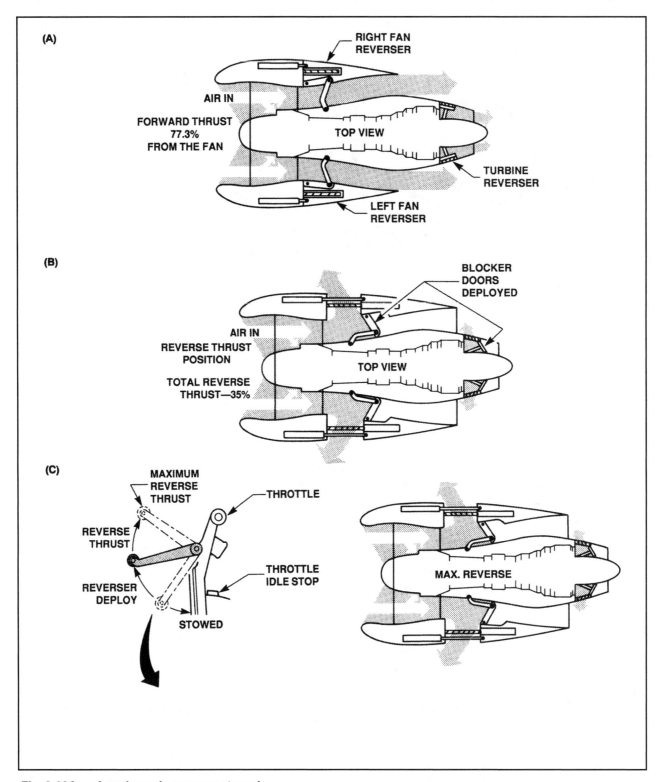

Fig. 3-82A — Aerodynamic reverser stowed.
Fig. 3-82B — Reverser deployed.
Fig. 3-82C — Cockpit control lever.

A mathematical definition or explanation of thrust reverse can be arrived at if we recall the thrust distribution example in Chapter II, section I.4.e. The jet nozzle had (-681.6) pounds of thrust with a rearward veloc-

ity of 1,900 feet/second. If the velocity direction (vector) is changed to an angle in the forward direction, this velocity component changes from a plus to a minus value. Because the angle is not straight forward,

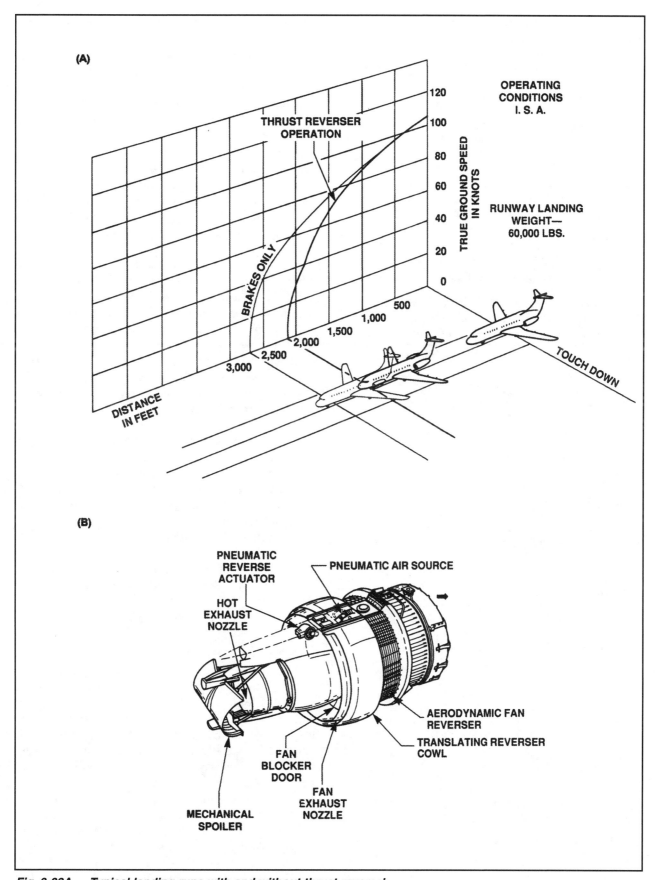

Fig. 3-83A — Typical landing runs with and without thrust reversal.

Fig. 3-83B — High bypass turbofan engine with unmixed exhaust, aerodynamic fan reverser and hot stream spoiler.

for reasons already explained, the resultant velocity vector will drop to approximately 60% of its former value. (as shown below.)

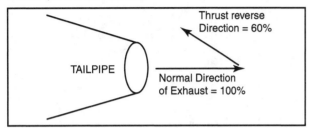

The example engine from the thrust distribution problem in Chapter II had 30 lbs. of mass airflow (Ms), an exhaust velocity of 1,900 feet per second (V2), and a choked nozzle creating an extra 525 pounds of thrust. The engine's total thrust was 2,295.2 lbs. The thrust distribution for the engine was as follows:

Compressor	+3,673.0 lbs. of thrust
Combustor	+5,631.0 lbs. of thrust
Exhaust Cone	+ 542.5 lbs. of thrust
	+9,846.5 lbs. of thrust
Turbine	-6,869.7 lbs. of thrust
Jet Nozzle	- 681.6 lbs. of thrust
	-7,551.3 lbs. of thrust

The numbers above show the total forward thrust equals 2,295.2 lbs.

Considering the jet nozzle of the engine to not be choked when the engine is in reverse thrust, and the exhaust velocity to be 60% of its normal value, the jet nozzle thrust shown above would change as follows:

$$Fg = \frac{Ms \times V}{g} - I$$

$$Fg = \frac{30 \, (-1,140)}{32.2} - 2,976.8$$

$$Fg = -1,062 - 2,976.8$$

$$Fg = -4,038.8 \text{ lbs.}$$

Where :

Ms = 30 lbs./sec.

V = - 1,140 ft./sec. (60% of 1,900)

I = 2,976.8 lbs. (value at exhaust cone)

g = 32.2 ft./sec.^{2}

By substituting the jet nozzle thrust when the engine is in reverse (-4,038.8) for the value that existed when it was in forward thrust (-681.3), the totals would be as follows:

Total Positive Thrust = +9,846.5 lbs.

Total Negative Thrust = -10,898.5

The difference, a negative 1,052 lbs., is the amount of thrust in reverse. This is 45.8% of the normal forward thrust.

1. Other Aspects Of Thrust Braking Systems

Mixed exhaust turbofans are configured with one reverser; unmixed exhaust turbofans often have both cold stream and hot stream reversers. Some high bypass turbofans will only have cold stream reversing, when most of the thrust is present in the fan discharge and a hot end reverser would be of minimal value and become a weight penalty.

Another system similar to thrust reverse is a thrust spoiler. It looks like a clamshell hot stream reverser, but the blocker panels direct the gases out radially rather than turning them forward. The spoiler system is used where reversal of the hot jet nozzle gas interferes with the aerodynamics of the fan section or causes hot gas re-ingestion into the flight inlet (Figure 3-83B).

Turboprop aircraft may also have a form of thrust reversing, namely, a full reversing propeller. This system, and turbofan reversers, work so well that they may be used to back the aircraft up into ground parking spots.

This procedure is referred to as a "power back operation". It is used with great caution due to the possibility of foreign object ingestion. Power back is not always used because it incurs a fuel cost which sometimes makes it more expensive than using the conventional tractor for a conventional push-back.

Another braking system, widely used by the military, is the drag chute. After landing, a fabric canopy similar to a parachute is deployed from a container in the tail section of the aircraft to produce a braking action. The chute is later released and recovered by ground personnel. A few fast landing business jets have been configured with this system as standard or emergency braking to be used in conjunction with thrust reversers.

One of the latest designs in thrust reversing for ultra-high bypass turbofan engines involves reversing the pitch of the fan blades. Presently, blade reverse is in extremely limited use but will probably be seen in many of the new generation aircraft presently being developed.

I. Noise Suppression

Noise is best defined for gas turbine engine purposes as "unwanted sound" because it can be both irritating and harmful. The sound level of the average business jet or airliner during takeoff, as heard by persons on the airport near the end of the runway, would probably be in the range of 90 to 100 decibels. This noise level would be similar to a subway train noise as heard from the boarding platform. Right at the aircraft the noise level could be as high as 160 decibels and painful to the ears (Figure 3-84).

Even the lower level of noise (90 to 100 effective perceived noise decibels) is felt by many people to be excessive and harmful. The industry has reacted to this by continually improving noise reduction techniques on every new generation of engine and aircraft to satisfy the public's need for more effective noise abatement.

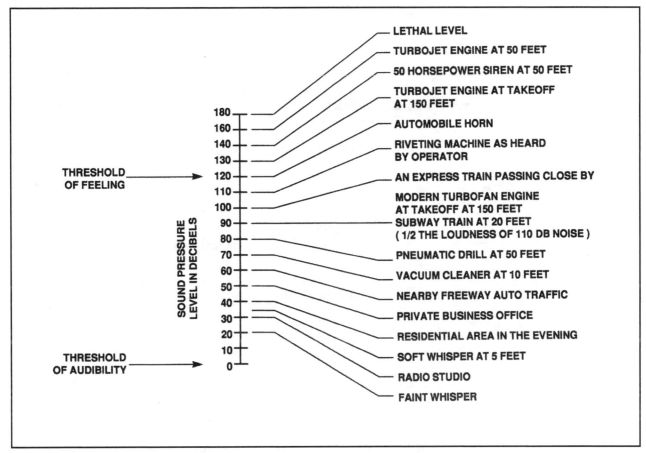

Fig. 3-84 — Noise levels in decibels.

Effective perceived noise decibels (Epndb) is a standard measure of the loudness (sound pressure) combined with the frequency and duration of sound and is used specifically for aircraft noises in the atmosphere. Epndb can also be an estimated value where atmospheric absorption prevents completely accurate measurement, such as an aircraft flying overhead where wind, temperature, moisture, etc., could interfere with accuracy.

In Figure 3-85A, observe the way in which the FAA measures noise levels in reference to aircraft taking off, landing, and sideline noise. Because of the location of the microphones used to measure takeoff noise, it is evident that an aircraft that climbs out more steeply could be sensed as being quieter. Figure 3-85B shows how a few example aircraft compare in reference to the FAR 36 noise limits. The Airbus A300, for example, has a noise level of 91 Epndb on takeoff and 101 Epndb on approach. The reason the measured noise and the noise limit are higher on approach is because of the relatively shallow angle the aircraft would be at, versus the steep angle that is typical of climbout.

Noise suppression units are not generally required on new business jets or airliners today, but FAR Part 36 requires their use on many older commercial jet aircraft. Newer aircraft have inlets and tailpipes lined with noise attenuating materials to keep sound emission within the established effective perceived noise decibel limits (Figure 3-86). These noise absorbing materials convert acoustic energy (air pressure) into heat energy. However, one can still find what looks like the old style noise suppressor being fitted to some newer engines to meet the new noise standards (Figure 3-87 and Figure 3-88).

Noise generated as the exhaust gases leave the engine is at a low frequency level, such as from a ship's fog horn, and in the same way carries for long distances. It is this low frequency noise that tends to be most bothersome to people who live close to airports.

The noise generated by a turbofan engine is much less than that generated by a turbojet. This is principally because the turbofan will generally employ more turbine wheels to drive the compressor and the fan. This, in turn, causes the hot exhaust velocity and noise level to be lessened. Figure 3-87 shows an old style hot stream noise suppressor, called an "increased perimeter" or "multi-lobed" design.

Most fully ducted turbofan engines are designed with what is termed exhaust mixing to blend the fan and hot airstreams more effectively and lessen the sound emission coming from a common exhaust duct. On these engines the sound from the inlet is likely to be louder than from the tailpipe. This is also the case today with the high by-pass fan engines which draw so much

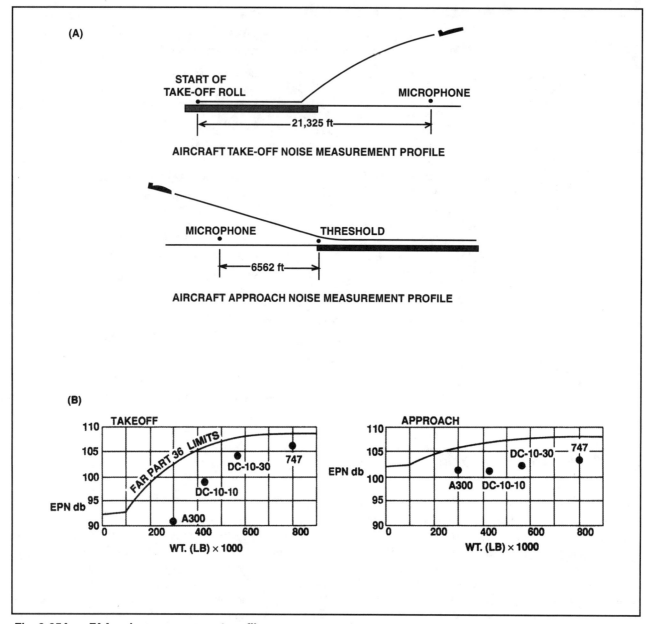

Fig. 3-85A — *FAA noise measurement profiles.*
Fig. 3-85B — *Typical take-off and landing noise emission limits. Approach limits higher due to low approach altitudes.*

energy from the hot gases to drive the fan, compressor, and accessories that the fan emits the greatest noise (Figure 3-88).

Because of the characteristic of low frequency noise to linger at relatively high volume, noise reduction is achieved by raising the frequency. Frequency change is accomplished by increasing the perimeter of the exhaust stream, which provides more cold and hot air mixing space. This reduces the tendency of hot and cold air molecules to shear against each other and also to break up the large turbulence in the jet wake which produces the low frequency (loud) noise.

In other words, reducing large eddy turbulence to fine grain turbulence changes the frequency of noise to

a higher state which is more readily absorbed by the atmosphere. The noise is then lessened for any given distance from the noise source and the effective perceived noise reading on a decibel meter will be lower (Figure 3-89).

As stated previously, some older model Boeing 707 and DC-8 aircraft with turbojet powerplants have the type suppressors shown in Figure 3-87. However, most today have turbofan engines with a treatment kit installed, commonly called a "hush kit". The kit is somewhat in the style of Figure 3-86A.

Other newly designed noise suppressor units for older commercial aircraft are shown in Figure 3-90. They are called ejectors because they induce cold air into a mixing

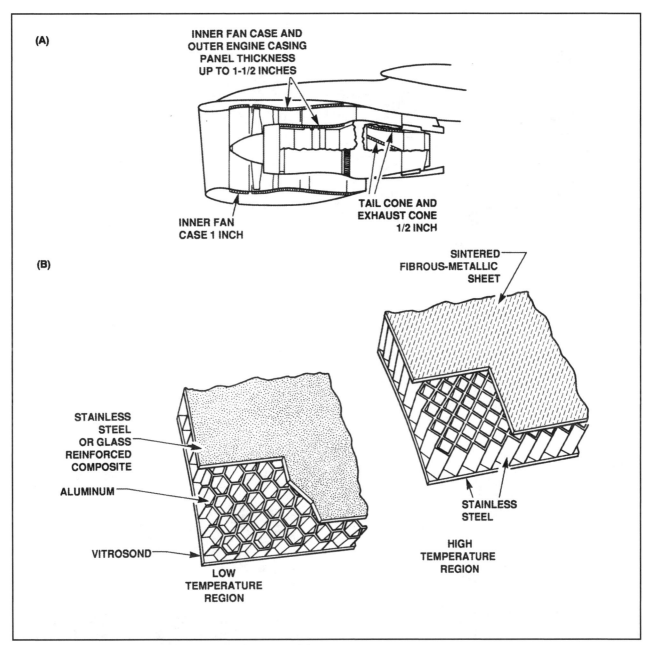

Fig. 3-86A — Location of noise suppression materials.
Fig. 3-86B — Noise suppression materials convert acoustic energy (pressure) to friction heat energy.

Fig. 3-87 — Old style multi-lobed noise suppressors.

space with the hot exhaust, then eject the mixture into the atmosphere. The ejectors combine the old style multi-lobed and multi-tubed designs with present technology sound suppression materials. At this time, ejectors are in limited use.

J. Engine Compartment Ventilation And Cooling

Engine nacelle ventilation and cooling is required because of the high heat radiation through engine outer cases and the presence of fuel, oil, and electrical systems located on, or adjacent to, those outer cases. Air is

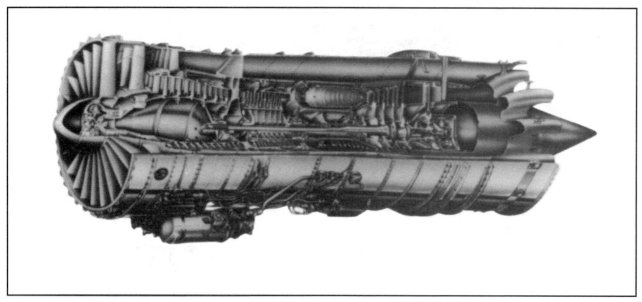

Fig. 3-88 — Pratt & Whitney JT8D-200 series engine with exhaust mixer.

changed in these locations five or more times per minute. Figure 3-91 shows the cooling arrangement for a turbojet engine nacelle. A turbofan engine nacelle would utilize fan air discharge and perhaps some ram air for cooling.

Figure 3-92 shows typical temperature values along the length of a dual-spool engine with a peak temperature load at the turbine area. The figure also shows the two compartments to be cooled. The cold section is cooled and ventilated by ram air and is separated from the hot section by a fireproof seal. The hot section is also cooled by ram air but in higher quantity than the cold section. The fire seal prevents the high heat in the hot section from moving forward into the cold section which contains all or most of the volatile fluid, lines, and electrical wiring.

K. Engine Mounts

Engine mounts for gas turbine engines are of relatively simple construction, as seen in Figure 3-93. Except for the turboprop, gas turbine engines produce little torque,

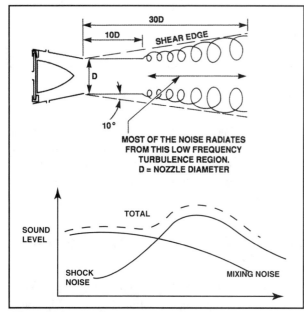

Fig. 3-89A — Hot exhaust noise pattern.
Fig. 3-89B — Total sound vs frequencies.

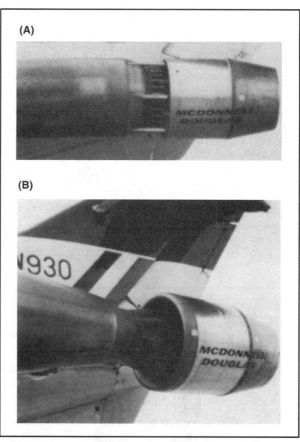

Fig. 3-90A — New style multi-tube noise suppression ejector.
Fig. 3-90B — New style multi-lobed noise suppression ejector.

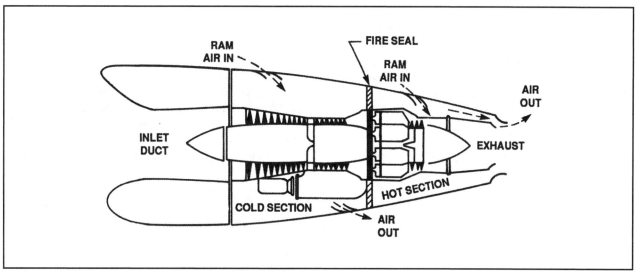

Fig. 3-91 — Engine compartment cooling and ventilation.

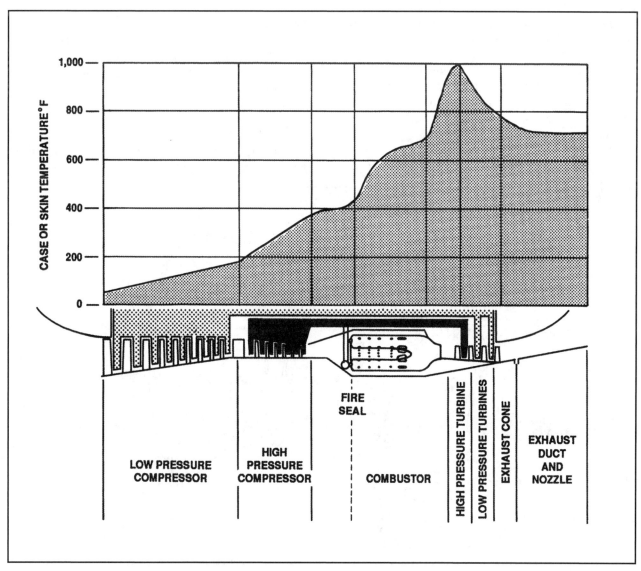

Fig. 3-92 — Typical outer case temperatures.

and their mounts do not need to be of heavy construction. The mounts do, however, support the engine weight and also allow for transfer of stresses created by the engine into the aircraft structure. Because of induced propeller loads, the turboprop develops higher torque loads and mountings are proportionately heavier.

L. Bearings

Bearings are an important construction and design feature of any gas turbine engine, and will be discussed in Chapter V under Main Bearings And Seals.

M. Construction Materials

1. Cold Section

Aluminum and magnesium alloys are extensively used for construction of compressor cases, inlet cases, and accessory cases where low heat and moderate strength is the primary consideration. These materials have approximately 30 to 40 percent the weight of steel.

Titanium alloys are used in the manufacture of fan cases, fan blades, compressor blades, compressor disks, and centrifugal impellers where lower weight rather than high temperature steel strength is required. Titanium is an expensive material, and it is not as resistant to foreign object damage as steel. Titanium, however, has the strength of some steels of moderate to high quality but only half the weight.

Titanium is used in turbine engines because of its low density, high specific strength, and corrosion resistance.

While these are significant benefits, titanium has some unique properties that make it unsuited for some applications within turbine engines.

Particularly, titanium has two properties that can combine to make it vulnerable to combustion: (1) unlike most other structural metals, titanium ignites at a lower temperature than its melting temperature, and, (2) it has a lower conductivity of heat. Thus, heat may not be readily conducted away from its source, thereby permitting the titanium to more rapidly reach its ignition temperature.

Hard rubs are the most common source of heat buildup. Rubs may result from foreign object damage (FOD), stall damage, bearing failure, rotor imbalance, and/or case deflection. During a rub, the low thermal conductivity of a titanium component may rapidly rise to the ignition temperature.

In the compressor high pressure stages, nickel-chromium alloys, referred to as stainless steels, and nickel-base alloys are often employed. Nickel-base alloys are also very expensive and are primarily used in the hot section.

Epoxy-resin materials, called composite materials, have been developed for cold section construction of cases and shroud rings where lower strength is permissible and light weight is the major consideration. This family of materials is presently undergoing major development for use in the construction of primary airfoils, such as fan blades.

2. Hot Section

For hot sections, a variety of high strength to weight materials have been developed, often referred to as super

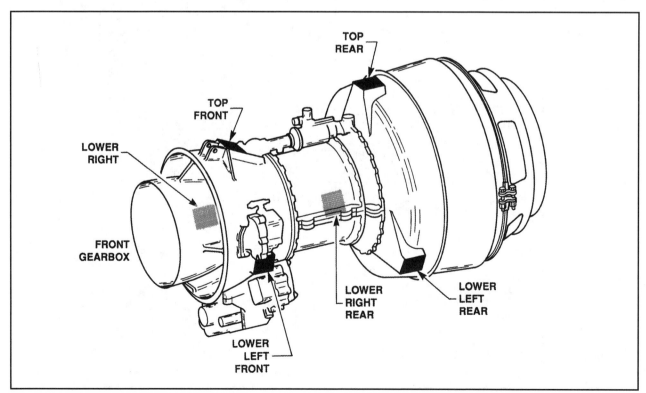

Fig. 3-93 — Engine mount arrangement of a turboshaft engine.

alloys. These alloys have a maximum temperature limit of 2000°F when uncooled and 2600°F when cooled internally. Super alloys were developed for use in high temperature areas where oxidation resistance is needed and where high thermal, tensile, and vibratory stresses are present.

Super alloys are complex mixtures of many critical metals, namely: Nickel, chromium, cobalt, titanium, tungsten, carbon, and other metallic elements.

General agreement on precise mixtures by manufacturers of turbine parts is still the subject of much debate. One reason for this is that the strength properties these metals ultimately have depends on the mixture. However, the stronger the metal, the more difficult and expensive it is to form and machine into the intricate shapes necessary for turbine engine parts.

Also, exotic materials and processes mean expensive initial and replacement costs. It is not uncommon to see a single, two to three inch long turbine blade, that costs $300 or a large blade that costs $3,000. The technician's decision to change these parts soon becomes a significant cost to the customer (Figure 3-94).

Many manufacturing processes are utilized in the production of hot section parts. Forging, casting, and plating are the traditional methods. Newer procedures include powder metallurgy, single-crystal casting, and plasma spraying.

Powder metallurgy is a forging process in which powdered super metal is hot-pressed into a solid state. This results in a very high density material of high temperature strength. These metals have long slender crystals with axial grain boundaries, but few traverse grain boundaries, and are very creep resistant.

Another process which produces even stronger materials is single crystal casting in which only one grain of material forms in the mold rather than millions of grains bound together, as is the case with traditional casting. With only one grain and no grain boundaries, corrosion due to expansion is all but eliminated.

Ceramic and aluminum alloy thermal barrier coating of super alloy parts and some titanium parts are also processes which give high surface strength and resistance to corrosion. These coatings are generally referred to as plasma sprays and, when applied under high heat, melt into the surface of the base metal. This coating is said to give the best protection against the scaling type corrosion or erosion which occurs at high gas temperatures. Scaling is a condition caused by sodium (salt) in the air and sulfur in the fuel reacting chemically with the base metals.

The alloy itself, in conjunction with the process involved in forming it, usually determines its strength and workability. In some cases, the combustion liner is constructed of material as thin as 0.040 inch and must be easily weldable. For this reason, nickel-base alloys are

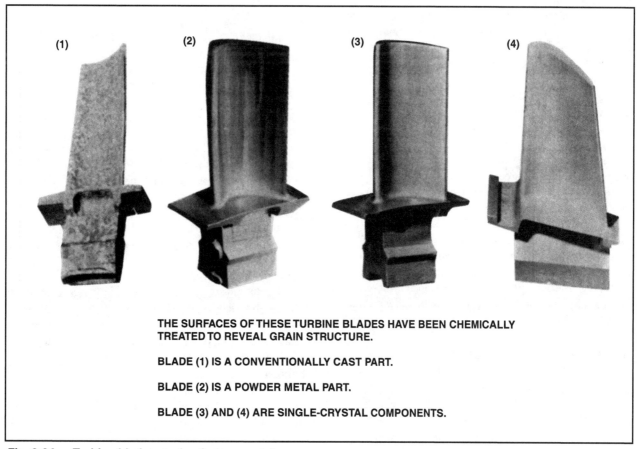

THE SURFACES OF THESE TURBINE BLADES HAVE BEEN CHEMICALLY TREATED TO REVEAL GRAIN STRUCTURE.

BLADE (1) IS A CONVENTIONALLY CAST PART.

BLADE (2) IS A POWDER METAL PART.

BLADE (3) AND (4) ARE SINGLE-CRYSTAL COMPONENTS.

Fig. 3-94 — Turbine blades made of super metals.

generally used today rather than the stainless steel alloys of a few years ago. Nickel-base alloys contain little or no iron, are noncorrosive, and can be worked in thin weldable sheets.

Combustion liners sometimes experience surface erosion which supports carbon buildup on the inner surfaces. Today, one might see a whitish coating applied to some liners, called magnesium zirconate. It is a material which helps combat carbon deposits. A property of this coating is that it wears away during operation taking carbon with it and thereby maintaining cleanliness on the surfaces. During heavy repair the coating is replaced.

Combustor cases and turbine cases are often constructed from nickel-base alloys, often referred to as Inconel (a trade name).

Turbine blades and vanes are either forged by newer powder metallurgy technique or by traditional methods, or investment cast from nickel-base alloys. They are also cast by single-crystal methods mentioned previously. These materials have very high temperature strength under centrifugal loads and are highly corrosion resistant.

Turbine disks are almost exclusively constructed from cobalt-base alloys for high thermal strength under extreme mechanical and thermal loads. Temperatures as high as 2500°F are experienced in the first stage vane area of large engines. Cobalt, representing the current state-of-the-art in metallurgical development for turbine engines, is used to combat these high temperatures.

Because of their ability to withstand higher heat than metal, and also their high strength to weight ratio, ceramic turbine components have been experimented with since early German development; but, because of its low mechanical strength under vibrating loads, only limited use has been made of ceramic material. Some non-flight engines are currently fitted with ceramic blades and disks, but flight engines to date are limited to ceramic coating of some stationary parts, such as combustion liners and turbine nozzle vanes. Ceramic coating can usually be recognized as a greenish glazed type finish.

As mentioned previously, the gas turbine engine could have unlimited power if there were no temperature limits imposed by material strength. The idea is that less and less cooling air would be needed as material heat strength increases. The engine then, in turn, could be scaled down and the power to weight ratio would increase significantly. But material strength today, as it was in Whittle's time, still remains the most limiting factor in the power output of the turbine engine.

3. Construction Processes

Today the most common process for producing compressor and turbine parts is as follows:

1. Turbine disk forging by use of powder metals.

   a) A forming case is filled with powder metal and placed in a vacuum chamber;

b) A forming case case is vibrated to tightly pack the powder. The vacuum prevents air voids in the mixture;

c) The metal powder is subjected to very high mechanical pressure of approximately 25,000 pounds per square inch. High heat is supplied sufficient to fuse the metal particles together into a disk-shaped piece;

d) The disk is machined to its final shape.

2. Compressor blade and vane investment casting.

   a) Molten metal is poured into a ceramic mold in a furnace then taken out to cool;

   b) The mold is broken away and the blade or vane comes out in a near-net shape;

   c) The part is machined to its finer shape.

3. Turbine vane and blade casting by the "lost wax method" (Figure 3-95).

   a) A wax copy of the piece is made in a metal mold;

   b) The wax piece is dipped in liquid ceramic to form a coating;

   c) Molten metal is poured into the ceramic casting in a casting furnace and the wax leaves the mold;

   d) During cooling, the casting is centrifugally loaded in a spin-chamber to provide a directional solidification to the piece resulting in a long grain structure. After solidification the ceramic shell is broken off and the piece is processed into a finished part;

4. Turbine vane and blade casting by the "single-crystal method". Accomplished as above for directional solidification except that the molten metal is drawn into the mold through a small corkscrew channel at one end while the other end is chilled.

N. Engine Stations

For ease of identification, engine manufacturers number locations, either along the length of the gas path or along the length of the engine. Station numbers start at either the flight cowling inlet or the engine inlet. Typical of this station numbering concept is the Pratt & Whitney PT6 turboprop, a single spool two shaft engine shown in Figure 3-96A. Figures 3-96B and C show the numbering sequence for a dual and single spool engine. Figure 3-97 shows the station numbering sequence for a high bypass turbofan, the General Electric CFM56. As can be seen by these figures, manufacturers do not always number engine stations the same way. The purpose of the numbering scheme is always the same.

Engine symbols such as Pt and Tt are often used in conjunction with station numbers.

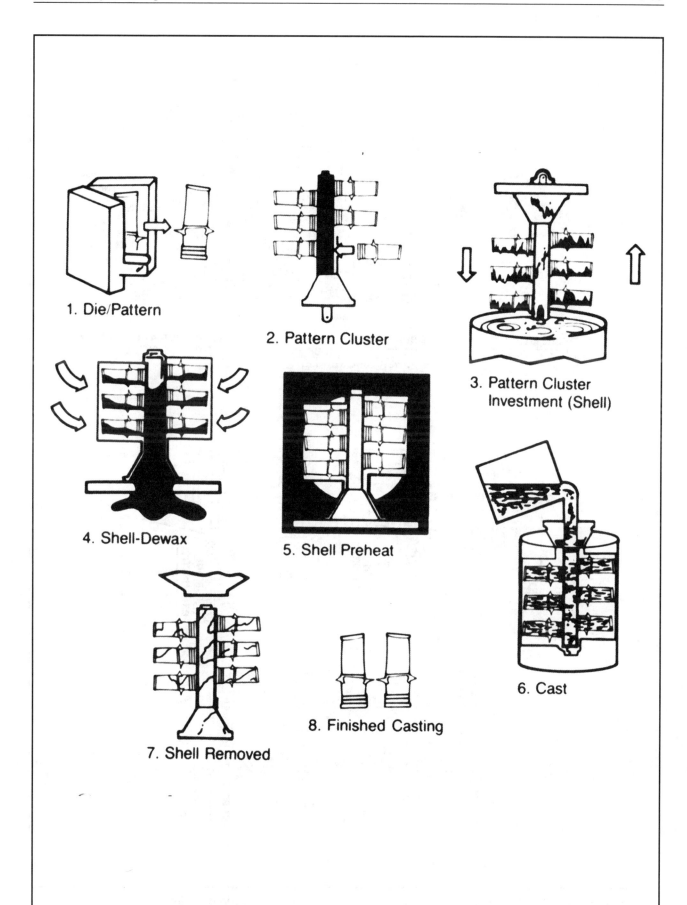

1. Die/Pattern

2. Pattern Cluster

3. Pattern Cluster Investment (Shell)

4. Shell-Dewax

5. Shell Preheat

6. Cast

7. Shell Removed

8. Finished Casting

Fig. 3-95 — Steps in " lost wax casting" method, cluster of six blades.

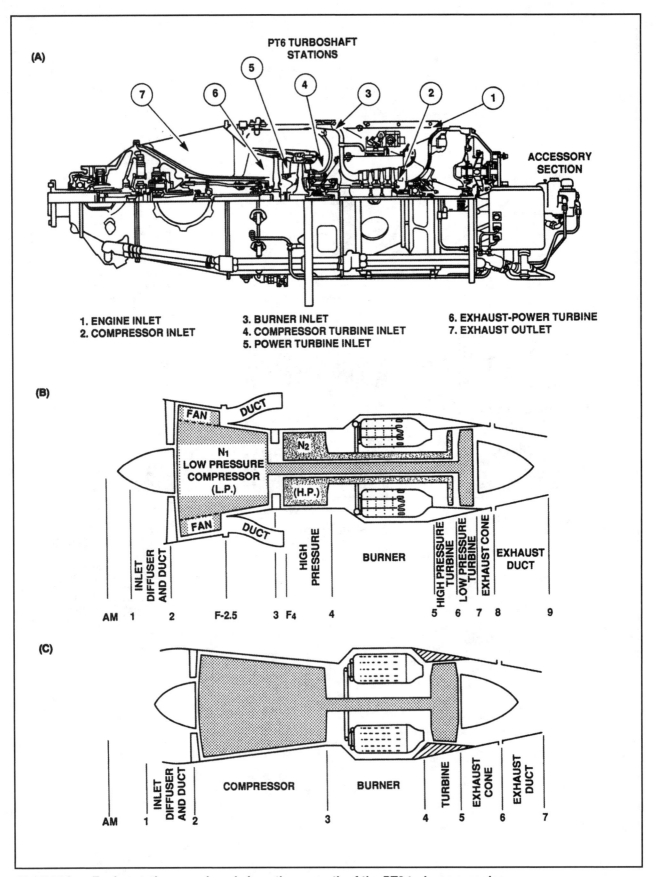

Fig. 3-96A — Engine stations numbered along the gas path of the PT6 turboprop engine.
Fig. 3-96B — Engine stations along the length of a dual spool engine.
Fig. 3-96C — Engine stations along the length of a single spool engine.

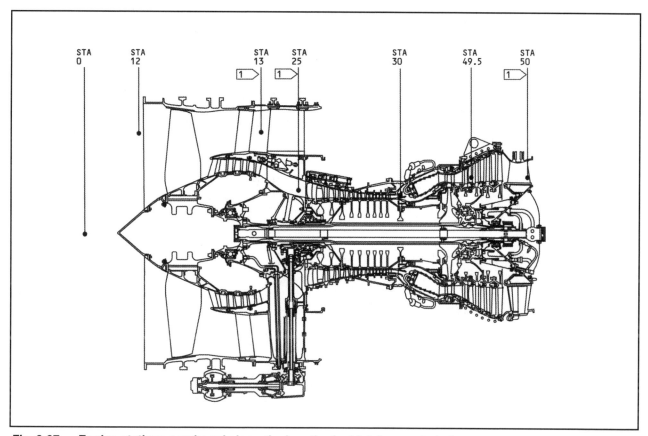

Fig. 3-97 — Engine stations numbered along the length of a high bypass turbofan.

For example: To describe Pressure Total at Station-2 (the engine inlet), Pt_2 is used. To describe Temperature Total at Station-7, the turbine outlet on a dual-spool engine, Tt_7 is used. From this discussion it is evident that station numbers, when used as a subscript to an upper case prefix, help greatly in abbreviating cumbersome terminology in describing locations and functional data of the engine.

O. Directional References

For purposes of identifying engine construction points, or component and accessory placement, directional references are used along with station numbers. These references are described as forward at the engine inlet and aft at the engine tailpipe, with a standard 12 hour clock orientation. The terms right- and left-hand, clockwise and counterclockwise, apply as viewed from the rear of the engine looking forward toward the inlet (Figure 3-98).

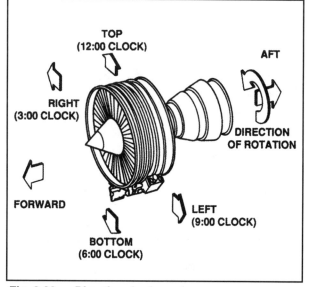

Fig. 3-98 — Directional references.

QUESTIONS:

1. Is the shape of a subsonic turbofan inlet duct convergent, divergent, or both?

2. What is the principle involved in inlet duct design, to increase static pressure or to increase velocity of the mass airflow?

3. The centrifugal compressor is more common to which type of gas turbine engine today, turboshaft or large turbofan?

4. The primary function of an axial flow compressor stator vane is to act as a diffuser. What is its secondary function?

5. What is the name given to the reduced thickness at the tip of some compressor blades?

6. Name another advantage of a gas turbine engine with an axial flow compressor besides a small frontal area.

7. At what location in the turbine engine would one find the point of highest static pressure?

8. What approximate percentage of total airflow is used for combustion?

9. What is the main purpose of the combustion section "secondary air"?

10. What makes the reverse-flow annular combustor an efficient design?

11. Is the most common low pressure turbine blade design the open-tip type or the shrouded type?

12. At what location on an impulse-reaction turbine blade can the impulse design be seen?

13. From what construction materials are the turbine components generally made?

14. What is the name given to the opening in the end of the tailpipe?

15. What are the two names given to the common types of thrust reversers?

16. Why does a turbofan produce less noise than a turbojet of the same thrust?

Chapter IV
Engine Familiarization

Four different Gas Turbine Engines are discussed in detail in this section. The engines are as follows:

1. The Pratt & Whitney JT8D Turbofan, a low bypass airliner sized engine.

2. The General Motors Allison Company Model 250 Turboshaft used in helicopters (now a Rolls Royce engine).

3. The Pratt & Whitney Company of Canada PT6 Turboprop, a commuter and business aircraft-sized engine.

4. The GE/Snecma CFM56 Turbofan, a high bypass airliner sized engine.

NOTE: Specifications for the above four engines appear at the end of this chapter

These engines represent four of the most widely produced gas turbine engines in current use worldwide.

The JT8D is produced only as a turbofan and is an outgrowth of a Navy turbojet with the designation J-52. The Allison-250 was originally developed as both the military T-63 and the commercial 250 model. It is produced in turboshaft and turboprop models, the shaft model being the most popular. The PT6 was originally developed as both a military T-76 and the commercial PT6. It is produced in turboprop and turboshaft models, the turboprop model being the most popular. The CFM56 is the engine used in all the Boeing 737 models from the dash 300 up to the new dash 900. It is also used in a number of Airbus airplanes, and for engine retrofits on DC-8 and KC-135 aircraft.

A. Familiarization With The Pratt & Whitney JT8D Turbofan Engine

The Pratt & Whitney JT8D turbofan engine is the most widely used airliner-sized engines in the history of aviation. It is used as the powerplant of the Boeing 727, Boeing 737, and McDonnell Douglas DC-9 and MD-80. It is a low bypass ratio, fully ducted engine, with its various models ranging from 12,500 to 20,000 pounds of thrust.

The following material will show the construction features and some of the operational data of the JT8D-17A so that the reader can compare and contrast this engine to the various engine designs contained in the preceding portions of this text.

1. Engine Design Features (Figures 4-1, 4-2)

The JT8D is a front fan turbofan engine of the dual-spool type. It is fully ducted and has a mixed exhaust.

The full bypass duct allows the cold and hot gas streams to merge before discharging to the atmosphere. It is of low bypass design, indicating that approximately the same amount of air is flowing through the fan duct (labeled secondary airflow in Figure 4-1) as is flowing through the core portion of the engine (labeled primary airflow in Figure 4-1).

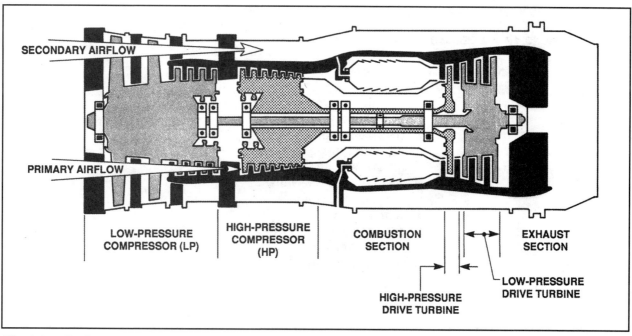

Fig. 4-1 — Engine design features—JT8D.

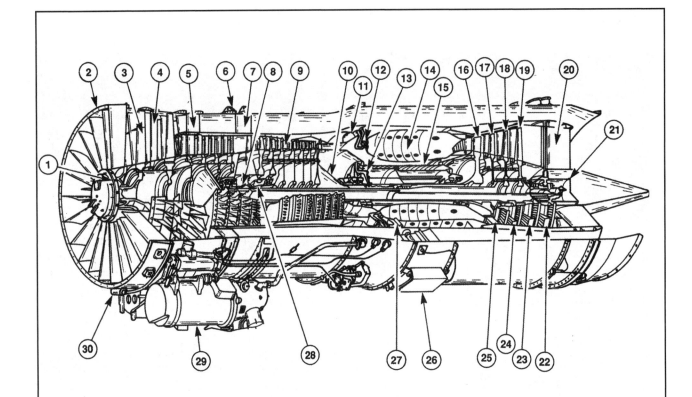

LEGEND:
1. ANTI-ICING AIR DISCHARGE PORTS
2. FAN INLET CASE
3. 1ST STAGE FAN BLADES
4. FRONT COMPRESSOR ROTOR
5. FAN DISCHARGE VANES
6. FAN DISCHARGE INTERMEDIATE CASE
7. FAN DISCHARGE INTERMEDIATE CASE STRUTS
8. NO. 2 AND 3 BEARINGS OIL NOZZLE
9. REAR COMPRESSOR ROTOR
10. REAR COMPRESSOR ROTOR REAR HUB
11. DIFFUSER CASE AIR MANIFOLD
12. FUEL NOZZLE
13. NO. 4 BEARING OIL NOZZLE
14. COMBUSTION CHAMBER
15. COMBUSTION CHAMBER INNER CASE
16. 1ST STAGE TURBINE BLADES
17. 2ND STAGE TURBINE DISK AND BLADES
18. 3RD STAGE TURBINE DISK AND BLADES
19. 4TH STAGE TURBINE DISK AND BLADES
20. EXHAUST STRUT
21. NO. 6 BEARING HEATSHIELD
22. 4TH STAGE TURBINE VANES
23. 3RD STAGE TURBINE VANES
24. 2ND STAGE TURBINE VANES
25. 1ST STAGE TURBINE VANES
26. IGNITION TRANSFORMER
27. IGNITER PLUG
28. GEAR BOX DRIVE BEVEL GEAR
29. MAIN GEARBOX
30. NO. 1 BEARING TUBE CONNECTOR

Fig. 4-2 — Cutaway view—JT8D.

Dual-spool refers to the split compressor design, meaning that the low pressure compressor (LP) and the high pressure compressor (HP) rotate independently of each other. This is possible because the LP compressor drive shaft is located coaxially within the HP compressor shaft.

The six-stage low pressure compressor, also called the N_1 compressor, located in front, is driven by a three-stage axial flow turbine rotor located at the rear of the high pressure turbine.

The first two stages of the N_1 compressor also serve as the front fan. The inner portion of the fan blades act as compressor blades to provide primary airflow. The outer portion of the blades act as fan blades providing secondary airflow.

The seven-stage, high-pressure compressor, also called the N_2 compressor, is driven by a single-stage axial flow turbine rotor located immediately to the rear of the combustor.

The two rotor systems, N_1 and N_2, are supported by two double, and five single, main bearings which are positioned within the main cases of the engine. Chip detectors are provided at four of the bearing locations.

Three borescoping ports are provided for performing both scheduled and unscheduled internal inspections.

2. Major Engine Sections And Views Of Ongoing Maintenance (Figure 4-3)

The JT8D is of Modular construction. Any of the Modules can be replaced as an entire unit during overhaul. The Modules are later overhauled as a separate repair function. This expedites the overhaul procedure of the engine.

The total time in service on the engine and the total time in service on modules is carefully analyzed by management personnel to ensure a cost-effective match is made. This is done to ensure that a low time module is not placed on a high time engine, unless no other choice is possible from existing stock. In some instances, a module will be repaired instead of being replaced to prevent mismatching.

3. Low-Pressure Compressor — N_1

(Figure 4-4)

The low-pressure compressor (N_1) has six stages of compression: Two fan stages and four more compressor stages. At rated thrust, the N_1 has a compression ratio of 4.33 to 1, with a discharge pressure of 63.6 pounds per square inch - absolute at standard day conditions.

The N_1 compressor has two functions. The first is to accelerate secondary airflow into the fan duct at the rate of 164 pounds/second, at 8,589 RPM, which is 100% takeoff speed. Compression ratio of the fan is 2.1 to 1 with a fan discharge pressure of 31.0 pounds per square inch - absolute. The second function of the N_1 compressor is to provide the N_2 compressor with supercharged primary air of 4.33 times atmospheric, at 160 pounds/second mass airflow.

A single-roller bearing, No. 1, located in the inlet case, supports the front of the compressor for radial loads, and a double ball bearing, No. 2, supports the rear of the N_1 rotor for both axial and radial loads.

The first-stage fan blades are attached to the disk by a dovetail blade root and are retained by a locking ring. The second-stage fan blades are attached by a dovetail attachment and retained by tab locks.

The six stator stages are individual, continuous welded ring assemblies. To assemble the N_1 compressor, this design requires that the compressor be stacked, starting with the last stator, then the last rotor, and so forth through the successive stages up to the number one stage. Each rotor stage has a shroud ring acting as a spacer between stator assemblies.

The N_1 compressor is mechanically coupled to the N_1 turbine shaft at the No. 2 bearing area. The turbine shaft runs co-axially through the N_2 compressor shaft.

4. High-Pressure Compressor — N_2

The high-pressure compressor (N_2) has seven stages of compression. At rated thrust, the N_2 compressor has a compression ratio of approximately 4 to 1, with a discharge pressure (total of N_1 and N_2) of 254 pounds per square inch - absolute at standard conditions.

The function of the N_2 compressor is to provide the combustor with sufficient air at all operating conditions. At rated power, 160 pounds/second of mass airflow is moved by the N_2 compressor.

A single ball bearing, No. 3, supports the front of the compressor and a double ball bearing, No. 4, supports the rear for both axial and radial loads. An air balance chamber at the No. 4 bearing assists in absorbing thrust loads.

The seventh stage blades (first stage of N_2) are pin-mounted and retained with rivets. Stages 8 through 13 are dovetail slotted to the disk and retained by tablocks.

The seven stator stages are continuous welded ring assemblies. The N_2, like the N_1, is stacked from the rear, rotor on stator during reassembly.

The N_2 compressor is mechanically coupled to the N_2 turbine shaft at the No. 4 bearing area.

5. Diffuser Case (Figure 4-5)

The diffuser case is the mid-supporting member of the engine. It contains the thirteenth-stage stators and the thirteenth-stage rotor shroud ring. The No. 4 bearing is housed within the diffuser to support the rear of the high-pressure compressor.

The outer case contains air extraction points for Customer Bleed Air, Engine Anti-Ice Air, and Anti-Surge Bleed Air. It also contains external bosses to which the fuel nozzles mount.

The main function of the diffuser is to straighten airflow and to diffuse airflow to the correct pressure and velocity in preparation for combustion.

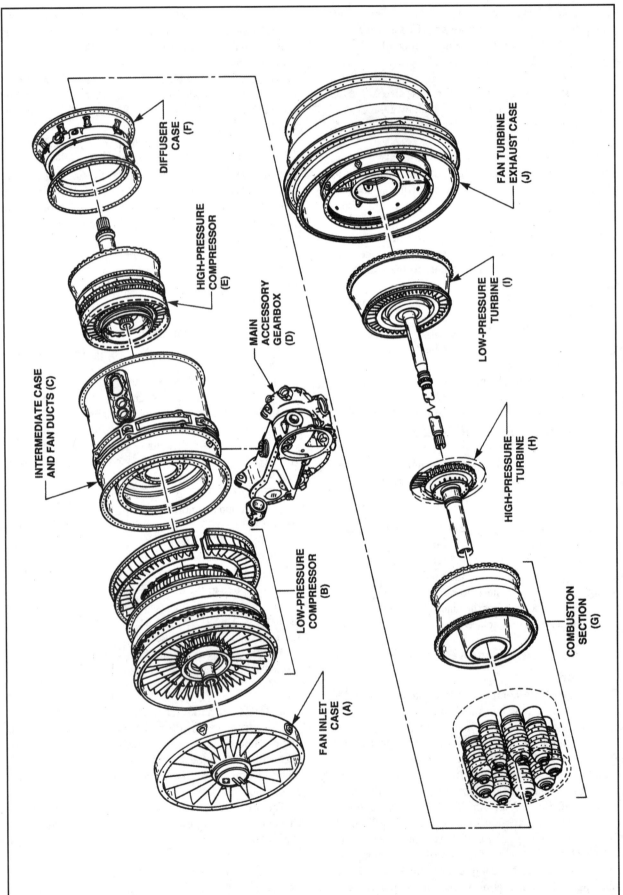

Fig. 4-3 — Major engine sections—JT8D.

DIFFUSER CASE (F)

HIGH-PRESSURE COMPRESSOR (E)

MAIN ACCESSORY GEARBOX (D)

INTERMEDIATE CASE AND FAN DUCTS (C)

LOW-PRESSURE COMPRESSOR (B)

FAN INLET CASE (A)

FAN TURBINE EXHAUST CASE (J)

LOW-PRESSURE TURBINE (I)

HIGH-PRESSURE TURBINE (H)

COMBUSTION SECTION (G)

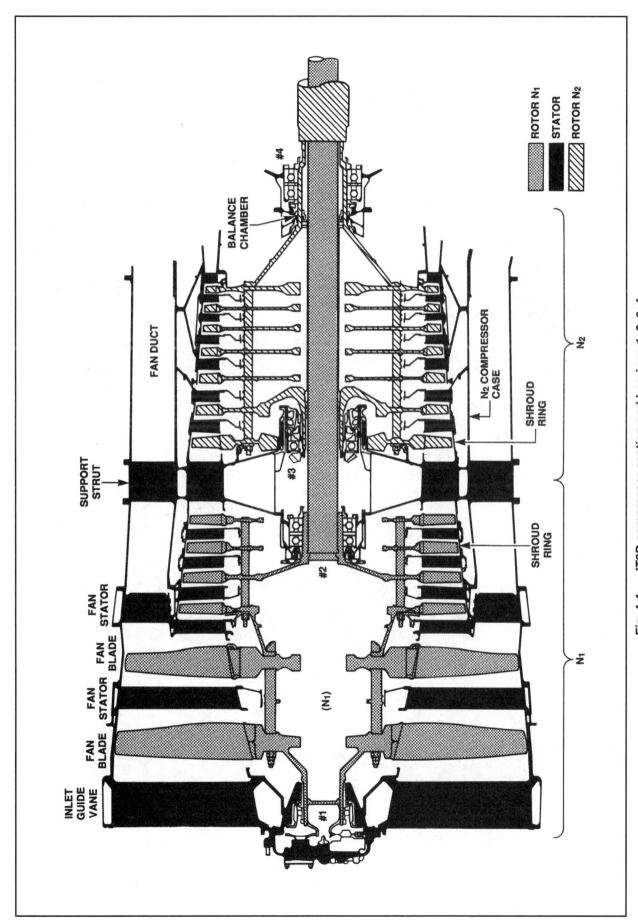

Fig. 4-4 — JT8D compressor section and bearings 1, 2, 3, 4.

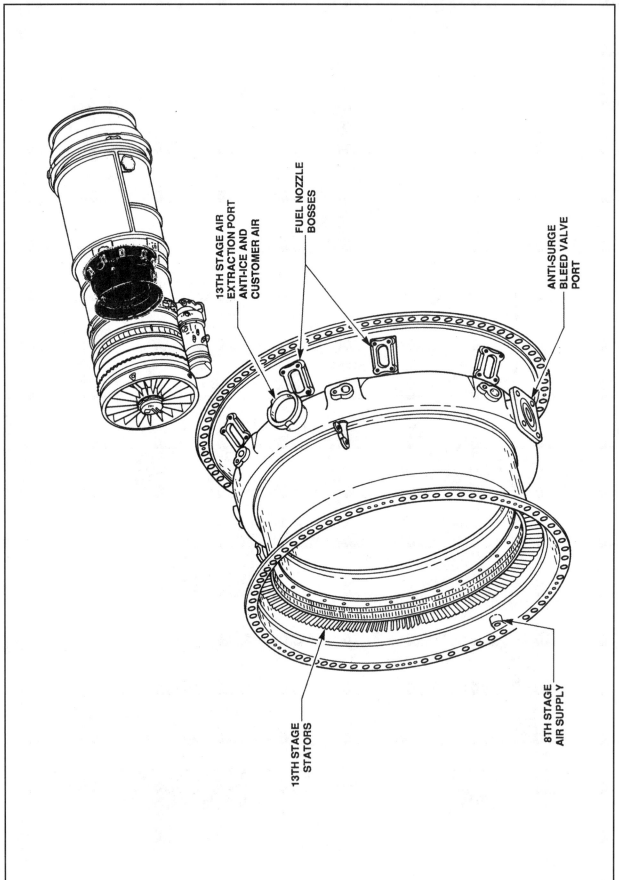

13TH STAGE AIR
EXTRACTION PORT
ANTI-ICE AND
CUSTOMER AIR

FUEL NOZZLE
BOSSES

ANTI-SURGE
BLEED VALVE
PORT

13TH STAGE
STATORS

8TH STAGE
AIR SUPPLY

Fig. 4-5 — Diffuser case—JT8D.

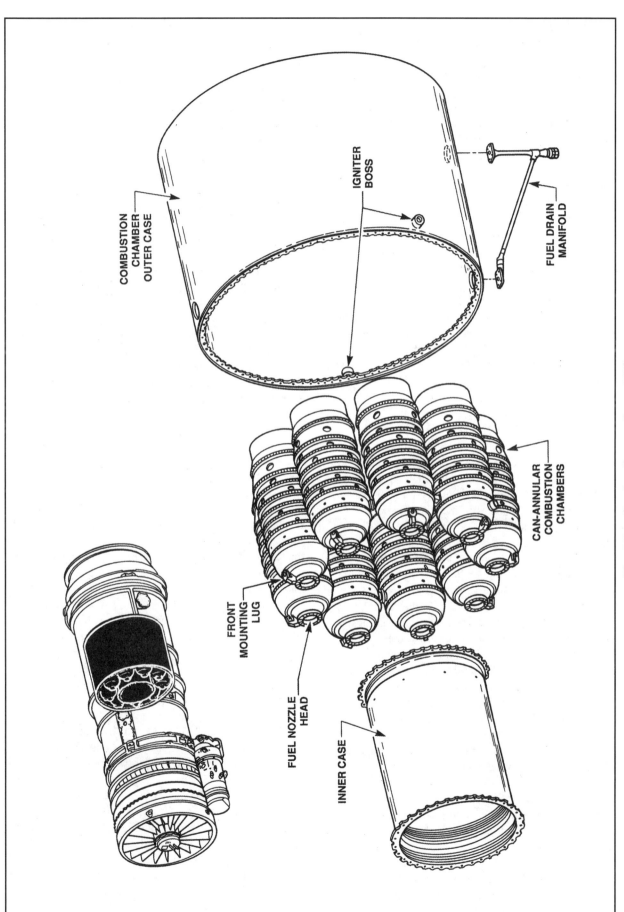

COMBUSTION CHAMBER OUTER CASE

IGNITER BOSS

FUEL DRAIN MANIFOLD

CAN-ANNULAR COMBUSTION CHAMBERS

FRONT MOUNTING LUG

FUEL NOZZLE HEAD

INNER CASE

Fig. 4-6 — Combustion section—JT8D.

6. Combustion Case (Figure 4-7)

The combustion section houses the combustion liners. The inner case forms the inner walls of the combustion chamber. The turbine shaft passes through this case. The outer case forms the outer walls of the combustion chamber.

The nine can-annular combustion liners are supported on the front end by a locating lug on the liner and a hangar pin within the diffuser case. The liners are held in place at the aft end to the rear support assembly by circular clamps.

The combustor rear support and outlet assembly supports the rear of the nine liners and has two configurations, louvered and non-louvered. Both perform essentially the same task, but the louvered-type is a newer design and is cooled by thirteenth-stage air. This gives the assembly a higher tolerance to thermal shock and increases its expected service life.

The front portion of the liners provides the entry point of air for combustion and also the fuel nozzle head mounting points. The purpose of the combustion section is to add thermal energy to the air passing through it, to enclose the fuel-air mixture during combustion, and to discharge that mixture to the turbine via the outlet duct assembly.

7. Turbine Nozzle Vanes (Figures 4-8 and 4-9)

The Turbine Nozzle Vanes are individually installed in all four stages of turbine. The first stage contains 46 vanes, which are located in front of the first-stage N_2 turbine wheel. The N_1 turbines have, respectively, 95 vanes in the second stage, 79 vanes in the third stage, and 77 vanes in the fourth stage.

The first-stage vanes can be removed individually from the front by sliding the outer combustion case back, removing the liners, and sliding the vanes forward. In the "Unit Module" low-pressure turbine, the three turbines and stators are removed as one piece. In the "Non-Unit" low-pressure turbine, the wheels and stators are unstacked one at a time starting at the No. 4 turbine wheel.

The first-stage vanes are air-cooled by both convection (through-flow cooling) and film cooling from a combination of trailing edge slots and cambered-side slots. The difference can be seen in the vanes for the -9, -15, and -17 model engines.

The turbine outer air seals act as turbine blade shroud rings and reduce air leakage at the blade tips. They also act as spacers between vane stages.

The vane trailing edges act as nozzles and form an effective flow area, which helps to maintain correct back-pressure of gas flow through the turbine system. Airseals also accelerate and direct the gases at the most effective angle onto the turbine blades.

All vanes come in several sizes, called classes, by which the effective flow area can be adjusted by maintenance personnel to meet certain operational performance requirements of an engine.

8. High-Pressure Turbine Rotor (N_2) (Figure 4-10)

The high-pressure turbine rotor is a single stage axial flow type with shrouded, impulse-reaction turbine blades. The blades are designed with fir tree-shaped bases which fit into turbine disk slots of the same shape. The blades are retained in place by rivets on models -1, -7, -9, -11, -15, and by side plates on the -17 model engines.

On early model engines, the shrouded tips contain no knife-edge seals, the seals being located in the turbine outer air seal and shroud ring. On the -15 and -17 engines, the knife-edge seals are located on the blade tip shrouds. It has been discovered that better sealing results with this method. The outer air seal for the -15 and -17 models are of the honeycomb design which allows for tighter running clearances and lower air leakage.

The N_2 turbine is supported by the No. 5 bearing. The N_2 turbine shaft houses the No. 4-1/2 bearing, which centers the N_1 turbine shaft, located coaxially within the N_2 shaft. Splines on the front end of the N_2 turbine shaft connect to the N_2 compressor rear shaft.

The function of the N_2 turbine is to convert a portion of the combustor discharge energy into shaft horsepower to drive the N_2 compressor and the main accessory gearbox.

9. Low-Pressure Turbine (N_1) (Figure 4-12)

The low-pressure turbine has two configurations, the Non-unit and the Unit-module. The Non-unit is removed and unstacked during repair and the Unit-module is removed and replaced as a single assembly.

The N_1 turbine is a three-stage axial-flow type with shrouded, impulse-reaction turbine blades. The blade bases are configured with firtree serrations which fit into the turbine disk serrations. The blades are retained in the disk by rivets. The turbine blade tips are sealed by continuous ring shrouds containing knife-edge seals.

The N_1 turbine shaft houses the No. 4-1/2 bearing on its outer diameter. The outer race of this bearing is located within the N_2 turbine shaft. This bearing prevents the N_1shaft from whipping at high torque loads.

The function of the N_1 turbine is to convert the gas energy, which spills over from the N_2 turbine into horsepower to drive the N_1 compressor.

10. Main Accessory Gearbox (Figure 4-13)

The main accessory gearbox is located at the six o'clock position on the fan outer case below the N_2 compressor front shaft. The gearbox is driven by a radial (tower) shaft which connects to a bevel gear drive mechanism located at the front of the N_2 compressor.

The gearbox provides reduction gearing to the drive pads on which components and accessories are mounted, such as the fuel pump/fuel control unit, constant speed drive (C.S.D.), starter, hydraulic pump, and tachometer generator. The front face of the gearbox is a mounting point for the main oil tank.

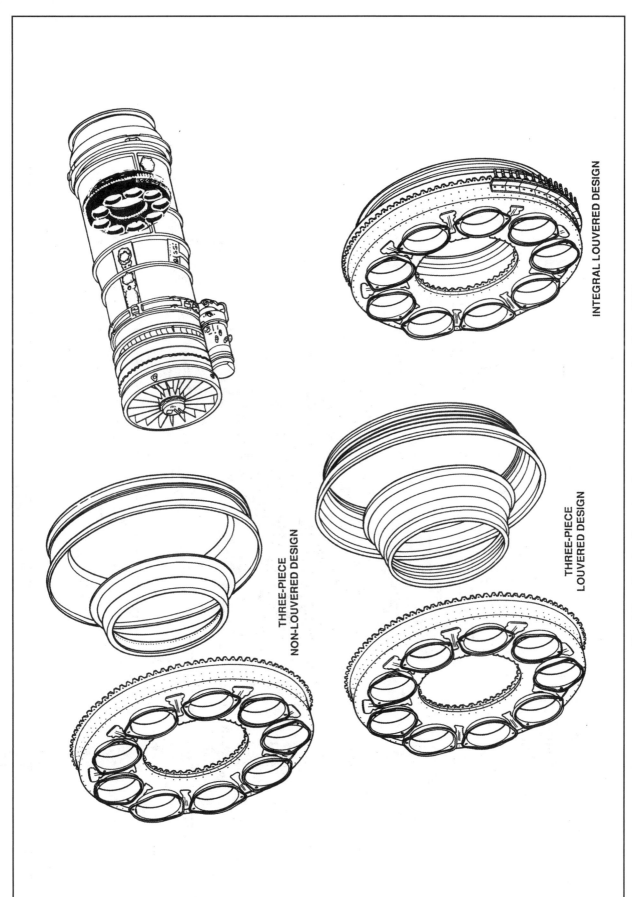

INTEGRAL LOUVERED DESIGN

THREE-PIECE
NON-LOUVERED DESIGN

THREE-PIECE
LOUVERED DESIGN

Fig. 4-7 — Combustion chamber rear support and outlet—JT8D.

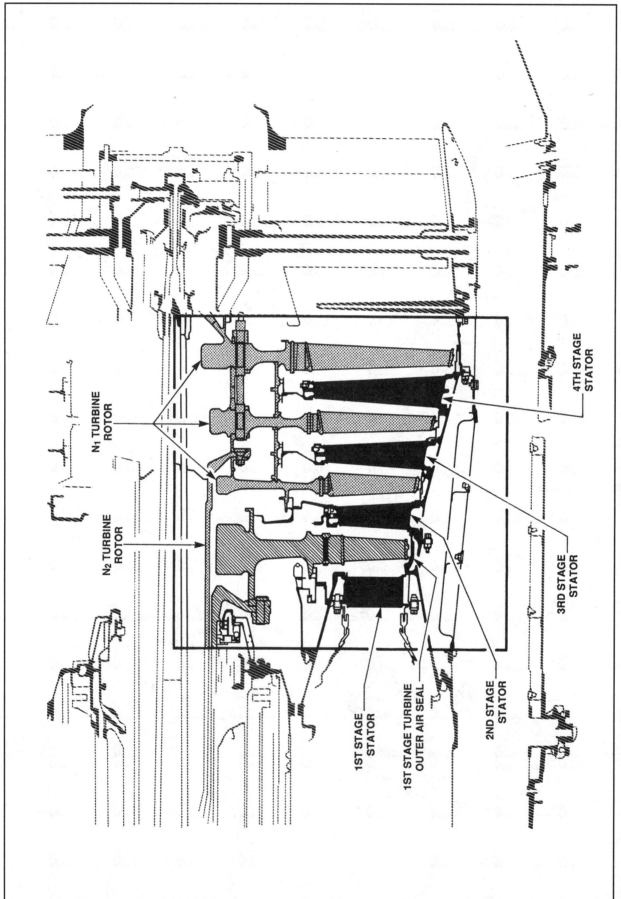

Fig. 4-8. Turbine nozzle vanes—JT8D.

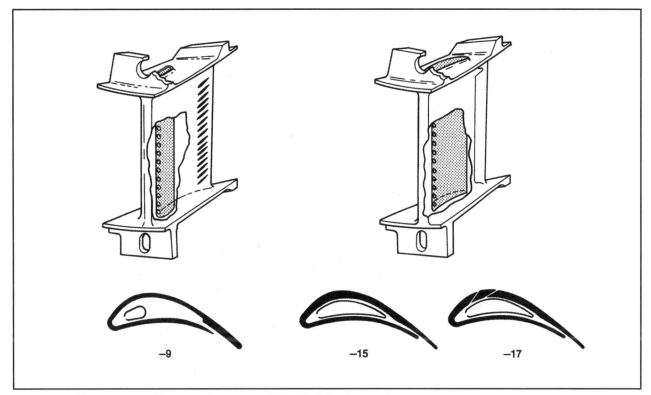

Fig. 4-9 — First stage turbine nozzle vanes—JT8D Models -9, -15, -17.

The gearbox housing also contains integral mounting points for the main oil pump, scavenge oil pump, oil filter, oil pressure regulating valve, and vent system air-oil separator (de-oilers).

11. Turbine Exhaust Case (Figure 4-14)

The turbine exhaust case forms the exhaust nozzle for primary airflow through the core portion of the engine. The rear part of the fan duct forms the combined primary and secondary exhaust nozzle.

The turbine exhaust case houses the turbine exhaust duct, which is supported by four airfoil shaped struts designed to provide the final straightening of primary air flow before discharge into the mixed-flow duct. This case also contains the No. 6 bearing, which supports the rear of the low-pressure turbine. The bearing housing is positioned by four support rods which pass through the struts of the turbine exhaust duct.

The outer case also provides mounting points for six turbine discharge, total-pressure (Pt_7) probes, which are part of the Engine Pressure Ratio (EPR) cockpit indicating system. The eight turbine discharge total temperature (Tt_7) probes shown installed in this case are part of the Exhaust Gas Temperature (EGT) cockpit indicating system.

12. Main Bearings (Figure 4-15)

There are seven main bearings of the ball and roller-type supporting the rotor systems. Four bearings support the N_1 system, and three bearings support the N_2 system as follows:

No. 1 bearing is a roller bearing which supports the front of the N_1 compressor for radial loads. It is mist and vapor lubricated. Oil leakage into the gas path is prevented by labyrinth air-oil sealing which is pressurized with sixth-stage bleed air.

No. 2 bearing is a duplex-ball bearing which supports the rear of the N_1 compressor for both radial and axial loads. It is directly lubricated by a fluid oil stream and fitted with labyrinth air-oil sealing. It is also pressurized with sixth-stage bleed air.

No. 3 bearing is a single-ball type which supports the front of the N_2 compressor. It is directly lubricated by an oil jet and is fitted with a labyrinth air-oil sealing and pressurized by sixth and seventh-stage bleed air.

No. 4 bearing is a duplex-ball type which supports the rear of the N_2 compressor. It is directly lubricated by an oil jet and is fitted with labyrinth air-oil sealing and pressurized by eight-stage bleed air.

No. 4-1/2 is a single-roller type bearing. Its outer race is located midway within the N_2 turbine shaft, and the roller and cage assemblies are located on the N_1 turbine shaft. This bearing prevents the N_1 shaft from whipping at high rotational speeds. It is directly lubricated by an oil jet and utilizes a carbon seal of the ring-type to prevent loss of oil to the gas path.

No. 5 bearing is a single-roller bearing which supports the front of the N_2 turbine shaft. It is mist-lubricated and is sealed by the use of face-type carbon seals. Last stage(thirteenth) air is used to pre-load the carbon seal to its rub ring.

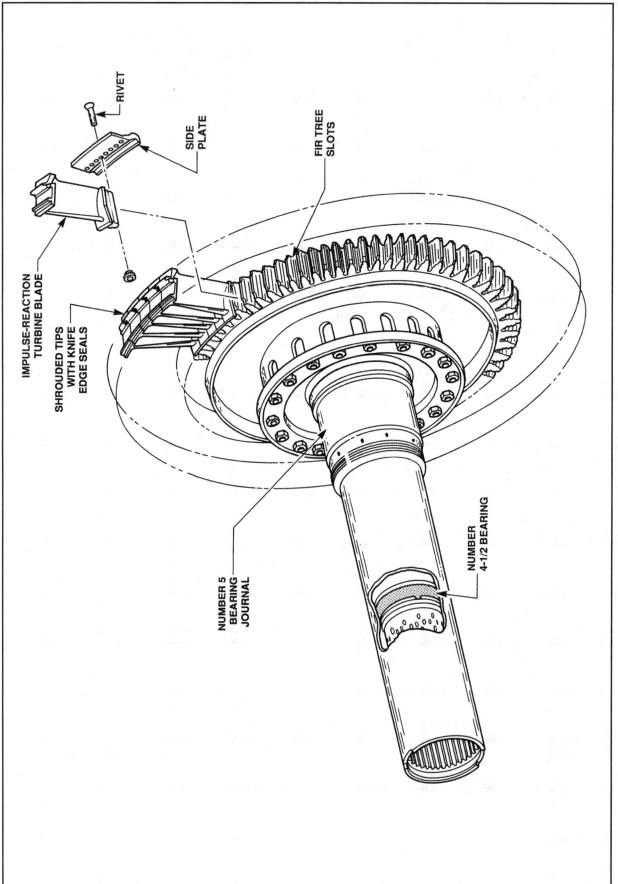

Fig. 4-10 — *High-pressure turbine—JT8D.*

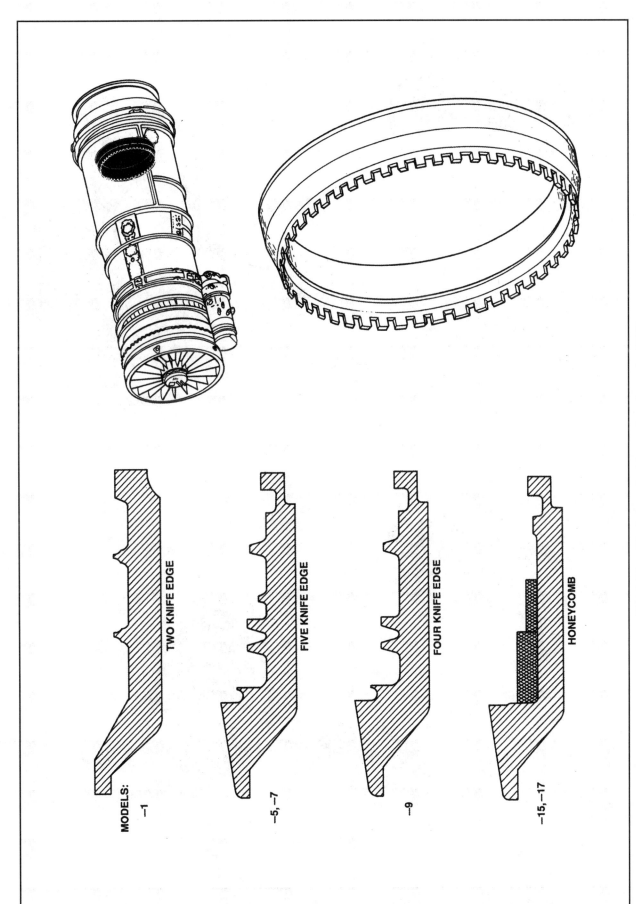

MODELS:

−1 TWO KNIFE EDGE

−5, −7 FIVE KNIFE EDGE

−9 FOUR KNIFE EDGE

−15, −17 HONEYCOMB

Fig. 4-11 — First stage turbine outer air seal—JT8D.

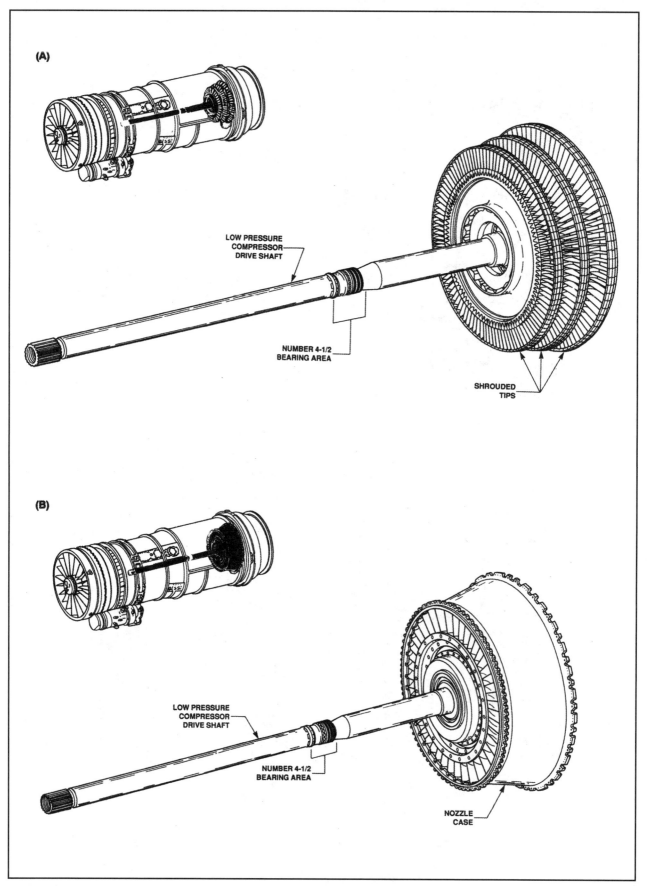

Fig. 4-12A — Low-pressure turbine (non-unit)—JT8D Models.
Fig. 4-12B — Low-pressure turbine (unit type)—JT8D Models (9, 15, 17)

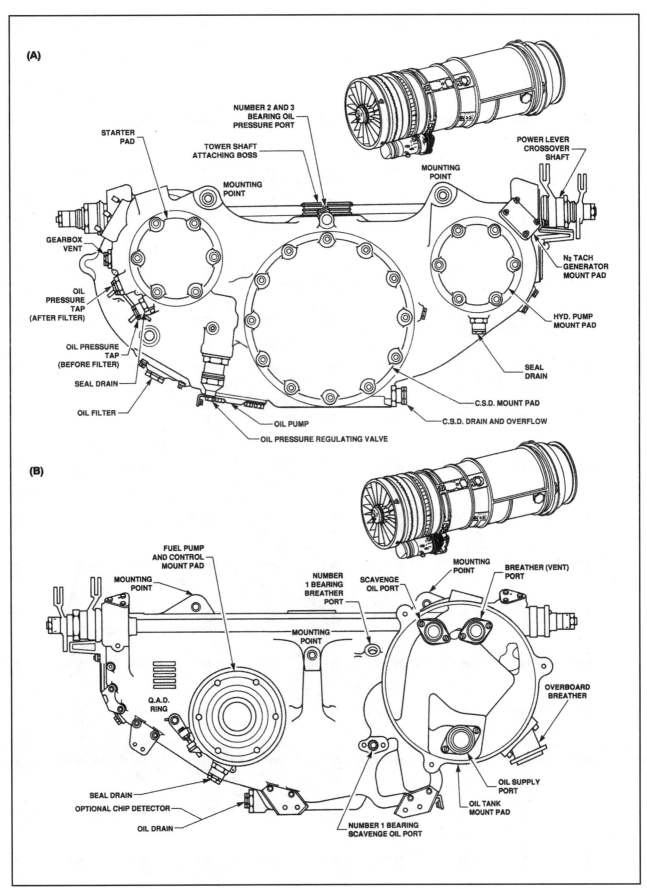

Fig. 4-13A — Main accessory gearbox-rear—JT8D.
Fig. 4-13B — Main accessory gearbox-front—JT8D.

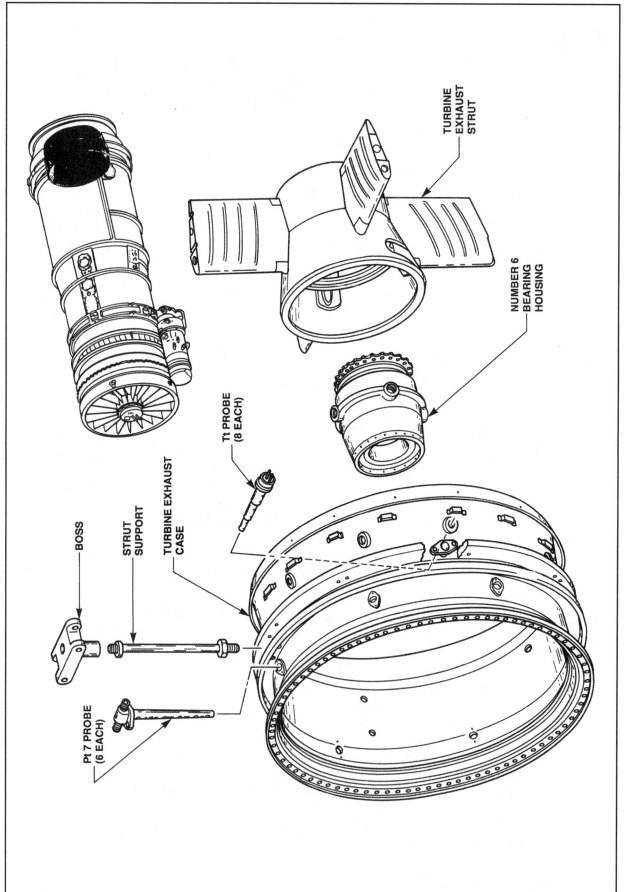

TURBINE EXHAUST STRUT

NUMBER 6 BEARING HOUSING

Tt PROBE (8 EACH)

BOSS

STRUT SUPPORT

TURBINE EXHAUST CASE

Pt 7 PROBE (6 EACH)

Fig. 4-14 — Turbine exhaust case—JT8D.

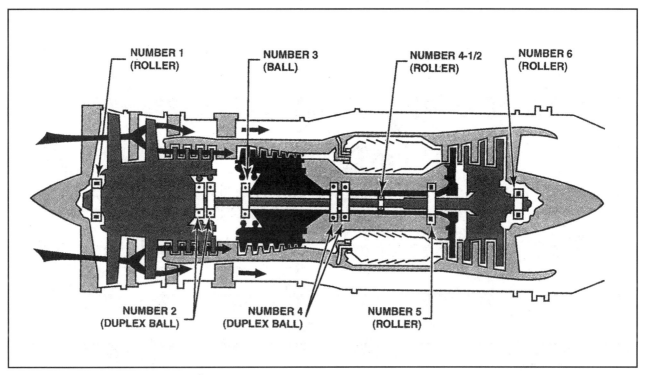

Fig. 4-15 — Bearing locations—JT8D.

No. 6 bearing is a single-roller type which supports the rear of the N_1 turbine. It is a direct lubricated bearing and protected from leakage by carbon ring-type seals. The seal is pressurized by last (thirteenth) stage bleed air.

13. Additional Information

Engine stations, directional references, and construction materials are given in Figures 4-16, 4-17, and 4-18.

Performance figures are given in Figures 4-19, 4-20, 4-21, and 4-22.

The lubrication system of the JT8D is given in detail in Chapter VI.

B. Familiarization With The Allison-250 Turboshaft Engine (Figure 4-23)

The Allison-250 turboshaft engine is produced by the Allison Division of General Motors. At the present time, this engine is the most widely used helicopter engine in the world. There are several different models of the Allison-250, including some turboprop models. Only the C-20B, F, and J models will be described here.

The C-20 is a two-shaft turboshaft with a combination compresssor, a six-stage axial attached to a one-stage centrifugal compressor. It has a reverse-flow can-type combustor, a two-stage high-pressure turbine, also referred to as the gas producer turbine or N_1 turbine, and a two-stage low-pressure turbine called the power turbine or N_2 turbine.

1. Gas Path Of The Allison-250

The model C-20 has a compressor pressure ratio of 7.1:1 and a mass airflow of 3.6 pounds/second at 52,000 RPM.

Airflow along the engine's gas path is as follows: From the flight inlet, air moves straight into the compressor first stage and out of the centrifugal last stage into two external air transfer tubes and to the combustor at the very rear of the engine. The gases then turn forward and through a two-stage compressor turbine (N_1) and a two-stage power turbine (N_2). Finally the gases are directed out of the exhaust duct and upward through two outlets which are twenty degrees from top center at the midpoint on the engine.

2. Four Major Engine Sections (Modules)

The four major engine sections are:

a. The Compressor Section, consisting of inlet housing, combination axial-centrifugal compressor, and diffuser at the rear.

b. The Combustor Section, consisting of two external air transfer tubes which carry air from the diffuser to a single basket type, reverse-flow annular combustor. The combustor contains one duplex fuel nozzle and a single igniter plug.

c. The Turbine Section, consisting of a two-shaft, four-stage turbine assembly and a dual exhaust outlet duct.

d. The Power and Accessory Gearbox Section consisting of a power outlet reduction gear, ratio 5.534:1. The output drive to the helicopter transmission is 6,016 RPM at 100% power turbine speed. For different aircraft applications, a connecting pad is located at both the front and rear of the gearbox. The gearbox also provides mounting pads for the various engine components and accessories.

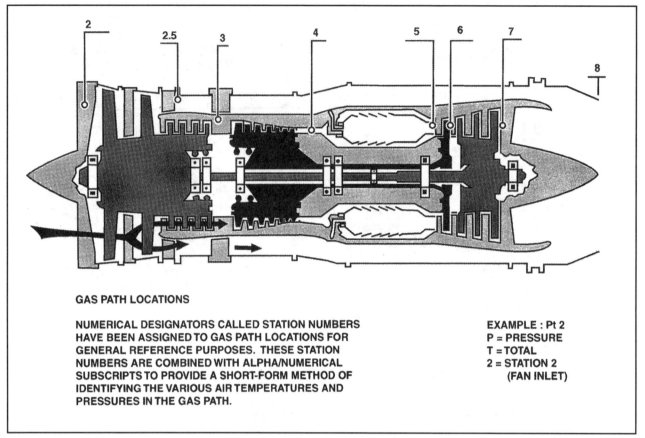

GAS PATH LOCATIONS

NUMERICAL DESIGNATORS CALLED STATION NUMBERS
HAVE BEEN ASSIGNED TO GAS PATH LOCATIONS FOR
GENERAL REFERENCE PURPOSES. THESE STATION
NUMBERS ARE COMBINED WITH ALPHA/NUMERICAL
SUBSCRIPTS TO PROVIDE A SHORT-FORM METHOD OF
IDENTIFYING THE VARIOUS AIR TEMPERATURES AND
PRESSURES IN THE GAS PATH.

EXAMPLE : Pt 2
P = PRESSURE
T = TOTAL
2 = STATION 2
   (FAN INLET)

Fig. 4-16 — Engine station locations—JT8D.

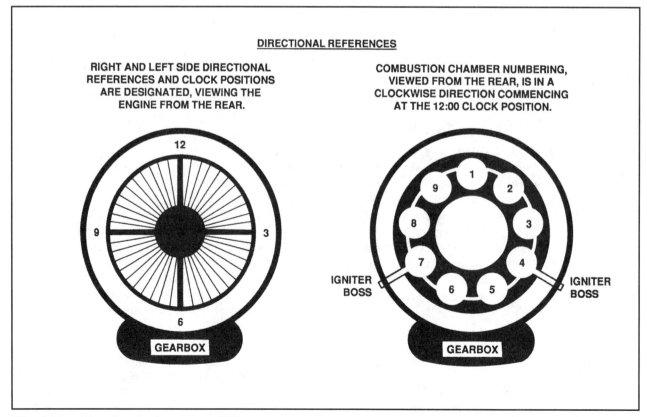

DIRECTIONAL REFERENCES

RIGHT AND LEFT SIDE DIRECTIONAL
REFERENCES AND CLOCK POSITIONS
ARE DESIGNATED, VIEWING THE
ENGINE FROM THE REAR.

COMBUSTION CHAMBER NUMBERING,
VIEWED FROM THE REAR, IS IN A
CLOCKWISE DIRECTION COMMENCING
AT THE 12:00 CLOCK POSITION.

Fig. 4-17 — Directional references—JT8D.

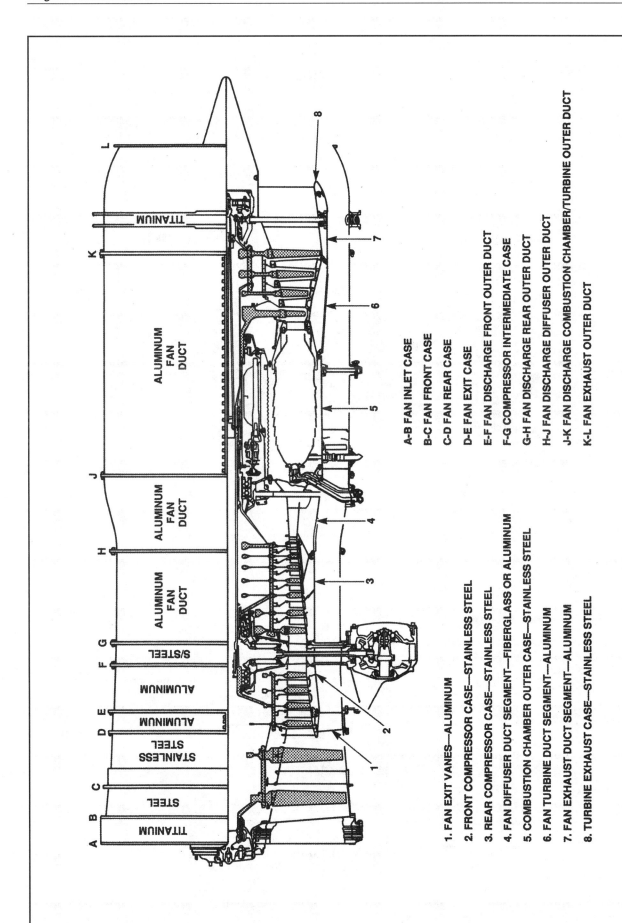

ALUMINUM
FAN
DUCT

ALUMINUM
FAN
DUCT

ALUMINUM
FAN
DUCT

TITANIUM

S/STEEL

ALUMINUM

ALUMINUM

STAINLESS
STEEL

STEEL

TITANIUM

A B C D E F G H J K L

A-B FAN INLET CASE

B-C FAN FRONT CASE

C-D FAN REAR CASE

D-E FAN EXIT CASE

E-F FAN DISCHARGE FRONT OUTER DUCT

F-G COMPRESSOR INTERMEDIATE CASE

G-H FAN DISCHARGE REAR OUTER DUCT

H-J FAN DISCHARGE DIFFUSER OUTER DUCT

J-K FAN DISCHARGE COMBUSTION CHAMBER/TURBINE OUTER DUCT

K-L FAN EXHAUST OUTER DUCT

1. FAN EXIT VANES—ALUMINUM

2. FRONT COMPRESSOR CASE—STAINLESS STEEL

3. REAR COMPRESSOR CASE—STAINLESS STEEL

4. FAN DIFFUSER DUCT SEGMENT—FIBERGLASS OR ALUMINUM

5. COMBUSTION CHAMBER OUTER CASE—STAINLESS STEEL

6. FAN TURBINE DUCT SEGMENT—ALUMINUM

7. FAN EXHAUST DUCT SEGMENT—ALUMINUM

8. TURBINE EXHAUST CASE—STAINLESS STEEL

Fig. 4-18 — Identification of cases, flanges, and materials—JT8D.

Total weight of the engine is 158 pounds. At 420 rated shaft horsepower, this is equal to a power-to-weight ratio of 2.66:1 or 2.66 shaft horsepower per pound of weight.

3. Compressor Section

The compressor assembly consists of a compressor front support assembly, compressor rotor assembly, compressor case assembly, and compressor diffuser assembly.

The compressor consists of one double and four single axial wheel segments and one centrifugal segment. The compressor blades, both axial and centrifugal, are cast as part of the wheel and cannot be removed individually. If a blade is damaged beyond blend repair limits, the entire wheel segment must be replaced.

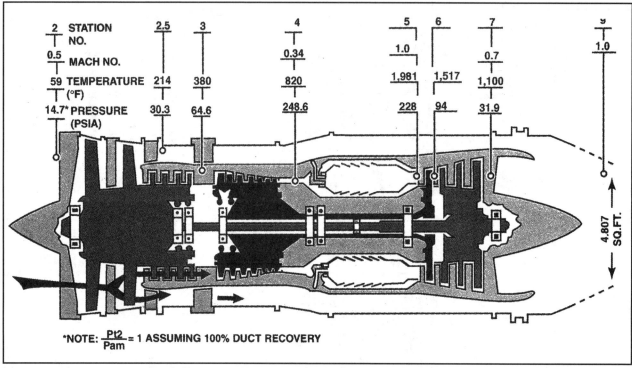

Fig. 4-19 — Typical take-off values—JT8D-17A (average performance).

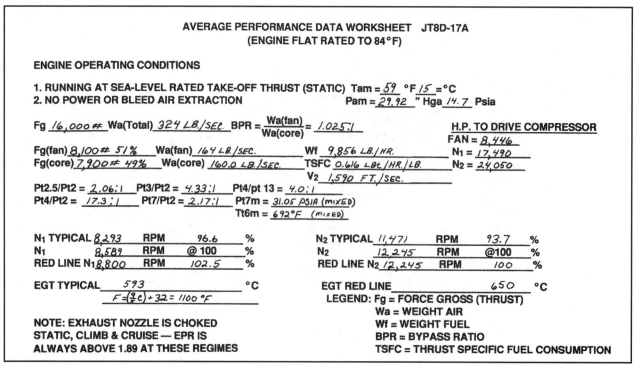

Fig. 4-20 — Engine test-run worksheet.

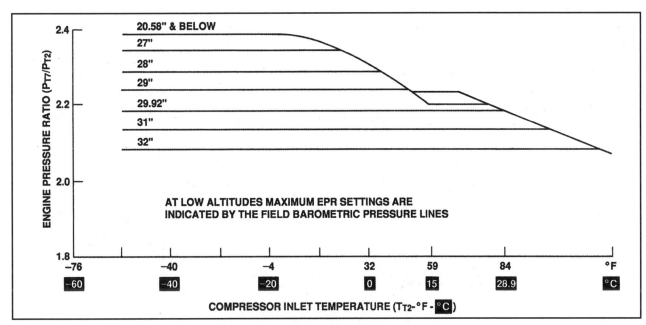

Fig. 4-21 — Take-off EPR setting JT8D-17.

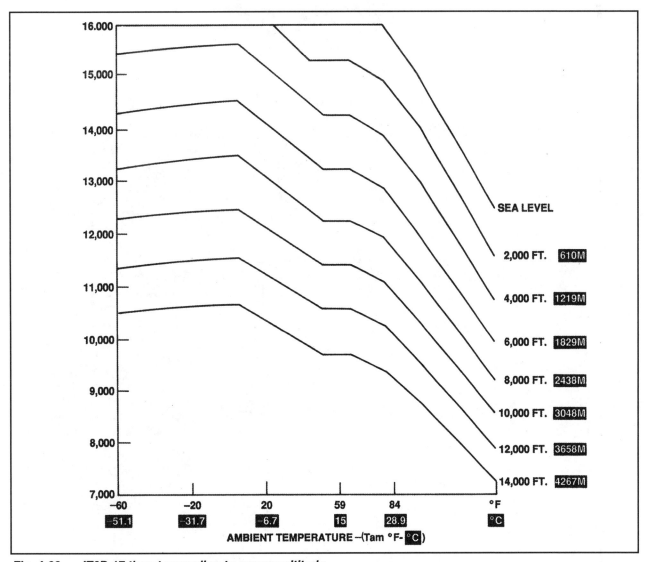

Fig. 4-22 — JT8D-17 thrust according to runway altitude.

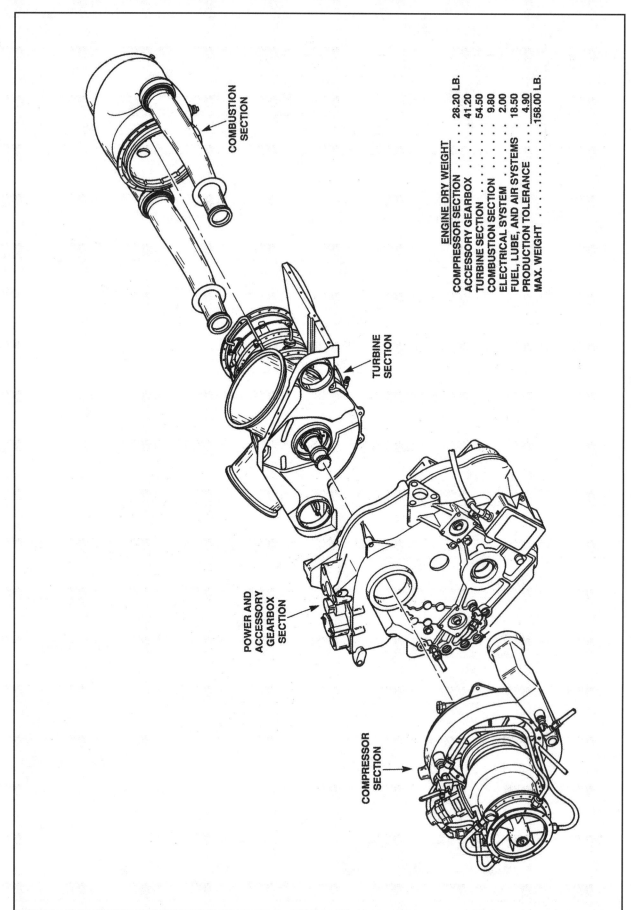

ENGINE DRY WEIGHT

COMPRESSOR SECTION	28.20 LB.
ACCESSORY GEARBOX	41.20
TURBINE SECTION	54.50
COMBUSTION SECTION	9.80
ELECTRICAL SYSTEM	2.00
FUEL, LUBE, AND AIR SYSTEMS	18.50
PRODUCTION TOLERANCE	4.90
MAX. WEIGHT	158.00 LB.

COMBUSTION SECTION

TURBINE SECTION

POWER AND ACCESSORY GEARBOX SECTION

COMPRESSOR SECTION

Fig. 4-23 — Four major engine sections 250-C20B, F, J.

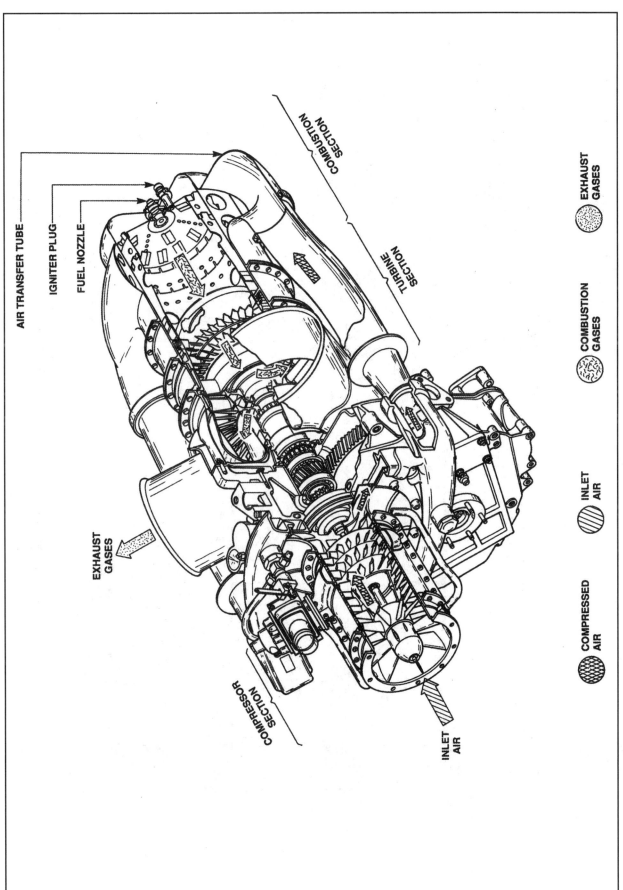

AIR TRANSFER TUBE

IGNITER PLUG

FUEL NOZZLE

COMBUSTION SECTION

TURBINE SECTION

COMPRESSOR SECTION

EXHAUST GASES

INLET AIR

EXHAUST GASES

COMBUSTION GASES

INLET AIR

COMPRESSED AIR

Fig. 4-24 — Gas path of the Allison 250-C20B, F, J.

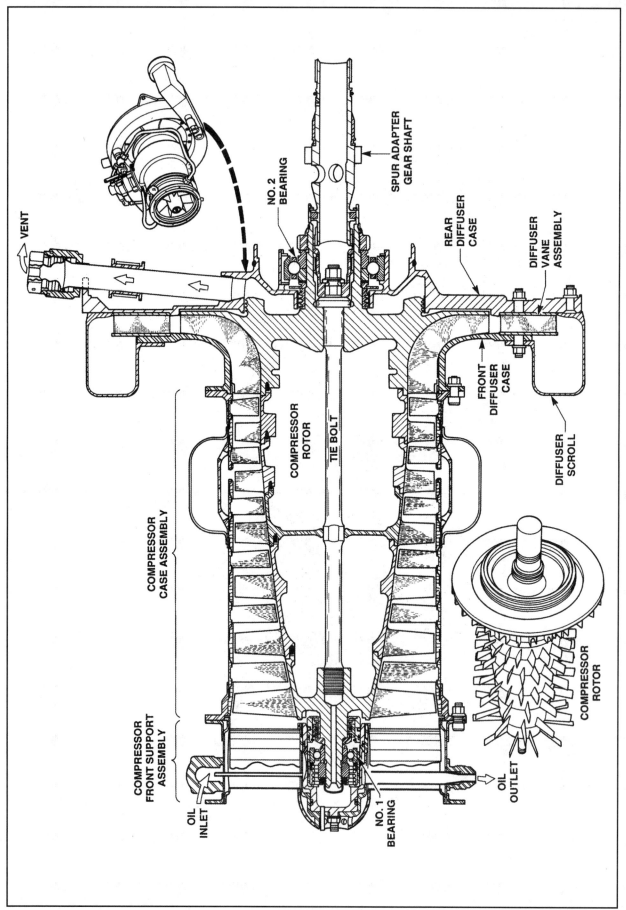

Fig. 4-25 — Compressor section schematic 250-C20B, F, J.

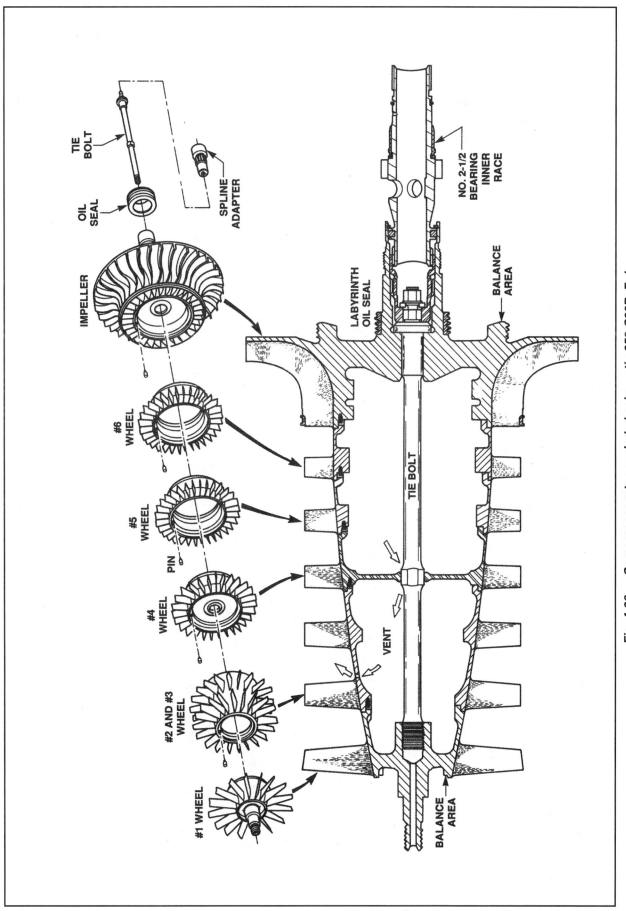

Fig. 4-26 — Compressor rotor exploded schematic 250-C20B, F, J.

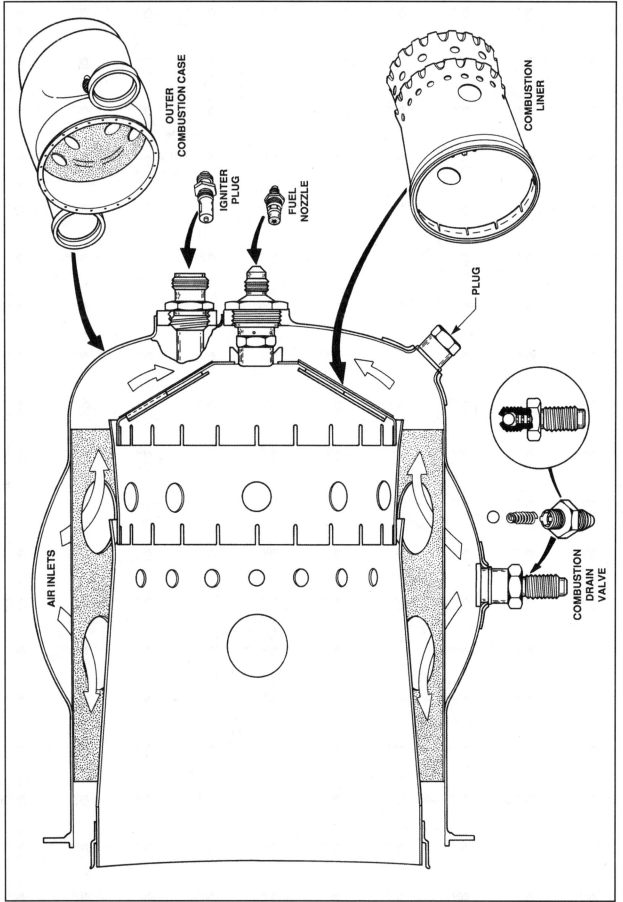

Fig. 4-27 — Combustion section schematic 250-C20B, F, J.

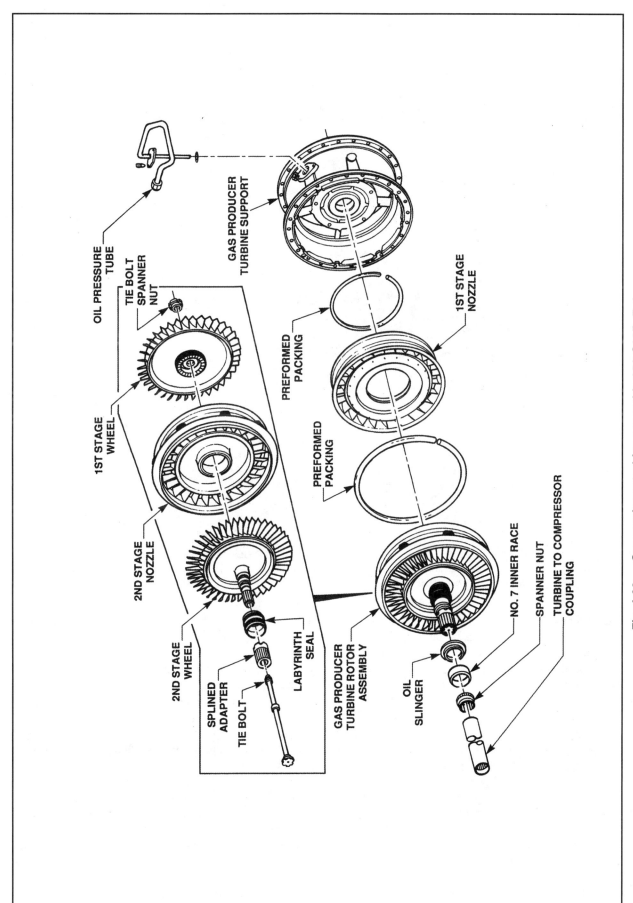

Fig. 4-28 — Gas producer turbine assembly 250-C20B, F, J.

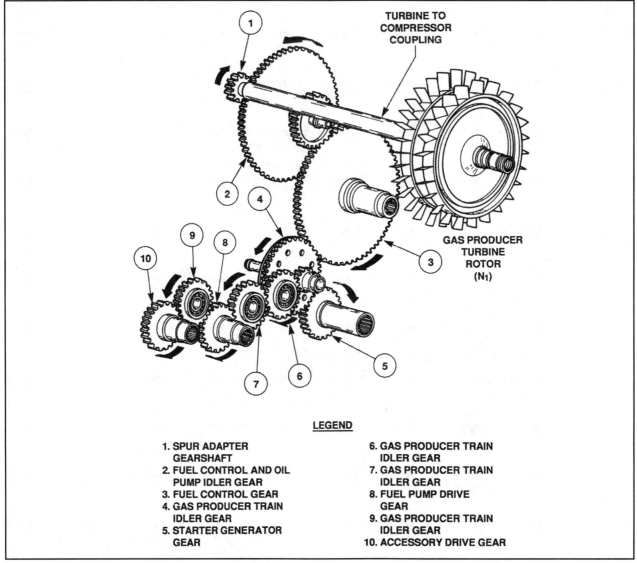

Fig. 4-29 — Gas producer gear train 250-C20B, F, J.

The compressor is a combination axial-centrifugal type with six stages of axial compression and one stage of centrifugal compression. The wheel and blade assemblies and the impeller are made of stainless steel. The compressor rotor front (No. 1) ball bearing is housed in the compressor front support, and the compressor rotor rear (No. 2) ball bearing is housed in the compressor rear diffuser. The No. 2 bearing serves as the thrust bearing for the compressor rotor assembly.

The compressor case assembly consists of an upper and lower case, constructed of stainless steel. The stator vanes are also made of stainless steel and are brazed to stainless steel bands which, in turn, are welded to the compressor case halves. Thermal setting plastic is centrifugally cast to the inside surface of the case halves and vane outer bands. To obtain maximum compressor efficiency, it is necessary to maintain as tight a clearance as possible between the compressor blade tips and the inside surface of the compressor case halves. If the blade tips

contact the plastic, the plastic will be scraped away to the extent that minimum blade tip clearance will be attained without damage to either the case halves or blades.

The compressor case assembly has provisions for mounting a bleed air control valve which bleeds air from the fifth stage of the axial compressor during starting and acceleration.

The compressor diffuser assembly consists of stainless steel front and rear diffuser cases and a magnesium alloy diffuser scroll.

The scroll collects the air and delivers it to two elbows. Each elbow contains stainless steel turning vanes which redirect the airflow from an outward to a rearward direction. Compressor discharge air tubes deliver compressed air from the outlet side of the elbows to the combustor outer case. The diffuser scroll has five ports from which air can be bled, or from which compressor discharge air pressure can be sensed. Two of these ports are customer bleeds, and the remaining ports are utilized by

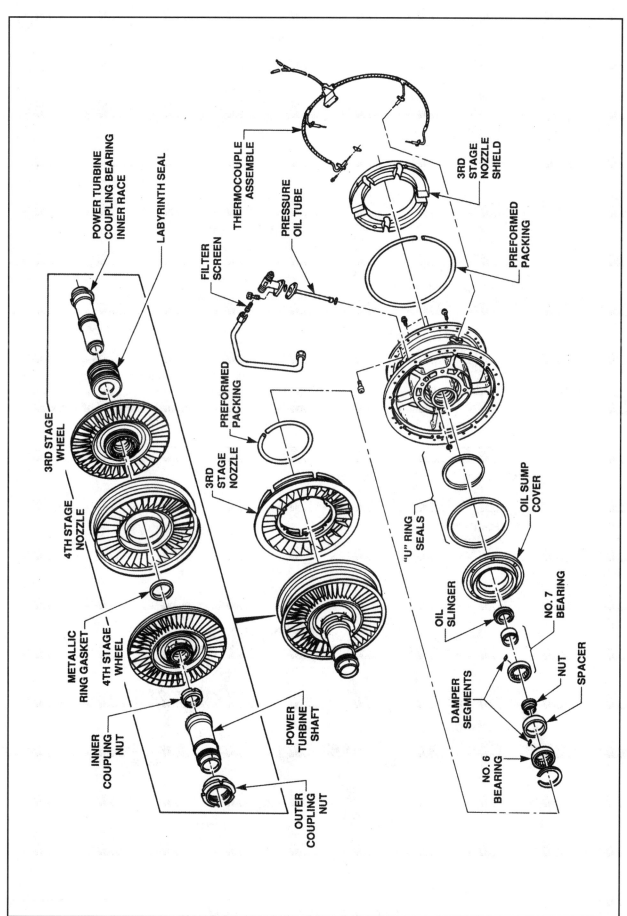

Fig. 4-30 — Power turbine assembly 250-C20B, F, J.

the anti-icing valve, fuel control system pressure sensing, and compressor bleed air control valve pressure sensing.

4. Combustion Section

The combustor assembly is comprised of two compressor discharge transfer air tubes, combustor outer case, and the combustor liner. The combustor outer case is a stainless steel part with tapped bosses for mounting a combustor drain valve, a fuel nozzle, and an igniter plug.

Two combustor drain valve bosses are provided. The combustor drain valve threads into the boss nearest to the 6 o'clock position with the engine installed in the aircraft, and the other boss is plugged.

The fuel nozzle positions and supports the aft end of the combustion liner, and the igniter locates the combustion liner in a circumferential position.

The combustion liner provides for rapid mixing of fuel and air, and it controls the flame length and position so that the flame does not contact any metallic surface. Approximately 25% of the total airflow passes through the liner to the combustion zone, and is referred to as primary air. The remaining 75% is utilized for cooling, and is referred to as secondary air.

5. Gas Producer Turbine

The gas producer turbine (N_1), also called the compressor turbine, is a two-stage unit consisting of Turbines No. 1 and No. 2, with No. 1 located at the rear of the engine and nearest to the combustor.

The function of the N_1 turbine is to drive the compressor and accessory gearbox directly from combustor discharge gases. Turbine blades are of the open-tip, integral type. (Its blades are cast as part of the turbine disk and cannot be removed individually.)

The first and second turbine nozzles are located in front of the first and second turbine wheels. They increase the velocity of exhausting gases and direct the gases at the correct angle onto the turbine rotor blades of their respective stages.

6. Power Turbine

The power turbine (N_2) is a two-stage unit consisting of No. 3 turbine and No. 4 turbine, with No. 4 turbine located nearest the exhaust outlet. The function of the N_2 turbine is to drive the power output gear through a pinion gear coupling. The power turbine rotor receives the gas energy spill-over from the gas producer turbine and converts gas energy into power delivered to the output shaft.

The power output gear can couple from either end to the power output shaft which drives the helicopter transmission. The power turbine blades are of the shrouded tip, integral type.

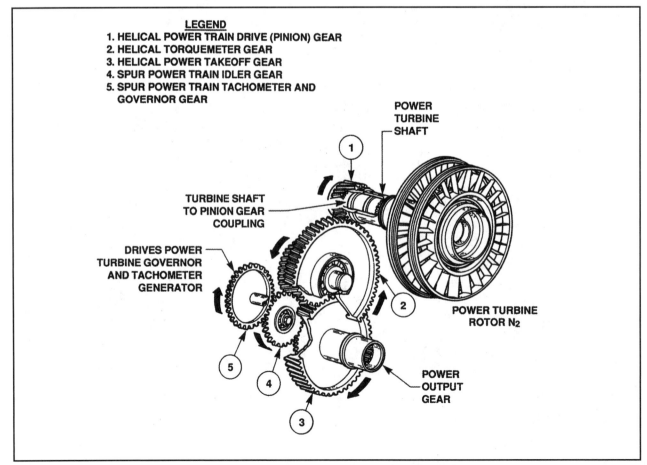

LEGEND
1. HELICAL POWER TRAIN DRIVE (PINION) GEAR
2. HELICAL TORQUEMETER GEAR
3. HELICAL POWER TAKEOFF GEAR
4. SPUR POWER TRAIN IDLER GEAR
5. SPUR POWER TRAIN TACHOMETER AND GOVERNOR GEAR

POWER TURBINE SHAFT

TURBINE SHAFT TO PINION GEAR COUPLING

DRIVES POWER TURBINE GOVERNOR AND TACHOMETER GENERATOR

POWER TURBINE ROTOR N2

POWER OUTPUT GEAR

Fig. 4-31 — Power turbine gear train 250-C20B, F, J.

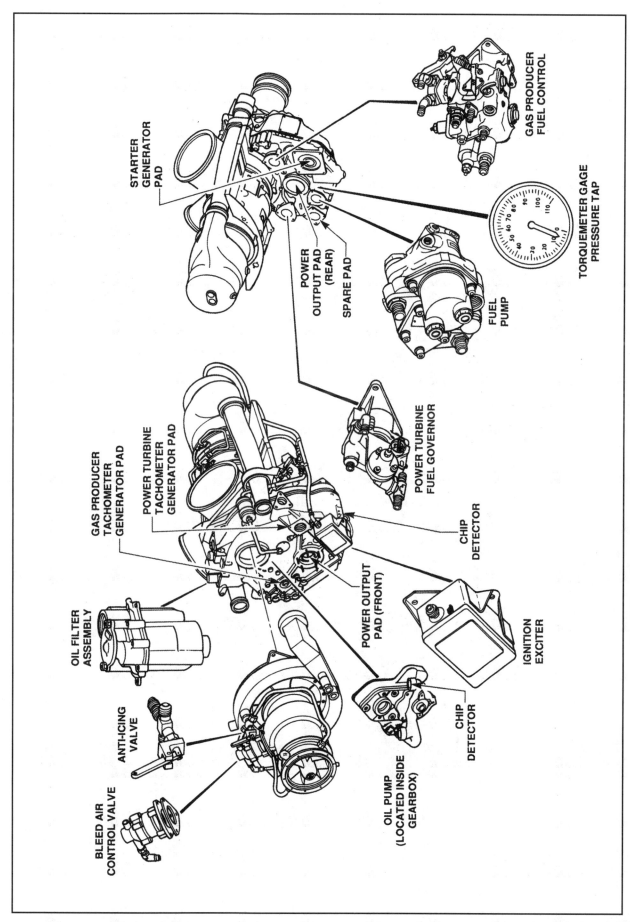

Fig. 4-32 — Component and accessories location, 250-20B, F, J.

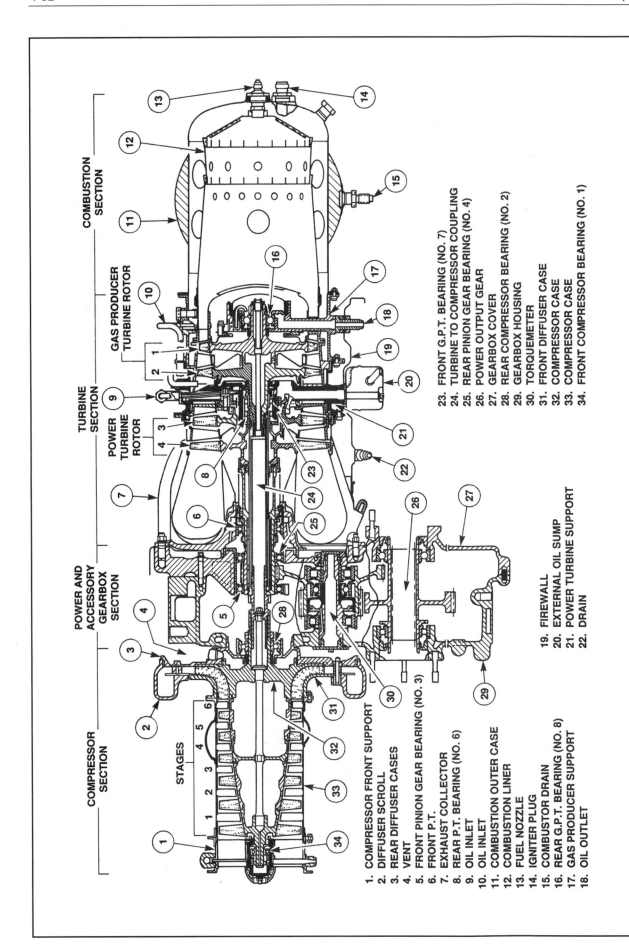

COMPRESSOR SECTION

POWER AND ACCESSORY GEARBOX SECTION

TURBINE SECTION

POWER TURBINE ROTOR

GAS PRODUCER TURBINE ROTOR

COMBUSTION SECTION

STAGES

1. COMPRESSOR FRONT SUPPORT
2. DIFFUSER SCROLL
3. REAR DIFFUSER CASES
4. VENT
5. FRONT PINION GEAR BEARING (NO. 3)
6. FRONT P.T.
7. EXHAUST COLLECTOR
8. REAR P.T. BEARING (NO. 6)
9. OIL INLET
10. OIL INLET
11. COMBUSTION OUTER CASE
12. COMBUSTION LINER
13. FUEL NOZZLE
14. IGNITER PLUG
15. COMBUSTOR DRAIN
16. REAR G.P.T. BEARING (NO. 8)
17. GAS PRODUCER SUPPORT
18. OIL OUTLET

19. FIREWALL
20. EXTERNAL OIL SUMP
21. POWER TURBINE SUPPORT
22. DRAIN

23. FRONT G.P.T. BEARING (NO. 7)
24. TURBINE TO COMPRESSOR COUPLING
25. REAR PINION GEAR BEARING (NO. 4)
26. POWER OUTPUT GEAR
27. GEARBOX COVER
28. REAR COMPRESSOR BEARING (NO. 2)
29. GEARBOX HOUSING
30. TORQUEMETER
31. FRONT DIFFUSER CASE
32. COMPRESSOR CASE
33. COMPRESSOR CASE
34. FRONT COMPRESSOR BEARING (NO. 1)

Fig. 4-33 — Cutaway view including bearing locations 250-C20B, F, J.

PERFORMANCE RATINGS—STANDARD, STATIC SEA LEVEL CONDITIONS

MODEL 250-C20 B, F, J RATINGS	OUTPUT SHP (MIN.)	N_1 GAS PRODUCER RPM (EST.)	OUTPUT SHAFT RPM	POWER TURBINE RPM	S.F.C. LB/HR/SHP (MAX)	F.F. FUEL FLOW LBS/HR (MAX)	RAM POWER RATING AT OUTPUT SHAFT TORQUE FT-LBS (MAX)	RAM POWER RATING AT OUTPUT SHAFT SHP (MAX)	T.O.T. MEASURED RATED GAS TEMPERATURE °F	T.O.T. MEASURED RATED GAS TEMPERATURE °C	NET JET THRUST LBS. (MIN.)
TAKEOFF (5 MIN.) *30-MINUTE POWER	420	52,000 102%	6,016 100%	33,290 100%	0.630	265	367	420.4	1460	793	40
MAX. CONTINUOUS	405	51,490 101%	6,016 100%	33,290 100%	0.633	256	336	385	1430	777	39
MAX. CRUISE	366	50,200 98.5%	6,016 100%	33,290 100%	0.645	236	302	346	1358	736	36
CRUISE A(90%)	331	49,180 96.5%	6,016 100%	33,290 100%	0.661	218	302	346	1301	705	33
CRUISE B(75%)	280	47,900 94%	6,016 100%	33,290 100%	0.698	195	302	346	1245	674	30
GROUND IDLE	45 MAX.	33,000 64.8%	4500-75% TO 6300-105%	24,968-75% TO 34,950-105%	----	70	---	----	800 ±100	427 ±38	10
FLIGHT AUTOROTATION	0	33,000 64.8%	5900-98% TO 6480-106%	32,725-98% TO 35,280-106%	----	70	---	----	775 ±100	413 ±38	10

*THIS RATING IS APPLICABLE ONLY DURING ONE-ENGINE-OUT OPERATION OF MULTI-ENGINE AIRCRAFT

100% N_1 = 50,970 RPM
100% N_2 = 33,290 RPM
T.O.T. = GAS PRODUCER TURBINE OUTLET TEMPERATURE
F.F. = FUEL FLOW
S.H.P. = SHAFT HORSEPOWER
S.F.C. = SPECIFIC FUEL CONSUMPTION

$$S.F.C. = \frac{F.F.}{S.H.P.} = \text{THUS, TAKEOFF S.F.C.} = \frac{265\ \text{LBS./HR}}{420\ \text{S.H.P.}} = 0.630\ \text{LBS./HR./S.H.P.}$$

$$S.H.P. = \frac{\text{TORQUE} \times N_2 \times 0.18071}{5252} = \frac{367 \times 6016}{5252}$$ WHERE TORQUE IS IN FT. LBS. & N_2 IS POWER TURBINE RPM.

$$\text{THUS TAKEOFF RAM POWER RATING S.H.P.} = \frac{367 \times 6016}{5252} = 420.4$$

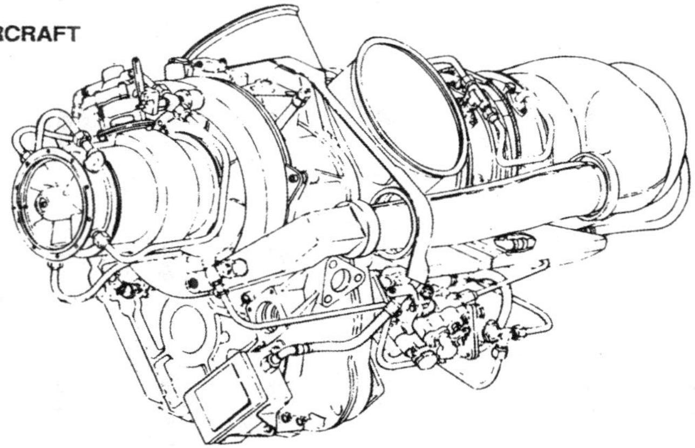

Fig. 4-34 — Performance Allison 250 Models 20B, F, J.

The power turbine is a "free turbine" since it is free to rotate at a different speed than the gas producer turbine. This design has several advantages, which are as follows:

a. Added operational flexibility in that there is an independent selection of speeds between the N_1 and N_2 rotors.

b. Improved overall engine performance because each turbine can be operated at a point of maximum efficiency for a given power requirement.

c. Ease of starting in that the starter rotates only the N_1 rotor during the start cycle.

The power turbine is supported for thrust loads by the No. 5 main ball bearing at the front and the No. 6 roller bearing at the rear, which absorbs only radial loads.

The third and fourth turbine nozzles are located in front of the power turbine wheels to accelerate and direct gases onto the turbine blades.

7. Power and Accessory Gearbox

The combined power and accessory gearbox is the primary structural member of the engine because it provides mounting and support for the compressor and turbine assemblies. The accessory gearbox contains most of the lubrication system components and incorporates two separate gear trains. The power turbine gear train reduces power turbine speed from 33,290 RPM to 6,016 RPM. Therefore, the gear reduction ratio is 5.53 to 1. The power turbine gear train also incorporates the torquemeter assembly and drives the power turbine tachometer generator and the power turbine governor. The gas producer gear train drives the oil pump, the fuel pump, gas producer fuel control, the gas producer tachometer generator, and the starter generator. During starting, the starter-generator rotates the engine through the gas producer gear train.

The gearbox housing and cover are magnesium-alloy castings. They house the bearings used to support the power turbine and gas producer gear trains.

The oil pump assembly, which incorporates a single pressure element and four scavenge elements, is mounted partially within the gearbox and on the housing. An oil filter is mounted on, and extends into, the top of the accessory gearbox housing.

There are two indicating type chip detectors. One is located at the bottom of the accessory gearbox and the other is at the engine oil outlet of the gearbox.

Other non-driven accessories shown are the anti-surge bleed air control valve, anti-icing valve, and ignition unit.

8. Engine Bearings And Lubrication System

a. Main Bearing Numbering

The main bearings are numbered 1 through 8 in a front to rear direction. The compressor rotor assembly is supported by the No. 1 and No. 2 main bearings. The helical power train drive (pinion) gear is supported by the No. 3

and No. 4 main bearings. Power turbine support bearings are numbered No. 5 and No. 6, and the gas producer turbine rotors are supported by the No. 7 and No. 8 main bearings.

b. Lubrication Of Bearings

The lubrication system is a circulating dry sump type with an external oil tank and oil cooler, both of which are mounted and furnished by the helicopter manufacturer.

Oil jet lubrication is provided to all compressor, gas producer turbine, and power turbine rotor bearings and to bearings and gear meshes of the power turbine gear train, with the exception of the power output shaft bearings. All other gears and bearings are lubricated by oil mist.

9. Additional Information

Performance figures are given in Figure 4-34.

C. Familiarization With The Pratt & Whitney PT6 Turboprop Engine.

The PT6 Turboprop engine is produced by the Pratt & Whitney Company of Canada, a division of United Technologies Corporation of Hartford, Connecticut.

It is the most widely used corporate/commuter sized turboprop engine in the world. There are several different models of the PT6, including some turboshaft models. All PT6 models have the same basic shape, with a circular air inlet, and dual exhaust parts located on the sides of the engine. The output drive shaft and main accessory gearbox are located at the front and back. This engine is designed to be used in either a puller or pusher configuration. Small models of the PT6 are in the 500 shaft horsepower class and weigh approximately 300 pounds. Large models are in the 1,800 shaft horsepower class and weigh approximately 600 pounds. Only the PT6-34 engine for fixed-wing aircraft will be discussed here.

The PT6-34 is a two-shaft turboprop with a combination three-stage axial and single-stage centrifugal compressor. It has an annular reverse flow combustor, a single-stage high-pressure turbine, called the Gas Producer Turbine (N_1), and a single-stage low-pressure turbine called the Power Turbine (N_2).

The PT6-34 has a compression ratio of 7.0 to 1, a mass airflow of 6.5 pounds/second, and 823 shaft horsepower at 38,100 RPM, 101.5% (N_1).

1. Gas Path Of The PT6 And Engine Station Numbering

Air flows along the engine's gas path as follows:

Station 1 — Air enters the flight inlet (not shown) and is directed radially inward through a screened opening which encircles the entrance of the compressor. The screen is located towards the rear of the engine, just forward of the accessory gearbox which is the rearmost section of the engine.

Station 2 — Air flows into a curved compressor inlet which angles the air 90° forward into the compressor first stage.

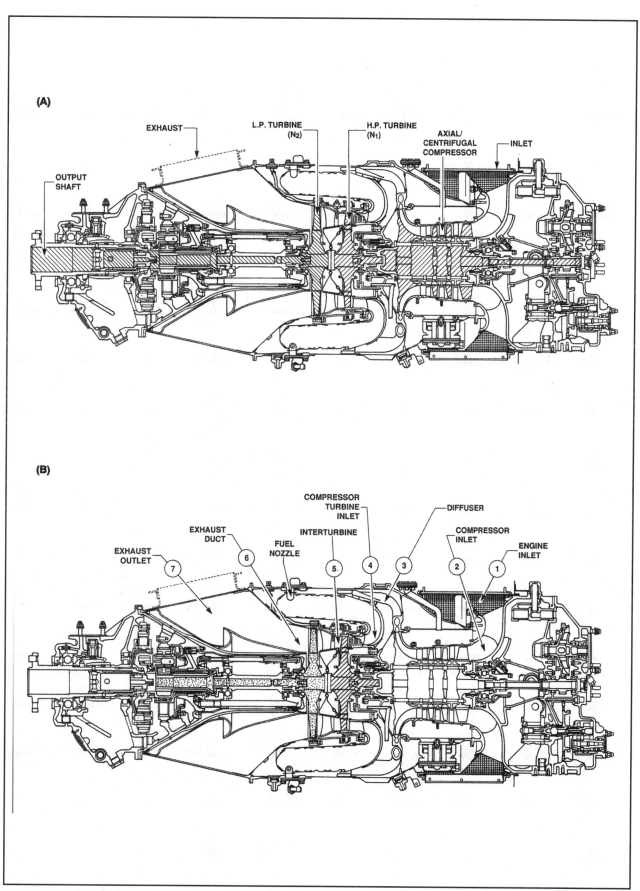

Fig. 4-35A — PT6A-34 Engine—Cross sectional view.
Fig. 4-36B — Engine stations along the gas path.

Station 3 — Air then moves axially through the first three stages of compression and then radially out of the last (ccntrifugal) stage into a diffuser (stations). From there, it continues to move forward between the combustion liner and the combustor outer case to the area of the fuel nozzle. At the forward end of the combustion liner, approximately one-fourth of the air enters the flame zone and the remainder seeps through and surrounds the liner, forming a cooling air blanket. The total airflow is now reversed in direction.

Stations 4 and 5 — Air flow again reverses and passes through the single-stage Gas Producer Turbine and the single-stage Power Turbine.

Stations 6 and 7 — Finally the gases exit the turbines and flow radially outward from a dual exhaust duct located just in front of the power reduction section.

2. Five Major Engine Sections

The five major engine sections are as follows:

a. The Propeller Reduction Gearbox Section, consisting of a planetary reduction gearbox of 15 to 1. The output flange to the propeller rotates at 2,200 RPM when the power turbine is operating at 100% speed of 33,000 RPM. Mounting pads are provided for accessories on the outer case.

b. The Turbine and Exhaust Section, consisting of a two-shaft, two-stage turbine assembly, and a dual exhaust outlet.

c. The Combustor Section, consisting of an outer casing and an annular reverse-flow, single basket-type liner. The liner contains fourteen fuel nozzle openings and two igniter plug openings.

d. The Compressor Section, consisting of an air inlet screen, a compressor inlet case, a combination axial-centrifugal compressor, and a diffuser case.

e. The Accessory Gearbox Section, consisting of a reduction gear train and mounting pads for the various engine components and accessories.

3. Compressor Section

The compressor section is made up of the Inlet Case, the Compressor Rotor and Stator Assembly, and the Diffuser.

The compressor inlet case consists of a circular aluminum casting, the front of which forms a plenum chamber for the passage of compressor inlet air. The rear portion forms the front of a hollow compartment which is used as an integral oil tank. A large area, circular wire mesh screen is located around the air inlet to preclude foreign object ingestion by the compressor.

The compressor rotor and stator assembly consists of three axial rotor stages, three inter stage spacers, three stators, and a single-stage centrifugal impeller and diffuser. The first stage blades are made of titanium and the remainder are made of stainless steel. The impeller is made of aluminum alloy.

The wide chord of the first stage blades provides increased impact tolerance. All blades are fitted to the disk by dovetail-shaped roots. The vanes are all made of stainless steel.

The compressor assembly is a stacked unit, held together by six, long tie bolts.

The No. 1 main ball bearing and its labyrinth sealing are contained within the inlet case centerbore. This bearing supports the front of the compressor rotor for both axial and radial loads. It is directly lubricated by an oil jet and this oil is prevented from leaking into the gas path by the labyrinth sealing.

The No. 2 main roller bearing supports the rear of the compressor for radial loads. It is located in the centerbore of the rear gas generator case. This bearing is directly lubricated by an oil jet and is protected from leaking oil into the gas path by labyrinth sealing.

The compressor delivers pressurized air radially into the diffuser which is located within the rear portion of the gas generator case. Here the static pressure makes its final increase as air diffuses to the correct pressure and velocity for combustion. The diffuser contains straightening vanes to turn the air back to an axial direction into the combustor.

4. Combustor Section

The front of the gas generator case forms the outer housing of the combustion section. The gas generator case consists of two stainless steel sections fabricated into a single structure. The case is circular and contains fourteen mounting bosses for the fuel nozzles. It also contains two bosses for mounting of the igniter plugs. Two different types are used in the PT6 for initiation of combustion. Ignition systems are explained in Chapter XI.

The combustion liner is an annular reverse flow type and is constructed of rolled sheet stainless steel.

The combustion section receives the total airflow discharged by the diffuser. The air is channeled first to the forward (domed) end of the liner where the primary air passages are formed. Approximately 25% of the air is directed into the liner around the fuel nozzle openings. The remaining 75% of the total airflow acts as a cooling air blanket. The outside of the liner is cooled directly and the louvers provide a film cooling airflow inside of the liner.

5. Gas Producer Turbine

The gas producer turbine (N_1), also called the compressor turbine, is a single-stage unit, consisting of No. 1 turbine nozzle and No. 1 turbine rotor. The turbine nozzle is made up of fourteen cast nickel alloy, air-cooled vanes. The vane assembly forms a calibrated, effective flow area for combustion gases to accelerate through and discharge into the turbine blades at the correct angle. Refer to Figure 4-40.

The N_1 turbine is fitted with individually removable blades. Each blade has a fir tree root which attaches it to the turbine disk and a rivet which retains the blade in its serrated slot.

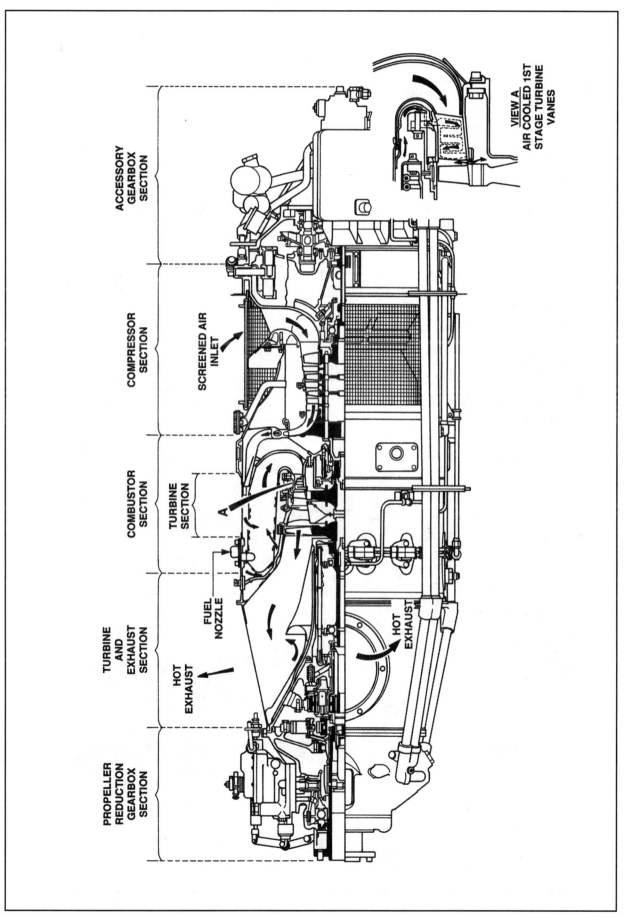

Fig. 4-36 —Five major sections.

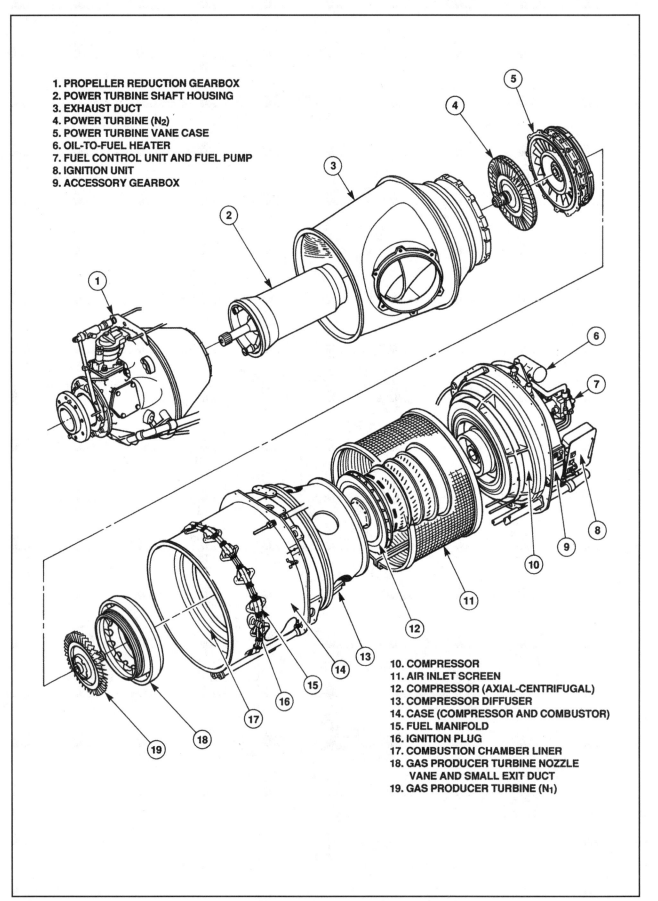

1. PROPELLER REDUCTION GEARBOX
2. POWER TURBINE SHAFT HOUSING
3. EXHAUST DUCT
4. POWER TURBINE (N_2)
5. POWER TURBINE VANE CASE
6. OIL-TO-FUEL HEATER
7. FUEL CONTROL UNIT AND FUEL PUMP
8. IGNITION UNIT
9. ACCESSORY GEARBOX

10. COMPRESSOR
11. AIR INLET SCREEN
12. COMPRESSOR (AXIAL-CENTRIFUGAL)
13. COMPRESSOR DIFFUSER
14. CASE (COMPRESSOR AND COMBUSTOR)
15. FUEL MANIFOLD
16. IGNITION PLUG
17. COMBUSTION CHAMBER LINER
18. GAS PRODUCER TURBINE NOZZLE
    VANE AND SMALL EXIT DUCT
19. GAS PRODUCER TURBINE (N_1)

Fig. 4-37 — Components of major sections.

The blades are made of cast nickel alloy and are of the open-tip variety. They are designed with a reduced thickness at the tips, called squeeler tips, to provide minimum rubbing on the shroud ring if contact occurs.

The N_1 turbine is supported by the No. 2 bearing which also supports the rear of the compressor. The function of the N_1 turbine is to drive the compressor and accessory gearbox directly from combustor discharge gases.

6. Power Turbine

The power turbine (N_2) is a single-stage unit, consisting of the No. 2 turbine nozzle and No. 2 turbine rotor. It is located toward the front of the engine, directly in front of the gas producer turbine.

The turbine nozzle consists of 19 uncooled, cast steel vanes which direct the flow of gases from the N_1 turbine into the power turbine at the most effective angle.

The power turbine (N_2) is a free turbine, meaning that it has an independent operating speed from the compressor turbine (N_1). The advantages of the free turbine can be found in the power turbine information of the Allison-250 turboshaft engine earlier in this chapter.

The power turbine is supported forward of the turbine disk by the No. 3 main bearing. It is a roller bearing and supports radial loads. The No. 4 main bearing is a ball

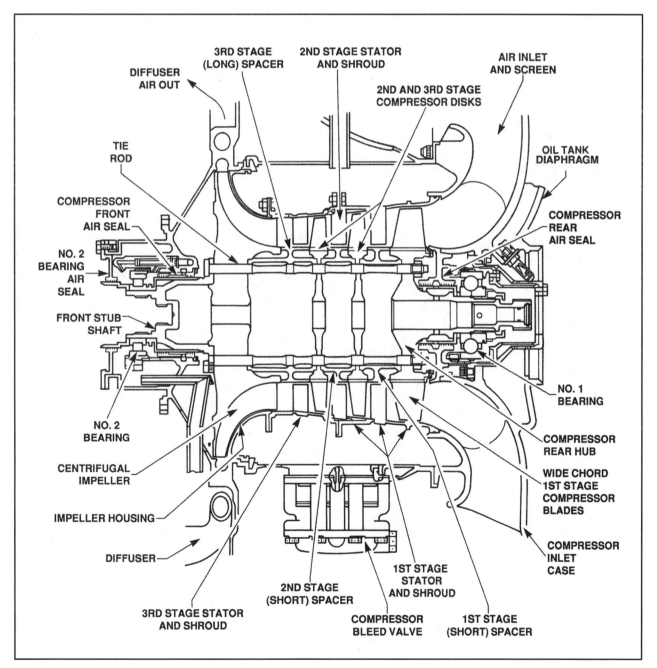

Fig. 4-38 — Compressor section.

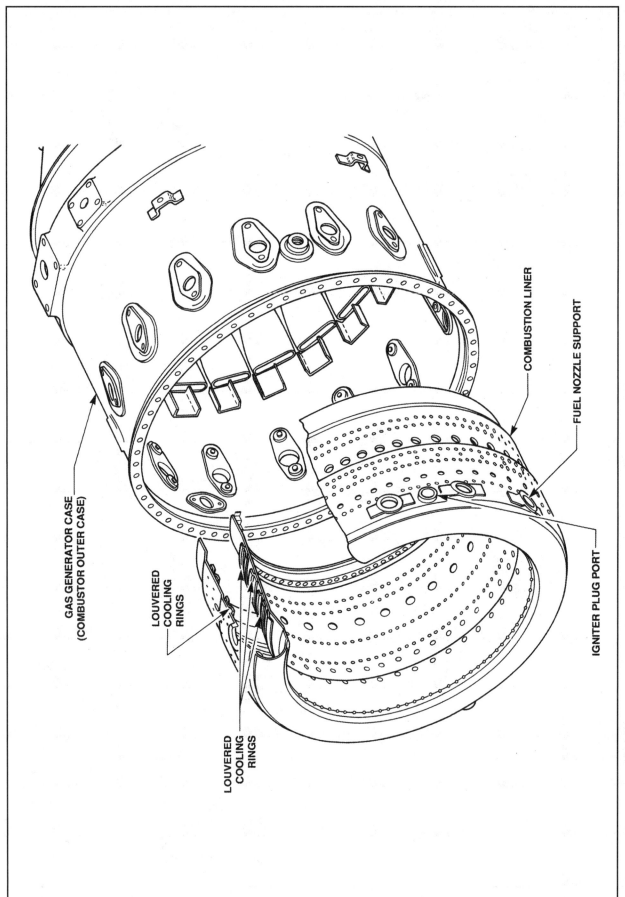

GAS GENERATOR CASE
(COMBUSTOR OUTER CASE)

LOUVERED
COOLING
RINGS

LOUVERED
COOLING
RINGS

COMBUSTION LINER

FUEL NOZZLE SUPPORT

IGNITER PLUG PORT

Fig. 4-39 — Combustor section.

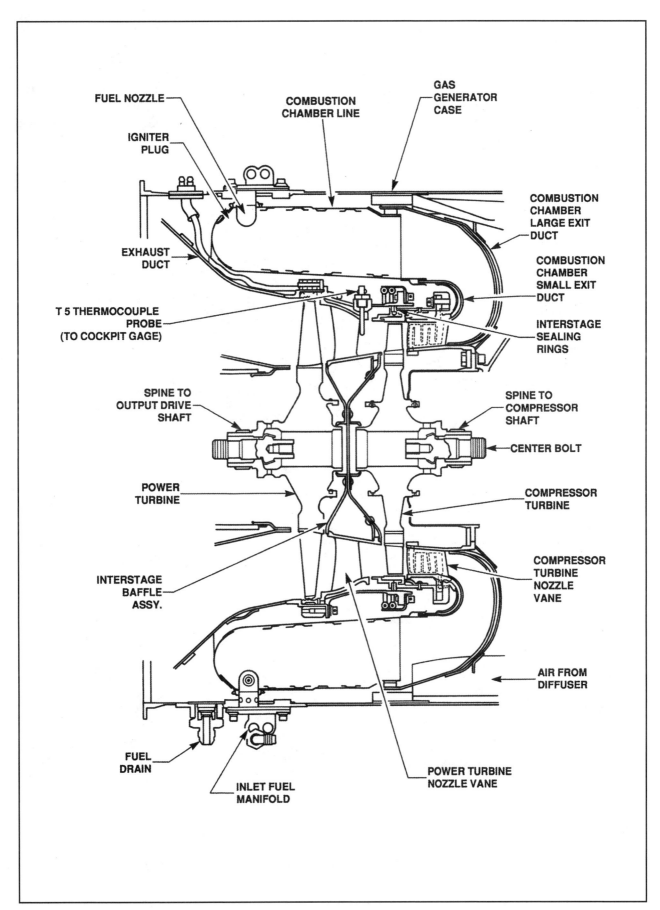

Fig. 4-40 — Combustor and turbine sections.

bearing. It supports the front of the N_2 turbine shaft for both radial and axial loads.

Power turbine blades are made of cast nickel alloy and have fir tree roots similar to the N_1 turbine, but the blade tips are different in that they are shrouded to form a circular support ring. This support ring rides within an outer shroud ring fitted with a double knife-edge seal. This reduces tip leakage and increases turbine efficiency by

extracting the required energy before the gases exit the engine via the exhaust duct.

The function of the power turbine is to receive the gas energy spill-over from the N_1 turbine and convert most of this energy into power delivered to the propeller reduction gearbox. Approximately 95% of the power is delivered to the propeller, and 5% of the hot exhaust power remains to create thrust.

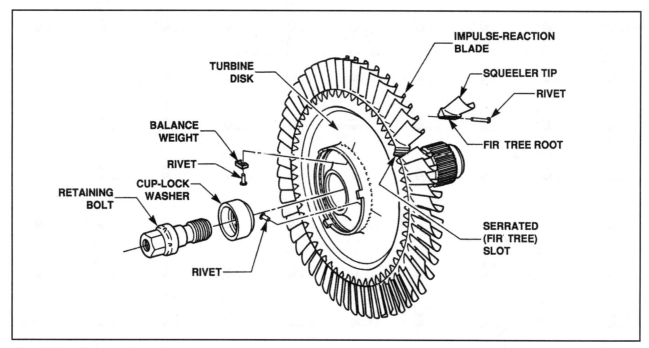

Fig. 4-41 — Gas producer (compressor) turbine.

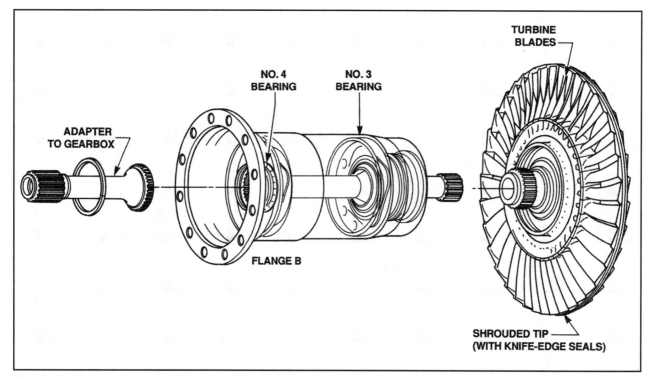

Fig. 4-42 — Power (free) turbine N_2.

7. Exhaust Duct

The exhaust duct is made of heat-resistant sheet stainless steel and provides two outlet ports. The duct is attached to the front flange of the gas generator case and consists of an inner and an outer section. The outer conical section contains the flanged outlet ports and forms the outer gas path. The aircraft tailpipe attaches to these outlet ports and carries the exhaust away from the aircraft in the reverse (aft) direction, producing approximately 82 pounds of jet thrust at takeoff power.

The inner section forms a compartment for the power reduction gearbox rear case.

The insulation blanket shown keeps the high temperature exhaust gases from heating the power turbine shaft which runs through it to connect into the power reduction gearbox.

8. Propeller Reduction Gearbox

The propeller reduction gearbox is located at the front of the engine. It consists of magnesium alloy cases which attach to the front of the gas producer case.

Torque from the power turbine is transmitted into the first-stage planet gear to start the reduction in speed of the propeller shaft. The first-stage planet reduction system is located in the rear of the propeller reduction case. The

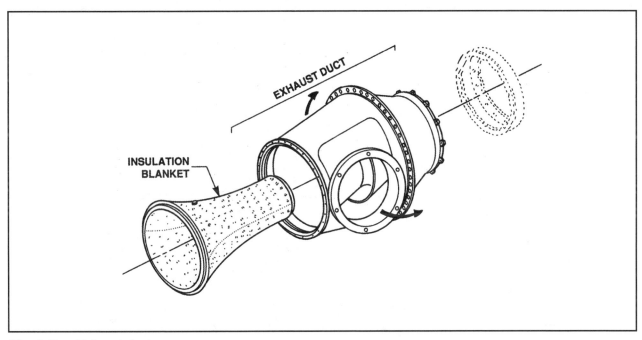

Fig. 4-43 — Exhaust duct.

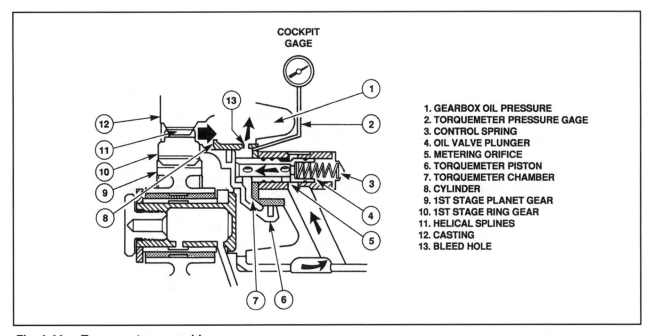

1. GEARBOX OIL PRESSURE
2. TORQUEMETER PRESSURE GAGE
3. CONTROL SPRING
4. OIL VALVE PLUNGER
5. METERING ORIFICE
6. TORQUEMETER PISTON
7. TORQUEMETER CHAMBER
8. CYLINDER
9. 1ST STAGE PLANET GEAR
10. 1ST STAGE RING GEAR
11. HELICAL SPLINES
12. CASTING
13. BLEED HOLE

Fig. 4-44 — Torquemeter assembly.

power turbine shaft adapter splines into this reduction system.

The first-stage planet gear is connected to the second-stage planet gear by a shock absorbing coupling and the second stage planet gear is connected to the propeller shaft. In the second stage, the final reduction takes place, converting, at takeoff power, 33,000 RPM at the power turbine to 2,200 RPM at the propeller shaft.

There are two bearings located within the power reduction gearbox. The rear roller bearing supports loads from the planet gear system and the ball bearing supports the propeller for thrust loads. The bearings located here are

not considered engine main bearings and are not numbered as such. However, engine lubricating oil supplied to the main engine bearings is also routed to the gears, bearings, and torquemeter of the power reduction gearbox.

The torquemeter (Figure 4-44) is located within the power reduction gearbox. It is a hydro-mechanical device connected to the first-stage reduction gear to provide an accurate indication of engine power output. The mechanism consists of a cylinder, piston, and oil metering-type plunger valve. Rotation of the first-stage reduction output drive ring gear is resisted by a helical spline which imparts an axial movement to the first stage ring gear and

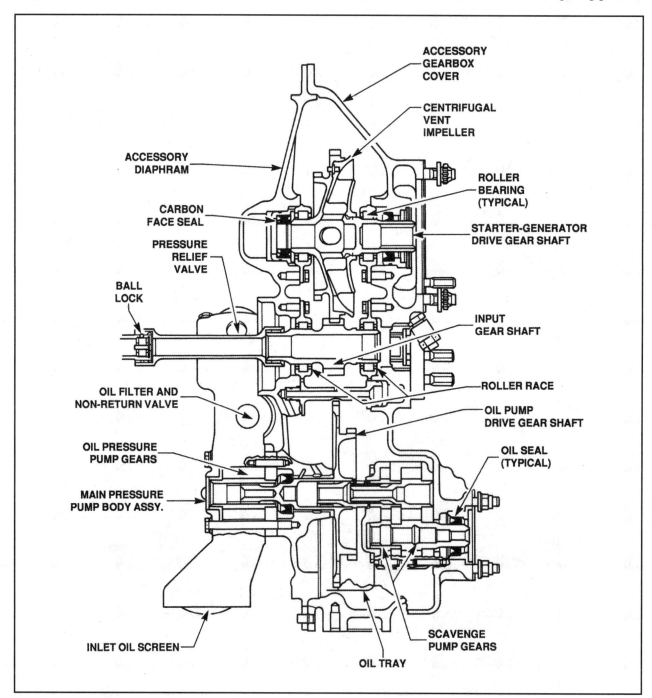

Fig. 4-45 — Accessory gearbox.

to the torquemeter piston. This in turn forces the piston onto the oil valve plunger allowing engine lubricating oil to enter the cylinder. This movement continues until the oil pressure within the torquemeter is equal to torque being applied to the first stage ring gear. A bleed hole is located in the torquemeter cylinder to allow a continuous flow of oil and to bleed pressure off when engine power is reduced.

When engine oil pressure is supplied to the plunger valve, it acts as a variable inlet metering orifice. The bleed hole acts as a fixed calibrated leak. On acceleration, there is more oil supplied than is bleeding away, so pressure builds up in the torquemeter cylinder. This pressure is directed to an electrical transmitter which operates either a cockpit "%" torque gauge or a "psi" torque gauge. When power is reduced, more oil is bled away through the calibrated leak than is entering the system and the cockpit gauge reading diminishes, showing the reduction in engine power.

9. Accessory Gearbox

The Accessory Gearbox consists of two magnesium alloy casings and is attached to the rear of the compressor inlet case. It provides gear reduction and drive pads for the following: starter/generator, fuel pump/fuel control unit, tachometer generator, vacuum pump, propeller reduction section scavenge pump, and two optional mounting pads.

The gearbox housing also contains mounting points for the oil pressure relief valve and the main oil filter.

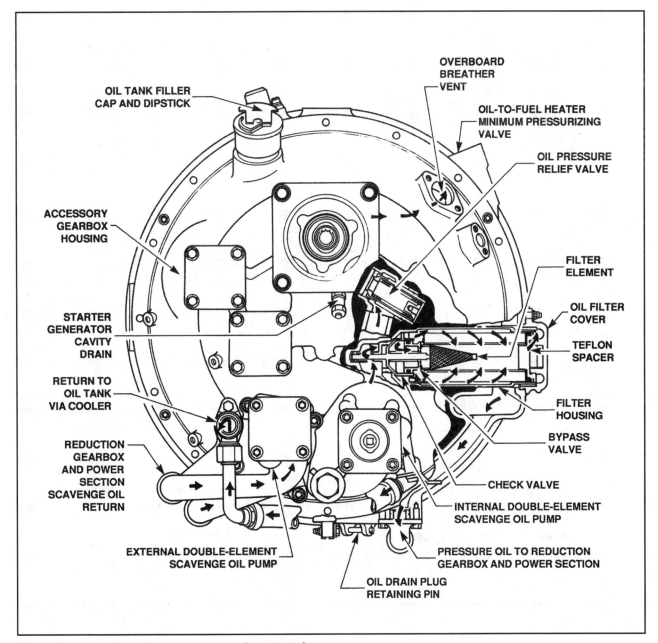

Fig. 4-46 — Location of components and accessories.

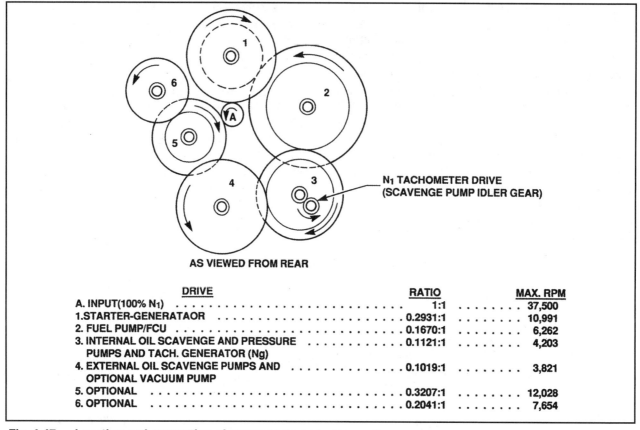

AS VIEWED FROM REAR

DRIVE	RATIO	MAX. RPM
A. INPUT(100% N1)	1:1	37,500
1.STARTER-GENERATAOR	0.2931:1	10,991
2. FUEL PUMP/FCU	0.1670:1	6,262
3. INTERNAL OIL SCAVENGE AND PRESSURE PUMPS AND TACH. GENERATOR (Ng)	0.1121:1	4,203
4. EXTERNAL OIL SCAVENGE PUMPS AND OPTIONAL VACUUM PUMP	0.1019:1	3,821
5. OPTIONAL	0.3207:1	12,028
6. OPTIONAL	0.2041:1	7,654

Fig. 4-47 — Location and gear ratios of components and accessories.

The gearbox housing contains a pressure oil pump for the entire engine lubricating system, a scavenge pump for the accessory case sump, an impeller type air-oil separator and vent to the atmosphere, and an oil tray, designed to prevent oil foaming during engine operation. The tray inhibits splashing of scavenged oil which drains down to the sump.

The forward bulkhead of the accessory gearbox, called the accessory diaphragm, forms one of the walls of the integral dry sump oil tank compartment. The other oil-tight wall is formed by the compressor inlet case.

10. Additional Information
a. Bearing locations are shown in Figure 4-48.
b. Engine leading particulars are shown in Figures 4-49A and B.
c. The PT6 lubrication system is explained in Chapter VI and the fuel system in Chapter VII.

D. Familiarization With The GE/Snecma CFM56 Turbofan Engine (Figure 4-50)
The CFM56 turbofan engine is manufactured by a multi-national company which combines General Electric of the U.S. and Snecma of France. A number of different models have been made since the engine was introduced in 1978, but this familiarization section will concentrate on the -7B model used in the Boeing 737-600 through 737-900.

The CFM56-7B is available in several different thrust ratings, ranging from 19,500 pounds to 27,300 pounds. The engine is a two spool, high bypass turbofan. It has a single stage fan plus four additional stages making up the low pressure compressor. It has a nine stage high pressure compressor. The combustion chamber is an annular type, available as either a single or dual annular design. The high pressure turbine is a single stage and the low pressure turbine has four stages. The engine weighs in at 5300 pounds, is 99 inches in length, 72 inches high, and 83 inches wide.

The CFM56-7B is a modular concept design engine. It has 17 different modules that are enclosed within three major modules and an accessory drive module. The four modules, as shown in Figure 4-51, are:
• The Fan Major Module.
• The Core Engine Major Module.
• The Low Pressure Turbine Major Module.
• The Accessory Drive Module.

1. Fan Major Module
The fan major module is at the front of the engine downstream from the air inlet cowl. The fan major module is made up of four modules, which are the fan and booster module, the number 1 and 2 bearing support module, the fan frame module, and the inlet gearbox and number 3 bearing module. The main purposes of the fan major module are:

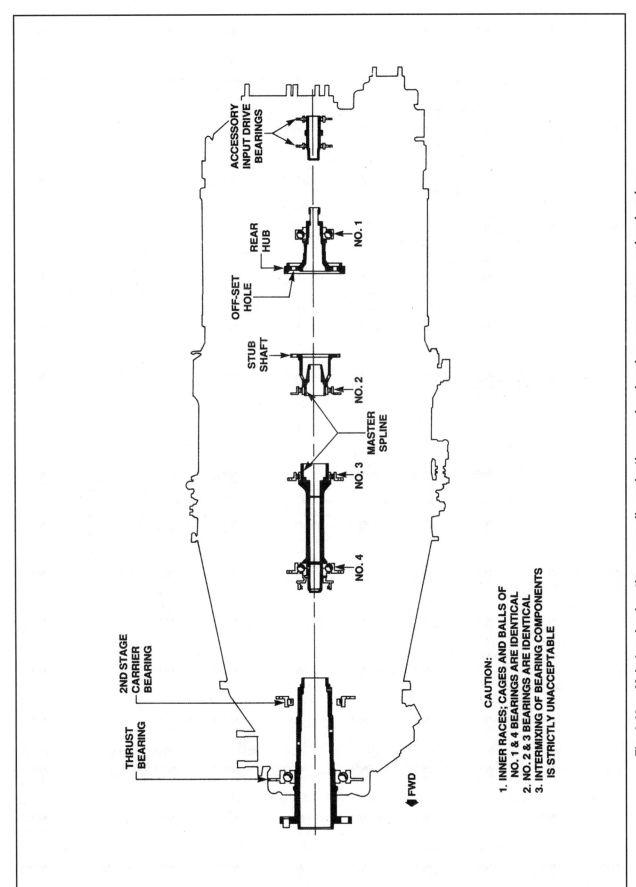

Fig. 4-48 — Main bearing locations, propeller reduction gearbox bearings, accessory gearbox bearings.

(A)

RATING PT6A-34/-34B/-34G	ESHP	SHP	PROP. RPM	JET THRUST LBS.	FUEL CONSUMPTION (LB./ESHP/HR) AT 15°C (59°F)
TAKEOFF	823	790*	2200	82	0.595
MAX CONTINUOUS/ ENROUTE EMERG.	823	790	2200	82	0.595
MAX CLIMB	769	736	2200	82	0.604
MAX CRUISE	700	667	2200	82	0.604

NOTE: 1. *AVAILABLE TO +30°C (+87°F) AMBIENT
2. H.P. (JET) = JET THRUST ÷ 2.5 = 33
3. CORRESPONDING ROTOR SPEEDS: GAS GENERATOR—38,100 RPM MAX.
POWER TURBINE—33,000 RPM

ENGINE TYPE . . . . .FREE TURBINE
TYPE OF COMBUSTION CHAMBER . . . . ANNULAR REVERSE FLOW
COMPRESSOR RATIO 7.0.:1
PROPELLER SHAFT ROTATION (LOOKING FORWARD) . . . . CLOCKWISE
PROPELLER SHAFT CONFIGURATION . . . . .FLANGED
PROPELLER SHAFT GEAR RATIO 0.0668:1
ENGINE DIAMETER, BASIC AT ROOM TEMPERATURE . . . . 19 INCHES
ENGINE LENGTH, BASIC AT ROOM TEMPERATURE . . . . 62 INCHES
OIL CONSUMPTION, MAXIMUM AVERAGE . . . . 0.2 LB/HR.
DRY WEIGHT (APPROXIMATELY) . . . . 292 LBS.

(B)

OPERATING CONDITIONS			PT6A-34/-34B/-34G			LIMITS				
POWER SETTING	TEMP. AVAILABLE TO	MAX. ESHP	N_1(100 = 37500 RPM) % RPM		N_2 (100 = 2200 RPM) % RPM		MAXIMUM OBSERVED ITT(T_{t5})	MAXIMUM TORQUE FT. LB. PSI	NORMAL OIL PRESSURE (PSIG)	OIL TEMPERATURE RANGE
TAKEOFF AND MAX. CONTINUOUS, ENROUTE EMERGENCY	30.6°C (87°F)	823	101.5	38,100	100	2200	790°C	1970　64.5	85 TO 105	+10° TO +99°C (+50° TO +210°F)
MAX. CLIMB	28.3°C (83°F)	769	101.5	38,100	100	2200	765°C	1840　60.2	85 TO 105	+10° TO +99°C (+50° TO +210°F)
MAX. CRUISE	19.4°C (67°F)	700	101.5	38,100	100	2200	740°C	1840　60.2	85 TO 105	0° TO +99°C (+32° TO +210°F)
GROUND IDLE			52.5	19,750 (TYPICAL)			685°C		40 (MIN)	-40° TO -99° (-40° TO +210°F)
STARTING							1090°C			-40° (MIN.)
MOMENTARY ACCELERATION			102.6	38,500	110	2420	850°C	2100　68.4	85 TO 105	0° TO 99°C (+32° TO +210°F)
MAX. REVERSE		750	101.5	38,100	95(± 1%)	2100	790°C	1970　64.5	85 TO 105	0° TO 99°C (+32° TO +210°F)

Fig. 4-49A — PT6A-34 Engine leading particulars.
Fig. 4-49B — Operating conditions and limits.

- To provide approximately 80% of the engine thrust.
- To provide the engine/pylon front attachment.
- To enclose the fan stage and low pressure compressor stages.
- To provide structural rigidity in the front section.
- To provide containment for front section major deterioration and/or damage.
- To provide noise reduction for the fan section.
- To provide attachment for gearboxes and nacelle equipment.
- To provide attachment for the core engine.

a. Fan And Booster (Figure 4-52)

The fan and booster is located at the front of the engine downstream from the air inlet cowl, and consists of:

- A spinner front cone.
- A spinner rear cone.
- A single stage fan rotor.
- A three stage axial booster.

Its rotating assembly is mounted on the fan shaft and its fixed assembly is secured to the fan frame.

The spinner front cone is made of a black sulfuric anodized aluminum alloy, and is designed to minimize ice build-up. The spinner rear cone smoothes airflow at the inlet of the engine and provides anti-rotation of the fan retaining ring. It also accommodates the fan retaining flange and balancing screws used in fan trim and static balance procedures.

The fan disk is a titanium alloy forging. The outer front flange provides attachment for the rear cone and the

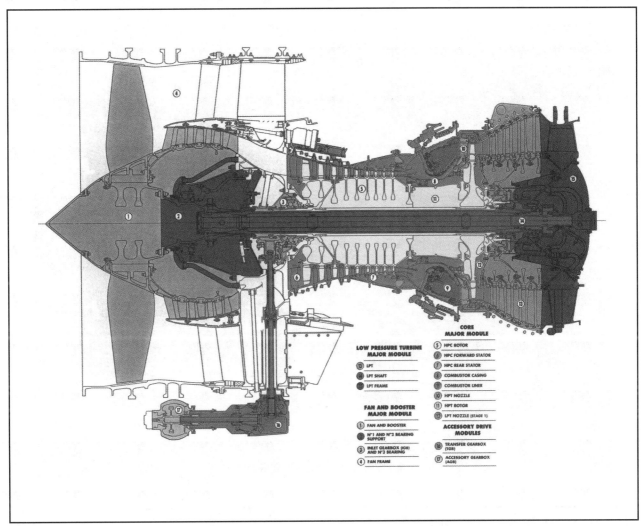

Fig. 4-50 — G.E./Snecma CFM56-7 high bypass turbofan, dual annular combustor.

retaining flange. The outer rim of the fan disk has 24 curved dovetail slots designed for fan blade retention.

The fan blades form the first stage of the low pressure compressor and accelerate the air entering the engine through the air inlet cowls. There are 24 titanium alloy, wide chord fan blades, each with a dovetail base, that slide into a recess on the fan disk outer rim. A retainer lug, machined at the rear end of the blade root, engages the forward flange of the booster spool and limits axial movement.

Each blade has specific indications engraved on the bottom of the root, and includes the part number, the serial number, the moment weight, and the manufacturer code. The fan blade root faces have an anti-friction plasma coating and a top coat of cured molybdenum-base varnish, which acts as a lubricant.

The three stage booster rotor consists of a booster spool, forged and machined from titanium alloy, that is cantilever mounted on the rear of the fan disk. The inner front flange acts as a stop for the fan blades. The booster rotor blades are installed in dovetail slots and serve, primarily, to supercharge the air going into the high speed compressor.

b. Number 1 and 2 Bearing Support Module (Figure 4-53)

The number 1 and 2 bearing support module belongs to the fan major module and its purpose is:
- To support the fan booster rotor.
- To enclose the front section of the forward oil sump.
- To support one of the vibration sensors.
- To vent the forward sump.
- To provide the fan speed indication.
- To direct bearing lubrication.

The number 1 bearing support is a titanium casting. The front flange of the support holds the number 1 ball bearing and its rear outer flange is bolted to the fan frame center hub. The support front flange provides an attachment to the number 1 bearing stationary air/oil seal and for the number 1 bearing vibration sensor. The number 1 bearing is a ball type and takes up the axial and radial loads generated by the low pressure rotor system.

The number 2 bearing support is a titanium casting. Its front inner flange holds the number 2 bearing outer race and also allows for the installation of the number 2 bearing oil nozzle. The support also accommodates a

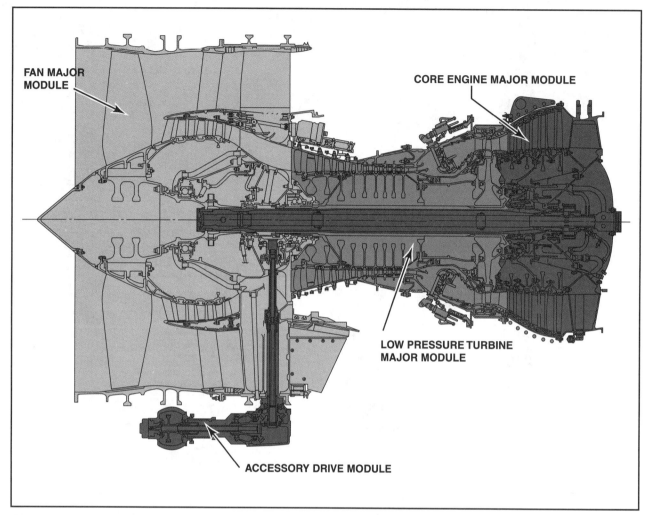

Fig. 4-51 — CFM56-7 Modular design.

guide sleeve for installation of the N_1 speed sensor probe. The number 2 bearing is a roller type and takes up some of the radial loads from the fan and booster rotor.

c. Fan Frame Module (Figure 4-54)

The fan frame module is the structure at the front of the engine. It consists of the major assemblies known as the containment case, the outlet guide vane assembly, the fan frame assembly, and the radial drive shaft housing. Its main purposes are:
• To provide ducting for both the primary and secondary airflows.
• To transmit the engine's thrust to the aircraft.
• To support the low pressure compressor rotor, through the number 1 and 2 bearing support.
• To support the front of the high pressure compressor rotor through the number 3 bearing support.
• To enclose the fan and the booster.
• To support various engine accessories.
• To minimize fan area noise levels.
• To provide attachment for the forward engine mounts, front handling trunnions and lifting points.

• To support the fan inlet cowl.
• To provide a connection between gearboxes and core engine rotor.

The containment case is a single part made of aluminum alloy. Its outer rear flange is bolted to the outer front flange of the frame shroud. The outer surface has flanges and ribs to give more strength to the case during engine operation and to provide attachment for equipment brackets. Its inner surface houses an abradable shroud, located radially in line with the fan rotor blades.

The outlet guide vane assembly is housed at the rear of the containment case. Its purpose is to direct and smooth the secondary airflow to increase thrust efficiency. The assembly consists of the fan outlet guide vane inner shroud and 76 vanes, made of aluminum alloy.

The fan frame assembly is the major structure at the forward section of the engine. It consists of the fan frame shroud, a 12 strut hub, and a radial drive shaft housing. The fan frame shroud is made of aluminum alloy and the strut hub is made of titanium alloy.

The strut at the 9 o'clock position contains both the forward sump oil supply tube and the radial drive shaft

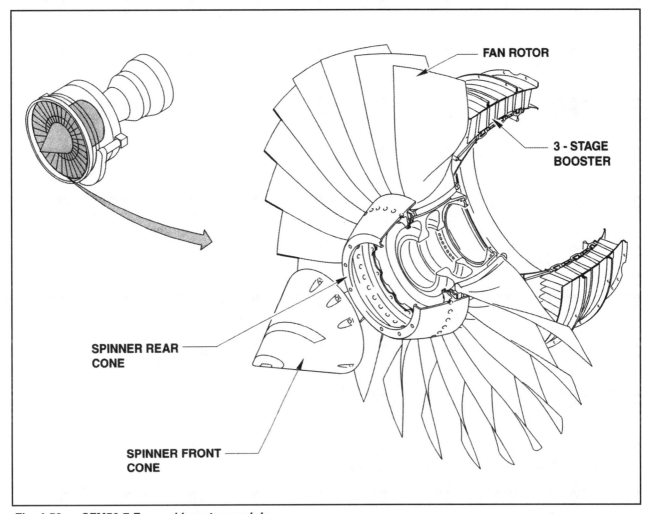

Fig. 4-52 — CFM56-7 Fan and booster module.

housing. The radial drive shaft is the mechanical rotating link between the inlet gearbox and the transfer gearbox.

2. Core Engine Major Module (Figure 4-55)

The core engine major module is made up of the high pressure compressor rotor, the combustion case and combustion chamber, and the high pressure turbine. These three components break down further into eight separate smaller modules. See Figure 4-50.

a. High Pressure Compressor

The high pressure compressor consists of nine stages. It is housed in the compressor case and the rotor front end is supported by the number 3 bearing (combination ball and roller).

Stages 1 and 2 are cantilever mounted on the front face of the rotor shaft flange, and are welded together as one unit. The disks are titanium alloy, with 38 blades fitted to stage 1 and 53 blades fitted to stage 2 by a dovetail attachment. The blades are made of titanium alloy.

The stage 3 disk mates with the rotor shaft flange and supports the stage four through nine spool. It is made of titanium alloy and has individual axial dovetail slots for

its 60 blades, also made of titanium alloy. Retainer hooks are machined on either side of the disk to provide a slot for the installation of split-ring type blade retainers.

The spool made up of stages 4 through 9 is bolted onto the stage 3 disk rear face. It is made from a nickel based alloy. The outer surface of each disk has a circumferential dovetail groove for the installation of the blades. Each blade tip has a reduced thickness, known as a profile or squealer tip. The blades are all made of nickel alloy. The blade count is as follows:

- Stage 4 has 68 blades.
- Stage 5 has 75 blades.
- Stage 6 has 82 blades.
- Stage 7 has 82 blades.
- Stage 8 has 80 blades.
- Stage 9 has 76 blades.

The high pressure compressor case forms the load carrying structure between the fan frame and the combustion case. The case is made up of a front and a rear section, each with a top and a bottom half.

The front case, shown in Figure 4-56, is for the first five stages of the high pressure compressor, with the two

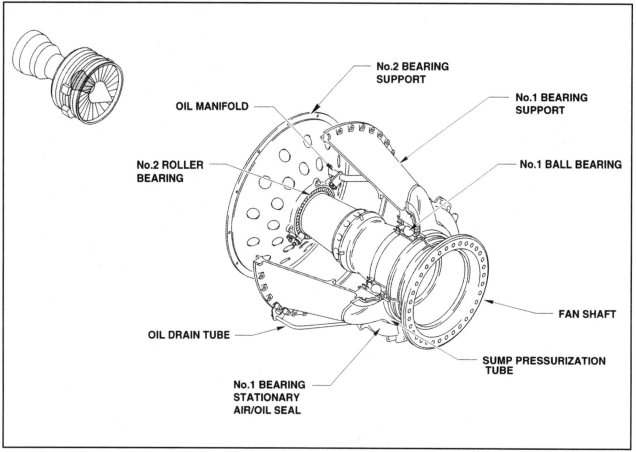

OIL MANIFOLD

No.2 ROLLER
BEARING

No.2 BEARING
SUPPORT

No.1 BEARING
SUPPORT

No.1 BALL BEARING

FAN SHAFT

SUMP PRESSURIZATION
TUBE

OIL DRAIN TUBE

No.1 BEARING
STATIONARY
AIR/OIL SEAL

Fig. 4-53 — CFM56-7 Number 1 and 2 bearing support module.

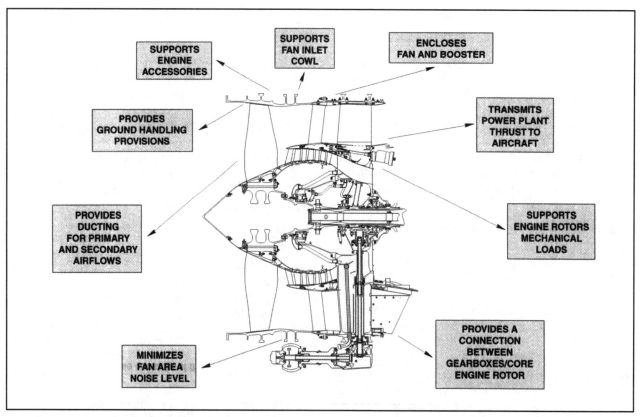

SUPPORTS
ENGINE
ACCESSORIES

SUPPORTS
FAN INLET
COWL

ENCLOSES
FAN AND BOOSTER

PROVIDES
GROUND HANDLING
PROVISIONS

TRANSMITS
POWER PLANT
THRUST TO
AIRCRAFT

PROVIDES
DUCTING
FOR PRIMARY
AND SECONDARY
AIRFLOWS

SUPPORTS
ENGINE ROTORS
MECHANICAL
LOADS

MINIMIZES
FAN AREA
NOISE LEVEL

PROVIDES A
CONNECTION
BETWEEN
GEARBOXES/CORE
ENGINE ROTOR

Fig. 4-54 — CFM56-7 Fan frame module main purposes.

halves being machined as a matched set from a steel forging. Housed within the front case are the inlet guide vanes, the variable stator vanes for stages 1, 2, and 3, and the fixed stator vanes for stages 4 and 5. The inner surface of the case is machined to provide a smooth air flow path through all five stages.

There are ports at the 4th and 5th stages to accommodate pipes that supply bleed air for both engine and aircraft use. Bleed air from the 4th stage is extracted for high pressure turbine cooling and clearance control and for low pressure turbine cooling. Bleed air from the 5th stage is for customer service air.

The rear case, shown in Figure 4-57, is for stages 6 through 9 of the high pressure compressor, with the two halves being machined as a matched set from a zinc-nickel-cobalt alloy forging. Housed within the rear case are the fixed stator vanes for stages 6, 7, and 8. The fixed stator vane for stage 9 is part of the combustion case.

b. Combustion Section (Figure 4-58)

The combustion section is located between the high pressure compressor and the low pressure turbine, and is made up of a combustion case and a combustion chamber. There are two versions of combustion chamber available, one known as a single annular combustor (SAC) and one known as a dual annular combustor (DAC). Air from the compressor is mixed with fuel, supplied by 20 fuel noz-

zles, and burned. The combustion case also provides the ports for high pressure compressor 9th stage bleed air.

The combustion case is a weldment structure, which provides the structural interface between the high pressure compressor, the combustor and the low pressure turbine, and transmits the engine axial loads. It incorporates the compressor outlet guide vanes and a diffuser, which slow down the air flow prior to delivering it to the combustion area. The mounting pads around the outer surface accommodate 20 fuel nozzles and 2 igniter plugs.

The combustion chamber is a short annular structure housed in the combustion case. It is installed between the high pressure compressor stage 9 stator and high pressure turbine nozzle. The chamber is made of a nickel-chrome alloy and coated with a thermal barrier material.

c. High Pressure Turbine (Figure 4-59)

The high pressure turbine converts the kinetic energy in the gasses leaving the combustion chamber into torque to drive the high pressure compressor. It is housed in the aft portion of the combustion case and is a single-stage, air cooled assembly. The assembly consists of the high pressure turbine nozzle and rotor, the high pressure turbine shroud, and the stage 1 low pressure turbine nozzle.

The high pressure turbine nozzle consists of 21 nozzle segments, each containing two vanes. The two vanes in

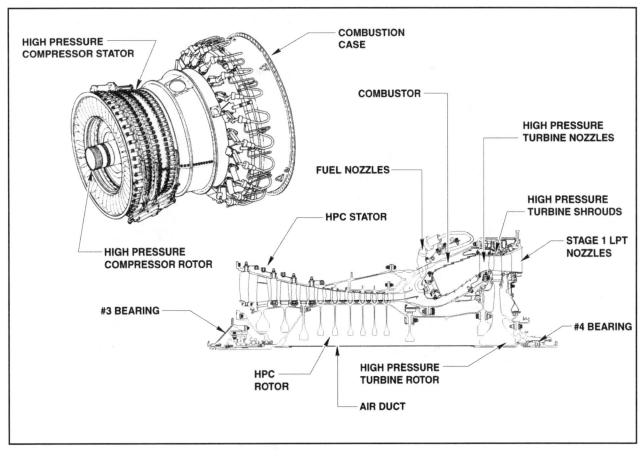

Fig. 4-55 — CFM56-7 Core engine major module.

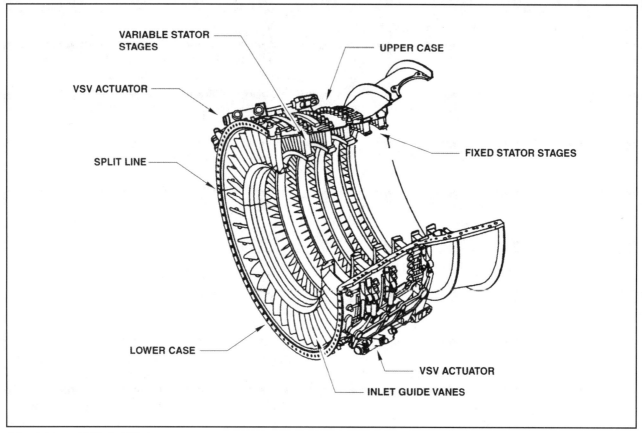

Fig. 4-56 — CFM56-7 High pressure compressor front stator design.

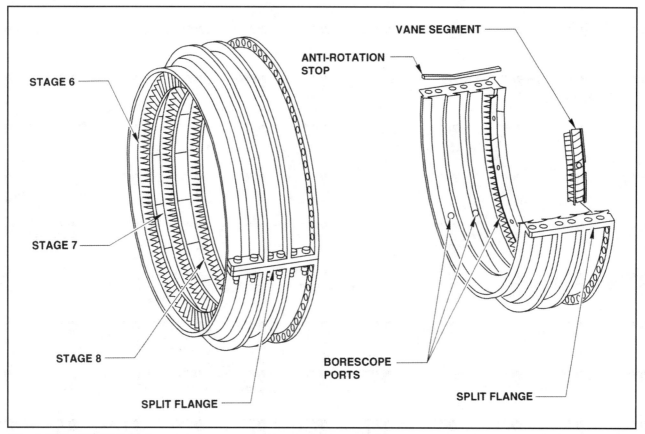

Fig. 4-57 — CFM56-7 High pressure compressor rear stator assembly.

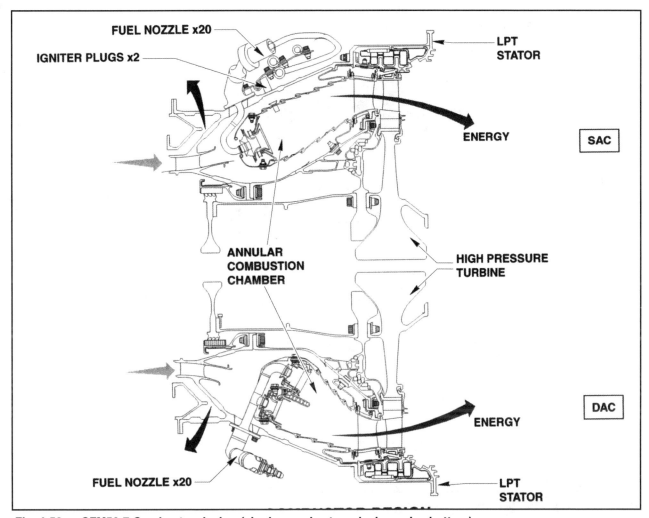

Fig. 4-58 — CFM56-7 Combustor design (single annular, top; dual annular, bottom).

each segment are brazed to inner and outer platforms. Each vane is a cast shell divided into forward and aft cooling compartments by an inner rib.

The vanes and platforms are cooled by compressor discharge air which enters the vane compartments through inserts in the inner and outer ends of the vanes. The air exits through holes in the vane's leading edge and slots in the trailing edge. The vanes are made of a nickel base alloy and covered with a thermal protective coating.

The high pressure turbine rotor front shaft forms the structural connection between the high pressure compressor and the high pressure turbine. It is made of a nickel-chrome alloy. The front flange on the shaft is bolted to the high pressure compressor, stages 4 to 9. It includes a damper sleeve on its inner surface to change vibration frequency.

The high pressure turbine disk is a forged and machined part, with individual axial dovetail slots that retain the turbine blades. The blades are held in position at the front by a rotating air seal and at the rear by blade retainers and a seal ring. The inner part of the disk, as well as the front and rear faces, are cooled by compressor bleed air.

The high pressure turbine blades are made of a high temperature single-crystal nickel alloy. There are 80 individually replaceable blades, with open tips. They are internally cooled by compressor bleed air which enters through the blade root and exits through holes in the leading edge, tip and trailing edge.

The high pressure turbine rear shaft provides aft support for the rotor through the number 4 bearing, which is a roller type. 36 radial and axial holes allow the passage of oil to cool the number 4 bearing outer race. It also has holes providing passages for booster discharge bleed air to cool the low pressure turbine, and booster air to pressurize the aft sump.

The high pressure turbine shroud and stage 1 low pressure turbine nozzle assembly form the connection between the core section and the low pressure turbine module of the engine. It is located inside the aft end of the combustion case and performs 2 main functions, as follows:

• The shroud is part of the high pressure turbine clearance control mechanism and uses high pressure compressor bleed air to maintain close clearances with the high pressure turbine rotor blades throughout flight operations.

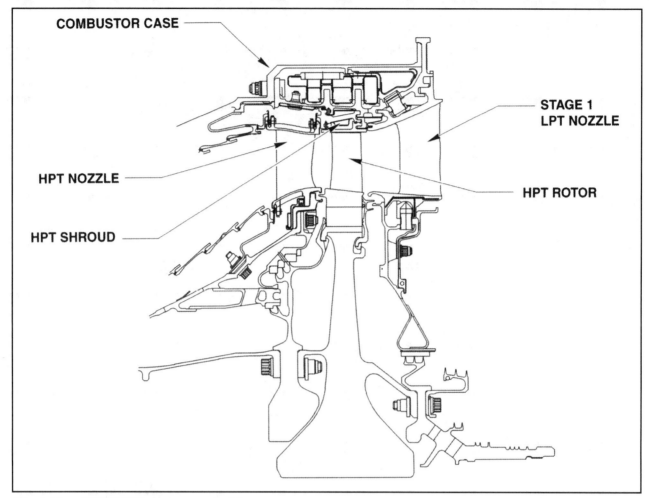

Fig. 4-59 — CFM56-7 High pressure turbine.

• The stage 1 low pressure turbine nozzles direct the core engine exhaust gas onto the stage 1 low pressure turbine blades.

Between the combustion case and the high pressure turbine case, there is an air impingement manifold that circulates 4th and 9th stage bleed air for active clearance control of the high pressure turbine blades and for cooling of the low pressure turbine nozzle. There are 3 air supply tubes on the manifolds inner surface, which circulate the air to cool down the high pressure turbine shroud.

The low pressure turbine nozzle directs high velocity gasses from the high pressure turbine rotor onto the blades of the low pressure turbine rotor stage 1. The assembly consists of 24 nozzle segments of 4 vanes each. The nozzle is air cooled by using air from the 4th stage of the high pressure compressor.

3. Low Pressure Turbine Major Module
(Figure 4-60)

The low pressure turbine major module is made up of three sub-modules; the low pressure turbine and stator module, the shaft module, and the rear frame module. The purpose of the low pressure turbine is to transform the pressure and velocity of the gasses coming from the

high pressure turbine into torque to drive the fan and booster module. Its case also provides support for the high pressure system and a rear mount location for installation on the aircraft. It is a 4 stage axial flow design.

a. Turbine Case

The turbine case is made of nickel alloy. The case incorporates 8 thermocouple mounting pads and 3 borescope ports. The case is air cooled, for active clearance control, and uses 6 cooling air tubes which surround the engine. The tubes are pressurized with fan discharge air.

b. Turbine Nozzles And Disks

The low pressure turbine module incorporates the nozzles for the 2nd, 3rd, and 4th stage turbine wheels. The nozzle for the first stage wheel is part of the high pressure module. The nozzle assemblies are made of nickel alloy, protected against oxidation by a vapor-phase aluminization treatment. There are 108 vanes in the stage 2 nozzle, 140 vanes in the stage 3 nozzle, and 132 vanes in the stage 4 nozzle.

The turbine disks in the low pressure turbine are made of nickel alloy. They have dovetail slots to accept the turbine blades.

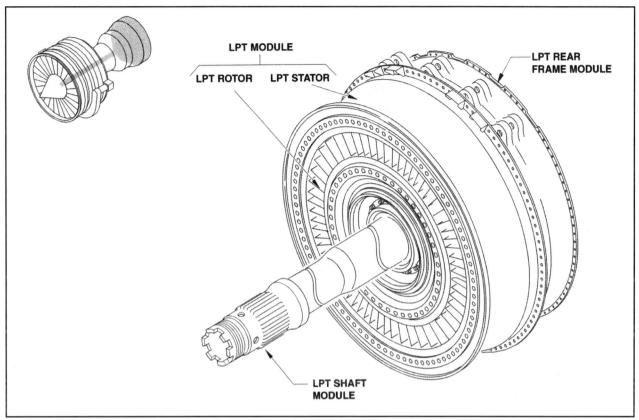

Fig. 4-60 — CFM56-7 Low pressure turbine major module.

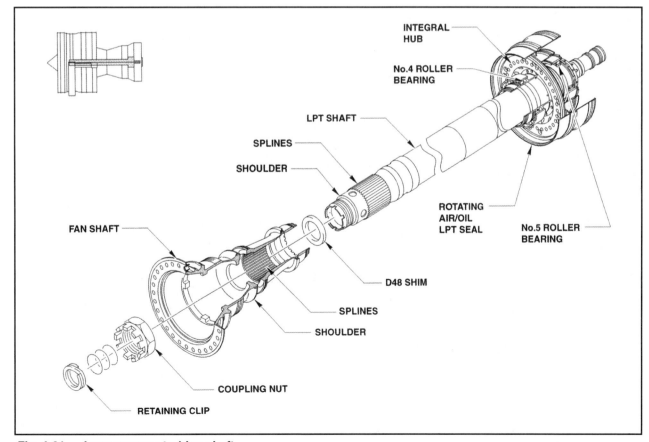

Fig. 4-61 — Low pressure turbine shaft.

c. Turbine Blades

The 4 stages of the low pressure turbine have shrouded tip blades made of nickel alloy. On stages 1 and 2 only, the blades are protected against oxidation by a vapor-phase aluminization treatment. There are 162 blades in stage 1, 150 blades in stage 2, 150 blades in stage 3, and 134 blades in stage 4. Three blades of each stage have a hard coating on their tips, to rub against the honeycomb material of the stator seal segments.

d. Turbine Shaft

The low pressure turbine shaft is made of steel alloy (Figure 4-61), and transmits torque from the turbine to the fan and booster module. It is installed concentrically inside the high pressure rotor system. The shaft is supported by the number 5 main bearing, which is a roller type.

The forward end of the low pressure turbine shaft has outer splines that engage into inner splines on the fan shaft. It also has a shoulder that is secured against a mating shoulder in the fan shaft, by the installation of a coupling nut. The shoulder and the coupling nut provide axial retention of the low pressure turbine shaft.

Running through the middle of the low pressure turbine shaft is a vent tube that provides overboard venting for the engine forward and rear oil sumps. A centrifugal air/oil separator is installed at the end of the tube to separate the vaporized oil from the aft sump pressurization

air. The separated oil joins the oil supply going to the number 4 and 5 main bearings. The air that vents overboard exits through a flame arrestor in the middle of the last low pressure turbine stage.

e. Rear Frame

The low pressure turbine rear frame is one of the engine major structural assemblies, and is located at the rear of the engine. It is made of nickel alloy. Its front section is bolted to the rear flange of the low pressure turbine case, and its rear section provides attachment for the exhaust nozzle and exhaust plug which are both part of the nacelle.

4. Accessory Drive Module (Figure 4-62)

The accessory drive module is made up of the accessory gear box and the transfer gear box. At engine start, the accessory drive system transmits external power from the engine's air turbine starter to drive the core engine. When the engine is running, the accessory drive system extracts part of the core engine power and transmits it through a series of gearboxes and shafts in order to drive the engine and aircraft accessories.

The accessory drive system is located at the 9 o'clock position and consists of the following components:

- The inlet gearbox, that takes power from the high pressure compressor front shaft.

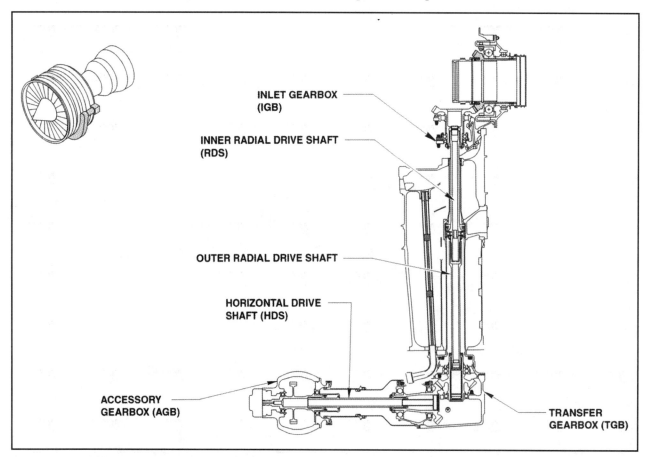

Fig. 4-62 — CFM56-7 Accessory drive section design.

- The radial drive shaft, that transmits the power to the transfer gearbox.
- The transfer gearbox, that redirects the torque.
- The horizontal drive shaft, that transmits power from the transfer gearbox to the accessory gearbox.
- The accessory gearbox, that supports and drives both engine and aircraft accessories.

a. Inlet Gearbox

The inlet gearbox transfers torque between the high pressure compressor front shaft and the radial drive shaft. It also supports the front end of the core engine. The inlet gear box is located in the fan frame sump and is bolted to the forward side of the fan frame aft flange. It is only accessible after many of the other engine modules have been removed.

The inlet gearbox contains the following parts:
- The horizontal bevel gear, with a coupling/locking nut.
- The radial bevel gear.
- The number 3 main bearing (ball and roller).
- The rotating air/oil seal.

b. Radial Drive Shaft

The radial drive shaft transmits power from the inlet gearbox to the transfer gearbox. The assembly is installed inside the fan frame number 10 strut at the 9 o'clock position. It consists of an inner radial drive shaft and housing, a shaft mid-length bearing and an outer radial drive shaft and housing.

c. Transfer Gearbox

Driven by the radial drive shaft, the transfer gearbox reduces rotational speed and redirects the torque from the inlet gearbox to the accessory gearbox, through the horizontal drive shaft. It is secured under the fan frame module at the 9 o'clock position.

d. Horizontal Drive Shaft

The horizontal drive shaft provides power transmission between the transfer gearbox and the accessory gearbox. It consists of an outer tube, made of steel and aluminum, which encloses the inner drive shaft. The drive shaft is made of steel and is splined at both ends for connection to the transfer and accessory gearboxes.

e. Accessory Gearbox (Figure 4-63)

The accessory gearbox supports and drives both aircraft and engine accessories. It is mounted on the left hand side of the fan frame at the 9 o'clock position. The accessory gear box is driven by the inlet gear box and the transfer gear box via drive pad 47 as shown in Figure 4-64. The housing is an aluminum alloy casting.

The accessory gearbox consists of a gear train that reduces and increases the rotational speed to meet the specific drive requirements of each accessory. Figure 4-64 shows the gearbox arrangement, and the relationship of rotational speeds. The front face of the gearbox has mount pads for the following accessories:

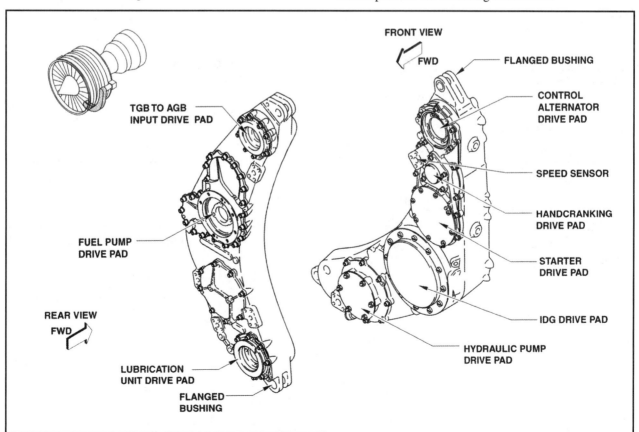

Fig. 4-63 — CFM56-7 Accessory gearbox housing.

- The hydraulic pump, with a ratio to the N_2 of 0.257.
- The integrated drive generator, with a ratio to the N_2 of 0.565.
- The starter, with a ratio to the N_2 of 1.002.
- The hand-cranking drive, with a ratio to the N_2 of 0.986.
- The EEC control alternator (FADEC power supply),

with a ratio to the N_2 of 1.301.

The rear face of the gearbox has mount pads for the following accessories:
- The lubrication unit, with a ratio to the N_2 of 0.423.
- The scavenge oil filter.
- The fuel pump and hydromechanical unit, with a ratio to the N_2 of 0.426.

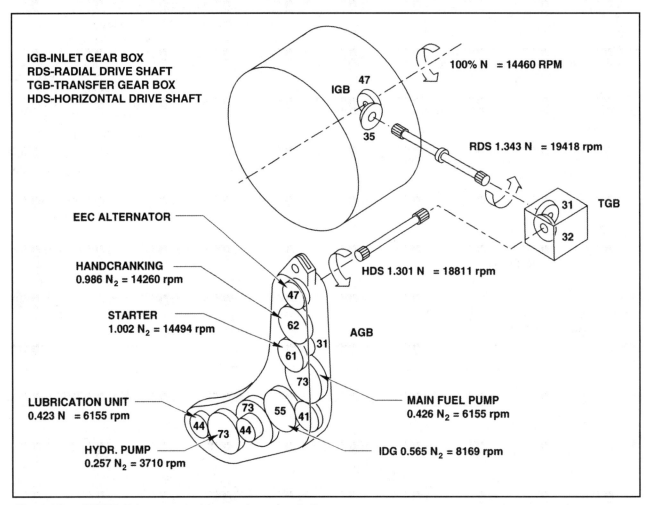

Fig. 4-64 — CFM56-7 Accessory drive system gear train.

E. Engine Data Sheets (Figures 4-65 to 4-68)

The Engine Data Sheets show data and specifications for the four engines mentioned in this chapter. A complete set of specifications for nearly every current engine in the world is available by this publisher in a book entitled; *Encyclopedia of Jet Aircraft and Engines.*

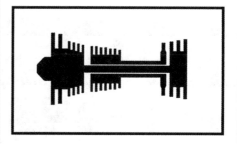

USA TURBINE ENGINE COMPANIES

MANUFACTURER: **UNITED TECHNOLOGIES CORP.**
(Pratt & Whitney Aircraft Group)
Commercial Products Division, East Hartford, Conn.

DESIGNATION: JT8D-17A.

BACKGROUND: Derivative of the Military J52 Turbojet. Originally developed for the Boeing B727 Airliner.
Date First J52 Engine Produced: 1958.
Date First JT8D Engine Produced: 1963 .

ENGINE TYPE: Turbofan
Dual-Shaft, Low-Bypass, Front Fan.

COMPRESSOR TYPE: 13-Stage Dual-Spool, Axial Flow Compressor including: 2-Stage Front Fan and 4 Axial Stages in the Low Pressure Compressor, 7-Stage High Pressure Compressor.

COMPRESSOR DATA (Take-Off): Compressor Pressure Ratio: 16.9 : 1, Fan Pressure Ratio: 2.11 : 1, Fan Bypass Ratio: 1.0 : 1, Total Mass Airflow: 331 lb/sec (150 kg/sec). Fan Diameter: 42.5 inch.

TURBINE TYPE: 4-Stage Axial Flow Turbine including: 1-Stage High Pressure Turbine, 3-Stage Low Pressure Turbine.

COMBUSTOR TYPE: Can-Annular, Through-Flow, with (9) Combustion Liners.

POWER (take-off) RATING: 16,000 lbt (71,2 kN thrust). Rating Approved to: 84°F (29°C). Cruise TSFC: 0.806 lb/hr/lbt.

TAKE-OFF SPECIFIC FUEL CONSUMPTION (SFC): 0.62 lb/hr/lbt (17,56 mg/Ns).

ENGINE WEIGHT (less tailpipe): 3,500 lbs (1,588 kg).

POWER/WEIGHT RATIO: 4.97 : 1 lbt/lb.

APPLICATION: Boeing B727, B737, McDonnell-Douglas DC-9-30, -50 Airliners.

OTHER ENGINES IN SERIES:
JT8D-1 in Boeing B727 Airliner and McDonnell-Douglas DC-9-5 and DC-9-10 Airliners.
JT8D-7 (14,000 lbt) in B727, DC-9, Aerospatiale Caravelle and Super Caravelle Airliners.
JT8D-9,-9A (14,500 lbt) in B727, B737, DC-9, Caravelle Airliners.
JT8D-11 (15,000 lbt) in DC-9, Dassault Mercure And Caravelle Airliners.
JT8D-15 (15,500 lbt) in B727, B737, DC-9, Dassault Mercure-2 Airliners; Boeing C-22B.
JT8D-15AR (16,400 lbt) in B727-100/200, B737, DC-9 Airliners .
JT8D-17 (16,000 lbt) also in Indonesian "Surveiller" Patrol Aircraft.
JT8D-17R in Boeing B727-100, and -200 Airliners.
JT8D-9 (14,500 lbt) In Kawasaki C-1 Transport Aircraft.

Fig. 4-65 — Data Sheet Pratt & Whitney, USA, JT8D-17A Turbofan engine.

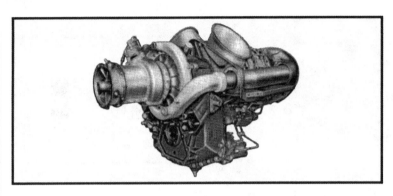
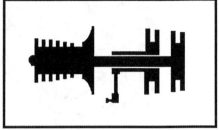

USA TURBINE ENGINE COMPANIES

MANUFACTURER: **ALLISON GAS TURBINE COMPANY** (DIVISION OF ROLLS-ROYCE) **Indianapolis, Indiana.**

DESIGNATION: 250-C20B.

BACKGROUND: Civil version of the military T-63 Turboshaft.
Date First 250-C20R Engine Produced: 1970.

ENGINE TYPE: Turboshaft
Dual-Shaft, Single Compressor.

COMPRESSOR TYPE: Combination Compressor: 6-Stage Axial, 1-Stage Centrifugal.

COMPRESSOR DATA (Take-Off): Compressor Pressure Ratio: 7.2 : 1, Total Mass Airflow: 3.8 lb/sec (1,72 kg/sec).

TURBINE TYPE: 4-Stage Axial Flow Turbine, including a 2-Stage Gas Producer (compressor drive) Turbine, 2-Stage Power (free) Turbine.

COMBUSTOR TYPE: Reverse-Flow, Can Type Combustor.

POWER (take-off) RATING: 420 shp (314 kw). Rating Approved to: 59°F (15°C).

TAKE-OFF SPECIFIC FUEL CONSUMPTION (SFC): 0.65 lb/hr/shp (0,39 kg/hr/kw).

ENGINE WEIGHT (less tailpipe): 161 lbs (78 kg).

POWER/WEIGHT RATIO: 2.6 : 1 shp/lb (4,28 : 1 kw/kg).

APPLICATION:

250-C20B, F, J; in:	Bell 206B/L, Bell TH-67, and Hughes 500D/E, USA.
250-C20B in:	MBB BO.105, Germany.
	Brenda-Nardi 369D, India.
	Agusta AB 206, Italy.
	IPTN NBO.105, Indonesia.
	Kawasaki OH-6D, Japan.
	WSK-PZL Mi-2, Poland.
	Rogerson-Hiller UH-12, USA.
250-C20R in:	Agusta A.109A, Italy.MDHC MD-500/530, USA, Rhein-Flugbugbar,
	FT-400 "FanTrainer" Ducted Fan type Helicopter.
250-C20W in:	Enstrom TH-28 & Enstrom 480, USA.
	Schweizer TH-330, USA.

Fig. 4-66 — Data Sheet Allison, Rolls-Royce, USA, 250-C20B Turboshaft engine.

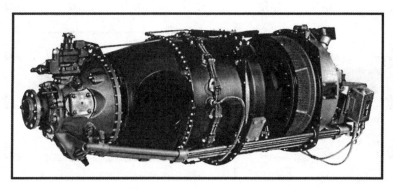
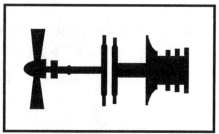

INTERNATIONAL TURBINE ENGINE COMPANIES

COUNTRY: **CANADA**

MANUFACTURER: PRATT & WHITNEY OF CANADA, INC.
LONGUEUIL, QUEBEC.

DESIGNATION: PT6A-34.

BACKGROUND: Military version designated T-74-CP-701. The PT6 Series ranges in power output from 500 eshp (373 ekw) to 1,875 eshp (1,398 ekw). It is the most widely used Small Gas Turbine Engine in world service.
Date First PT6 Produced: 1963.

ENGINE TYPE: Turboprop
Rear Drive, Dual-Shaft (Compressor Drive & Power Output Drive).

COMPRESSOR TYPE: Combination, Axial-Centrifugal Flow Compressor including: 3-Stages of Axial Flow Compression, 1-Stage of Centrifugal Flow Compression.

COMPRESSOR DATA (Take-Off): Compressor Pressure Ratio: 7 : 1, Total Mass Airflow: 6.5 lb/sec (2,95 kg/sec).

TURBINE TYPE: 2-Stage Axial Flow Turbine including: 1-Stage Gas Producer (compressor drive) Turbine, 1-Stage Power (free) Turbine.

COMBUSTOR TYPE: Annular, Reverse Flow.

POWER (take-off) RATING: 750 eshp (559 ekw). Includes 80 shp (59,7 kw) from 200 lbt (0,89 kN thrust). Rating Approved to: 71°F (22°C).

TAKE-OFF SPECIFIC FUEL CONSUMPTION (SFC): 0.59 lb/hr/eshp (0,36 kg/hr/ekw).

ENGINE WEIGHT (less tailpipe): 331 lbs (150 kg).

POWER/WEIGHT RATIO: 2.27 : 1 eshp/lb (3,58 : 1 ekw/kg).

APPLICATION: Embraer EMB-110 and EMB-111.

OTHER ENGINES IN SERIES: PT6A Series: -10, -11, -11AG, -112, -15AG, -21, -25, -25A, -25C, -27, -28, -34B, -34AG, 110, -112, 114, -135, -135A, -36, -41, -41AG, -42, -45, -45R, -50, -60, -65B, -65R, -66, -67. PT6B Series: -35F, -36. PT6T Series: -3B, -6. ST6L-73. In many models of fixed-wing aircraft including: Avtec, IAI Arava, Ayres, Basler, Beech, Cessna, Cinair, Commuter, DeHavilland, Dornier, Embraer, Gates, Harbin, IMP, LearFan, Maul, Mooney, New-Cal, Norman, Omac, Omni, Pezetel, Piaggio, Pilatus, Pox, iper, Shorts, TBM (Aerospatiale-Mooney), Valmet. Also Rotor-Wing aircraft including: Agusta-Bell, Bell, SikorskyT-74 US Army applications include: RC-12, UV-18, UV-20, RU-21, UV-21, UV-24 ,UV-27. T-74 US Navy Applications include: T-34, T-44, UC-12.

Fig. 4-67 — Data Sheet Pratt & Whitney, Canada, PT6A-34 Turboprop engine.

 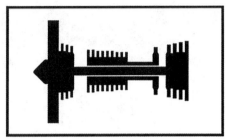

MULTI-NATIONAL TURBINE ENGINE COMPANIES

**MANUFACTURER: CFM INTERNATIONAL (CMFI): GENERAL ELECTRIC AND SNECMA
Cincinnati, Ohio, USA.**

COUNTRY: USA, FRANCE.

DESIGNATION: CFM56-7B27

BACKGROUND: The original CFM56 Utilized a General Electric, F101 Engine as its core.
Date First CFM56 Engine Produced: 1978.

ENGINE TYPE: Turbofan
Dual-Shaft, High-Bypass, Front Fan.

COMPRESSOR TYPE: 13-Stage Dual-Spool, Axial Flow Compressor including: 1-Stage Front Fan
and (3) additional Axial Stages in the Low Pressure Compressor, 9-Stage High Pressure
Compressor. Fan Diameter 72.3 inch.

COMPRESSOR DATA (Take-Off): Compressor Pressure Ratio: 28.9 : 1, Fan Pressure Ratio:
1 : 1, Fan Bypass Ratio: 6.5 : 1, Total Mass Airflow: 1,045 lb/sec (474 kg/sec).

TURBINE TYPE: 5-Stage Axial Flow Turbine including: 1-Stage High Pressure Turbine,
4-Stage Low Pressure Turbine.

COMBUSTOR TYPE: Annular (ring), Through-Flow.

POWER (take-off) RATING: 27,300 lbt (144,56 kN thrust). Rating Approved to: 86°F (30°C).

TAKE-OFF SPECIFIC FUEL CONSUMPTION (SFC): 0.38 lb/hr/lbt (9,35 mg/Ns).

ENGINE WEIGHT (less tailpipe): 5,234 lbs (2,561 kg).

POWER/WEIGHT RATIO: 5.75 : 1 lbt/lb.

APPLICATION:
Boeing and Airbus Airliners.

OTHER ENGINES IN SERIES: As of this writing: CFM56-7B18 (19,500 LBT), -7B20 (20,600 LBT), -7B22
(22,700 LBT), 7B24 (24,000 LBT) , -7B26 (26,300 LBT).

Fig. 4-68 — Data Sheet CFM Int'l, USA/France, CFM-56-7B27 Turbofan engine.

Chapter V
Inspection And Maintenance

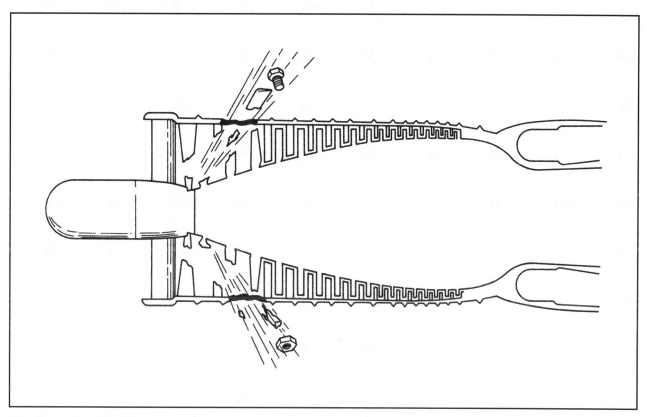

Fig. 5-1 — Foreign object damage.

The basic maintenance concept of the gas turbine engine is that there are two levels of maintenance performed. They are line maintenance and shop maintenance. The term maintenance includes inspection, parts replacement, repair, and overhaul. Although the tendency today is to perform more maintenance on the flight line, the really heavy maintenance is performed on engines removed from the aircraft and in shop maintenance facilities. Shop maintenance is also referred to as heavy maintenance or overhaul maintenance.

A good point to remember as a manager, technician, or pilot when working on turbine engines is that all are lightweight, high speed machines which are manufactured to very close tolerances; therefore, extreme care is required in their maintenance. This includes rigid adherence to established technical procedures, correct use of tools, and especially cleanliness of parts and shop environment (Figure 5-1).

A. Line Maintenance (Figure 5-2)

Line maintenance encompasses all the inspections, parts replacement, and repairs that can be made to the power plant while it is installed in the aircraft.

An airline repair program may include module replacement in the line maintenance category. Others may have a separate maintenance category for modular maintenance, discussed later in Section E, which fits in between line maintenance and shop maintenance.

Fig. 5-2 — DC-10 Aircraft, General Electric CF6 engine undergoing flight line maintenance.

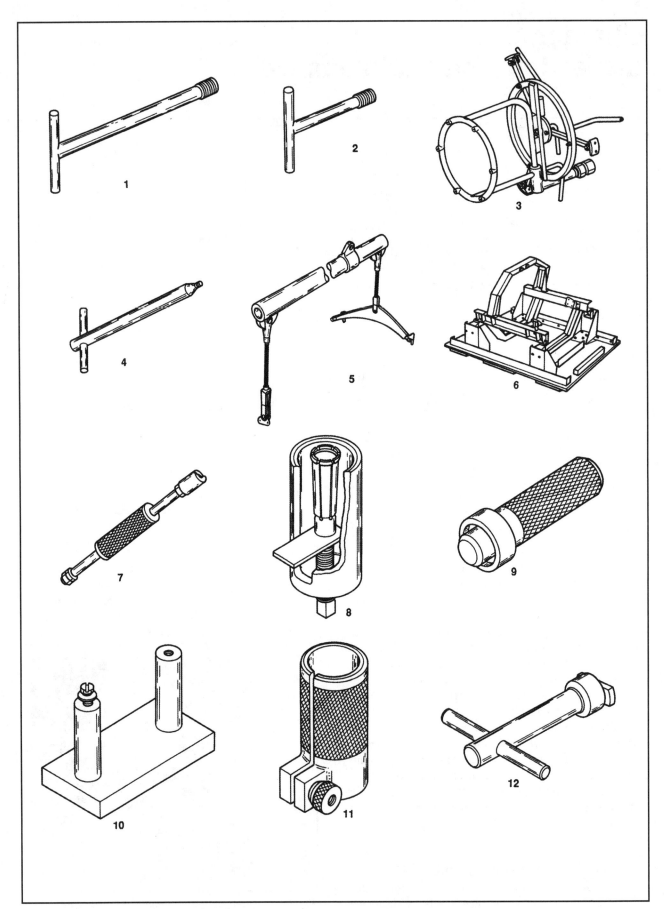

Fig. 5-3A — Special tools, Pratt & Whitney JT15 Turbofan, line maintenance.

REF. NO.	PART NUMBER	NOMENCLATURE	APPLICATION
1	CPWA30128-02	PULLER	ANTI-ICING LINE TRANSFER TUBE
2	CPWA30123-07	PULLER	OIL FILLER PLUG
3	CPWA31498	WASH RIG	LOW COMPRESSOR
4	CPWA30271	SPREADER	EXHAUST DUCT AND GAS GENERATOR CASE SHANK NUTS
5	CPWA31001	SLING	ENGINE ASSEMBLY COMPLETE
6	CPWA31002	SKID	LINE MAINTENANCE ENGINE HANDLING
7	CPWA31013-00	PULLER	ACCESSORY GEARBOX RETAINING PIN
8	CPWA31061-00	PULLER	CENTRIFUGAL BREATHER CARBON SEAL
9	CPWA31062-00	DRIFT	CENTRIFUGAL BREATHER CARBON SEAL
10	CPWA31063	SUPPORT	CENTRIFUGAL BREATHER CARBON SEAL
11	CPWA31080	PULLER	CHECK VALVE HOUSING
12	CPWA31081	ADJUSTING TOOL	OIL PRESSURE RELIEF VALVE

Fig. 5-3B — Identification of special tools, Pratt & Whitney JT15 Turbofan

1. Gas Turbine Special Tools (For Line Maintenance) (Figure 5-3)

The special tools and fixtures necessary to carry out line maintenance on the engine and to prepare the Pratt & Whitney of Canada JT15D Turbofan engine for storage or service are listed here. Standard tools, which normally form part of a technician's tool kit, are not included. Shop maintenance tools are also too numerous to include here.

2. Foreign Object Damage And Erosion

a. Foreign Object Damage (Figures 5-4 and 5-5)

Much of the damage to the compressor section encountered on the flight line arises from foreign matter being drawn into the engine inlet. Damage to compressor blades results in a compressor geometry change which can cause malfunctions such as performance deterioration, compressor stalls, and even engine failure. Foreign object damage can also be caused by objects dropped into the engine gas path or internal parts during maintenance.

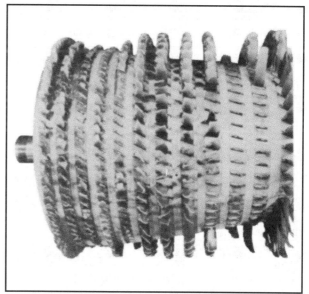

Fig. 5-4 — Compressor completely destroyed by foreign object ingestion.

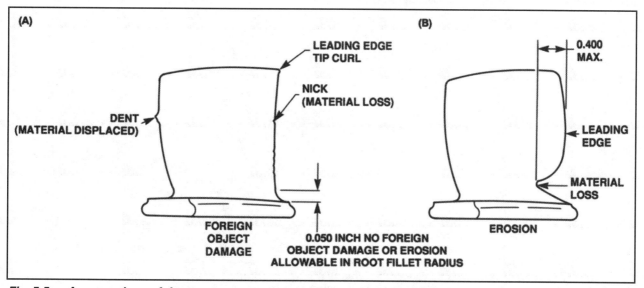

Fig. 5-5 — A comparison of damage to a compressor blade done by (A) FOD, and (B) erosion.

Foreign object damage (F.O.D.) prevention is a concern of all flight line personnel. Sometimes the most harmless looking piece of debris can cause thousands of dollars in maintenance costs to the aircraft owner. The following is a list of suggested F.O.D. prevention methods for managers, technicians and pilots. Ensure that:

1) Maintenance personnel keep ramp and hangar areas clean;
2) Other flight line personnel are appraised of the importance of cleanliness in work areas;
3) All personnel keep articles of clothing and materials in pockets secured when working on operating aircraft;
4) Engine operators check inlets for foreign objects before engine run-up and that they avoid run-ups and taxiing into exhaust blasts of other operating aircraft;
5) Everyone who maintains jet aircraft keeps the inlet and exhaust covers in place when the engine is static (not operating) to prevent contamination and windmilling.

NOTE: *Damage incurred in the gas path from material failure of aircraft or engine parts is normally termed Domestic Object Damage (D.O.D.) rather than foreign object damage.*

b. Erosion (Figure 5-5)

Gas path erosion occurs from ingestion of sand, dirt, dust, and other fine airborne contaminants. This ingestion affects both the compressor and the turbine sections. The abrasive effect of repeated ingestion can wear through the surface coating and even into the base metals of the fan, the compressor blades and vanes. It can even cause similar damage to the turbine before leaving the engine via the exhaust.

Designers of modern aircraft better understand this problem today and try to engineer the slip-streams around the aircraft to carry contaminants around rather than into the inlets. However, many older aircraft have ingestion problems. Also, some have been reconfigured from narrow nacelles to wide, high bypass fan engine nacelles and have very low ground clearance. These aircraft, especially, are experiencing performance loss and an increase in maintenance and fuel costs due to the effects of erosion on compressor and turbine parts (Figure 5-6).

3. Compressor Field Cleaning

Accumulation of contaminants in the compressor reduces aerodynamic efficiency of the blades, thereby reducing engine performance. Contaminants, mainly salt, airborne pollutants from smokestacks, and agricultural chemicals, all pass through the engine and build up over time on internal surfaces.

Two common methods for removing dirt, salt, and corrosion deposits are a fluid wash and an abrasive grit blast. Before field cleaning, it may be necessary to blank off certain sensing and bleed ports to prevent contamination or blockage.

a. Fluid Cleaning Procedure

The fluid cleaning procedure is easily accomplished by first spraying an emulsion type surface cleaner and then applying a rinse solution into the compressor. This is done while the engine is being motored over by the starter or during low speed operation. Figure 5-7 depicts a Pratt & Whitney PT6 turboprop performance recovery wash apparatus. It cannot be over stressed that the wash procedure must be performed in strict accordance with the instructions set forth in the manufacturer's maintenance manual.

There are two methods of performing compressor washes:
1) While motoring the engine with starter only;
2) While running the engine.

Depending on the nature of the operating environment and the type of deposits in the engine gas path, either of the two wash methods can be used to remove salt or dirt and other baked on deposits which accumulate over a period of time and cause engine performance deterioration.

When the water wash is performed solely to remove salt deposits, the compressor wash is known as a "desalination wash".

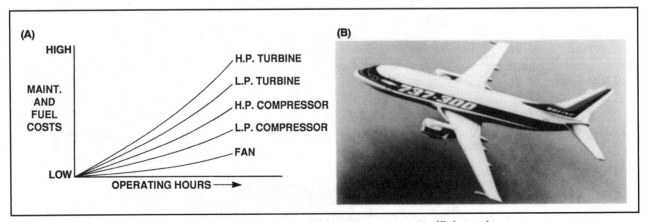

Fig. 5-6A — Typical maintenance and fuel cost increase due to component efficiency losses.
Fig. 5-6B — High bypass engine conversion to Boeing 737 aircraft.

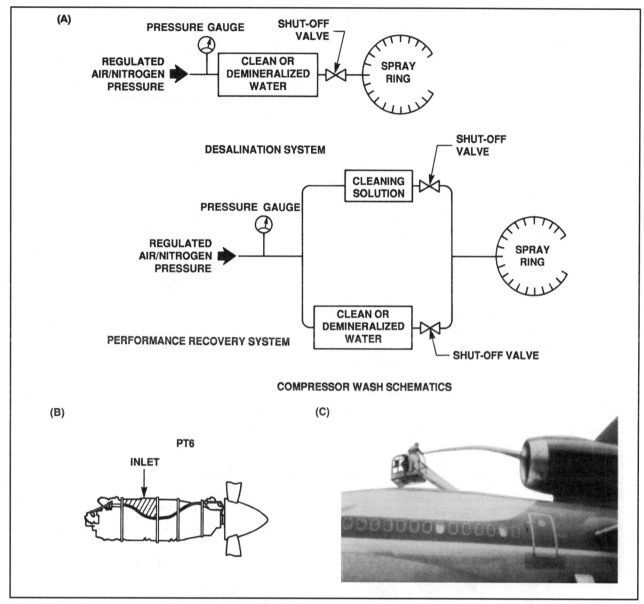

Fig. 5-7A — Compressor wash schematic of the PT6 turboprop.
Fig. 6-7B — Water is introduced into engine inlet.
Fig. 5-7C — Large engine compressor wash

When the solution wash is performed solely to remove baked on deposits to improve engine performance, the compressor wash is known as a "performance recovery" wash.

The motoring wash is carried out at engine speeds of 14% to 25% and with the cleaning mixture injected at a pressure of 30 to 50 pounds per square inch.

The running wash is carried out at engine speeds of approximately 60%, with the cleaning mixture and rinsing solution injected at a pressure of 15 to 20 pounds per square inch gage.

See Typical Wash Schedule (Figure 5-8).

NOTE: Multiple motoring wash procedures should be performed to the extent permitted by the starter operating limitations. Observe starter cooling period (Reference: Starter Manufacturer's Manual). A five minute drying out period at idle speed is required after motor washing has been accomplished.

The fluid wash method also cleans the turbine area. Turbine sulfidation (sulfur deposits from burning fuel which collect on turbine components) causes surface damage over time, and the frequent use of surface cleaning solvents in a motoring wash procedure has been found to be an added benefit in terms of extended engine service life for some engines (Figure 5-9).

The timely use of fresh water rinsing, where prescribed, to remove salt deposits, and use of inlet and exhaust plugs will greatly reduce the need for these heavy cleaning procedures. Some manufacturers of small engines have authorized fogging of the compressor with anti-corrosive fluids after the wash procedure to slow the contamination process.

OPERATING ENVIRONMENT	NATURE OF WASH	RECOMMENDED FREQUENCY	RECOMMENDED METHOD	REMARKS
Continuously salt laden	Desalination	Daily	Motoring	Strongly recommended after last flight of day.
Occasionally salt laden	Desalination	Weekly	Motoring	Strongly recommended. Adjust washing frequency to suit condition.
All	Performance Recovery	100 to 200 hours	Motoring or Running	Strongly recommended. Performance recovery required less frequently. Adjust washing frequency to suit engine operating conditions as indicated by engine condition monitoring system. Motoring wash for light soil and multiple motoring or running wash for heavy soil is recommended.

NOTE: On some engines, a turbine wash is possible via the ignitor plug opening.

Fig. 5-8 — Typical compressor wash schedule.

b. Abrasive Grit Process (Figure 5-10)

A second more vigorous method of compressor cleaning is to inject an abrasive grit (one popular material being ground walnut shells or apricot pits, trade name Carboblast) into an engine operating at selected power settings. The amount of material and the operation procedure is prescribed by the manufacturer for each particular engine. The greater capability of this procedure over the solvent and water methods allows the time interval between cleaning to be longer, but because the cleaning grit is mostly burned up in combustion, the agent does not clean the turbine vanes and blades as effectively as the fluid wash.

4. Scheduled Line Maintenance

Scheduled line maintenance includes inspections, such as the 100-hour, annual, continuous and progressive, which are frequent tasks performed by the maintenance technician. FAR Parts 43, 65, and 91 describe the scope of these inspections, and the manufacturer publishes the specific inspection procedures for the particular engine being inspected (Figure 5-11).

A typical 100 hour inspection on the turbine engine in a small business jet would include, but not be limited to, the following items:

1) An oil change every third inspection (300 hours).
2) The oil filter inspected and then cleaned or replaced.

BEFORE A COMPRESSOR WASH
(A)

AFTER A COMPRESSOR WASH
(B)

Fig. 5-9 — PT6 turboprop engine compressor.

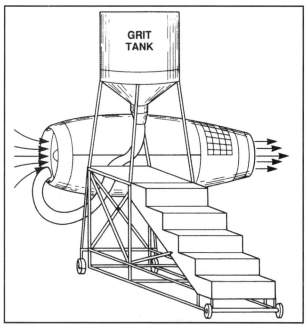

Fig. 5-10 — Abrasive grit compressor cleaning.

*Fig. 5-11 — Engine Cowling arrangement
Rolls-Royce Dart Engine ready for inspection.*

3) An analysis of the oil filter and chip detector debris.

4) The oil analyzed by means of a spectrometer check.

5) The igniter plugs visually inspected and operationally checked.

6) The fuel pump filter(s) cleaned or replaced.

7) A visual inspection of the engine inlet and exhaust, to check for possible FOD and turbine distress.

8) A visual inspection of the engine's exterior, checking for leaks and the condition of the lines and electrical leads.

9) The engine operationally checked and a compressor wash done.

10) An engine vibration analysis performed.

A turbine engine powered business or commuter aircraft might undergo a set of routine inspections to

insure the engine remains in an airworthy condition. An example of a typical inspection schedule would be as follows:

Transit checks after each flight - These consist of checking the engine cowling for signs of leaks, the intake and low pressure compressor rotor blades for damage, the engine exhaust for damage and metal deposits, and checking the oil level and oil filter blockage indicator.

Check 1 at 25 hours of run time - This consists of the transit checks plus:

Checking the last stage of the low pressure turbine for cracking and damage by using a strong spotlight.

Checking the nose cone fairing for damage and security, the low pressure compressor lining and rotor blades, the low pressure compressor outlet guide vanes, and the intermediate compressor inlet guide vanes.

Check 2 at 150 hours or 3 months - This consists of the transit checks and check 1, plus:

Checking the two master chip detectors.

Checking the fan bypass duct, exhaust cone and fairings for damage.

Audibly checking the igniter plugs.

Checking the low pressure and high pressure air supply ducting and joints for damage and leaks.

Checking the fuel system for contamination.

Checking the freedom and security of mechanical controls and greasing those controls.

Check 3 at 600 hours or 12 months - This consists of the transit checks, and check 1 and check 2, plus:

Replacing the fuel filter element.

A functional test of the temperature control system.

Large commercial aircraft, like Boeing 767's or Airbus A340's, undergo what is called a Continuous Airworthiness Inspection Program. This program involves daily inspections, known as layover inspections, and what are called letter or alphabet checks. The letter checks are typically broken down into what are called "A", "B", "C" and "D" checks.

Each higher letter check incorporates all the previous inspection items, plus a more detailed look at the aircraft and its engines. By the time the "D" check takes place, the aircraft is ready to be completely stripped to its shell and rebuilt. What will happen to the engines at this point in time depends on how long it has been since they were overhauled. They may just be removed, inspected, and reinstalled as the aircraft goes back together.

5. Unscheduled Line Maintenance

Unscheduled line maintenance is performed as the maintenance technician corrects discrepancies found during flight, walk-around inspections, scheduled inspections, while performing Airworthiness Directives (AD's) etc. The engine system Chapters, VI to XII of this text, include the line maintenance repairs and troubleshooting necessary to locate and correct common malfunctions (Figure 5-12).

B. Shop Maintenance (Heavy)

Whenever the engine cannot be repaired in the airplane, it is removed for shop maintenance or for test cell operation and troubleshooting. The Federal Aviation Administration (FAA) requires that this level of maintenance be accomplished only at a manufacturer's facility or at a certified repair station which has the necessary tooling, technical data, and trained personnel.

The FAA divides heavy maintenance for most engines into the two categories of limited and unlimited (Figure 5-12).

1. Limited Heavy Maintenance

Many privately owned repair stations and factory-operated repair stations are in the limited category. They normally are authorized to perform any maintenance up to removal and replacement of the entire hot section. They can perform some cold end repairs, but cannot rebuild the compressor.

2. Unlimited Heavy Maintenance

Privately owned and factory operated overhaul facilities fall into this category. They can remove and replace any part, perform limited remanufacture of parts, and zero out the engine time.

a. Remanufacturing Facility

Some manufacturers offer a remanufacture option to users wherein the engine is repaired and updated by remanufacture of parts and returned to service with added capabilities and greater expected service life than on overhauled engines.

In terms of FAA categories of minor and major repairs, all line maintenance is considered minor, including

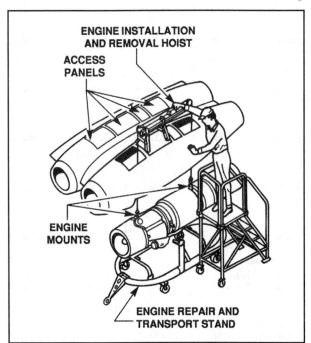

Fig. 5-12 — Engine installation with two-cable hoist.

ENGINE INSTALLATION
AND REMOVAL HOIST

ACCESS
PANELS

ENGINE
MOUNTS

ENGINE REPAIR AND
TRANSPORT STAND

changing of modules (discussed later in Section E), and only the overhaul of modules is considered major. At the time the repair shop facility completes a major repair, it will prepare a FAA Form 337 or a FAA approved Manufacturer's Release Form as a certification of the repairs performed (Figure 5-13).

3. Examples Of Heavy Repairs

a. Power Plant Removal

Power plants are fully removed from the aircraft by one of two methods. One method involves lowering the engine from its mounting location using a hydraulically operated installation stand which looks similar to a large scissors jack. This method is generally used when working with large engines. The other method, more common to general aviation, requires a sling and hoist arrangement to lower the engine into its transportation dolly (Figure 5-14).

4. Shop Maintenance

Once in the shop, the engine to be repaired is usually installed on a maintenance stand. Some stands are on casters while others look similar to the one in Figure 5-15. Many stands are designed to keep the engine perfectly horizontal. Figure 5-16 shows a turbine wheel being removed with a special tool, a sling, and a shop hoist. The turbine, as well as many of the large components, will be placed in its own roll-around maintenance stand.

At some point engine disassembly is usually completed vertically, such as for removal of the compressor (Figure 5-17). On some engines, the entire disassembly is accomplished vertically so the weight will assist in component alignment. One standard maintenance practice during disassembly is to cover all openings as they are exposed, using plugs, caps, and other suitable material to prevent contamination and to maintain the utmost in shop cleanliness and safety procedures.

Another general rule that applies during any maintenance is never to reuse lock wire, lock washers, tab locks, cotter pins, gaskets, packings, or rubber O-rings and to reuse locknuts and other fasteners only within the limits prescribed in the manufacturer's instructions.

In Figure 5-18, we see an expanded view of an entire General Electric CJ-610 engine, as it would appear disassembled during heavy maintenance.

C. Cold Section And Hot Section Inspections And Repairs

For the purpose of inspection and maintenance, the basic engine is divided into two main sections, the cold section and the hot section. The cold section includes the engine inlet, compressor, and diffuser sections. The hot section includes the combustor, turbine, and exhaust sections (Figure 5-19).

AIRWORTHINESS INSPECTOR'S HANDBOOK, SECTION 15 "POWERPLANT REPAIRS" FAA ORDER 8300.9 -EXCERPT-

630. PURPOSE. THIS SECTION PROVIDES GUIDANCE TO FIELD PERSONNEL CONCERNING MAJOR/MINOR REPAIRS TO POWERPLANTS AND CLASSIFIES THE STRUCTURAL PARTS OF TURBINE ENGINES.

631. BACKGROUND. FIELD PERSONNEL ARE BEING ASKED TO PROVIDE GUIDANCE CONCERNING REPAIRS TO STRUCTURAL PARTS OF AIRCRAFT POWERPLANTS. FAR 43, APPENDIX A (B) (2), DEFINES POWERPLANT MAJOR REPAIRS AND SPEAKS TO STRUCTURAL ENGINE PARTS, HOWEVER, THE SECTION ADDRESSES ITSELF SPECIFICALLY TO RECIPROCATING ENGINES. THIS LEADS TO A PARTICULAR NEED FOR GUIDANCE CONCERNING TURBINE ENGINE REPAIRS AND THE CLASSIFICATION OF TURBINE ENGINE STRUCTURAL PARTS. THEREFORE, IN ORDER TO ARRIVE AT A UNIFORM POLICY CONCERNING REPAIRS TO TURBINE AND RECIPROCATING ENGINES, THE FOLLOWING CRITERIA ARE OFFERED AS GUIDANCE.

632. TURBINE ENGINE PARTS. EACH MANUFACTURER MAY NOT USE THE IDENTICAL TERMINOLOGY USED BELOW, HOWEVER WHAT IS USED WILL BE EQUIVALENT TO THESE TERMS.

    A. THE STRUCTURAL ENGINE PARTS:
        (1) ALL FRAMES.
        (2) ALL CASINGS OR HOUSINGS.
        (3) ENGINE MOUNTS, AND ASSOCIATED ENGINE STRUCTURE.
        (4) COMPLETE ROTOR ASSEMBLY.

    B. THE ENGINE FRAMES:
        (1) FRONT FRAMES OR FRONT BEARING SUPPORT.
        (2) COMPRESSOR REAR FRAME.
        (3) TURBINE MIDFRAME
        (4) TURBINE REAR FRAME OR REAR BEARING SUPPORT.

    C. THE ENGINE CASINGS OR HOUSINGS:
        (1) FAN CASING.
        (2) COMPRESSOR, BOTH LOW AND HIGH PRESSURE.
        (3) COMBUSTOR CASING OR HOUSING.
        (4) TURBINE CASING OR HOUSING.
        (5) ACCESSORY GEAR CASE HOUSING.

633. TURBINE ENGINE REPAIRS. REGARDING MODULAR AND NON-MODULAR DESIGNED TURBINE ENGINES THE FOLLOWING WOULD APPLY:
A. MODULAR DESIGN TURBINE ENGINES: THE CHANGING OF MODULES SHOULD "NOT" BE CONSIDERED A MAJOR REPAIR. THE DISASSEMBLY OF A MODULE SHOULD BE CONSIDERED A MAJOR REPAIR.
B. NON-MODULAR DESIGN TURBINE ENGINES: THE DISASSEMBLY OF ANY OF THE MAIN SECTIONS OF A TURBINE ENGINE SHOULD BE CONSIDERED A MAJOR REPAIR. THE MAIN SECTIONS ARE:
    (1) FAN SECTION.
    (2) COMPRESSOR SECTION, BOTH LOW AND HIGH PRESSURE.
    (3) COMBUSTION SECTION.
    (4) TURBINE SECTION.
    (5) ACCESSORY SECTION.

Fig. 5-13 — Turbine engine major versus minor repair.

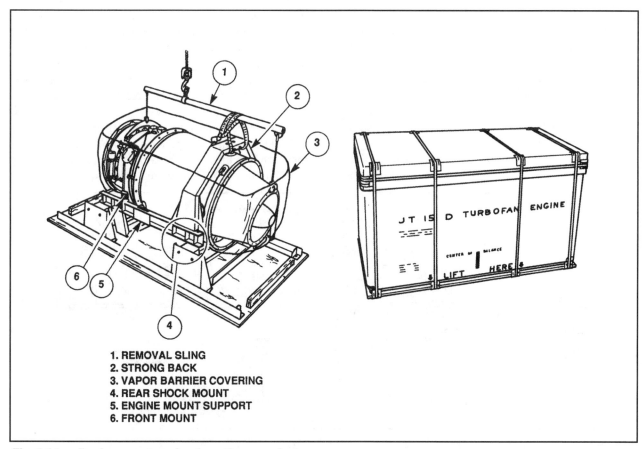

1. REMOVAL SLING
2. STRONG BACK
3. VAPOR BARRIER COVERING
4. REAR SHOCK MOUNT
5. ENGINE MOUNT SUPPORT
6. FRONT MOUNT

Fig. 5-14 — Replacement engine from the manufacturer.

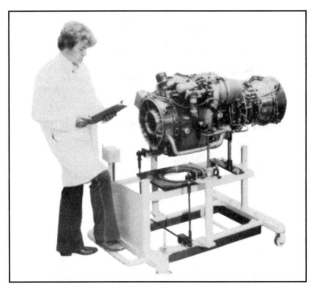

Fig. 5-15 — Small engine at overhaul
facility — General Electric CT-7 Turboshaft.

1. Borescoping

The fundamental inspection of engine inlets, exhausts, and other exterior areas of built up engines is to visually look for tell-tale signs of air, fuel, and oil leaks and items that are loose, chafed, broken, or otherwise damaged.

Borescoping of inner parts of the engine is another valuable inspection technique (Figure 5-21). The viewing eyepiece of the borescope is lighted, capable of magnification, and is adaptable to photography. The borescope can be rigid or flexible, with the flexible types having a fiber optics core for viewing in areas where the rigid type probe cannot reach.

Figures 5-20 and 5-21 show typical access port locations for inserting the eyepiece. The entire inner portion of the engine cannot be viewed with the borescope, only selected areas that are identified as critical by the manufacturer.

The photographs show the borescope views and the actual views with the piece out of the engine. It can

Fig. 5-17 — Engines being assembled vertically.

readily be seen that it will require a trained technician to interpret the findings when performing the borescope inspection (Figure 5-22).

Shown in Figure 5-23 is a more advanced borescope design equipped with a video viewing system, a camera, and a grinding tip. The rotary file or stone at the tip is designed for use in specific engine locations to blend out small areas of damage in order to remove stress points. In the picture, the area being accessed is the first stage of the high pressure compressor.

2. Other Nondestructive Inspections

Nondestructive inspection (NDI), sometimes referred to as nondestructive testing (NDT), is a means of checking the external and internal condition of aircraft and engine parts without changing their airworthiness. In a gas turbine engine, if these inspections are accomplished in a timely manner, they can avert costly unscheduled maintenance as a result of failures of parts due to fatigue and wear.

Some inspection methods require the part to be broken down into its basic components before testing, and other inspection methods can be accomplished on a built-up assembly or a complete engine assembly. The inspector

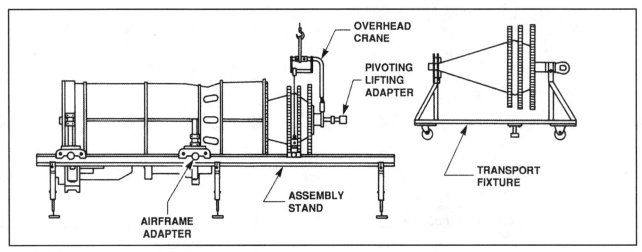

Fig. 5-16 — Turbine rotor removal.

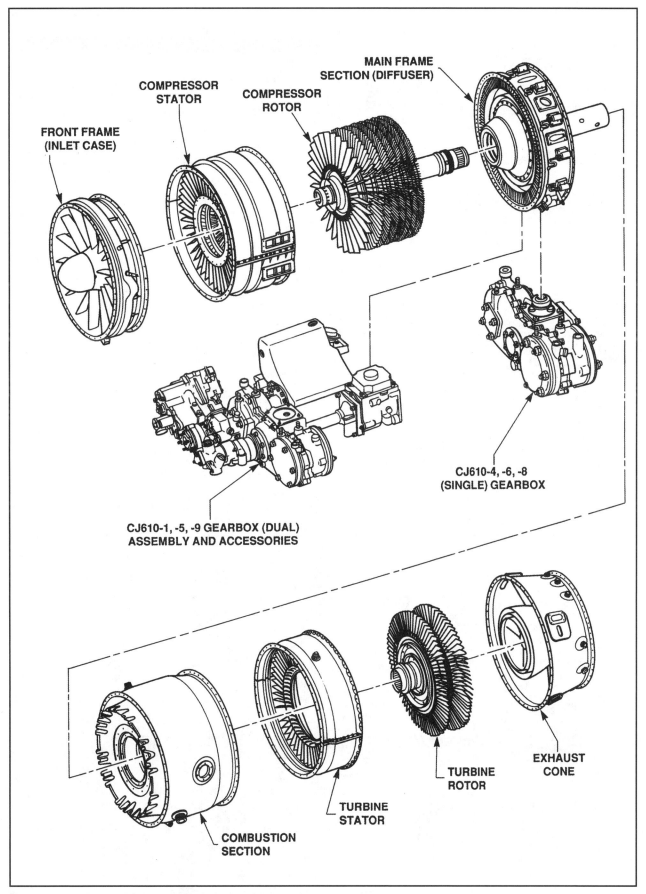

Fig. 5-18 — Major engine sections, General Electric CJ-610 turbojet.

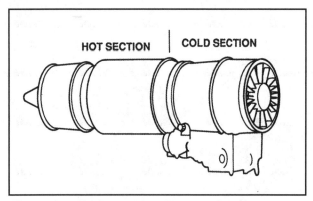

Fig. 5-19 — Engine cold and hot sections.

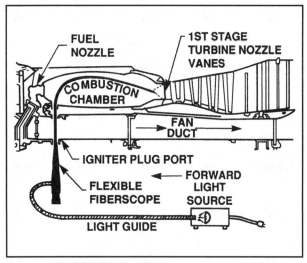

Fig. 5-20 — Flexible borescope.

must make the determination of the most appropriate method of inspection to be used and the extent to which the part needs to be disassembled to obtain the most accurate results.

There are many nondestructive inspection methods available in industry. The most commonly used methods in gas turbine engine overhaul are as follows:

a. Magnetic-Particle Method

The magnetic particle method requires use of special test apparatus and is most effective in detecting defects such as cracks, porosity, inclusions, and voids at or near the surface in ferrous materials.

The part to be inspected is first magnetized, and then a layer of fine test particles of magnetic material is applied to its surface. When the part is arranged in the magnetic field created by the test device, a material defect will create a magnetic field leakage which attracts the test particles. The particles form up in line with the defect, giving a visible indication of the shape and extent of the problem area.

The test particles can be applied in dry form or wet in a kerosene type fluid. Dry particles best detect subsurface defects in cast or forged parts which have rough surfaces. Wet fluorescent particles are best used for detection of fine cracks in smooth surfaces. An ultraviolet light is necessary for the wet inspection, and a room that is sufficiently darkened is required for the best visibility of the suspect area (See Figure 5-24A).

b. Dye-Penetrant Method

There are two common dye check methods used today in the aircraft industry, they are the Red-Dye Method and the Fluorescent Green-Dye Method.

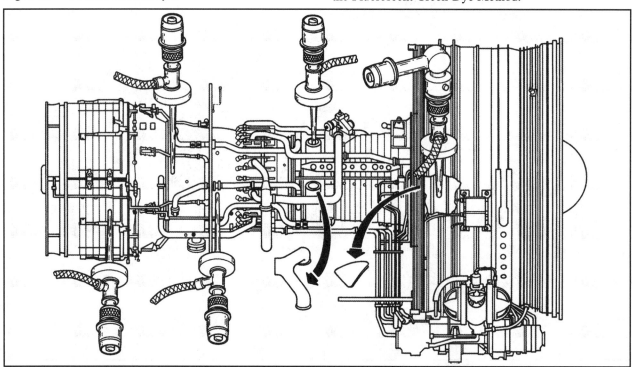

Fig. 5-21 — Borescope locations of a General Electric CF6 turbofan. Inspection interval 150 to 500 engine cycles.

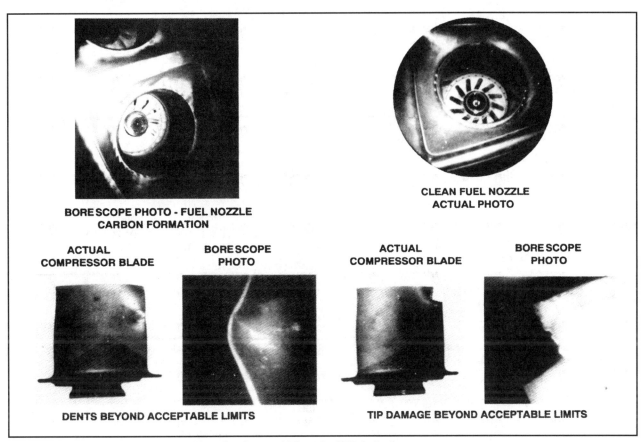

Fig. 5-22 — Borescope photography of a General Electric CF6 turbofan.

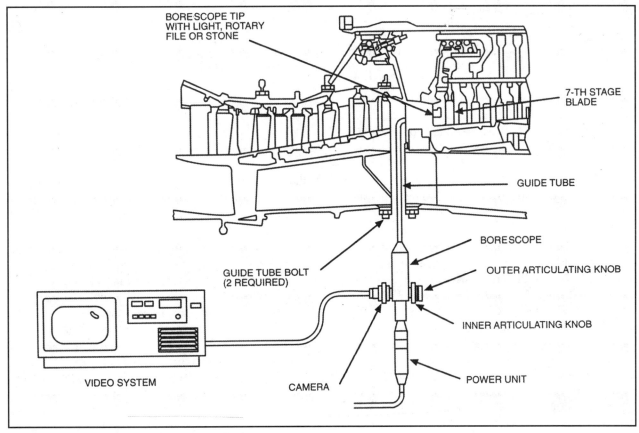

Fig. 5-23 — Borescope with Blending Tool.

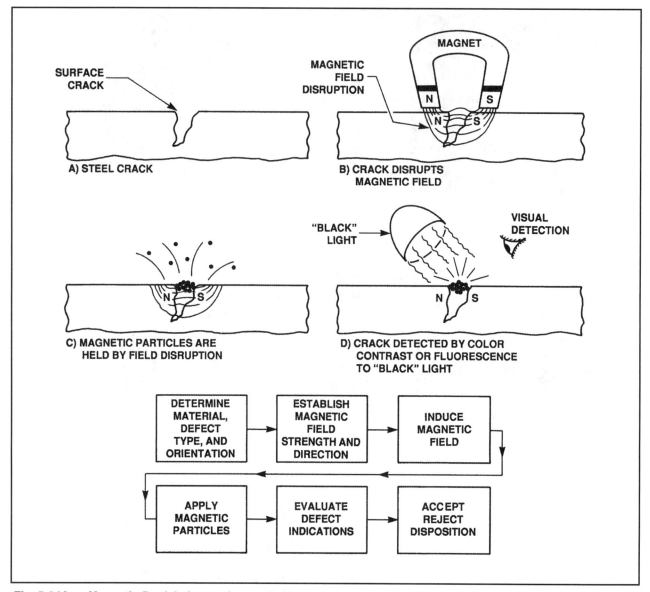

Fig. 5-24A — Magnetic-Particle inspection method.

The Red-Dye kit typically consists of three aerosol containers: A penetrating red dye, a cleaning fluid, and a developer.

The Red-Dye Method is used in daylight conditions to detect cracks and voids open to the surface in most ferrous and non-ferrous materials. The penetrating fluid, when applied to a clean surface, will seep into defects and will remain even after the surface is wiped dry of the penetrant. Then when the developer, a chalk colored spray, is applied any defect will appear as a red mark or red line on the whitened surface.

The Green-Dye Method is used for detecting the same type defects as the Red Dye, but it is sometimes more convenient when inspecting larger parts. The test item is placed in a drip tray, cleaned, and then sprayed with a green fluorescent penetrating fluid. Then, after a prescribed drying interval, usually five to thirty minutes,

the item is inspected visually under an ultraviolet light in a darkened room. Cracks show up as bright yellow-green lines, and voids show up as yellow-green marks defining the shape of the defect (See Figure 5-24B).

c. Radiographic Method

The Radiographic Method employs the use of X-rays, Gamma rays, and other penetrating radiation to reveal cracks, voids, or inclusions in the subsurface or deep interior of solid materials. Defects that will not show up in the magnetic-particle and dye-check nondestructive inspection procedures can be found with the radiographic inspection. Special test apparatus and licensed operators are needed for this inspection.

When penetrating rays are introduced into a part which contains a discontinuity in its interior, the rays create an image of the defect on a photographic plate which is positioned at the exterior surface opposite to the

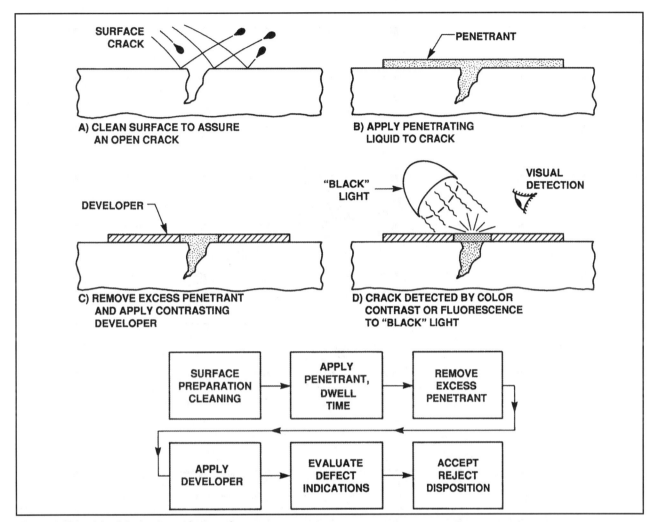

Fig. 5-24B — Liquid penetrant inspections.

point of introducing the rays. This method will detect flaws in most metallic and nonmetallic solids and even measure the thickness of plating surfaces.

The radiographic inspection provides a permanent record of the findings to compare against past and future Radiographic inspections and is valuable in that it can show progression of some types of defects from one inspection to the next (See Figure 5-24C).

d. Eddy Current Method

The eddy current inspection process is accomplished by placing a metallic part in a test device, then passing an electrical current through it. This creates a secondary magnetic field within an induced magnetic field created by the test device. The presence of a surface or subsurface flaw in the part alters the eddy current of the magnetic fields, which are then measured by a special detection coil in the test unit. This test can also be used to measure thickness of platings applied to metallic surfaces. It is widely used with simple parts, such as turbine and compressor blades, which can be tested in place or removed from the engine and placed into a fixture on the eddy current device (See Figure 5-24D).

e. Ultrasonic Method

The ultrasonic method introduces sound waves through a part and measures the time rate of pulses of energy. Discontinuities in the material will change this time factor from that of established time factors of a good part. This method is most effective in more dense metallic and nonmetallic materials of regular shape and smooth surfaces. The ultrasonic methods will detect very small surface and subsurface defects in parent material, discontinuities in bonded materials, and delamination of base materials (See Figure 5-24E).

3. Inspection Terminology

Inspection terms are listed and defined in Section K of this chapter.

4. Cold Section Inspection And Repair

a. Compressor Disassembly

It can be seen in Figure 5-25 that if only the N_1 compressor is in need of repair, it can be removed as follows: Remove the N_1 fan case, unfasten the N_1 compressor case from the N_2 compressor case, roll the N_1 compressor

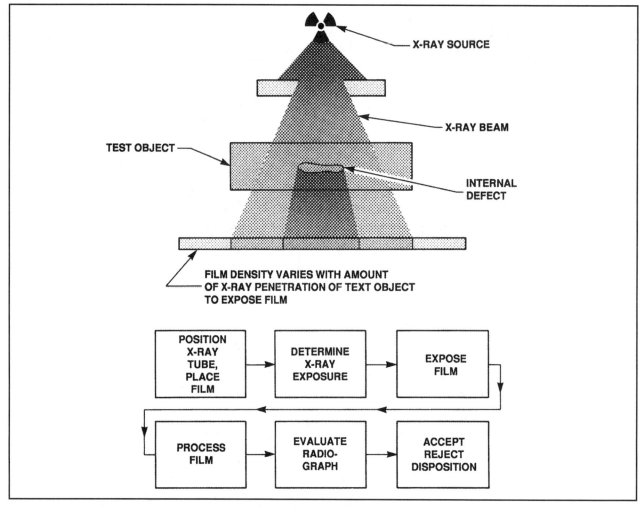

Fig. 5-24C — Radiographic inspection.

forward in the work stand, lift the N_1 compressor to a vertical position with an overhead hoist, and with the aft end high, unstack the stators and rotors down to the inlet case.

b. Axial Compressor Inspection And Repair

Minor impact damage to compressor blades can be repaired on the flight line or in the shop if the damage can be removed without exceeding allowable limits. When repairs are completed within the prescribed limits, there will be no compressor imbalance, and balancing checks are not usually required.

The following illustrations show typical gas turbine cold section repairs. This information is general in nature and information contained in the manufacturer's manuals is always required for making these repairs (Figures 5-27 and 5-28).

1) Typical Fan Blade Damage Limits

Repair to coded areas is accomplished by a procedure termed blending. Blending is a hand method of re-contouring damaged blades and vanes using common and dye sinker type files, crocus and emery cloth, and India or Carborundum stones. The use of power tools is

seldom permitted on installed blades due to the possibility of heat stress buildup and inadvertent damage to adjacent parts in what is usually a restricted working area.

Blending is performed parallel to the length of the blade to minimize stress points and to restore as smooth an aerodynamic shape as possible to the surface. Quite often this procedure can be completed on the flight line if damage is limited to the first one or two stages. Generally, blending of only the damaged blade is necessary. Occasionally, the manufacturer will require making an identical blend on the blade 180° opposite to maintain rotor balance.

Note that in Figure 5-26 no damage is allowed in Area E, the blade fillet area, because of the concentration of mechanical stresses that occur at these points during engine operation.

After repair, some manufacturers recommend covering the blend with a felt tip dye marking material or similar solution to identify it as a reworked area. This benefits those maintenance personnel who will later view it while performing inlet inspections.

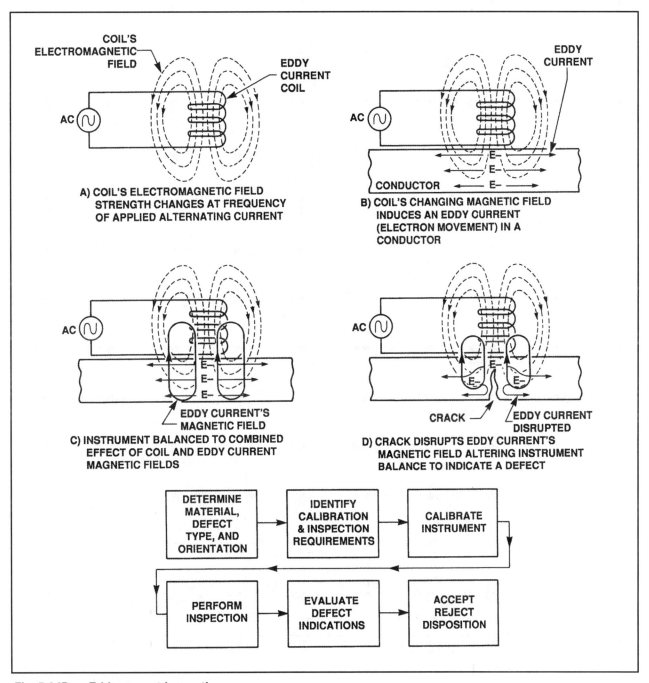

Fig. 5-24D — Eddy current inspection.

2) Electron Beam Welding

Welding and straightening of rotating airfoils usually requires special equipment and quite often is authorized to be done only at overhaul facilities or by the manufacturer. One new technique, called electron beam welding, now permits the reworking of many compressor blades formerly thought to be unserviceable. This beam welding procedure is especially useful on titanium alloy, from which many blades are made. A beam-weld results in a strength factor equal to a new blade.

Illustration 5-29 shows the apparatus which is used in electron beam welding. Notice that the piece being welded is in a vacuum chamber during the reworking

process. By controlling the oxygen level, the heat can be concentrated at the weld point better than if welded in atmospheric air.

Illustration 5-30 shows the result of a beam weld and the narrow bead which is made possible by concentrating the heat. A lower stress is placed on the base metal with this process than with conventional welding methods.

Figure 5-31 shows a compressor/fan blade with leading edge damage beyond the limits of a blend repair. The damaged area is ground off and an insert piece is beam-welded. The piece is then ground down to the blades original shape.

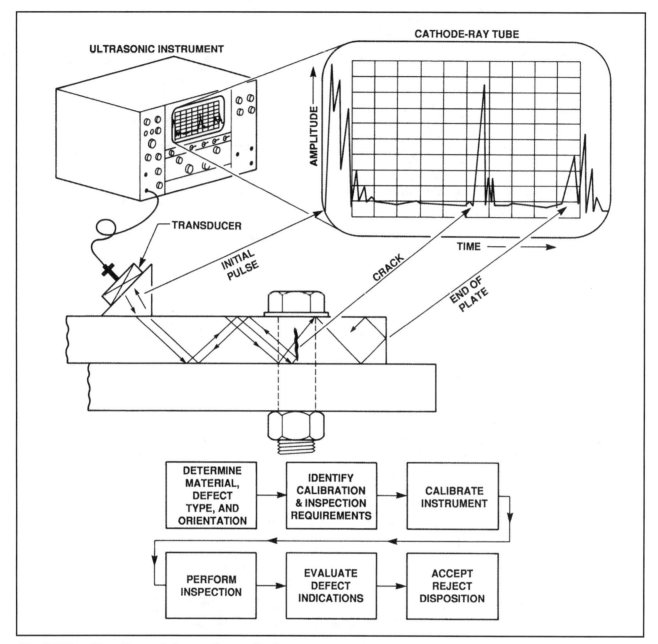

Fig. 5-24E — The ultrasonic inspection method.

Fig. 5-25 — Removal of the front compressor for repair — Pratt & Whitney JT8 turbofan.

3) Plasma Surface Repair Coating (Figure 5-32)

Another valuable overhaul process is to repair blades and vanes by applying a coating of material to its surface. If blade roots for instance are worn, a process called Plasma Coating can be accomplished to restore the root area to its original specifications.

The plasma spray process has in recent years become one of the most successful techniques in reclaiming formerly unusable parts. Information from industry indicates that a re-coated part typically costs approximately one-half the new replacement part cost.

The plasma spray process is accomplished by applying a metallic spray material, in an atomized state, to the base metal at high velocity and heat. The base metal is at room temperature, but the gas carrying the

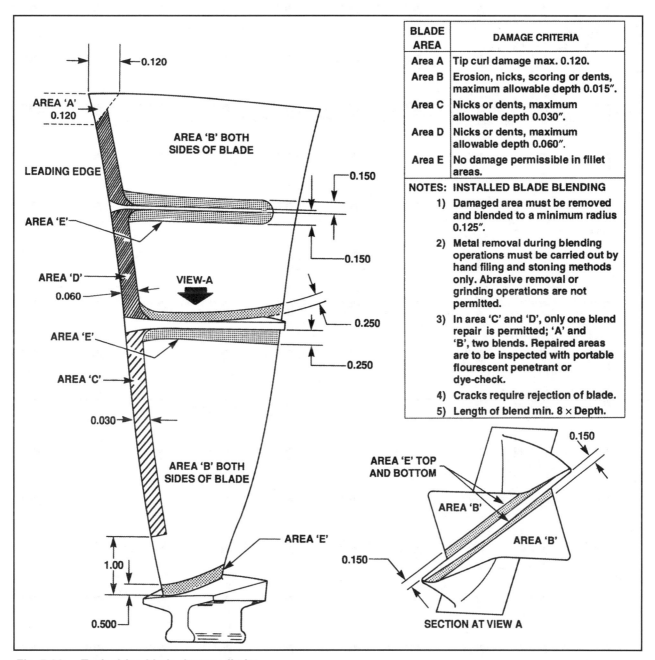

BLADE AREA	DAMAGE CRITERIA
Area A	Tip curl damage max. 0.120.
Area B	Erosion, nicks, scoring or dents, maximum allowable depth 0.015".
Area C	Nicks or dents, maximum allowable depth 0.030".
Area D	Nicks or dents, maximum allowable depth 0.060".
Area E	No damage permissible in fillet areas.

NOTES: INSTALLED BLADE BLENDING

1) Damaged area must be removed and blended to a minimum radius 0.125".
2) Metal removal during blending operations must be carried out by hand filing and stoning methods only. Abrasive removal or grinding operations are not permitted.
3) In area 'C' and 'D', only one blend repair is permitted; 'A' and 'B', two blends. Repaired areas are to be inspected with portable flourescent penetrant or dye-check.
4) Cracks require rejection of blade.
5) Length of blend min. 8 × Depth.

Fig. 5-26 — Typical fan blade damage limits.

spray is super-heated to as high as 50,000°F and travels at approximately Mach 2 velocity. Coatings as thin as 0.00025 inches are possible, and multiple coats can build up to several thousandths of an inch and be completely fused to the base metal. In many instances, the new surface will be stronger than the original. After the coating is applied, the piece is ground as necessary to its final shape and dimensions.

The plasma spray is equally applicable to hot-end parts as well as cold-end parts.

Spray coatings for anti-corrosion purposes and for enhancing airflow can be used on compressor parts. One such process is called Sermetal™. It is sprayed onto a prepared surface and when dry has a ceramic-like finish. This greatly reduces surface drag and air friction, thereby promoting good compression and reduced fuel consumption.

4) Tip Clearance

Plasma and other coating techniques are especially valuable in returning compressor blade tip clearances to original specifications. Correct clearances between blades and housings are important because compressor performance depends greatly on the controlled aerodynamic effect of its airfoils. For instance, a large engine with a 0.035 inch cold tip clearance might reduce typically to 0.002 inch clearance during operation. Case distortion and blade radial loading during operation can occasionally allow contact which will increase the running clearance by tip rubbing. The resulting loss of air over the blade tip, and the boundary layer distortion

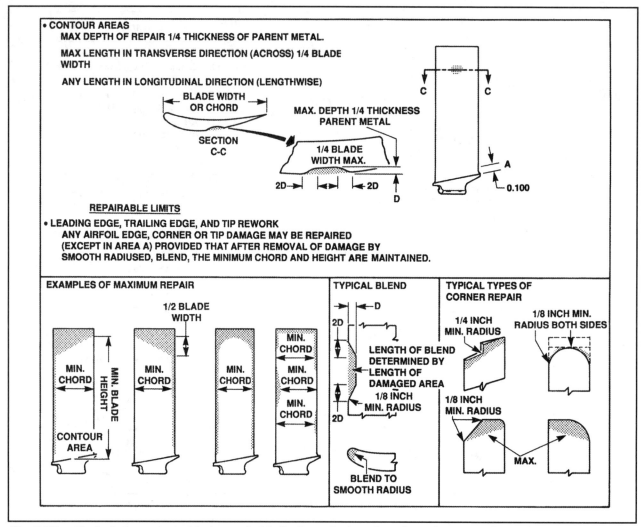

Fig. 5-27 — *Typical compressor blade repairable limits and examples of maximum repair by blending.*

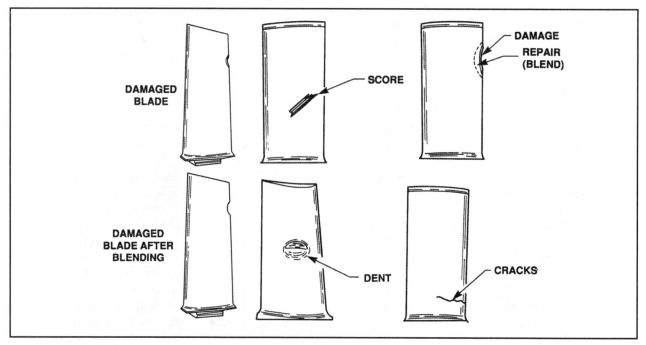

Fig. 5-28 — *Typical compressor blade damage and repairs.*

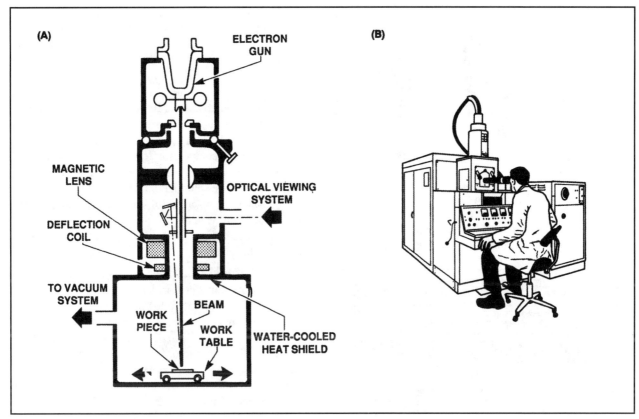

Fig. 5-29A — Piece being electron beam welded.
Fig. 5-29B — Electron beam welding apparatus.

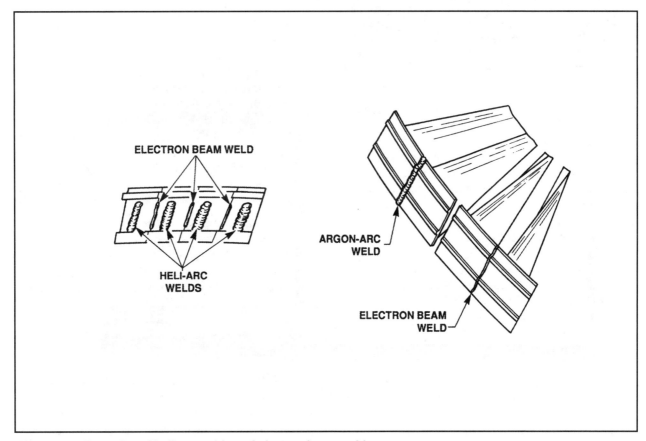

Fig. 5-30 — Examples of heli-arc welds and electron beam welds.

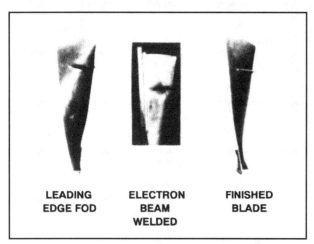

Fig.5-31— *Example of fan blade leading edge repair.*

Fig. 5-32 — *Plasma spray process used in rebuilding worn surfaces.*

which will occur, can cause serious loss of compression, compressor stalls, and over-temperatures.

On small engines, in which the clearance is a greater percentage of blade height, excessive clearance can greatly affect compressor efficiency. Tip clearances are generally taken with a thickness (feeler) gauge with the upper compressor case removed. Maintaining correct tip clearances is equally applicable to hot-end blading.

5) Blade Replacement (Figure 5-33)

Blade replacement is generally allowed, with a restriction placed on the number of blades replaced per stage and per entire rotor. The blades are moment-weighted and coded to provide a means of exact replacement for maintaining compressor balance. Moment-weight accounts for both the mass weight and the center of balance.

On compressor stages with an even number of blades, two blades can be replaced if one of the appropriate moment-weight is not available. The damaged blade and its opposite blade are replaced together as a pair.

If the compressor stage has an odd number of blades, three blades 120° apart can be replaced as a set under the

same circumstances. Under severe restrictions, some manufacturers allow replacement by mass weight, and certainly other replacement criteria also exists for specific installations. Some fan blades, for instance, are replaceable on the wing, while others are replaceable only during heavy maintenance.

If compressor blades are designed to be individually removed, there is generally a maximum number of damaged blades that can be replaced without re-balancing the compressor. If that maximum number of blades is exceeded, the unit will require a balance check after repair. The photograph (Figure 5-34) shows a typical balancing machine for small compressors. During the check, small weights are added or removed, or small portions of metal are ground off with a hand grinder to attain the balance.

c. Centrifugal Compressor Inspection

Inspect the impeller for nicks, dents, and cracks (See Figure 5-35.), using the following criteria:
1) Critical Area. No cracks or nicks allowed. Smooth dents are permitted, provided they do not exceed 0.030 inch in diameter and/or 0.010 inch in depth.
2) Leading Edge. No cracks allowed. Nicks or dents are permitted, provided they do not exceed 0.100 inch in depth and 0.300 inch in length after blend repair. Distance between repairs must be equal to or greater than length of longest repair.
3) Trailing Edge. No cracks are allowed. Nicks or dents are permitted, provided they do not exceed 0.060 inch in depth or 0.300 inch in length after repair. Distance between repairs must be equal to or greater than length of longest repair.
4) Blade Tips. No cracks are allowed. Six nicks or dents are permitted, provided they do not exceed 0.060 inch in depth or 0.300 inch in length after repair. Distance between repaired areas must be at least 3/8 inch.
5) Airfoil (sides of blades). No cracks are allowed. Nicks and dents are permitted, provided they do not exceed 0.030 inch in depth or 0.350 inch in length after repair. Distance between repaired areas, regardless of location, must be at least 1/2 inch.

d. Stator Vane And Compressor Case Inspection And Repair

Repairs of slight impact damage to stator vanes and compressor cases are generally made by blending. Cracks are usually weld-repairable with traditional inert gas welding apparatus. Typical observable damage is shown in Figures 5-36 and 5-37. If weld beads interfere with fits or airflow, they are ground back as nearly as possible to the original contour.

5. Hot Section Inspection And Repair
a. Combustion Section

Cracking is one of the most frequent discrepancies that will be detected while inspecting the combustion section of a turbine engine. The combustion liner is constructed

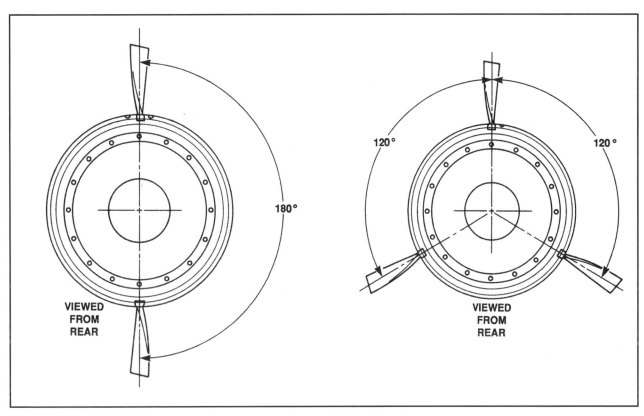

Fig. 5-33A — *Typical replacement of compressor blades (180° method).*
Fig. 5-33B — *Typical replacement of compressor blades (120° method).*

Fig. 5-34 — *Combination axial/centrifugal compressor rotor assembly installed in balancing machine after blade replacement.*

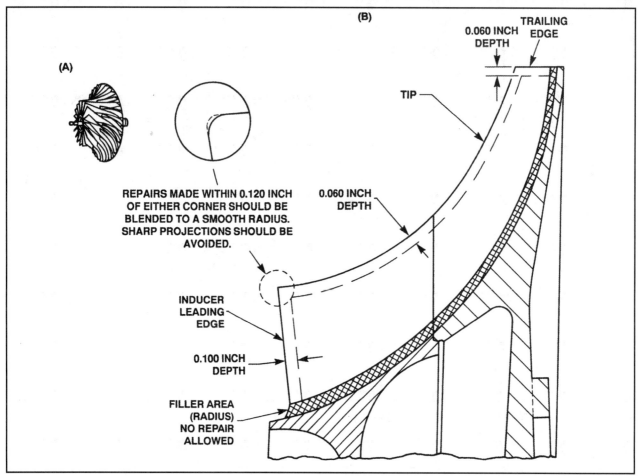

Fig. 5-35A — Centrifugal impeller.
Fig. 5-35B — Repair limits.

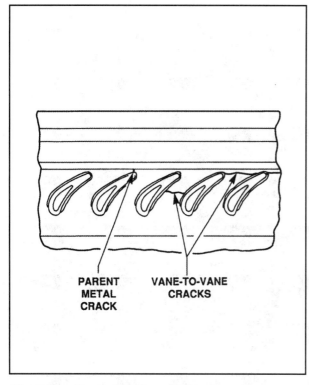

Fig. 5-36 — Typical weld repairable damage.

of thin stainless steel material that is subjected to high concentrations of heat.

1) Visual Inspection (Figure 5-38)

The most common method of checking for misalignment, cracks, and other hot distress on installed engines is by using an internal viewing device called a borescope. There are both rigid and flexible types available with different illumination and magnification capabilities similar to the units discussed for compressor inspection (See Figures 5-20 and 5-21).

With the borescope, the maintenance technician can easily view internal engine components and determine airworthiness of parts. During a borescope inspection, the operator looks for distress which is out of the manufacturer's limits, such as obvious cracking, warpage, burning, erosion, and sometimes obscure but tell-tale hot spots. These hot spots are possible indicators of a serious condition, such as malfunctioning fuel nozzles or other fuel system malfunctions, and require careful interpretation.

Another important aspect of borescoping is to check for misalignment of combustion liners. It has been determined that "burner-can shift", as it is called, can seriously affect combustor efficiency and engine performance.

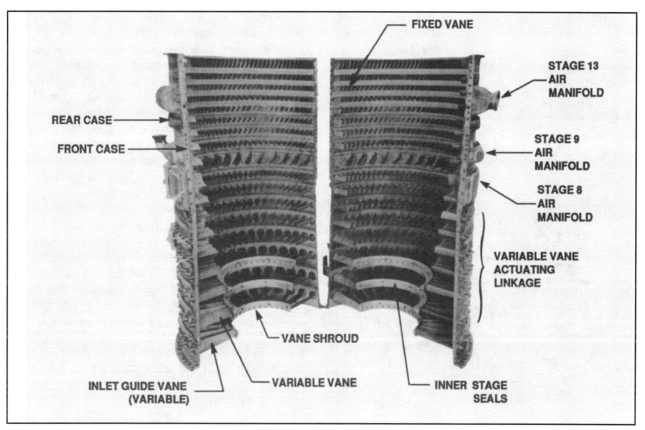

Fig. 5-37 — Compressor front and rear casing components.

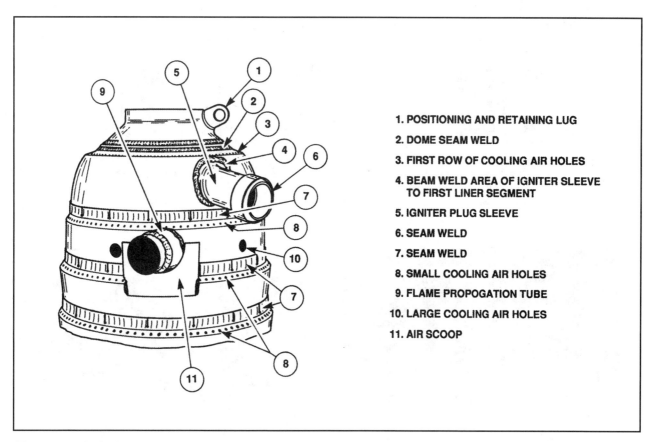

1. POSITIONING AND RETAINING LUG

2. DOME SEAM WELD

3. FIRST ROW OF COOLING AIR HOLES

4. BEAM WELD AREA OF IGNITER SLEEVE TO FIRST LINER SEGMENT

5. IGNITER PLUG SLEEVE

6. SEAM WELD

7. SEAM WELD

8. SMALL COOLING AIR HOLES

9. FLAME PROPOGATION TUBE

10. LARGE COOLING AIR HOLES

11. AIR SCOOP

Fig. 5-38 — Typical combustion chamber liner inspection points.

Whether the engine is fit to remain in service or needs to be disassembled for repair or replacement of combustor section parts must be determined by the technician. His or her expertise and training make this important determination possible.

b. Turbine Section (Figures 5-39 and 5-40)

Inspection of the inner turbine section is also done with a borescope, visually through the tailpipe with a strong light, mirror, and a magnifying glass, or by

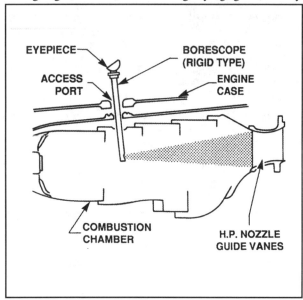

Fig. 5-39 — Borescoping the liner and first stage turbine stator.

disassembly of the engine. On the flight line, nondestructive inspection techniques such as the dye penetrant method are also useful in external inspection. As in other hot section inspections, the technician is most likely to see small cracks caused by compression and tension loading from heating and cooling. Other than on turbine blades, much of this type of distress is acceptable and requires no maintenance action because, after initial cracks relieve the stress, no elongation of cracks occur. Erosion is another common inspection finding. Erosion is the wearing away of metal either from the gas flow across its surfaces or impingement on the surfaces of impurities in the gas flow.

If hot spots are seen, they are generally the first indication of a malfunction in fuel distribution. A too rich mixture can cause lengthening of the flame until it reaches the turbine nozzle vanes. A condition called hot streaking can cause a flame to penetrate through the entire turbine system to the tailpipe. A hot streaking condition is caused by partially clogged fuel nozzles which do not atomize the fuel but allow a small fuel stream to flow with sufficient force to cut through the cooling air blanket and impinge directly on the turbine surfaces.

1) Turbine Wheel

Figure 5-41 shows turbine blade blend repair limits which are typical of either shop or flight line maintenance. According to this manufacturer, cracks are never acceptable (which is the case with most manufacturers).

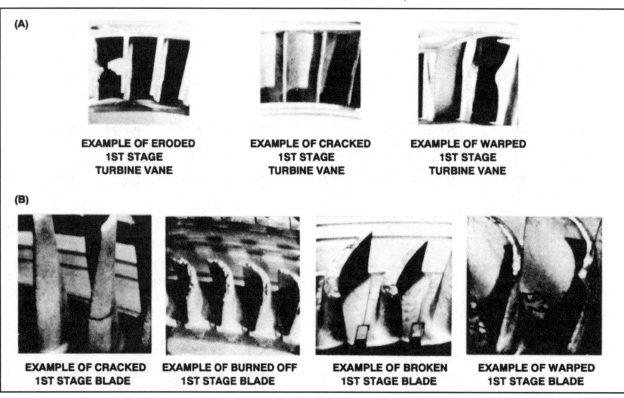

Fig. 5-40A — Borescope view of turbine vanes.
Fig. 5-40B — Borescope view of turbine blades.

INSPECTION	MAXIMUM SERVICEABLE	MAXIMUM REPAIRABLE	CORRECTION ACTION
BLADE SHIFT	Protrusion of any blade root must be equal within 0.015" either side of disk.	Not repairable	Return bladed disk assembly to an overhaul facility.
AREA A			
Nicks (3 max.)	0.015" long by 0.005" deep	.015 long by 0.010" deep	Blend out damaged area / Replace blade
Dents and pits (3 max.)	0.010" deep	.015 long by 0.010" deep	Blend out damaged area / Replace blade
Cracks	Not acceptable	Not repairable	Replace blade
AREA B			
Nicks, dents, and pits (No cracks allowed)	One 0.020" deep	Not repairable	Replace blade
LEADING AND TRAILING EDGES			
Nicks, dents, and pits	One 0.020" deep	Two 1/8" deep	Blend out damaged area/ Replace blade
Cracks	Not acceptable	Not repairable	Replace blade

(A)

1/4"
FILLET AREA
B
1/8"
TRAILING EDGE
LEADING EDGE
1/8"
A
1/8"
1/4"
1/8"
B
FILLET AREAS CRITICAL NO DAMAGE PERMITTED

NOTE:
RIPPLING OF TRAILING EDGE IS NOT ACCEPTABLE

(B)

REPAIRED BLADE

(C)

"W" WIDTH = (APPROX) 8 "D" DEPTH

D
W
A
A
VIEW A
ROUNDED EDGE
SECTION A-A

B
B
VIEW B
BLENDED
NICK, DENT, PIT, ETC.
D
W
SECTION B-B

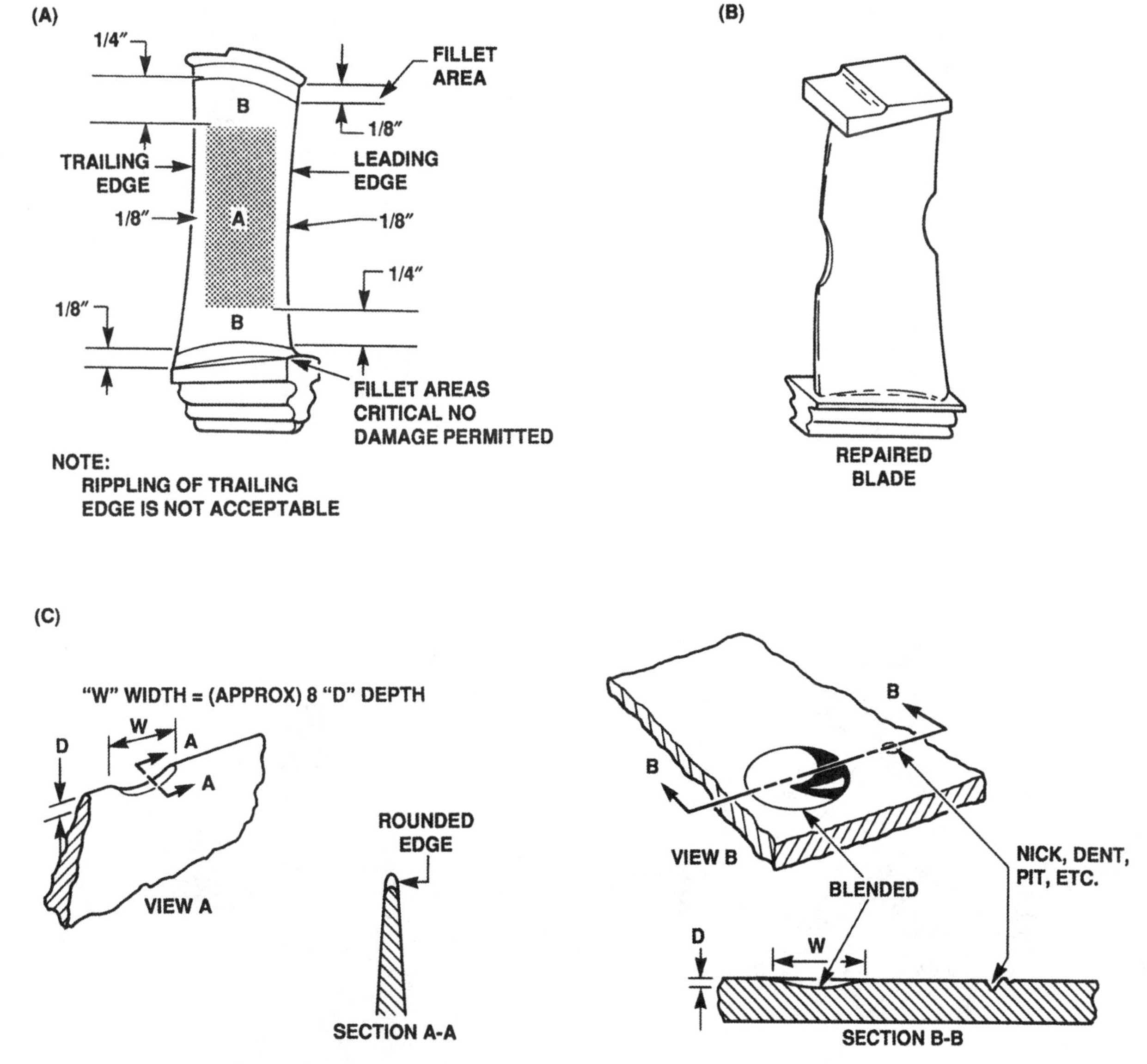

Fig. 5-41A — Power turbine blade repair limits.
Fig. 5-41B — Repaired blade.
Fig. 5-41C — Typical blending guides for turbine blade defects other than cracks.

Of particular concern during visual inspections are stress rupture cracks on turbine blade leading or trailing edges. Stress rupture cracks are perceptible as minute hairline cracks at right angles to the blade length. This condition, and rippling of the trailing edge, is an indication of a serious over temperature, and a special in-shop manufacturer's inspection will probably be required (Figure 5-42).

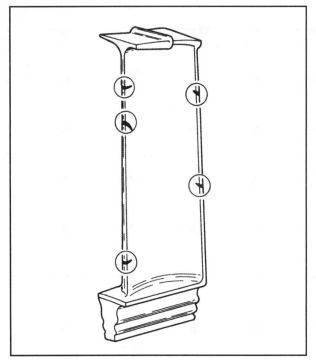

Fig. 5-42 — Stress rupture cracks.

To maintain turbine wheel balance, a single turbine blade replacement is generally accomplished by installing a new blade of equal moment-weight (Figure 5-43). If the blade's moment-weight cannot be matched, the damaged blade and one 180° out are replaced with blades of equal weight; or, the damaged blade and the blades 120° from it are replaced with three blades of equal moment weight in the same manner as was mentioned for compressor blades.

Turbine blades are rarely replaced on the wing today, however, shop procedures usually allow for entire turbine reblading, after which the rotor is checked on a special balancing device.

Code letters indicating the moment-weight in inch-ounces or inch-grams, are marked on the fir-tree section of the blade, as shown in Figure 5-44.

2) Creep And Untwist (Figure 5-45)

Creep is a term used to describe the permanent elongation which occurs to rotating parts. Creep is most pronounced in turbine blades because of the heat loads and centrifugal loads imposed during operation. Each time a turbine blade is heated, rotated, then stopped (referred to as an engine cycle), it remains slightly longer than it was before. The additional length may be only millionths of an inch under normal circumstances or, after an engine over temperature or over speed condition, very much longer.

Nevertheless, if the blade remains in service long enough, chances are that it will eventually make contact with its shroud ring and begin to wear away. When this occurs, an audible rubbing can be heard on engine

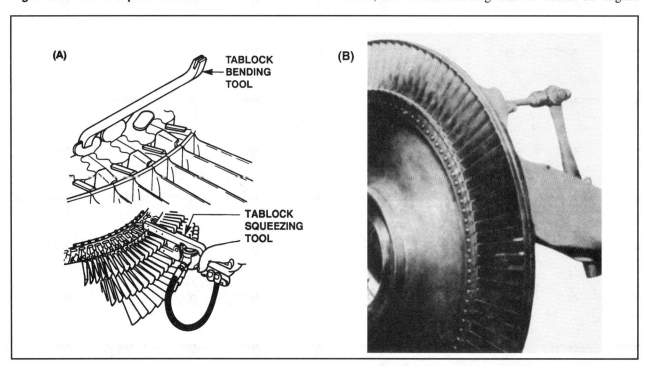

Fig. 5-43A — Replacing turbine blade and tab lock retainer.
Fig. 5-43B — Removing rivet retainer and turbine blade from disk.

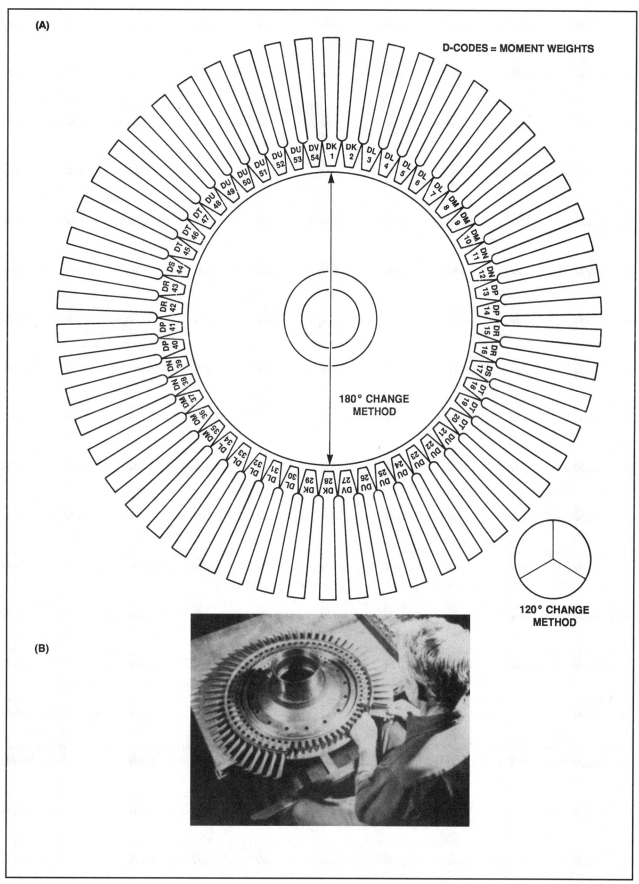

Fig. 5-44A — Typical turbine blade moment weight coding.
Fig. 5-44B — Blade replacement in high pressure turbine Pratt & Whitney PW2037.

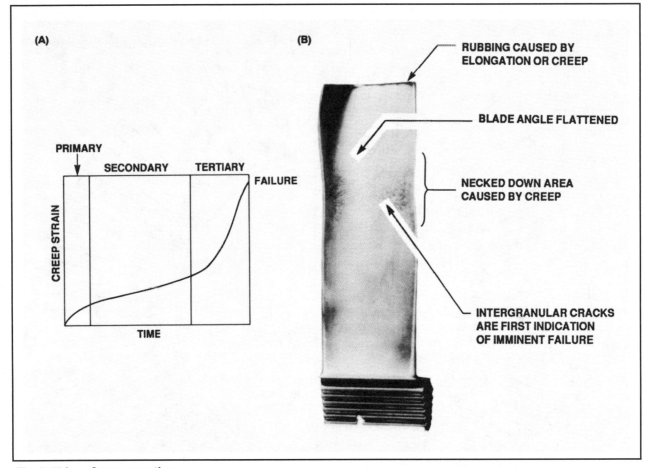

Fig. 5-45A — Creep over time.
Fig 5-45B — Turbine blade damage caused by excessive temperatures.

coast-down. Clearance checks are then taken and appropriate maintenance action is determined.

Creep can be thought of as occurring in three stages: Primary, secondary, and tertiary. The primary and tertiary stages occur relatively quickly. Primary creep occurs during the engine's first run, tertiary during operating overloads. But the secondary creep stage occurs quite slowly (flat portion on the strain/time graph). It is within the secondary creep region that the engine manufacturer bases the turbine's service life.

Accelerated (tertiary) creep during the engine's service life can be attributed to any of the following (Figure 5-45A):
a) Hot starts/over temperatures;
b) Extended operation at high power (high EGT and centrifugal loading);
c) Erosion of the blades from ingestion of sand or other foreign objects.

Untwist occurs in both turbine blades and turbine vanes from gas loads upon their surfaces. Loss of correct pitch affects efficiency of the turbine system, and engine performance deterioration results. The check for untwist is generally only possible after engine tear down when parts can be measured in special shop fixtures.

3) Turbine Case, Turbine Vanes, Exhaust Section

Turbine section parts, in effect, record all abuses in operation as well as the normal aging process in the form of cracking, warping, bowing, eroding, etc.

Certain types of small visible cracks result from thermal stresses and are commonly found after periods of normal operation. The progress of many such discrepancies with further operation is quite often negligible since the cracks in effect relieve the original stress condition. The manufacturer's limits, based on this consideration, allow certain distress conditions to be acceptable. The judgment for the technician performing the inspection is whether the part will remain airworthy until the next inspection or whether the cracks converge and are likely to permit a portion of the material to break away. This condition can cause impact damage to downstream components, as well as result in serious burn-through damage by misdirection of the hot gases (Figure 5-46).

a) Turbine cases that are worn or burned can be repaired by a process called plasma coating. Often the slots or channels that vanes fit into become worn and allow the vane to shift. Vane cases that form turbine blade shrouds erode after time. The plasma coating restores

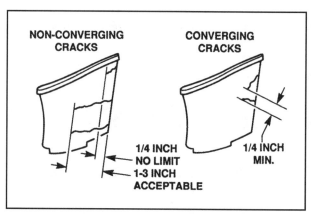

Fig. 5-46 — Converging and nonconverging cracks in turbine vanes.

the case to an "as-new" condition and is much less costly than replacement with a new part. Plasma coating was previously discussed in compressor blade repairs.

Turbine cases that are cracked or burned can be welded by conventional heli-arc methods, but the newer electron beam and laser beam welding techniques are quickly becoming the standard practice because they localize the heat and cause less stress to areas surrounding the welds.

b) Turbine vanes that are burned or eroded on their outer surfaces can often be repaired by applying the same types of plasma coatings as mentioned above for turbine cases.

Cracked or bowed vanes can be beam-welded or even restored by cutting away the damaged area and welding in a segment of new material. It is claimed that this process can produce a strength factor that exceeds the original. This is possible because the replacement material is of more current technology and of higher quality.

Figure 5-47A shows a vane that is ready for a bowing check on a flat plate. This check is accomplished by inserting a thickness gauge under the leading and trailing edge. If the piece is out of limits, it can be repaired by straightening if the material will permit such a process. If it cannot be straightened, a section can be removed and a new section welded in.

Illustration (B) shows a vane that was either bowed, cracked, eroded, or burned through such that repair by replacement of a section of material is the only possible solution. The damaged area will be ground out and a new section beam-welded in its place. The vane will be ground to its original shape and then placed in a heat oven to relieve stress and unify its strength. More than likely, the vane will be recoated by a plasma spray before being placed back in the engine.

Illustration (C) shows vane cracks which are acceptable without repair, provided they fall within the limits. When beyond these limits, welding of cracks or replacement of small sections will be repaired.

c) Exhaust cases are also susceptible to all of the hot gas path problems previously mentioned. Most of the material in this part of the engine is a type of rolled stainless steel and can be weld repaired by conventional or beam welding for cracking or patched at burned through areas. Figure 5-48 shows typical damage and repairs.

4) Engine Vibrations

The repairs described in this chapter for all rotating airfoils ensures that strength, aerodynamics, and balance are maintained. The original design of the engine provides for little or no inherent imbalance in the engine by engineering techniques to eliminate vibration, resonance, and harmonics.

These terms are defined as follows:

a) Natural frequency of vibration — the RPM at which a rotating object will vibrate. Engine parts are rotated so that natural frequency speeds are never reached. Improper repairs however, can lower the natural frequency into the operating RPM range.

b) Resonance — occurs when two mechanical systems, closely mounted, have the same natural frequency of vibration. If one malfunctions and reaches its natural frequency, the other will also vibrate along with the first, failing both systems.

c) Harmonics — severe vibrations that occur at one-times the magnitude of vibration at the natural frequency and, if unattended, two-times the natural frequency, and so on until the part fails.

5) Marking Of Parts

The general marking procedure for identifying areas to be repaired in both hot and cold section parts is to apply chalk, special layout dye or to mark with a commercial felt-tip applicator or special marking pencil. A note of caution to observe when marking any hot section parts is to refrain from using a substance which leaves a carbon, copper, zinc, or lead deposit. When the metal is heated, these deposits are drawn into the metal and can cause intergranular stress. Marking with a common graphite lead pencil is strictly prohibited. Specific marking procedures will always take precedence over general procedures.

The following caution note was excerpted from a current gas turbine engine maintenance manual.

CAUTION: Deposits left on stainless and high temperature alloy parts where marked with carbonaceous materials, such as graphite, wax, or grease pencils, may lead to failure of the parts in service. Even dychem (layout dye) is potentially hazardous if not completely removed. This type of failure occurs when parts are heat treated, welded, or exposed in any manner to elevated temperatures of 700°F or more. The exposure causes localized carbon enrichment and intergranular embrittlement, which can in turn lead to crack initiation and propagation.

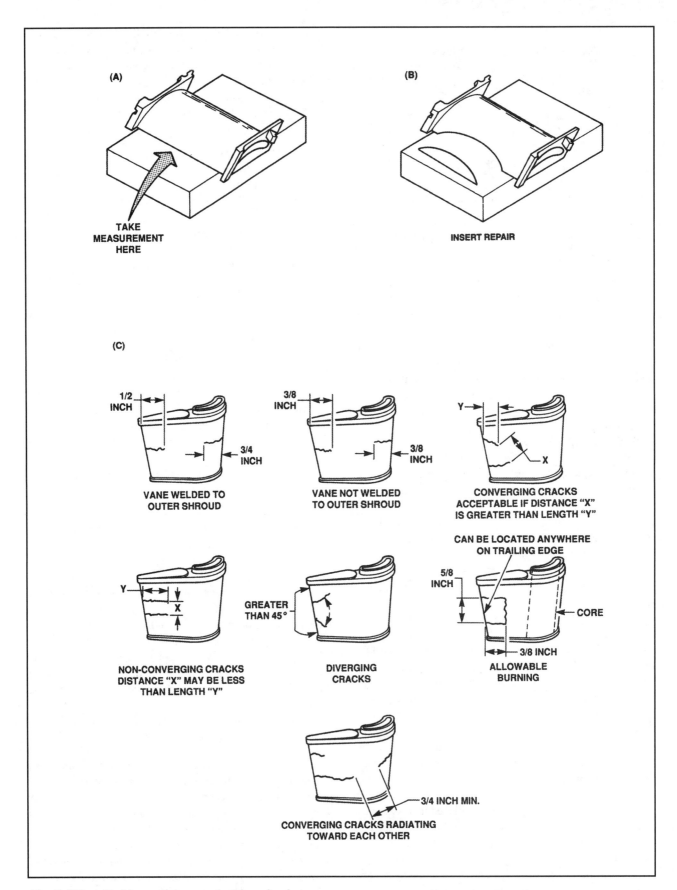

Fig. 5-47A — Turbine nozzle vane bowing check.
Fig. 5-47B — Vane repair by welding in a new segment.
Fig. 5-47C — Vanes acceptable if they do not exceed these limits (dimensions typical of small engines).

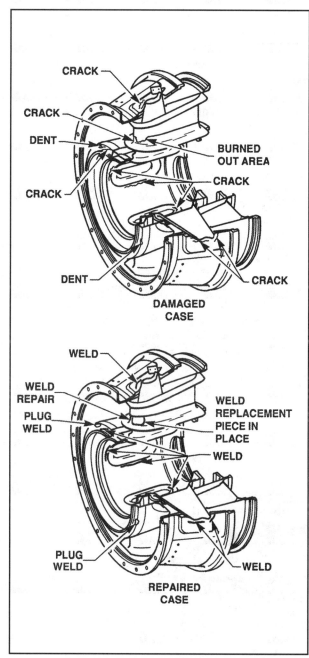

Fig. 5-48 — *Turboshaft engine exhaust collector showing typical damage and repairs.*

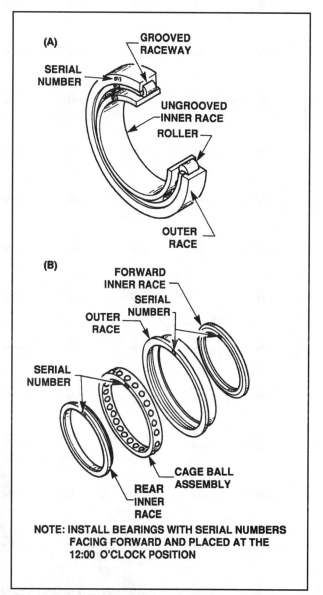

Fig. 5-49A — *Main bearing, roller type.*
Fig. 5-49B — *Main bearing, ball type.*

D. Main Bearings And Seals

1. Bearings

The main bearings of a gas turbine engine are either ball or roller anti-friction types. Ball bearings ride in a grooved inner race and support the main engine rotor for both axial (thrust) and radial (centrifugal) loads. The roller bearings ride on a flat inner race. Because of their greater surface contact area than the ball bearings, they are positioned to absorb the bulk of the radial loading and to allow for axial growth of the engine during operation. For this reason, tapered roller bearings are seldom used (Figure 5-49).

Plain bearings are not used as main bearings in turbine engines, as they are in reciprocating engines, because turbines operate at much higher speeds and friction heat buildup would be prohibitive. Plain bearings (bushings), however, are used in some minor load locations such as in accessories.

The primary loads acting on main bearings are from the following sources:

• Weight of the rotating mass (compressor and turbine) magnified many thousands of times by radial G-forces.

• Axial forces from power changes and thrust loading.

• Gyroscopic effect of heavy rotating masses trying to remain in place as the aircraft changes direction.

• Compression and tension loads between the stationary casings and the rotor system caused by thermal expansion.

• Vibrations induced by the airstream, the aircraft and the engine itself.

The main bearings support the rotor assemblies and then transfer the various loads through the bearing housings and support struts to the outer cases of the engine, and ultimately into the aircraft mountings.

The number of main bearings varies from one engine model to another. One manufacturer might prefer to install three heavy bearings and another five or six lighter bearings to accommodate the same load factors.

Construction features of ball and roller bearings are shown in Figures 5-49, and 5-50. A design feature to note is that only one of the roller bearing races is grooved, allowing the roller freedom to move axially when the engine expands and contracts during operation. The split inner race is a design feature of the ball bearing which allows for ease of bearing disassembly, maintenance, and inspection, once the bearing is removed from the engine.

The inner races of bearings are normally interference fitted to the rotor shafts to prevent movement on the shaft, and have to be removed with special puller tools. Also shown in Figure 5-50 is the oil damped bearing which is provided with an oil film between the outer race and the bearing housing to reduce vibration tendencies in the rotor system and to allow for a slight misalignment of up to five thousandths of an inch.

The component pieces of turbine bearings are generally identified by serial number to prevent intermixing. Gas turbine quality anti-friction bearings are matched sets of races, cages, etc. to conform to extremely close production tolerances. Recall that the gas turbine is referred to as a high speed, light-weight device, and this design requires that vibrations be kept to an absolute minimum even under great G-forces and gyroscopic loads. Typical dimension tolerances for the parts that make up a gas turbine engine's main bearing would be as follows:

sheet metal casings - ± 0.02"
machined casings - ± 0.002"
bearing races - ± 0.0002"
bearing rollers - ± 0.00005"
bearing balls - ± 0.00001"

Because of these tight mechanical tolerances, many bearings are installed with their serial numbers, alignment marks, and other manufacturing tolerance marks placed in a very specific manner, as prescribed by the manufacturer (See Figure 5-51).

The air balance chamber, shown in Figure 5-52, aids the compressor thrust bearing (No. 2) in combating high gas path pressures, which try to push the compressor forward. The balance chamber and the thrust bearings help restrain the compressor against the axial pushing

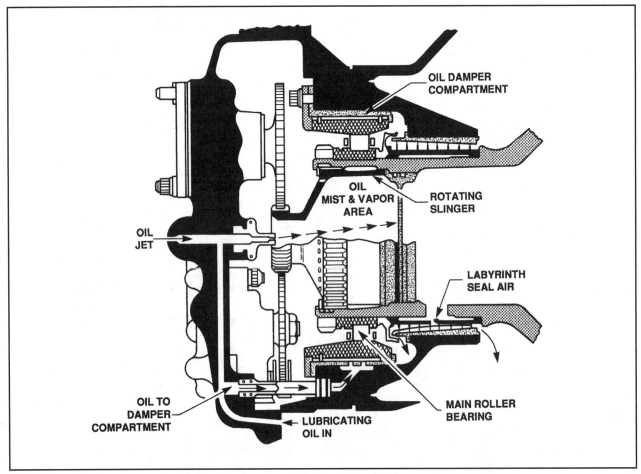

Fig. 5-50 — Front compressor main roller bearing with oil damped outer race.

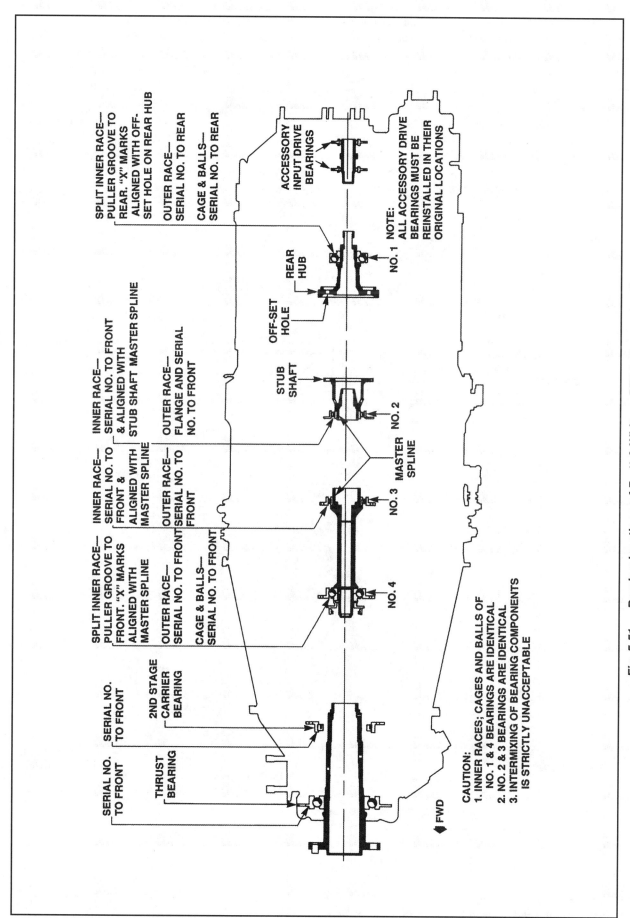

Fig. 5-51 — Bearing locations of Pratt & Whitney PT6 turboprop engine.

force. Some engines do not need an air balance chamber because the opposite (rearward) thrust load, at the turbine, adequately cancels out the forward pushing loads on the compressor.

2. Bearing Seals

Most bearing housings contain seals to prevent loss of oil into the gas path. Oil seals are usually of the labyrinth or carbon rubbing types, and it is common to see one or the other, or a combination of the two, in the same engine. The need for this arrangement arises due to temperature

gradient differences in the hot and cold sections of the engine. That is, if a labyrinth seal is used in some hot locations it might expand and contact its seal land, causing wear. The seal land is the name generally given to the rotating portion of the labyrinth seal.

a. Labyrinth Seals

The two labyrinth seals, as shown in Figures 5-52 and 5-53, form a compartment in which the bearing is housed. Air from the gas path that is present outside of the bearing compartment bleeds inward across grooves cut in the labyrinth seal. These grooves form sealing rings in

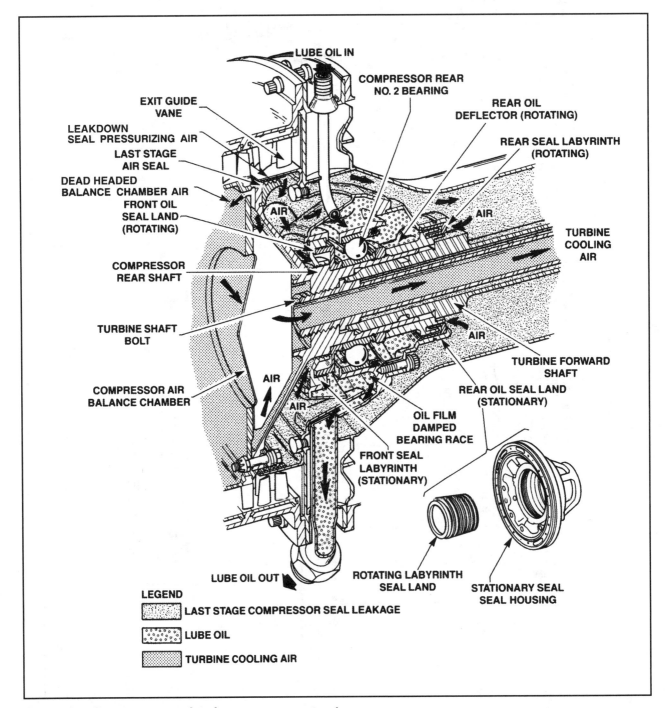

Fig. 5-52 — Compressor rear bearing sump arrangement.

either a concentric path similar to a screw thread or a non-concentric path with each ring in its own plane. In any case the seal dams formed by the rings allow for a metered amount of air from the engine gas path to flow inward. Pressure within the bearing compartment is in most engines maintained slightly above atmospheric level. This is discussed later in detail in Chapter VI of this text.

The oil mist created by the oil jet spraying on the rotating bearing is prevented from exiting the bearing compartment by the air entering across the labyrinth seal. The seal pressurizing air then leaves the bearing area, in Figure 5-52, by way of the scavenge oil system. The balance chamber uses dead headed air pressure to push against the compressor, and prevent sudden thrust loads from being absorbed totally by the bearing when the engine power changes. Most higher compression engines are designed with a separate vent subsystem as shown in Figure 5-53.

b. Carbon Seals

Carbon seals are a blend of carbon and graphite. They are similar in function and location to labyrinth seals but not in design. The carbon seal rides on a highly polished chrome carbide surface, while the labyrinth seal maintains an air gap clearance.

The carbon seal is usually spring-loaded and sometimes pressurized with air to create a uniform pressure drop across the seal. The pressurized air also preloads the carbon segment against its mating surface, and provides a more positive oil sealing capability.

The carbon seal shown in Figure 5-54A is classified as a carbon-ring type seal which rides on a seal surface attached to a rotating shaft. Another common design is the carbon-face type seal seen in Figure 5-54B. It is similar to those used as drive shaft seals in many fluid carrying accessories. The carbon surfaces are generally stationary with their highly polished mating surface, called a seal plate or seal race, attached to and turning with the main rotor shaft.

The carbon seal will be found where a more positive control over airflow into the bearing sumps is required, or where a full contact type seal is needed to hold back oil which might at times puddle before being scavenged. Conversely, labyrinth sealing will usually be associated with oil system locations designed with higher vent subsystem pressures. This system is discussed again in detail in the Lubrication Systems Chapter.

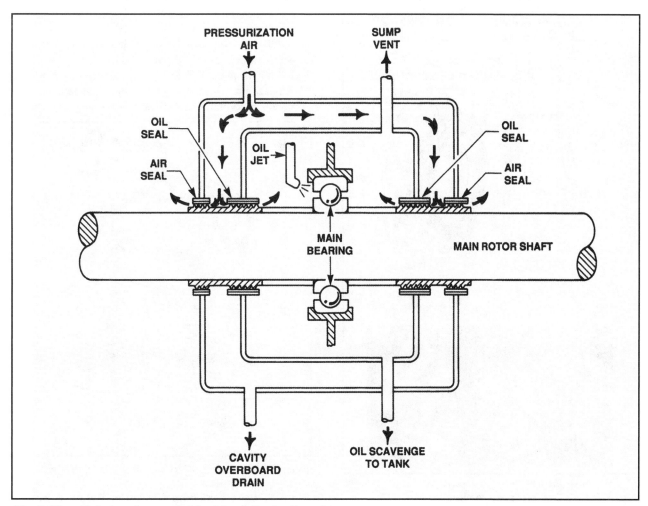

Fig. 5-53 — Main bearing sealed by labyrinth air-oil seals.

The newest generation of oil seal is the brush type, where a metal bristled element rides on a smooth rub ring. It is stated that this type of seal provides less air loss than the labyrinth type seal and an improved service life over the carbon seal.

The brush seal shown in Figure 5-54C is becoming more widley used in the turbine engine. It functions much like a labyrinth seal by taking a pressure drop across the interface of the stationary bristle section and its rotating rub-ring. Because the seal's bristles maintain

contact with its runner, its leakage rate is less than the Labyrinth Seal.

As the engine experiences thermal and mechanical trasient loading during power changes, gyroscopic deflections of the engine rotor system promote wear on both Labrynth and Carbon Seals. The Brush Seal has an advantage here in that it is able to accomodate rotor excursions, both radial and axial, without permanently opening up the seals clearance.

3. Bearing Handling And Maintenance

Most manufacturers require that bearings be cleaned and inspected in an environmentally-controlled bearing handling room. This prevents surface corrosion on bearings when out of the engine. Moreover, bearings are never left unprotected, to prevent even the slightest damage from occurring to their very close tolerance surfaces (Figure 5-55).

Proper bearing handling during inspection is accomplished with lint-free cotton or synthetic rubber gloves to prevent acid or moisture on the hands from contacting the bearing surfaces. Bearing inspection is usually conducted under strong lights and magnification to accurately determine their serviceability. Only very minor surface defects are allowable.

Bearings tend to gain work-hardness over time. They are often checked for excessive hardness with special equipment procedures because this condition makes bearings susceptible to chipping.

During inspection, bearings also receive a feel test. This is accomplished by an experienced technician who compares the rotational feel of one bearing against the

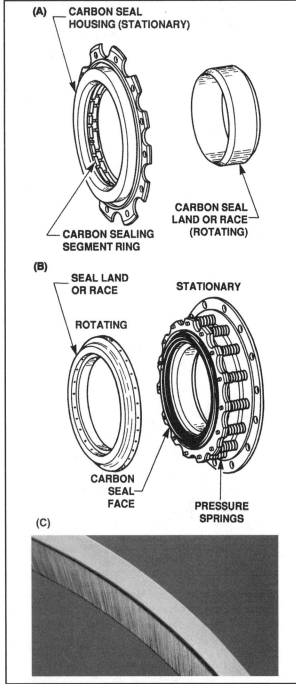

Fig. 5-54A — Carbon ring-type seal.
Fig. 5-54B — Carbon face-type seal.
Fig. 5-54C — Brush-type seal.

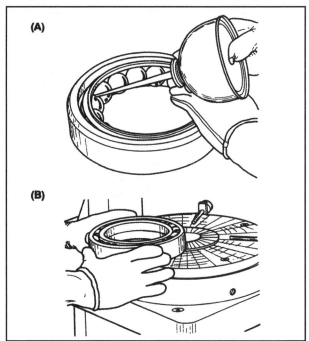

Fig. 5-55A — Lubricating bearings, handling with lint free gloves
Fig. 5-55B — Positioning bearing on flat plate for measurement check.

feel of a new one. After inspection many measurement checks are performed on the bearings with special measurement devices provided by the manufacturer.

a. Precautionary Measures

Managers and technicians should be made aware of several precautionary measures needed during bearing inspection. These are as follows:

Do not spin dry bearings because dust particles can scratch surfaces.

Do not blow bearings dry with shop air because moisture content in the air can cause corrosion.

Do not vapor degrease bearings because vapors support contaminants.

Do not use petroleum oils on bearings intended for use in engines which utilize synthetic oil. A chemical reaction can result.

Do not use the shop cleaning vat. Instead immerse bearings in clean fluid or wipe clean, using a lint-free cloth or suitable paper wiper and an approved cleaning solvent.

b. Magnetism Check

After inspection, bearings are checked for the presence of magnetism with a device called a magnetic-field detector. If magnetism is present, it must be removed with a suitable degausser to prevent the attraction of foreign ferrous particles into the bearing during engine operation.

It has been determined that magnetism occurs mainly from the effects of bearing rotation at high speeds, and from lightning strikes absorbed by the aircraft.

Another possible cause of bearing magnetism is electric arc welding of the assembled engine, and improper grounding of the equipment. The ground lead of the welding equipment must not be secured to an outer casing, but rather to the part being welded in a manner that prevents high electrical current flow through the entire engine. The result is that ferrous particles generated by normal engine wear in bearings and other ferrous materials will adhere to the bearing surfaces rather than be flushed away to the oil system filters.

c. Bearing Installation (Figure 5-56)

Bearings are stored in vapor proof paper until ready to install. Also, where appropriate, the inner and outer races are either heated in a clean bath of engine oil or chilled in a refrigerator before being fitted into their installation positions. Refer to Figure 5-51 which indicates some installation requirements.

d. Bearing Distress Terms (Figure 5-57)

Abrasion: A roughened area caused by the presence of fine foreign material between moving surfaces.

Brinelling (true): A shallow indentation sometimes found at one location on the surface of ball or roller bearing races, caused by shock loads to the bearing when not rotating.

Brinelling (false): A satin finish or a series of shallow depressions in the surface of ball or roller bearing races.

Burning: An injury to the surface caused by excessive heat. This is evidenced by discoloration or, in severe cases, by loss of material.

Burnishing: A mechanical smoothing of a metal surface by rubbing. It is not accompanied by removal of material but sometimes by discoloration around the outer edges of the area.

Burr: A sharp projection or rough edge.

Chafing: A rubbing action between two parts which have limited relative motion.

Chipping: Breaking out of small pieces of material.

Corrosion: Breakdown of the surface by chemical action.

Fig. 5-56A — Bearing and labyrinth seal ready for installation.
Fig. 5-56B — Installation of bearing retaining nut Pratt & Whitney JT8D Turbofan.

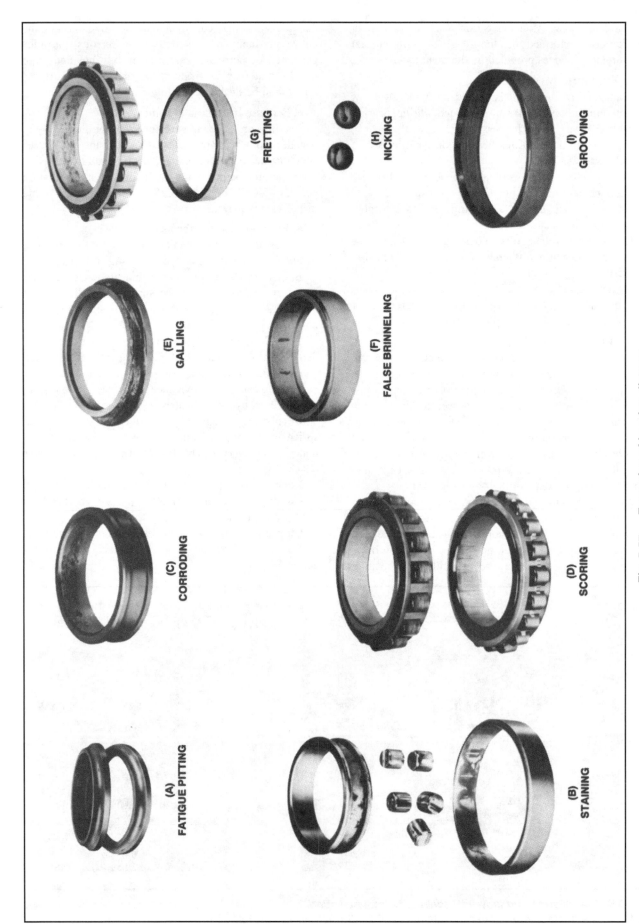

Fig. 5-57 — Examples of bearing distress.

Fretting: Discoloration on surfaces which are pressed or bolted together under high pressure. On steel parts the color is reddish brown. On aluminum, the oxide is white.

Galling: The transfer of metal from one surface to another, caused by chafing.

Gouging: The displacement of materials from a surface by a cutting, tearing, or displacement effect.

Grooving: Smooth rounded furrows, such as score marks, where the sharp edges have been polished off.

Guttering: A deep concentrated erosion, caused by overheat or burning.

Inclusion: Foreign material enclosed in the metal. Surface inclusions are indicated by dark spots or lines, an inherent discontinuity in the material.

Nick: A sharp indentation caused by striking one part against another metal object.

Peening: Deformation of the surface, caused by impact.

Pitting: Small, irregularly-shaped cavities in a surface from which material has been removed by corrosion or chipping. Corrosive pitting is usually accompanied by a deposit formed by the action of a corrosive agent on the base material.

Scoring: Deep scratches made by sharp edges or foreign particles during engine operation; elongated gouges.

Spalling: Sharply roughened area characteristic of the progressive chipping or peeling of surface material, caused by overloading.

E. Modular Maintenance (Figure 5-58)

A newer maintenance concept that combines many line and heavy maintenance tasks is referred to as modular maintenance. This is an engine construction concept wherein the engine is assembled as a set of separate modules. These modules are designed to be more easily removed and replaced with a minimum of man-hour expenditure. Each module has its own data plate so that operating time, cycles or hours, can be tracked by serial number. Most or all of the modules are pre-balanced and can be replaced while the engine remains installed in the aircraft. This eliminates engine removal and test cell running of the engine.

When rebuilt modules are installed in engines with high service time, achieving a good aerodynamic and thermodynamic match is extremely difficult and is becoming a science in itself for repair station and heavy repair shop managers. An engine's total time since new continues to increase, even though many of the engine's modules may have been replaced. Because of the nature of module maintenance, the FAA classifies the replacement of most modules as a minor repair, requiring no FAA Form 337. Overhaul of modules is considered a major repair, and requires the submission of FAA Form 337 to the local FAA Records Office (Figure 5-13).

F. Torque Wrench Use (Figure 5-59)

The torque wrench is a required tool for both line and shop maintenance. Before using a torque wrench, the technician should ensure that it is in calibration by means of a weight and lever arm tester. All gas turbine engine manufacturers require careful torquing (application of twisting force), and most recommend a calibration schedule for torque wrenches utilized in maintenance of their engines. A typical schedule is as follows:

a. Micrometer-type torque wrenches. Check once a week.

b. Non-set-type torque wrenches. Check once a month.

It is not uncommon in larger shops to have a torque wrench calibration tester available in all work stations where frequent daily use is made of torque wrenches. In this case the wrench can be checked for calibration daily or even before each use.

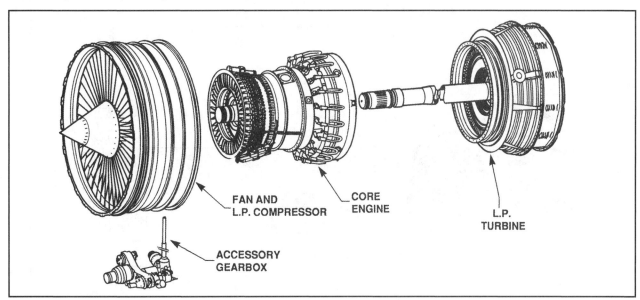

FAN AND
L.P. COMPRESSOR

CORE
ENGINE

L.P.
TURBINE

ACCESSORY
GEARBOX

Fig. 5-58A — G.E./Snecma CFM56 major modules.

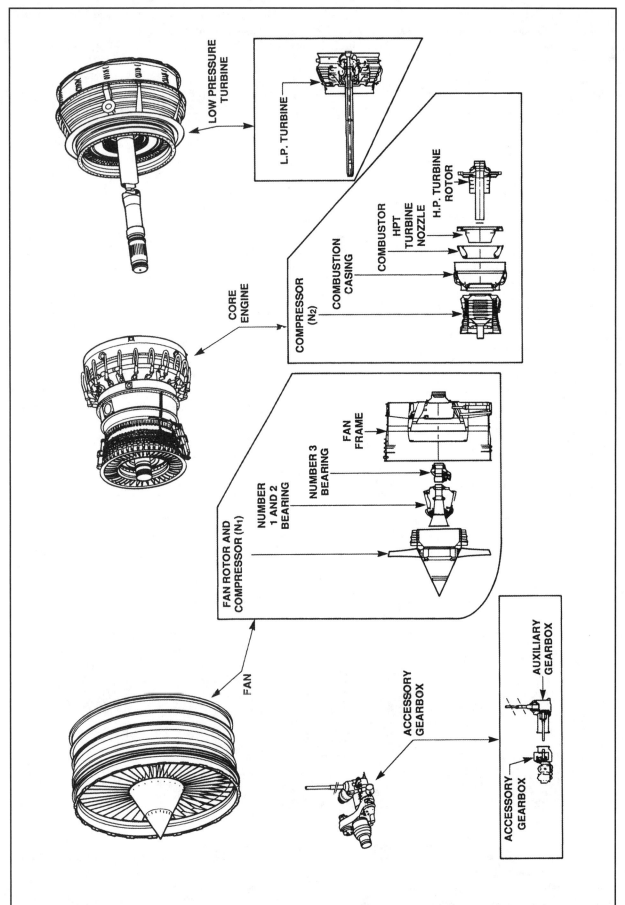

Fig. 5-58B — Makeup of major modules CFM56 turbofan.

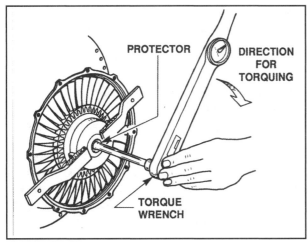

Fig. 5-59 — Use of torque wrench to install a turbine wheel.

To prevent loss of calibration of a micrometer type torque wrench, it should be returned to its lowest setting after use. The micrometer torque wrench is the most widely used in the industry because almost every fastener on a gas turbine engine requires a specific torque. This type wrench can be used quickly and accurately in positions and places difficult to work in with other types. Torque with this wrench is applied by feel. The correct torque is applied when the wrench breaks and the user does not have to see the scale.

The beam and dial torque wrenches are said to apply a more accurate initial torque if the user holds the torque for a few seconds after reaching the desired amount to allow a set to occur between mating parts. The user must, however, be positioned so that he always has an unobstructed, straight-on view of the scale or an inaccurate torque will result.

With the micrometer type wrench, if the manufacturer feels a set must occur between parts for accurate torque application, he will stipulate a procedure of: 1) Torquing a series of fasteners, loosening and retorquing; 2) Torquing a series of fasteners to minimum value, then a second torque to the required value; or, 3) Some other arrangement which will bring about the desired alignment of mating parts.

Another method of applying torque is to measure the stretch of a bolt, rather than measuring the amount of twist applied. This is more the case with large bolts found in larger engines.

In Figure 5-60A the technician is setting initial torque with a Beam Type torque wrench on nuts which attach to long hollow tie bolts (tie rods). The tie rods hold the fan to the front of the compressor.

In Figure 5-60B, the technician has installed an adapter plate containing a number of dial type depth micrometers, which fit into the hollow tie rods. He then applies final torque on the nut by measuring the stretch of the tie bolt using the dial micrometers.

1. Use Of Torque Wrench With Extension

Occasionally, an extension to a torque wrench is needed. The following information describes the procedure for calculating the indicated torque value as compared to the true torque being applied (Figure 5-61).

EXAMPLE: A torque of 1,440 pound inches is required on a part. A special extension having a length of 4 inches from the center of its wrench slot to its square drive is used. The torque wrench measures 16 inches from the center of its handle to the center of its square adapter. What would the indicated torque be on the wrench when the part is properly torqued?

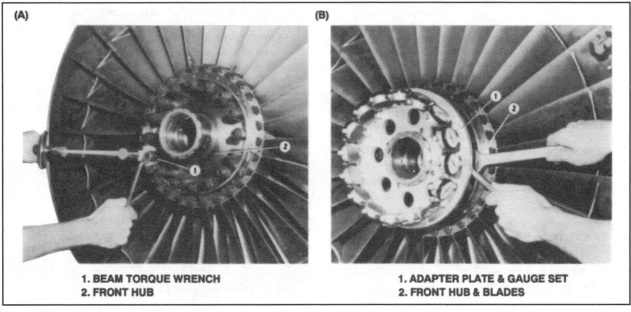

Fig. 5-60A — Tightening front compressor tie rod nuts.
Fig. 5-60B — Stretching front compressor tie rods.

$$R = \frac{L}{L + E} \times T$$

$$R = \frac{16}{16 + 4} \times 1{,}440$$

$$R = 1{,}152$$

With the axis of the extension and torque wrench in a straight line, tightening to a wrench reading of 1,152 inch pounds will provide a desired torque of 1,440 inch pounds.

2. Torque Procedure (Figure 5-62)

The manufacturer usually specifies the torque to apply and the torquing procedure to use. This procedure must be followed conscientiously so as to avoid setting up stresses between the mating flanges.

The turbine engine, being cylindrical in shape, has many circular bolt-ring sets. Often the manufacturer will stipulate stagger torquing the entire ring to the low limit and then loosening and retorquing to the median value. This procedure accomplishes two things: It allows an even "set" to take place between the two surfaces and then it allows for a small torque wrench calibration error. For example, if the manual torque chart indicates a torque of 90 to 100 inch pounds, the technician would torque all bolts initially to 90 inch pounds and then loosen and retorque to 95 inch pounds.

If a special procedure is not prescribed, the standard maintenance practice is to torque tighten gradually at staggered locations until the required torque value is reached. When torquing castellated nuts or nuts and bolts with tab-washers, the low torque should be applied and then additional torque applied up to the maximum value, if necessary, for alignment of the cotter key slot or the tablock slot. If alignment cannot be made, a new nut or bolt should be installed until the right combination of torque and alignment can be acquired.

Another widely used procedure is to initially torque one bolt at each 90° location and then stagger torque the remaining bolts in the ring at 180° locations.

If the bolt head rather than the nut is to be torqued because the nut is not accessible or the bolt is being installed into a nut-plate, the running torque will need to be calculated and this value added to the median torque value. The same is true when torquing steel locking and fiber locking nuts.

If a special torque value is not indicated by the manufacturer, the technician should use an appropriate standard torque table similar to the example in Figure 5-63.

G. Locking Methods

1. Lock Wiring (Figures 5-64 and 5-65)

Lock wiring, or safety wiring as it is sometimes called, is a common line and shop maintenance procedure. It is a method designed to prevent loosening of threaded parts after they have been tightened and torqued to required value. This is a significant airworthiness consideration on turbine engines because dangerous air, oil, and fuel leaks can occur at loose lines and flanges, and present serious flight hazards.

Care must be taken to select only the correct type and diameter lock wire as recommended by the manufacturer.

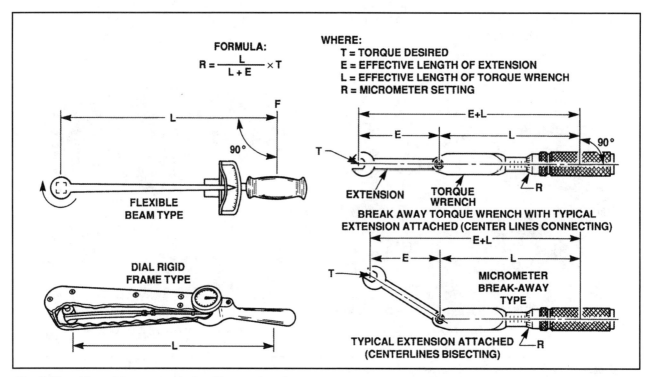

Fig. 5-61 — Use of torque wrench with an extension.

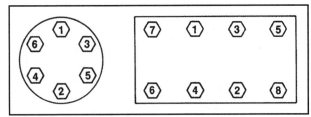

Fig. 5-62 — Stagger torque patterns.

The wire must not be over-twisted. If it is, it work-hardens and could break during service. For example, the twisting for 0.032 inch lock wire is usually recommended at 8 to 10 twists per inch and for 0.041 inch diameter lock wire, 6 to 8 twists per inch.

The common practice in the industry is to use stainless steel, aircraft grade lockwire of a sufficient heat range for the location intended, and to have a wire diameter of approximately three-fourths the diameter of the hole in the fastener. The maximum span between tension points, if possible, should be no longer than 6 inches. Nicks, kinks or other mutilation of the wire is not acceptable. Lockwire ends, commonly called pigtails, will be cut off at least three complete twists from the last tension point, then turned in to prevent snagging.

The commonly accepted lock wiring techniques are indicated in Figure 5-65A.

The latest lockwiring technique is the pre-twisted wire referred to as a cable and crimp-ferrule method, as shown in Figure 5-65B. The special installation tool tensions the cable, crimps the ferrule and cuts off the excess cable flush with the ferrule.

2. Lock Washers And Tabs (Figure 5-66A)

Lock washers typically found in Gas Turbine Engines are more often the lock tab and cup-washer varieties than the traditional split-ring type or the internal/external tooth types seen in other industries.

These locking devices are placed under the nuts or bolt heads with the locating tab(s) in a recess in the parent material. Then, after the nut or bolt is torqued, the locking tabs or crimp flanges are bent in such a way as to prevent or interfere with rotation and loosening.

O-Ring Seals (Figure 5-66B)

An o-ring seal is a type of elastomer, most often black in color, that is used at two mating surfaces to prevent the

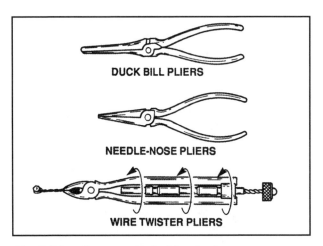

Fig. 5-64 — Common lockwiring tools.

loss of a fluid (liquid or gas). The o-ring is compressed between the two surfaces, typically fitting into a groove which holds it securely in place. The types of o-ring seals most common to aviation are as follows:

Nitrile - wide temperature range, good resistance to natural petroleum products.

Flurocarbon - a type of neopreme with a wide temperature range, good resistance to natural and synthetic lubricating products and jet fuels.

Silicones - wide temperature range, and when combined as flurosilicone it offers good resistance to fuel products.

Polyacrylate - excellent resistance to fuel and petroleum oil products and to oxidation.

Ethylene Propylene and Butyl Rubber - used mainly with ester type hydraulic fluids.

All o-ring seals are manufactured with a specific purpose in mind, and if selected improperly a serious engine malfunction can result. An o-ring seal must be the part number specified by the manufacturer, not just a seal of the proper size.

H. Test Cell Maintenance

After manufacture, heavy repair, and even some minor repairs the engine may require an integrity check in a specific test facility similar to the one illustrated in Figure 5-67. This facility is instrumented to provide operational data that is beyond the capability of the aircraft cockpit. The test bed, for instance, is configured

DIAMETER AND THREADS PER INCH	(NATIONAL COARSE) SIZE	TORQUE VALUES	DIAMETER AND THREADS PER INCH	(NATIONAL FINE) SIZE	TORQUE VALUES
NC-8-32	.164	13-16 LB-IN.	NF-8-36	.164	16-19 LB-IN.
10-24	.190	20-23 LB-IN.	10-32	.190	24-27 LB-IN.
1/4-20	.250	40-60 LB-IN.	1/4-28	.250	55-70 LB-IN.
5/16-18	.3125	70-110 LB-IN.	5/16-24	.3125	100-130 LB-IN.
3/8-16	.375	160-210 LB-IN.	3/8-24	.375	190-230 LB-IN.
7/16-14	.4375	250-320 LB-IN.	7/16-20	.4375	300-360 LB-IN.
1/2-13	.500	420-510 LB-IN.	1/2-20	.500	480-570 LB-IN.

Fig. 5-63 — Standard torque table for steel bolts and self-locking nuts.

(A)

NOTE: LOCKWIRING AROUND THE HEAD RESULTS IN BETTER LOAD DISTRIBUTION THAN ACROSS THE HEAD.

EXAMPLE 1   EXAMPLE 2   EXAMPLE 3   EXAMPLE 4

EXAMPLES 1, 2, 3, AND 4 APPLY TO ALL TYPES OF BOLTS, FILLSTER HEAD SCREWS, SQUARE HEAD PLUGS, AND OTHER SIMILAR PARTS WHICH ARE WIRED SO THAT THE LOOSENING TENDENCY OF EITHER PART IS COUNTERACTED BY TIGHTENING OF THE OTHER PART. THE DIRECTION OF TWIST FROM THE SECOND TO THE THIRD UNIT IS COUNTERCLOCKWISE TO KEEP THE LOOP IN POSITION AGAINST THE HEAD OF THE BOLT. THE WIRE ENTERING THE HOLE IN THE THIRD UNIT WILL BE THE LOWER WIRE AND BY MAKING A COUNTERCLOCKWISE TWIST AFTER IT LEAVES THE HOLE, THE LOOP WILL BE SECURED IN PLACE AROUND THE HEAD OF THAT BOLT.

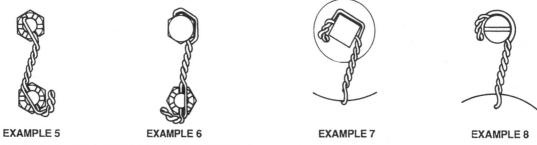

EXAMPLE 5   EXAMPLE 6   EXAMPLE 7   EXAMPLE 8

EXAMPLES 5, 6, 7, AND 8 SHOW METHODS FOR WIRING VARIOUS STANDARD ITEMS. NOTE: WIRE MAY BE WRAPPED OVER THE UNIT RATHER THAN AROUND IT WHEN WIRING CASTELLATED NUTS OR ON OTHER ITEMS WHEN THERE IS A CLEARANCE PROBLEM.

(B)

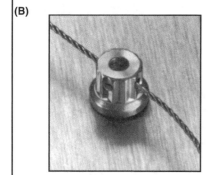

1. INSTAL CABLE THROUGH FASTENERS IN A NEUTRAL-TO-POSITIVE POSITION. INSERT LOOSE FERRULE ONTO CABLE WITH MAGAZINE LOADER.

3. CRIMP FERRULE AND CUT CABLE FLUSH IN ONE MOTION.

2. STRING END OF CABLE THROUGH TOOL AND TENSION ASSEMBLY TO THE PRESET LOAD.

4. TOTAL INSTALLED TIME AVERAGES LESS THAN HALF THAT OF LOCKWIRE.

Fig.5-65A — Twist lockwiring examples (1-8)
Fig.5-65B — Cable lockwiring method.

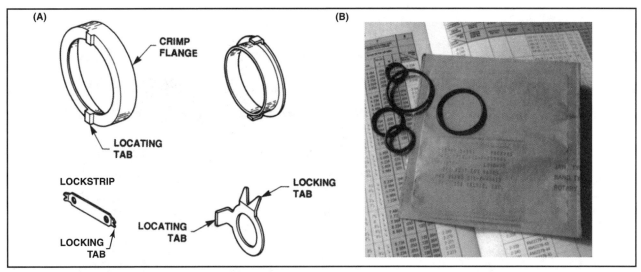

Fig. 5-66A — Types of lock tabs and lock cups.
Fig. 5-66B — O-ring seals, packaging, specifications.

to electronically measure engine power output which can be compared to other aircraft type performance gauges. In this manner, thrust parameters of turbojet and turbofan engines or torque output of the turboprop and turboshaft engines can be accurately measured.

Another primary engine inspection deals with vibration analysis during test cell operation. This is a very important inspection. It is used to check for component imbalance, a hazardous condition in the low weight, high speed turbine engine, where rapid wear can occur quickly from even very small induced vibration. Many larger aircraft cockpits are also fitted with vibration monitoring equipment.

While reciprocating engines have a visible vibration characteristic, gas turbine engines have minute vibration limits in the order of only 3 to 5 thousandths of an inch. Vibration is measured by using a meter and a special engine-mounted detector called a vibration transducer. This transducer is basically a small electrical generator which sends a signal to the vibration meter.

If an engine produces a vibration level beyond the limit during test cell operation, the rotating component causing the imbalance is identified and the engine is sent back to the repair facility for rework (Figure 5-68).

1. Analysis Of Test Cell Data (Figure 5-69)

Test cells are also used by repair facilities to troubleshoot engine malfunctions, leak test engines after minor repairs, perform research and development, and test after modifications and for various other maintenance support reasons.

When all parameters are recorded, test cell personnel plot observed reading against standard data to give a permanent record of the test run.

2. Run Data Corrections To Standard Day

In order to test run an engine and check its thrust performance on any given day and have meaningful data,

the gauge readings are corrected to Standard Day conditions. A comparison can then be made between observed data and present conditions of ambient temperature and pressure and Standard Day values of 29.92 inches Hg and 519°R (59°F). To use the same type data for in-flight recording and monitoring of engine performance, correction factors are programmed into the system which bias ambient conditions at altitude to Standard Day atmospheric conditions (See Appendix 7). The data then becomes a tool for both maintenance and management to use in determining such factors as engine economy of operation, maintenance planning and flight safety.

Consider the following run data taken on a test cell run-up of an engine when ambient temperature is 545°R (85°F), ambient pressure is 30.1 inches Hg, and engine data is as follows:

Example of engine run data recorded:
RPM = 15,000
EGT = 1,560°R (1,100°F)
Fuel flow = 1,500 lb./hr.
Mass air flow = 65 lb./sec.

To find out how these values relate to a standard day, two correction factors are needed, referred to as Delta (Δ), the pressure correction factor, and Theta (θ), the temperature correction factor.

Pressure correction factor ($\Delta t2$) calculations:

$$\Delta t2 = \frac{\text{observed ambient pressure}}{29.92 \text{ in. Hg}} = \frac{30.1}{29.92} = 1.006$$

Temperature correction factor ($\theta t2$) calculations:

$$\theta t2 = \frac{\text{observed ambient pressure}}{519°R} = \frac{545}{519} = 1.050$$

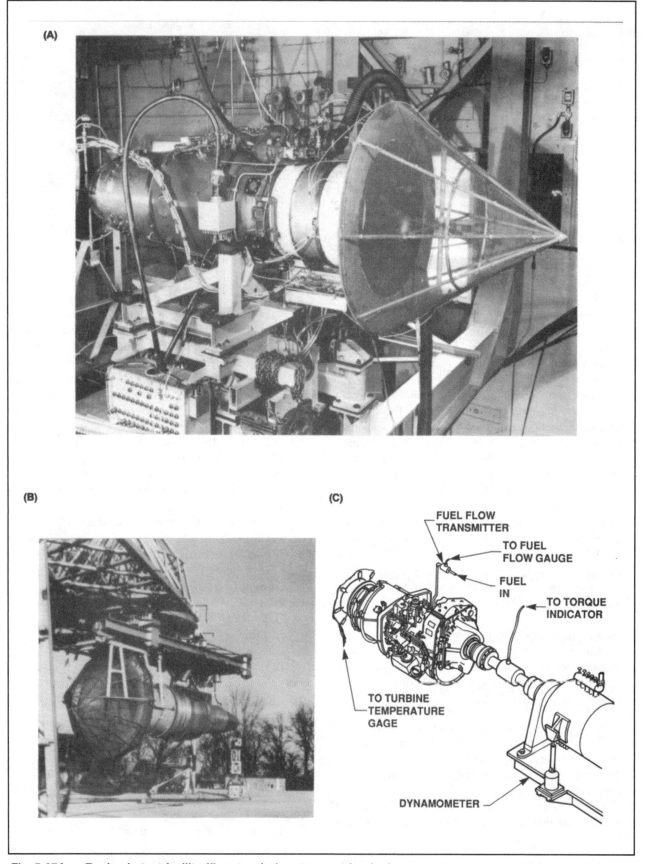

Fig. 5-67A — Engine in test facility (floor type), thrust measuring bed.
Fig. 5-67B — General Electric CF6, turbofan test facility (overhead type), thrust measuring bed.
Fig. 5-67C — Turboprop and turboshaft test facility, dynamometer providing a substitute load.

For ease of computations, Delta and Theta tables, such as provided in Appendix 9, are used by Test Cell personnel.

The following formulas can now be used in conjunction with the two correction factors:

$$\text{Corrected rpm} = \frac{\text{observed rpm}}{\sqrt{\theta t2}} = \frac{15,000}{\sqrt{1.050}} = 14,638.4$$

$$\text{Corrected EGT} = \frac{\text{observed EGT (°R)}}{\theta t2} = \frac{1,560}{1.050} = 1,485.7°\text{R}$$

$$\text{Corrected W}_f = \frac{\text{observed W}_f \text{ (pph)}}{\theta t2 \ x \sqrt{\theta t2}}$$

$$= \frac{1,500}{1.006 \ x \sqrt{1.050}} = 1,455.1 \text{ pph}$$

$$\text{Corrected m}_s = \frac{\text{observed m}_s \sqrt{\theta t2}}{\theta t2}$$

$$= \frac{65 \ x \sqrt{1.050}}{1.006} = 66.21 \text{ lbs./sec.}$$

It is a fact that gas turbine engine performance is sensitive to ambient conditions. When conditions are different from International Standard Day (ISD) values, the observed readings are not the same as they would be on a Standard Day. The values that were calculated above are those the engine would have if it were being run at ISD conditions. These values can now be compared with the manufacturer's specifications to determine engine condition. A further explanation of the corrections follow:

a. Corrected revolutions per minute (RPM). At higher than Standard Day ambient temperatures, RPM (observed compressor speed) is higher than Standard Day RPM because 85°F air requires more work than 59°F air to provide the necessary compressor pressure ratio and rated thrust.

b. Corrected exhaust gas temperature. In order to increase the RPM, as mentioned above, more fuel is required. This, of course, is what elevates the observed exhaust gas temperature.

c. Corrected Fuel flow (Wf). The increase in observed fuel flow over standard day fuel flow occurs because the operator adds fuel energy to increase RPM to obtain rated thrust.

d. Corrected Mass Airflow (Ms). When ambient temperature is 85°F, mass airflow is 65 pounds/second relative to a standard of 66.21 pound/second. See also Appendix 10 for typical flight correction data.

To discuss the above circumstances further, consider that 14,635.5 RPM represents 100% RPM. It then follows that 15,000 RPM represents 102.5% RPM. Percent of

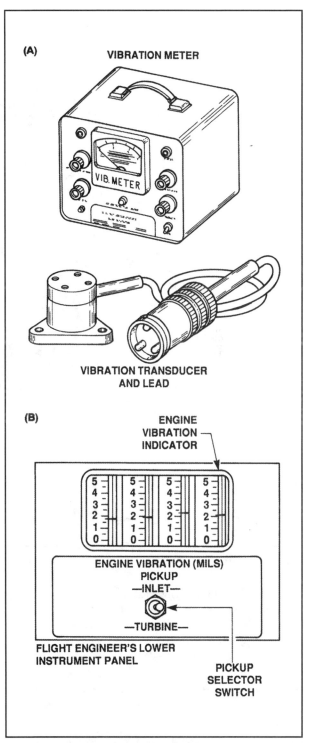

Fig. 5-68A — Test cell vibration meter and vibration transducer.

Fig. 5-68B — Cockpit vibration meter — four engine aircraft.

revolutions per minute is the traditional frame of reference for RPM and will be covered more thoroughly in the Instruments chapter of this text.

Note also that three parameters, RPM, exhaust gas temperature, and fuel flow are all set by the operator at higher than International Standard Day values in order to

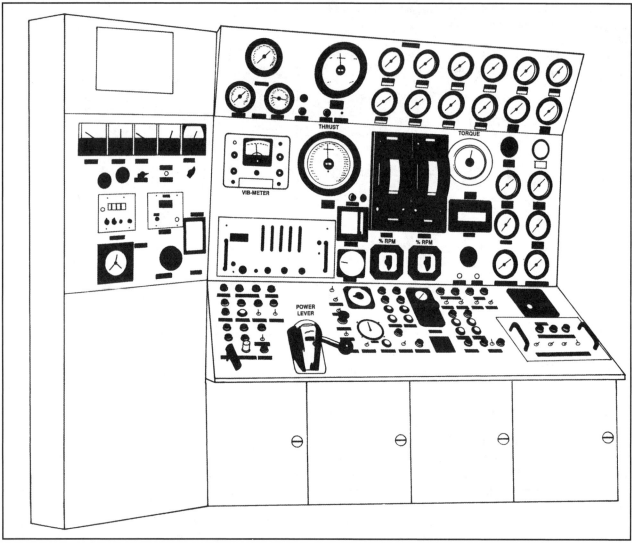

Fig. 5-69 — Test console.

maintain rated thrust. But observed Ms value is lower than ISD value. This indicates that RPM is at its limit of 102.5% and creating only 65 pound/second mass airflow. The reason that rated thrust can be maintained in the presence of low Ms value is that mass airflow energy losses within the engine are being replaced by a fuel energy increase. This is always the case with the gas turbine engine. Whenever mass airflow decreases for whatever reason, fuel flow has to be increased if the engine is to continue to produce the same thrust.

I. Time Between Overhaul (TBO) And Component Expected Service Life

1. Time Between Overhaul

Time between overhaul on gas turbine engines has changed greatly in recent years. Small gas turbine engines on an average may have a manufacturer's recommended time between overhaul of 3,000 to 5,000 hours, with a half-life hot section inspection in between. If a small engine is of modular construction, only its component parts have time between overhaul requirements. In fact the words "engine overhaul" are fast losing their meaning in terms of the gas turbine engine.

Large commercial turbine engines do not generally have hard-time between overhaul limits, in either hours or cycles. In conjunction with the Federal Aviation Administration (FAA), operators maintain an inspection schedule and trend analysis of engine performance upon which major component or module removal for overhaul is based. Using this method, some large engines remain on the wing for many thousands of hours until one of its components or modules requires removal. See Figure 5-70.

Hard time, also called "life limited cycle time", means a mandatory replacement of the unit. In this system, total time since new (TTSN) is tracked but the familiar time between overhaul (TBO) or time since overhaul (TSO) are not used.

Operators use hours and/or cycles upon which to base inspection intervals. A cycle is generally considered to be

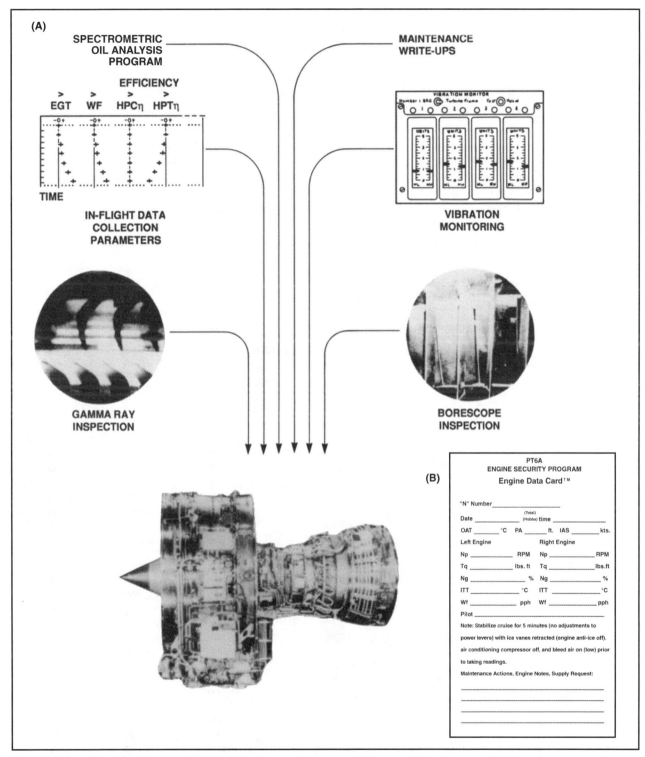

Fig. 5-70A — General Electric CFM-56 turbofan engine on-condition maintenance monitoring.
Fig. 5-70B — Manual trend monitoring data card of a PT-6A Turboprop.

one engine start, run and stop. Total time since new runs on through various component or module changes, so an engine can have a very high TTSN and still be airworthy and remain in service. The actual change interval used on many newer engines is based strictly on cycles rather than hours of operation.

Certain smaller engine parts also have life limited cycle time, meaning they have a scheduled hard-time cycle life between the time they are new or zero-timed and the time at which they must be replaced. Zero-timed means an overhauled part brought back to an as-new condition.

For all other non-life-limited parts the concept of on-condition maintenance prevails, meaning that the part will remain in place through successive inspections as long as it is felt to be in airworthy condition.

Cycle counters are installed in many aircraft. They usually function on the principle of electronically recording engine starts. If counters are not available, flight crew and ground crew must ensure accurate recording of hours or cycles so that all inspections, part changes, etc. are accomplished on time.

Turbine engines are expensive. The new price of the smallest flight engine is approximately $175,000, and a jumbo aircraft fan engine costs up to $12,000,000. From this standpoint alone, it is evident that good record keeping and proper recording of operating time becomes essential.

2. Component Expected Service Life

The Service Life design of modern gas turbine engines is much improved over engines of the past. This is true for business jet powerplants and for airliner powerplants alike.

As an example, the General Electric CF-6 high bypass fan engine, has a design life for the main engine structure of 50,000 hours or 35,000 flight cycles. The engine's expected service period is 15 years.

A partial list of component design life objectives of the CF-6 engine can be seen in Figure 5-71.

CF6-6 AND CF6-50
COMPONENT DESIGN LIFE OBJECTIVES

	NORMAL MAINTENANCE AND REPAIR ASSUMED SERVICE LIFE PER INSTALLATION (INSPECTION SCHEDULE)		TOTAL SERVICE LIFE (REPLACEMENT SCHEDULE)	
	HOURS	FLIGHT CYCLES	HOURS	FLIGHT CYCLES
STATIONARY COMPONENTS (UNLESS NOTED)	12,000	12,000	50,000	35,000
CASINGS	12,000	12,000	50,000	35,000
FRAMES	12,000	12,000	50,000	35,000
COMBUSTOR	6,000	6,000	18,000	15,000
HP TURBINE VANES	6,000	6,000	15,000	12,000
LP TURBINE VANES	6,000	6,000	18,000	15,000
TURBINE FRAME LINERS	6,000	6,000	18,000	15,000
NOISE SUPPRESSION PANELS	12,000	12,000	12,000	12,000
ROTATING COMPONENTS (UNLESS NOTED)	15,000	15,000	30,000	30,000
FAN BLADES	12,000	12,000	30,000	25,000
HP COMPRESSOR BLADES	12,000	12,000	30,000	25,000
HP COMPRESSOR DISCS	15,000	15,000	30,000	30,000
FAN DISCS	15,000	15,000	30,000	30,000
HP COMPRESSOR HUBS AND SHAFTS	15,000	15,000	30,000	30,000
HP TURBINE BLADES	6,000	6,000	15,000	12,000
LP TURBINE BLADES	6,000	6,000	18,000	15,000
HP TURBINE HUBS, SHAFTS, AND SPACERS	15,000	15,000	30,000	25,000
LP TURBINE DISCS	15,000	15,000	30,000	25,000
HP TURBINE DISCS	15,000	15,000	30,000	25,000
LP TURBINE HUBS, SHAFTS	15,000	15,000	30,000	25,000
GEARBOXES	12,000	12,000	50,000	35,000
GEARBOX BEARINGS	10,000	10,000	16,000	9,000
MAIN ENGINE BEARINGS	7,500	4,500	16,000	9,000
SEALS (MAIN ENGINE)	12,000	12,000	50,000	35,000
FAN THRUST REVERSER	6,000	4,000	30,000	20,000
TURBINE REVERSER	6,000	4,000	30,000	20,000

Fig. 5-71 — Table of component expected service life.

J. Troubleshooting Ground And Flight Data

1. Ground Troubleshooting

Troubleshooting is a major part of both line and heavy maintenance. Internal engine malfunction is likely to be a troubleshooting task for line or shop technicians and in many cases managers, engineers, and factory representatives. The troubleshooter in any case must adopt an intelligent sequence of procedures to ensure efficient correction of the problem. Too often a remove and replace philosophy prevails because the engine problem at hand looks similar to one that has happened in the past, and the troubleshooter makes a snap judgment that is incomplete or incorrect.

a. A few guidelines to follow might include:

1) Find all the facts surrounding the current problem by interviewing the flight crew, reading the logbook, reviewing the work order file, etc.
2) Review the same documents for previous related discrepancies.
3) Research the maintenance manual thoroughly for system operation and troubleshooting clues.
4) Make a written list in order of priority of possible causes.
5) Troubleshoot by inspecting, testing, and, if possible, duplicating the malfunction until cause of the problem is determined.
6) Make the necessary repairs to resolve the problem or remove the engine for shop repair.
7) Where possible flight line troubleshooting can give recommendations to shop maintenance for possible repairs needed.

b. A sequence of troubleshooting procedures is included at the end of Chapters VI through XII. A sample Troubleshooting Information and Priority List is as follows:

2. Analysis Of In-Flight Data For Troubleshooting

Another important troubleshooting technique is to analyze in-flight data gathered either manually or electronically. The data is then plotted into a trend analysis by the flight crew or later at a maintenance management facility. The trend analysis can be used to assist in making timely maintenance decisions or to pinpoint impending or actual parts failures.

The fundamental idea in gathering in-flight data is that it is obtained while the problem is ongoing in the engine rather than later during maintenance check runs. It then allows maintenance personnel to go quickly to the problem with little or no troubleshooting other than to study the data collected.

The data can be in either observed readings or corrected readings, as was discussed for test cell readings of engine parameters.

a. Engine Trends (Figure 5-72)

There are two categories of trend parameters available during engine operation, mechanical, and performance as follows:

1) Mechanical Monitoring. The traditional cockpit instrument readings of oil pressure, oil temperature, oil quantity, vibration, and also low oil pressure warning lights and filter bypass lights.
2) Performance Monitoring. The instrument readings that indicate how hard the engine is working to produce power such as: Engine Pressure Ratio, N_1 Speed, N_2 Speed, Exhaust Gas Temperature, and Fuel Flow.

The success of instrument analysis depends on the operator's ability to observe small shifts in operating parameters on one or more gauges and to accurately compare these data against standard or base line data supplied by the manufacturer. For instance, a small shift in only one gauge reading may likely be a problem in the gauge itself, whereas multiple small shifts may indicate

---

Troubleshooting Information and Priority Listing (To be filled out by personnel performing troubleshooting)

Aircraft No. _____542_____   Engine No. _#2_____   Date: _05/13/87_

1. Problem:
NO ENGINE OIL PRESSURE INDICATION ON COCKPIT
GAUGE ON START

2. Cockpit Indications:
   a. EPR: OK
   b. EGT: OK
   c. RPM N1: OK
      N2: OK
   d. Wf : OK
   e. Fuel Temp.: HIGH (21°C)
   f. Oil Temp.: SLIGHTLY HIGH (215°C)
   g. Oil Pressure: ZERO
   h. Oil Quantity: OK
   i. Warning Lights: NONE

3. Other Factors to Consider:
From flight log: SAME PROBLEM 4 FLIGHTS
PREVIOUS — CHANGED INDICATOR
Normal oil consumption: LAST SERVICE 1 PINT
Other information:
FLIGHT CREW INTERCHANGED INDICATORS #1
TO #2 STILL NO INDICATION

4. Suspect Causes: (in priority order)
   a. LOW OIL QUANTITY (COCKPIT QUANTITY)
      INDICATOR MAY BE INACCURATE)
   b. CIRCUIT BREAKER TRIPPED
   c. DEFECTIVE INDICATOR INPUT SIGNAL
   d. DEFECTIVE TRANSMITTER OR INPUT SIGNAL
   e. OBSTRUCTION IN LINE TO OIL PUMP
   f. DEFECTIVE OIL PUMP

engine performance change and possible contamination, wear, or damage within the engine.

The following information represents typical, but hypothetical trend analysis sheets, some plotted by calendar time, others plotted by engine time since overhaul:

b. Normal Engine (Figure 5-72)

Case 1 shows parameter plots and oil consumption data for a "normal" engine. It can be seen that all parameters are relatively flat and consistent. This is a good engine which shows no performance loss or mechanical problems.

c. Compressor Section Malfunction (Figure 5-73)

Case 2 shows compressor contamination from inlet water injection on a JT8D engine.

This is a plot of corrected flight log data for an engine water injection system which was probably serviced with water containing more solids than the 10 parts per million typically allowed. Exhaust Gas Temperature, fuel

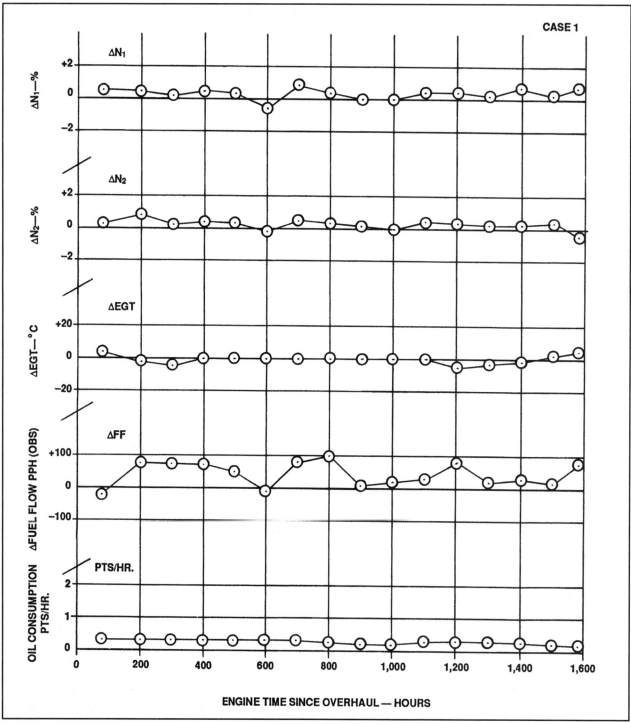

Fig. 5-72 — Case 1 — Trend analysis normal operation dual-spool engine.

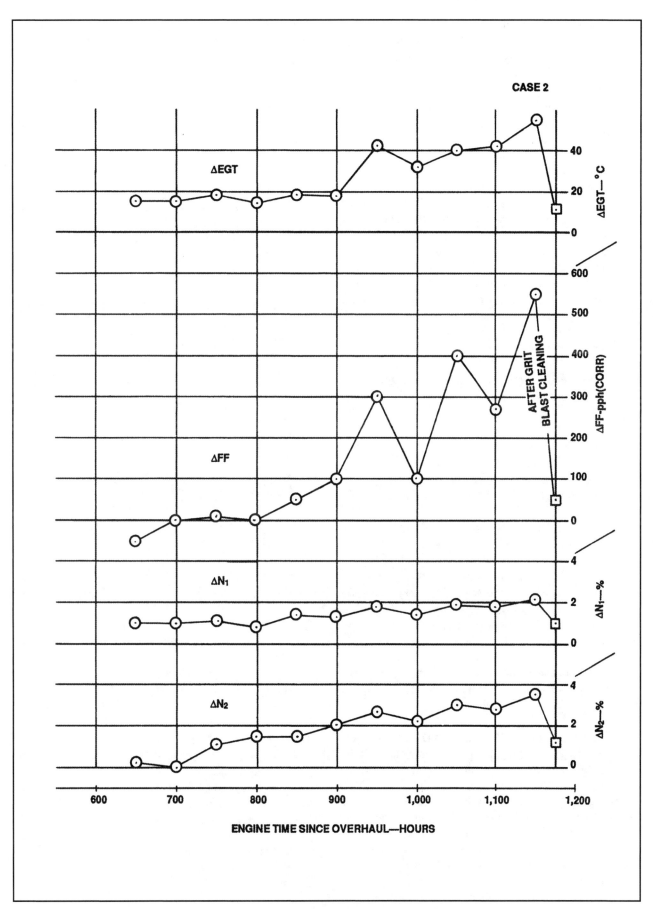

Fig. 5-73 — Case 2 — Compressor contamination from water injection dual-spool engine.

flow, and N_2 are up significantly while N_1 is up slightly. Abrasive grit cleaning this engine brought all parameters back down almost to their original level, as shown by the squares at 1175 hours time since overhaul (TSO).

Compressor contamination occurs mainly when the dissolved solids in the water adhere to blades and vanes, changing their aerodynamic shape, roughening their surfaces, and reducing the airflow area. This reduces compressor efficiency and airflow capacity. Consequently, the engine must work harder to produce a given thrust. One item of interest is that when water contamination occurs as the result of inlet water injection for thrust augmentation, the low pressure compressor (N_1) parts get little or none of these deposits. They normally settle out in the high pressure compressor (N_2). This is due to the combination of temperature and pressure existing in the N_2 compressor, plus the time element involved in vaporizing the water. In this case it can be seen that the operator needed to increase fuel flow to maintain engine thrust output.

d. Combustor Section Malfunction (Figure 5-74)
Case 3 shows a detached combustion chamber inner liner.

The engine was shut down in flight when it sustained a stall during operation at cruise. Subsequent disassembly and inspection revealed that a section of one of the combustion chamber liners had become detached and passed on through, lodging against the turbine nozzle vanes.

The flight engineer's log shows that on 4/28, the liner section became dislodged in the combustion chamber. The piece lodged in the nozzle vane area and the engine began to stall. The sudden depression in N_2 and increase in Exhaust Gas Temperature and Wf resemble a classic high turbine efficiency loss. Nozzle blockage blanks off a number of turbine vanes, decreasing turbine efficiency. The decrease in turbine efficiency is the overriding effect in this case causing N_2 to decrease. In this case, with a sudden component failure induced stall, the operator did not attempt to maintain engine thrust due to EGT limitations and shut the engine down in flight.

e. Turbine Section Malfunction (Figure 5-75)
Case 4 shows first stage turbine seal erosion.

Investigation revealed the knife edges of the first stage turbine outer seal to be eroded, allowing an excess of exhaust gases to bypass the first turbine, resulting in a rise in N_1 speed and a rise in exhaust gas temperature and fuel flow to obtain a given N_2 speed and thrust. It can be seen that the seal erosion began to be appreciable after about 1800 hours time since overhaul. This is one of the malfunctions which can be tracked accurately enough that maintenance action required can be planned in sufficient time to prevent major engine problems. In this case

with a failing turbine seal, higher fuel flow is maintaining N_2 speed, but at the same time N_1 is increasing with its seals remaining secure.

K. Inspection And Troubleshooting Terms
The following is a list of terms commonly used to describe inspection findings during gas turbine engine maintenance:

Abrasion: Wearing away of small amounts of metal as a result of friction between parts.

Blister: The raised portion of a surface, caused by separation of layers of material.

Bowing: A bend or curve in a normally straight or nearly straight line.

Buckling: Large scale deformation from original shape of a part, usually caused by pressure or impact of a foreign object, unusual structural stresses, excessive localized heating, or any combination of these.

Burn: Discoloration from excessive heat.

Burr: A sharp projection or rough edge.

Converging: Two or more lines (cracks) which approach one another and which, if allowed to continue, will meet at a single point.

Corrosion: A surface chemical action resulting in surface discoloration, a layer of oxide, or, in advanced stages, the removal of surface metal.

Crack: Fissure or break in material.

Crazing: Minute cracking which tends to run in all directions. It is often noticed on glazed or ceramic-coated surfaces and is occasionally referred to as "china cracking".

Deformation: Alteration of form or shape.

Dent: A smooth, round-bottomed depression.

Distress: An umbrella term to mean any of the problems included in this listing.

Distortion: A twisted or misshapened condition.

Erosion: Wearing away of metal and/or surface coating.

Flaking: Loose particles of metal on a surface or evidence of removal of surface covering.

Frosting: An initial stage of scoring caused by irregularities or high points of metal welding together with minute particles of metal transferring to the mating surface, giving a frosted appearance.

Galling: Chafing caused by friction.

Gouging: A removal of surface metal, typified by rough and deep depressions.

Grooving: Smooth, rounded indentation caused by concentrated wear.

Inclusion: Foreign matter enclosed in metal.

Metallization: Coating by failed molten metal particles sprayed through the engine.

Nick: A sharp-bottomed depression with rough outer edges.

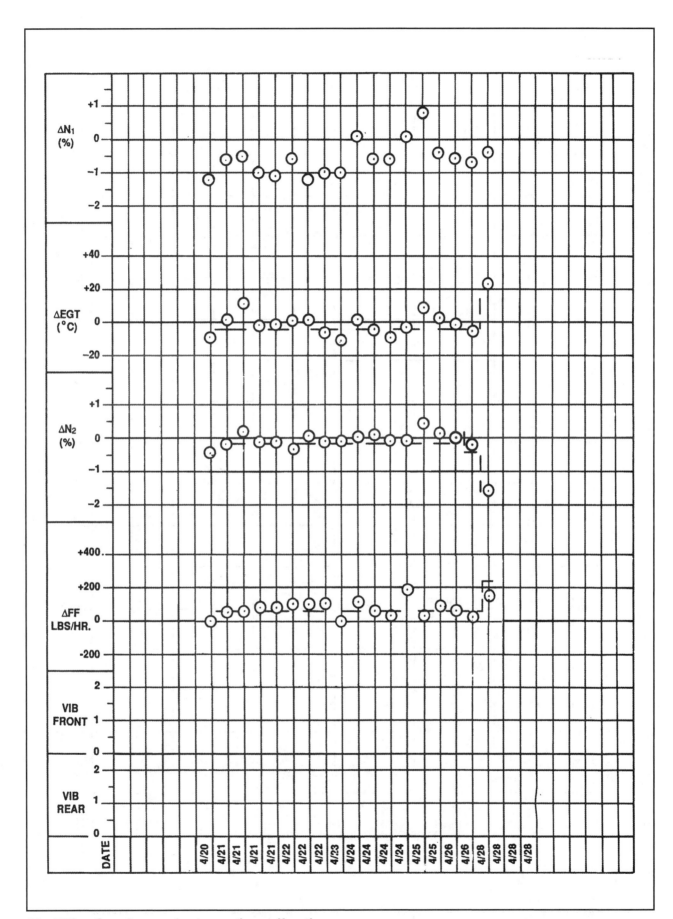

Fig. 5-74 — Case 3 — combustor section malfunction.

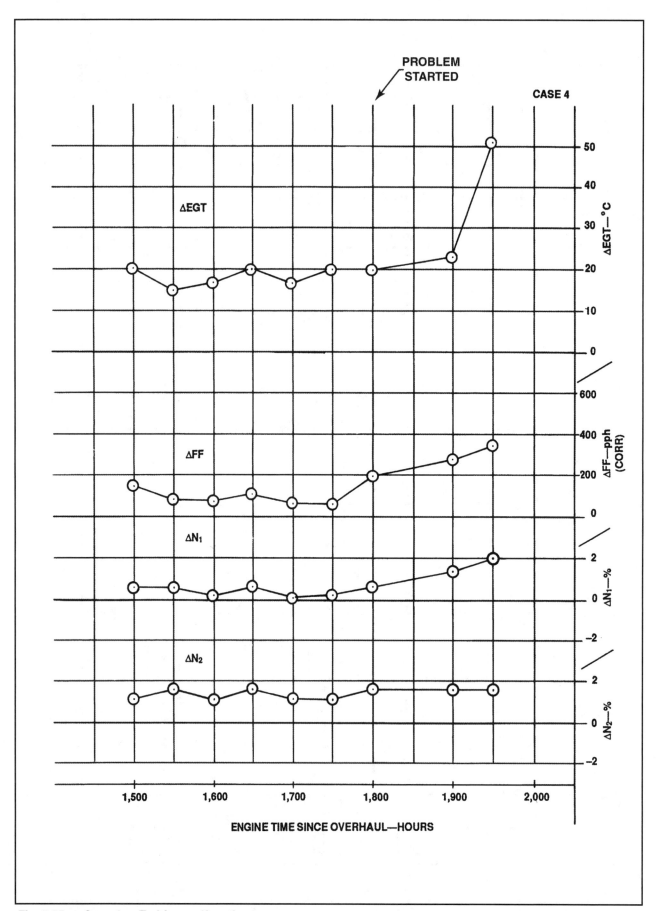

Fig. 5-75 — Case 4 — Turbine malfunction.

Peening: Flattening or displacing of metal by repeated blows. A surface may be peened by continuous impact of foreign objects or loose parts .

Pitting: A surface condition recognized by minute holes or cavities which occur on over stressed areas. The pits may occur in such profusion as to resemble spalling.

Scoring: A form of wear characterized by a scratched, scuffed, or dragged appearance with markings in the direction of sliding. It generally occurs at or near the top of a gear tooth.

Scratches: Narrow, shallows marks or lines resulting from the movement of a metallic particle of sharp-pointed object across a surface.

Scuffing: A dulling or moderate wear of a surface resulting from a slight amount of rubbing.

Seizure: A welding or binding of two adjacent surfaces, preventing further movement.

Spalling: A separation of metal by flaking or chipping.

Stress: Metal failure due to compression, tension, shear, torsion, or shock.

Tear: Parent metal torn by excessive vibration or other stresses.

Unbalanced: A condition created in a rotating body by an unequal distribution of weight about its axis. Usually results in vibration.

Wear: A condition resulting from relatively slow removal of parent material, frequently not visible to the naked eye.

L. Technical Data Identification System (ATA)

The Air Transportation Association of America, an organization of air carriers, has established many standards and procedures that make airline operation more effective and efficient. One of the specifications of value to us in the maintenance field is the A.T.A. Specification 100, which is a standard for the presentation of technical information. Because of this specification, maintenance information from any of the manufacturers of transport aircraft is presented in a specific manner.

For example, regardless of the aircraft manufacturer, chapter 72 of an aircraft maintenance manual will deal with the turbine engine powerplant. More specifically, section 30 of chapter 72 will deal with the engine's compressor.

The A.T.A. Specification 100 system has now found its way into all facets of aviation, including General Aviation aircraft. Figure 5-76 shows the breakdown of the system.

First Element	Second Element	Third Element
Chapter (System)	Section (Subsystem)	Subject (Unit)
Example		
71 Powerplant, general	- 50 Electrical harness	- 00 Unit of harness

Aircraft, General		Structure	
05-00-00	Time Limits/Maintenance Checks	51-00-00	Structures
06-00-00	Dimensions and Areas	52-00-00	Doors
07-00-00	Lifting and Shoring	53-00-00	Fuselage
08-00-00	Leveling and Weighing	54-00-00	Nacelles/Pylons
09-00-00	Towing and Taxiing	55-00-00	Stabilizers
10-00-00	Parking and Mooring	56-00-00	Windows
11-00-00	Placards and Markings	57-00-00	Wings
12-00-00	Servicing		
Airframe Systems		**Propeller/Rotor**	
20-00-00	Standard Practices, Airframe	60-00-00	Standard Practice - Propellers/Rotors
21-00-00	Air Conditioning	61-00-00	Propellers
22-00-00	Automatic Flight	65-00-00	Rotors
23-00-00	Communications		
24-00-00	Electrical Power		
25-00-00	Equipment/Furnishings	**Powerplant**	
26-00-00	Fire Protection		
27-00-00	Flight Controls	70-00-00	Standard Practices - Engine
28-00-00	Fuel	71-00-00	Powerplant, General
29-00-00	Hydraulic Power	72-00-00	Engine
30-00-00	Ice and Rain Protection	73-00-00	Engine Fuel and Control
31-00-00	Indicating and Recording Systems	74-00-00	Ignition
32-00-00	Landing Gear	75-00-00	Air
33-00-00	Lights	76-00-00	Engine Controls
34-00-00	Navigation	77-00-00	Engine Indicating
35-00-00	Oxygen	78-00-00	Exhaust
36-00-00	Pneumatic	79-00-00	Oil
37-00-00	Vacuum	80-00-00	Starting
38-00-00	Water/Waste	81-00-00	Turbines
39-00-00	Electrical/Electronic Panels and Multipurpose Parts	82-00-00	Water Injection
		83-00-00	Accessory Gearboxes
49-00-00	Airborne Auxiliary Power	91-00-00	Charts

Fig. 5-76 — ATA Standard for presentation of technical data.

QUESTIONS:

1. What is the name of the grit blast and wash procedure for removing the accumulation of dirt deposits on compressor blades?

2. Is the straightening of compressor blades typical of flight line maintenance?

3. What is one of the most frequent discrepancies that will be detected while inspecting the combustor?

4. On which hot section component will stress rupture cracking most commonly occur?

5. Why must turbine blade replacement procedures be strictly adhered to?

6. Why is rippling and stress cracking more critical on the turbine blade trailing edge than on the leading edge?

7. Hot spots are a possible indication of what component malfunction?

8. Ball bearings are positioned on the compressor or turbine shaft so that they will absorb which types of loads?

9. Why are main bearings of ball and roller types used in preference to plain types?

Chapter VI
Lubrication Systems

There are two basic types of self-contained lubrication systems used in today's gas turbine engines. They are known as the "pressure relief valve" system and the "full flow" system. The pressure relief valve system controls oil flow by limiting the pressure from the oil pump to a given value. In the full flow system, pressure changes with RPM change, and this is the system of choice when the bearing vent cavities contain high air pressures. Both systems will be discussed in detail later in this chapter.

The primary function of the lubrication system is to supply oil to the various parts within the engine which are subjected to friction loads from engine rotation and heat loads from the gas path. Engine heat rejection radiates outward and is dealt with by the nacelle ventilation system. Engine heat rejection inward is dealt with by the lubrication system. The oil is supplied under pressure along the main rotor shaft and to the gearboxes to reduce friction, to cool, and to clean. It is then returned by a scavenging system to the oil storage tank to be used again and again.

Oil consumption is low in gas turbine engines as compared to piston engines, and this accounts for the relatively small bulk oil storage tanks used. They can be as small as three to five quarts in capacity on business jet size engines and 20 to 30 quarts on large commercial type engines. The oil is not exposed to great quantities of combustion products and stays fairly clean by filtration. Heat, however, is a problem which can cause rapid oil decomposition and for this reason temperature is carefully controlled by automatic cooling devices and is carefully monitored by the engine operators.

A. Principles Of Engine Lubrication

In theory, lubricating fluids fill all surface irregularities providing oil films which slide against each other and prevent metal-to-metal contact. The primary purpose of a lubricant is to reduce friction between moving parts. As long as this oil film remains unbroken, metallic friction is replaced by internal fluid friction. The heated oil is then carried away to be cooled and reused.

Secondary purposes of an engine lubricant are to act as a cushion between metal parts, to cool, and to clean. As oil circulates through the engine, it collects foreign matter and deposits it into the filtration system. As it is circulating through the engine, it is absorbing engine heat.

B. Requirements Of Turbine Engine Lubricants

Gas turbine engine oil must have a high enough viscosity for good load carrying ability, but it must also be of sufficient low viscosity to provide good flow ability. Because of these requirements, synthetic, rather than petroleum base lubricants, are used in turbine engines.

1. Desirable Characteristics Of Synthetic Lubricants Are:

a. Low volatility: To minimize evaporation at high altitudes;

b. Anti-foaming quality: For more positive lubrication;

c. Low lacquer and coke deposits: Keeps solid particle formation to a minimum;

d. High flash point: The temperature at which oil, when heated, gives off flammable vapors that will ignite if near a flame source;

e. Low pour point: The lowest temperature at which oil will gravity flow;

f. Film strength: Excellent qualities of cohesion and adhesion, a characteristic of oil molecules allowing them to stick together under compression loads and stick to surfaces under centrifugal loads;

g. Wide temperature range: Approximately –60°F to +400°F, preheat not required to approximately –40°F;

h. High viscosity index: An indication of how well the oil will tend to retain its viscosity when heated to its operating temperature.

2. FAA Requirements Of Lubrication Systems

The following is a list of minimum oil system requirements from FAA Parts 23, 25 and 33.

a. The word "oil" must be stenciled in the area of the oil tank filler opening.

b. A means must be provided wherein it is impossible to inadvertently fill the oil tank expansion space.

c. An oil tank expansion space of 10% must be provided.

d. An oil tank scupper must be provided to carry spilled oil to a drain point on the engine.

e. The oil filter must be of a type through which all of the system oil flows.

3. Viscosity
a. Petroleum Oils

An SAE (Society of Automotive Engineers) rating for petroleum base lubricants is determined by heating 60 milliliters (cubic centimeters) of oil to one specific temperature, and measuring the flow time as the oil is poured through a calibrated orifice. One such device for this calculation is the Saybolt-Universal Seconds (S.U.S.) Viscosimeter. For example, refer to Figure 6-1 and determine that if the flow time of an oil at (0°F) is 24,000 seconds, it will have an SAE 20 W classification. If the flow time of an oil at (210°F) is 65 seconds, it will have an SAE 30 classification.

Many automotive and some aviation oils are now classified as multi-grade, for example, SAE 5W-20. This means that the oil when cold will have the viscosity of SAE-5 and when at its normal operating temperature will thin out no more than SAE-20. Viscosity, then, is a measure of an oil's pourability and multi-viscosity oils are designed to have low temperature fluidity for quick lubrication at low temperatures and remain thick enough for good lubrication at higher temperatures.

Although the SAE scale explained above eliminates some confusion in the designation of engine lubrication oils, it does not cover all important viscosity requirements. An SAE number merely indicates the viscosity grade and does not indicate the quality of an oil.

b. Synthetic Oils

Synthetic oils do not have SAE ratings indicating viscosity. Instead, synthetics have a Kinematic Viscosity Rating in centistokes. The term "kinematics" derives from the study of the motion of fluids, and centistoke is an international system (metric) measurement of viscosity. It can therefore be stated that in regard to viscosities of oils that centistoke numbers are to synthetic oils as SAE numbers are to petroleum (mineral) oils.

4. Viscosity Index

Viscosity index is determined by measuring the viscosity change when a liquid lubricant is heated to two different temperatures. An important quality of synthetic lubricants is determined in this way.

In Figure 6-2, the American Society of Testing Materials (ASTM) nomograph is used for determining viscosity index (VI) when the Saybolt Universal

Viscosity is known. Notice that the oil in the sample plot has a viscosity of 280 SUS at 100°F, and 60 SUS at 210°F on the appropriate scales. Plots extended to the viscosity index chart indicate a viscosity index rating of approximately 170.

What the nomograph reveals is a basic quality of the oil. The higher the viscosity index of the oil, the less tendency it has to thin out when heated.

If the viscosity of an oil is given as kinematic viscosity in centistokes (cSt) from a kinematic viscosimeter rather than in SUS units from a Saybolt Viscosimeter, Figure 6-3 can be used as a conversion chart and Figure 6-2 can then be used to find the V.I. The centistoke value must, however, be known at both 100°F and 210°F.

The centistoke value (metric viscosity measurement) can be seen on some container labels of synthetic lubricants. A rough equivalent to SAE values is as follows: three centistoke oils are approximately equal to SAE-5; five centistoke oils are approximately equal to SAE 5W-10 multi-viscosity oils; seven centistoke oils are approximately equal to SAE 5W-20 multi-viscosity oils. It follows then that it would be more common to see the heavier seven centistoke oil in use in a turboprop engine where high gear loading is present. Five centistoke oils are the most widely used in turbojet and turbofan engines.

C. Oil Sampling

After shutdown, and just prior to servicing, many air carriers require ground personnel to take an oil sample from a sediment free location in the main oil tank. From

VISCOSITY RANGE SAYBOLT UNIVERSAL SECONDS (SUS)				
SAE VIS-COSITY NO.	SECONDS POUR TIME AT 0°F.		SECONDS POUR TIME AT 210°F.	
	MIN	MAX	MIN	MAX
5W	—	LESS THAN 6,000	—	—
10W	6,000	LESS THAN 12,000	—	—
20W	12,000	LESS THAN 48,500	—	—
20	—	—	45	LESS THAN 58
30	—	—	58	LESS THAN 70
40	—	—	70	LESS THAN 85

Fig. 6-1 — Viscosity Rating by SAE numbers.

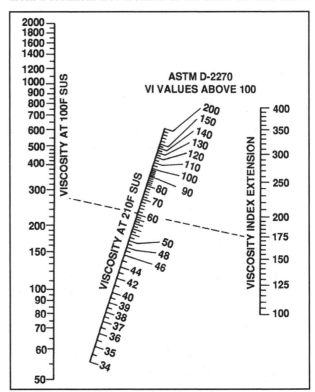

Fig. 6-2 — Viscosity index nomograph.

this, one can analyze the contaminants that are suspended in the oil.

These contaminants are a good indicator of engine wear when counted in a device known as an oil spectrometer. The procedure of reading parts per million of contaminants is referred to as spectrometric oil analysis. With a spectrometer, contaminant levels of silicon (dirt) and "wear metals", as they are called, are automatically registered by analyzing the color and measuring the intensity of brightness that occurs when the particles are burned in a certain light spectrum.

Many private companies offer this service to customers who, in turn, use the information to plot trend analyses of internal engine wear. Knowing the trends allows the operator to take timely action and avert costly repair or loss of equipment (Figure 6-6).

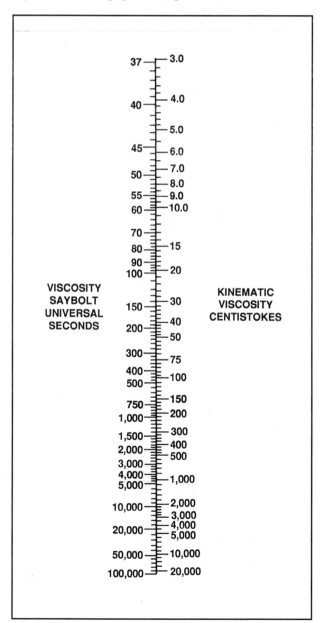

Fig. 6-3 — Conversion chart centistokes to SUS seconds.

1. Sampling Intervals

Sampling intervals are not standardized between one engine and another, or even between identical engines used by different operators. Intervals can be as low as 25 engine operating hours for smaller engines and up to 250 hours for large engines. Whatever the interval, when oil analysis trends start to rise, the interval is shortened to maintain a closer surveillance on the oil-wetted portions of the engine. Sometimes the interval is shortened to sampling after each flight.

When the first indication of excessive wear is encountered, the maintenance manager will probably make one of the following decisions based on the engine's past history and his fleet experience of oil analysis:

a. Shorten the sampling interval;
b. Back-flush the main oil filter to collect wear-metal particles for analysis;
c. Change the oil and perhaps shorten the sampling interval;
d. Flush the oil system, reservice, and perhaps shorten the interval;
e. Remove the engine from service and investigate the areas of the engine that contain the types of wear-metal found.

Notice in the example shown in Figure 6-4A that the parts per million trend is staying well below the guideline limit. In Illustration (b), on the sixth sample taken, the contaminant level rose significantly and maintenance action was determined to be necessary. Under the influence of different engine histories, perhaps the engine would have continued in service one or more flights. The wear-metal and silicon guideline in oil trend analysis is not a firm limit, but a point at which a management decision is required concerning the engine.

The contaminant levels typically plotted include: Iron, Tin, Bronze, Silver, Aluminum, Magnesium, Chromium, Copper, Silicon, and Nickel.

Maintenance personnel are aware of the points within the engine containing these types of metals and also the locations that are more suspect than others. High silicon levels are not generated by the engine but, rather, they come in on the airstream when operating in dust laden environments.

2. How the Analyzer Works

The spectrometer measures the contaminants present in the used oil samples as follows:

a. A film of the used oil sample is picked up on the rim of a rotating, high-purity graphite disk electrode (See Detail A of Figure 6-5);
b. Precisely controlled, high voltage AC spark discharge is initiated between the vertical electrode and the rotating disk electrode burning the small film of oil;
c. Light from the burning oil passes through a slit which is positioned precisely to the wavelength for the particular contaminants being monitored.

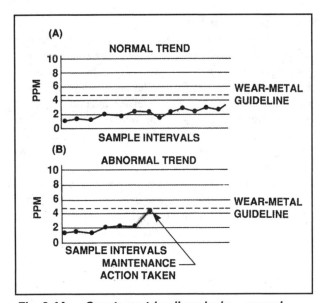

Fig. 6-4A — *Spectrometric oil analysis - normal trend.*

Fig. 6-4B — *Spectrometric oil analysis - abnormal trend.*

3. Measurement Of The Metals

The moving contact between the metallic surfaces of engine mechanical systems is always accompanied by friction. Even though this friction is reduced by a thin film of oil, some microscopic particles of metal do wear away and are carried in suspension in the oil. Thus, a potential source of information exists that relates directly to the condition of the system.

Under most conditions, the rate of wear will remain constant and quite slow. The wear-metal particles will be microscopic in size so that the particles will remain in suspension in the lubricating system.

Any condition which alters or increases the normal friction between the moving parts, will also accelerate the rate of wear and increase the quantity of wear-particles produced. If the condition is not discovered and corrected, the wear process will continue to accelerate, usually with secondary damage to other parts of the system and eventual failure of the entire system.

The important wear-metals produced in an oil lubrication mechanical system can be separately measured in extremely low concentrations.

Silver is accurately measured in concentrations down to one-half part by weight of silver in 1,000,000 parts of oil. Most other metals are measured accurately in concentrations down to two or three parts per million. The maximum amount of normal wear has been determined for each metal. This amount is called its "threshold limit" of contamination.

It must be understood that the wear-metals present can be of such microscopic size that they can not be seen by the naked eye, cannot be felt with the fingers, and they can flow freely through the system filters. As an example, wear-metals one-tenth the size of a grain of talcum powder are easily measured by the spectrometer. The spectrometer therefore measures the particles that move in suspension in the oil and are too small to appear in either the oil filters or on chip detectors (Figure 6-6).

D. Synthetic Lubricants

Synthetic lubricants have, by their structural makeup, multi-viscosity properties.

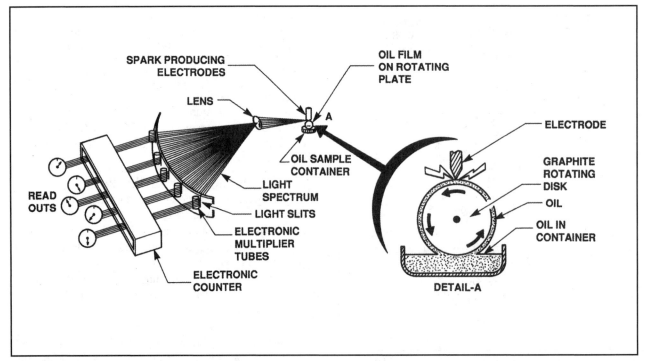

Fig. 6-5 — *Oil spectrometer.*

They are a blend of certain diesters, which are themselves man-made (synthesized) extracts of mineral, vegetable, and animal oils. In other words synthetic oils are made by synthesizing raw materials to form a base stock rather than refining base stock from crude oil.

The blending of these diesters with suitable chemicals in different amounts produces a lubricant which meets a prescribed specification of both the petroleum and the aviation industries. Synthetic oils are not compatible and cannot be mixed with petroleum (mineral) base oils. In addition, most manufacturers recommend that different brands or types of synthetic oils not be mixed or mixed only within strict guidelines of same-type and certain compatible brands. Inadvertent mixing can cause chemical shock and oil foaming and result in improper lubrication of the engine.

There are three different types of synthetic lubricants being used in turbine engines today: Type-1 (MIL-L-7808), Type-2 (MIL-L-23699), and Type-3 which currently does not have a MIL specification. Type-3 is the most recent synthetic lubricant to be developed and is used in many of the more modern engines. It is designed to meet current engine requirements and does not necessarily have the same chemical composition as Type-1 or Type-2. Engines originally designed to use Type-1 or Type-2 oil are still using this oil. Continuous modifications to the chemical structure of Type-1 has kept it essentially at the same quality as Type-2 or Type-3, when one considers the heat range for which it is intended. Type-2 and Type-3 were developed to withstand higher operating temperatures and to have improved anti-coking characteristics.

Changing over from Type-1 to the newer Type-2 or Type-3 is not generally recommended because the latter may have higher detergent quality, which could be detrimental to older engines. The idea here is that deposits which have formed over long periods of time are better left in place.

1. Discoloration Of Synthetic Lubricants

Synthetic oils of Type 1 and 2 are straw-colored when new but darken over time in service. Type-3 synthetic oil is slightly darker when new. The color change comes from an oxidation inhibitor added to the oil that darkens after coming in contact with oxygen. The gradual darkening effect is not an indication of oil degradation but rather the inhibitor performing its function of absorbing oxygen contained in air that is normally present in main bearing compartments and gearboxes.

However, abnormally rapid or heavy discoloration of oil can be an indicator of engine problems, mainly excessive air leakage into oil wetted areas. If this situation is present, the inhibitor breaks down and oxidation of oil will occur as oxygen molecules interact with molecules of oil products. Excessive oxidation results in viscosity increase or even sludge formation in the oil.

2. Typical Properties Of Turbine Oils

SPECIFICATIONS	TYPE I	TYPE II
United States	MIL-L-7808	MIL-L-23699
Great Britain	MIL-L-7808	MIL-L-23699
France	AIR 3513	PWA 521
Pratt & Whitney	PWA 521	D50TF1
General Electric	D50TFI	EMS-53
NATO Symbol	0-148	0-156
PROPERTIES:		
Specific gravity at 60°F(15.6°C)	0.95	0.975
Kinematic viscosity centistokes at 210°F(99°C)	3.26	5.09
at 100°F(38°C)	13.46	26.38
Flash point (open cup), °F(°C)	450(232)	480(249)
Pour point, °F(°C)	below 75(60)	75(60)
Evaporation loss in 6 1/2 hr, at 400°F 204°C), wt. %	17.0	4.2
Ryder gear test load, lb/in^2	2575	2796
Total acid number, mg KOH/gm	0.21	0.3

Common reminders one sees in oil company materials concerning synthetic lubricants are as follows:

WARNING: Synthetic turbine lubricants contain additives which are readily absorbed through the skin and are considered highly toxic. Excessive and/or prolonged exposure to the skin should be avoided.

CAUTION: Silicone based grease, such as that sometimes used to hold O-rings in place during assembly, can cause silicone contamination to the lube system. This contamination can cause engine oil to foam and result in oil loss through oil tank vents and also lead to engine damage from oil pump cavitation and insufficient lubrication.

CAUTION: Cadmium and zinc-plated parts and fasteners are not to be used in oil wetted areas. They are not compatible with synthetic lubricants. The lubricant can penetrate under the plating through small cracks or pin holes and cause the plating to flake off, contaminating the lubricating system.

E. Servicing

Before servicing an engine's oil system, the technician should refer to the engine or aircraft-type certificate data sheets or operations manual for the correct oil. (A sample "Data Sheet" is included at rear of this text.)

1. Common Synthetic Lubricants For Turbine Engines

A list of typical synthetic lubricants being widely used in the aviation industry is as follows:

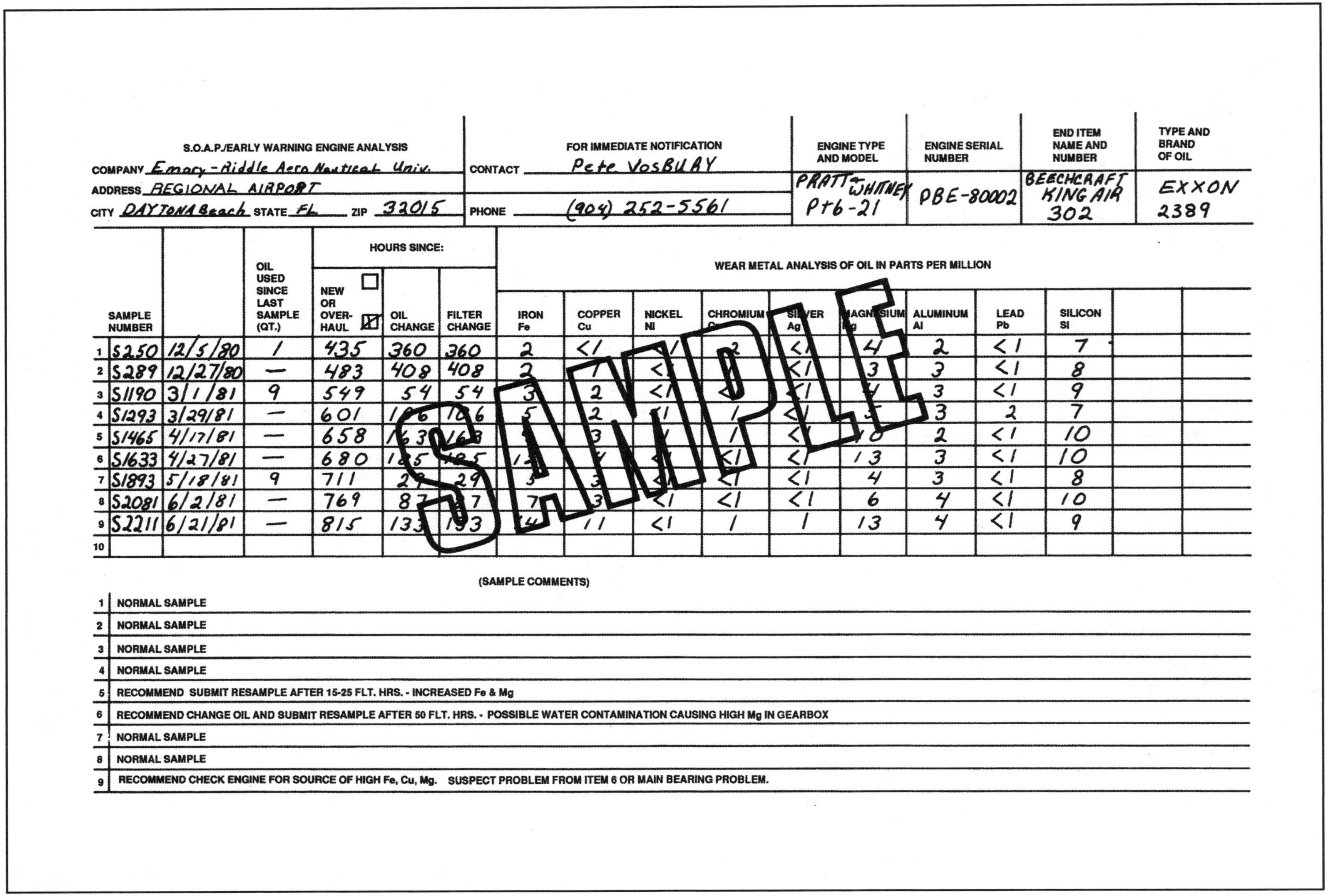

S.O.A.P./EARLY WARNING ENGINE ANALYSIS

COMPANY Emory-Riddle Aero Nautical Univ.
ADDRESS REGIONAL AIRPORT
CITY DAYTONA Beach STATE FL ZIP 32015

FOR IMMEDIATE NOTIFICATION
CONTACT Pete VosBURY
PHONE (904) 252-5561

ENGINE TYPE AND MODEL	ENGINE SERIAL NUMBER	END ITEM NAME AND NUMBER	TYPE AND BRAND OF OIL
PRATT-WHITNEY Pt6-21	PBE-80002	BEECHCRAFT KING AIR 302	EXXON 2389

	SAMPLE NUMBER		OIL USED SINCE LAST SAMPLE (QT.)	HOURS SINCE: NEW OR OVER-HAUL ☒	OIL CHANGE	FILTER CHANGE	WEAR METAL ANALYSIS OF OIL IN PARTS PER MILLION: IRON Fe	COPPER Cu	NICKEL Ni	CHROMIUM Cr	SILVER Ag	MAGNESIUM Mg	ALUMINUM Al	LEAD Pb	SILICON Si		
1	S250	12/5/80	1	435	360	360	2	<1	<1	2	<1	4	2	<1	7		
2	S289	12/27/80	—	483	408	408	2	1	<1	[illegible]	<1	3	3	<1	8		
3	S1190	3/1/81	9	549	54	54	3	2	<1	[illegible]	<1	4	3	<1	9		
4	S1293	3/29/81	—	601	106	106	5	2	<1	1	<1	5	3	2	7		
5	S1465	4/17/81	—	658	163	163	[illegible]	3	[illegible]	1	<1	10	2	<1	10		
6	S1633	4/27/81	—	680	185	185	[illegible]	4	<1	<1	<1	13	3	<1	10		
7	S1893	5/18/81	9	711	29	29	3	3	<1	<1	<1	4	3	<1	8		
8	S2081	6/2/81	—	769	87	87	7	3	<1	<1	<1	6	4	<1	10		
9	S2211	6/21/81	—	815	133	133	14	11	<1	1	1	13	4	<1	9		
10																	

(SAMPLE COMMENTS)

1 NORMAL SAMPLE
2 NORMAL SAMPLE
3 NORMAL SAMPLE
4 NORMAL SAMPLE
5 RECOMMEND SUBMIT RESAMPLE AFTER 15-25 FLT. HRS. - INCREASED Fe & Mg
6 RECOMMEND CHANGE OIL AND SUBMIT RESAMPLE AFTER 50 FLT. HRS. - POSSIBLE WATER CONTAMINATION CAUSING HIGH Mg IN GEARBOX
7 NORMAL SAMPLE
8 NORMAL SAMPLE
9 RECOMMEND CHECK ENGINE FOR SOURCE OF HIGH Fe, Cu, Mg. SUSPECT PROBLEM FROM ITEM 6 OR MAIN BEARING PROBLEM.

Fig. 6-6 — Spectrometric oil analysis report to user.

Type I	Type II	Type III
(MIL-L-7808)	(MIL-L-23699)	No MIL Spec
3 cSt	5 cSt	5 cSt
Exxon 2389	Mobil Jet-2	Mobil 254
Aeroshell 308	Aeroshell 500	Aeroshell 560
Castrol 399	Exxon 2380	Aeroshell 750
Castrol 5000	Stauffer Jet-2	

From this list, it can easily be seen that no standard identification system is currently in use. In fact, only a few oil companies include the type number or Mil Spec. on the oil can label. If needed, the technician would have to refer to oil company literature for these specifications.

Synthetic oil for turbine engines is usually supplied in one quart containers to minimize the chance of contaminants entering the lubrication system. Ground personnel should pay careful attention to cleanliness during servicing to maintain the integrity of the lubricant. In addition, use of a clean, service station type oil spout is recommended instead of can openers, which tend to deposit metal slivers in the oil.

If bulk oil rather than quart containers is used, filtering with a 10 micron filter or smaller is generally required.

2. Inadvertent Mixing Of Oils

In the event of inadvertent mixing of incompatible lubricants, many manufacturers require the oil system be drained and flushed before refilling. Also, when changing to another approved oil, a system drain and flush would most likely be required if the oils are not compatible.

Draining is usually accomplished at the oil tank, the accessory gearbox sump, the main oil filter, and other low points in the lube system. Flushing generally means reservicing and draining a second time after motoring the engine over with the starter and no ignition.

After final re-service, the engine will generally be run for a short period of time to resupply the lines, sumps, etc., with the residual oil normally held within the system.

If a new oil has been used, the placard stencil near the filler opening or metal oil identification tag, whichever is used, should be changed accordingly.

3. When To Service

Oil servicing is generally required after the terminating flight of the day and whenever requested by the flight crew. Another important consideration when servicing the oil system is to insure that servicing is accomplished within the prescribed time after engine shutdown. Manufacturers normally require this in order to prevent overservicing. Over servicing may occur on some engines which have the tendency to allow oil in the storage tank to seep into lower portions of the engine after periods of inactivity (Figure 6-7).

When the oil level is checked later than the prescribed time after shutdown, a typical procedure is as follows:

a. If the oil level is within one quart of full, servicing is generally optional;
b. If the oil level is low but still visible on the dipstick or sight gauge, motor the engine over with the starter for 20-30 seconds, then recheck the oil level;
c. If the oil level is not visible on the dipstick or sight gauge, add oil until an indication appears, then motor the engine for 20-30 seconds and recheck the oil level.

An important consideration after oil servicing is recording the amount of oil serviced. A steady oil consumption within allowable limits provides a valuable trend analysis to indicate that wear at main bearing oil-seal locations is normal.

4. Storage Of Turbine Oils

Most companies that produce turbine engine oil state that it must be used immediately after opening the container. Unlike most other oils, turbine engine synthetic oil is hygroscopic, meaning it easily absorbs moisture from the atmosphere. If a container is opened and not used in a short period of time, the oil will tend to absorb moisture from the air.

5. Oil Consumption - Oil Change

Oil consumption of turbine engines is very low. Many business-jet-sized engines may require only one quart of oil replenishment per 200 to 300 flight hours. A typical oil change interval is 300 to 400 operating hours or six months on a calendar interval.

On larger engines, one could expect to service no more than 0.2 to 0.5 quarts per operating hour. By comparison, an 18-cylinder radial engine could consume as much as 20 quarts per operating hour and still be considered airworthy.

Many airlines do not establish oil change intervals. The reason is that in the average 20 to 30 quart capacity oil tank, normal replenishment automatically changes the oil.

F. Wet Sump Lubrication Systems

The wet sump system is the oldest design, and it is still seen in auxiliary power units and ground power units but rarely seen in modern flight engines. Components of a wet sump system are similar to a dry sump system, except for the location of the oil supply. The dry sump carries its oil in a separate tank, whereas the wet sump oil is contained integrally in an engine sump.

Figure 6-8 shows an engine with a wet sump lubrication system and the oil contained in its accessory gearbox. The bearings and drive gears within the sump are lubricated by a splash system. The remaining points of lubrication receive oil from a gear-type pressure pump, which directs oil to oil jets at various locations in the engine.

Most wet sump engines do not incorporate a pressure relief valve and are known as variable pressure systems.

With this system the pump output pressure depends directly on engine revolutions per minute.

Scavenged oil is returned to the sump by a combination of gravity flow from the bearings and also suction created by a gear-type scavenge pump located within the pump housing.

The vent line is present to prevent over-pressurization of the gearbox. Gas path air seeping past main bearing seals finds its way to the gearbox via the scavenge system and the vent line returns this air to the atmosphere.

G. Dry Sump Systems

Most gas turbine engines utilize a dry sump lubrication system consisting of pressure, scavenge, and breather vent subsystems.

The main oil supply is carried in a tank mounted either integrally within the engine or externally on the engine or in the aircraft. A smaller supply is contained in a gearbox sump which also houses the oil pressure pump, oil scavenge pump, oil filter, and other lube systems components. Another small amount of oil is residual within the oil system lines, sumps, and components.

1. System Components

a. Oil Tank

The oil supply reservoir is usually constructed of sheet aluminum or stainless steel and is designed to furnish a constant supply of oil to the engine during all authorized flight attitudes. In most tanks, a pressure build-up is desired to assure a positive flow of oil to the oil pump inlet and to suppress foaming in the tank which in turn prevents pump cavitation. This buildup is accomplished by running the tank overboard vent line through a relief valve to maintain a positive pressure of approximately

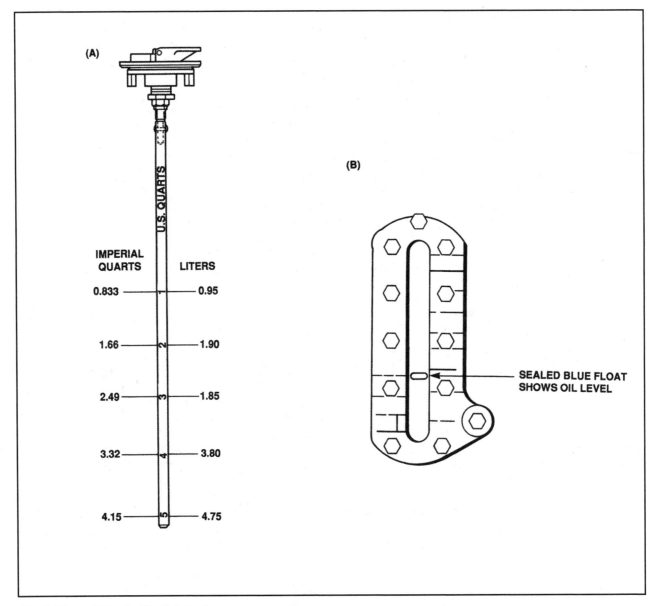

Fig. 6-7A — Oil tank dip stick and cap
Fig. 6-7B — Oil tank sight gauge.

three to six pounds per square inch—gauge (psig). That is, the tank vent relief valve will release excess air at a pressure differential of three to six pounds per square inch—differential (psid) between the tank and ambient, (Figure 6-27) or tank and vent subsystem. (Figure 6-34) After shutdown, a small bleed orifice in the relief valve allows for depressurization of the tank.

Some dry sump oil tanks are of the integral type. While the external sheet metal type is a separate assembly located outside the engine, the integral oil tank is formed by space provided within the engine. It can be a propeller reduction gearbox that houses the oil or sometimes a cavity between major engine cases (Figure 6-33).

The distinction between the wet sump and dry sump is that the wet sump is located in the main gearbox at the lowest point within the engine, facilitating splash lu brication. The dry sump is seldom located at the low point on the engine. It may or may not gravity flow oil to the main oil pump inlet. Refer to Figure 6-9 and Figure 6-10.

Figure 6-9 shows an illustration of an oil tank with a dwell chamber, often referred to as an oil tank de-aerator, which provides a means of separating entrained air from the scavenge oil. The tank shown is of typical oil capacity for a business jet, approximately five quarts of oil, three of which are usable, plus a two-quart expansion space. The location of the outlet in this example tank keeps one quart as residual oil and provides a low point for sediment and condensation to collect until drained. Other tanks could take oil from a bottom location using a standpipe.

Today, some oil tanks are configured with a remote pressure fill capability. An oil pumping cart can be attached to the tank and the oil hand pumped into the tank until it is at the proper level, at which time oil starts to flow from the overflow. The oil filler cap is usually removed during this operation to prevent over-servicing in case the oil overflow is not properly connected (Figure 6-11). The hand gravity oil tank filling method is, however, still the most common. The scupper shown on the illustration is present to catch oil that is spilled during servicing or during cap blow off and to route this spillage through a drain point location at the bottom of the engine. Due to the position of the filler cap, it is not possible to over-service by the hand gravity method. Many of the new filler openings are fitted with a flapper seal, in the event the oil filler cap is inadvertently left off.

In place of a dipstick, some oil tanks incorporate a sight gauge (Figure 6-7B) to satisfy the requirement for a visual means of checking oil level. However, these glass indicators tend to cloud over after prolonged use, and many operators have gone back to the dipstick.

b. Oil Pumps

The function of the oil pressure pump is to supply oil under pressure to the parts of the engine that require lubrication. Many oil pumps consist not only of a pressure lube element but one or more scavenge elements as well, all in one housing. By its nature, an oil pump is designed to provide a volume of flow to the engine. How much oil pressure it creates is a function of how much

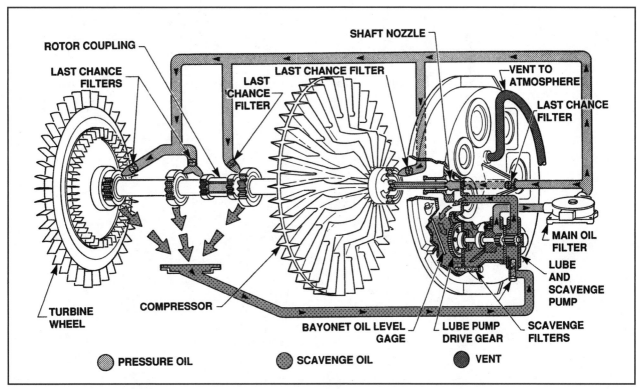

Fig. 6-8 — Wet sump lubrication system (variable pressure system with no relief valve).

resistance to flow there is. The more the flow is restricted, the higher the oil pressure will tend to be. For example, as an oil filter starts to clog, the resistance to flow increases in front of the filter and the pressure increases.

The three most common oil pumps are: The vane, gerotor, and gear types. All are classed as positive displacement pumps because they deposit a fixed quantity of oil in the pump outlet per revolution. All three types of pumps are also self-lubricating. These category pumps are also referred to as constant displacement types because they displace a constant volume per revolution.

1) Vane Pump

The pump in Figure 6-12 could be a single element type or one element of a multiple pump. Multiple pumps of this type generally contain one pressure element and one or more scavenge elements, all of which are mounted on a common shaft. The drive shaft mounts to an accessory gearbox drive pad and all pumping elements rotate together.

Pumping action takes place as Rotor Drive Shaft and Eccentric Rotor, which act as one rotating piece, drive the

sliding vanes around. The space between each vane pair floods with oil as it passes the oil inlet opening and carries this oil to the oil outlet. As the spaces diminish to a zero clearance, the oil is forced to leave the pump. The downstream resistance to flow will determine the pump output pressure unless a relief valve is present to regulate pressure.

Vane pumps are considered to be more tolerant of debris in the scavenge oil. They are also lighter in weight than the gerotor or gear pumps and offer a slimmer profile. They may not, however, have the mechanical strength of other type pumps.

2) Gerotor Pump

Figure 6-13A shows one pumping element mounted on a multiple-element pump main shaft. The gerotor pump, sometimes referred to as gear-rotor, utilizes a principle similar to the vane pump. The gerotor uses a lobe-shaped drive gear within an elliptically-shaped idler gear to displace oil from an inlet to an outlet port.

Notice that the inner driving gear in Figure 6-13 has six lobes (teeth) and that the outer idling gear has seven

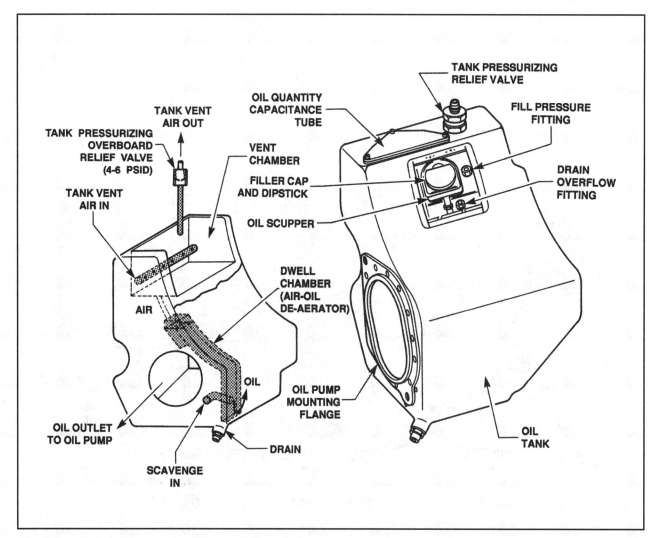

Fig. 6-9 — External dry sump oil tank, small engine.

openings. This arrangement allows oil to fill the one open pocket and move inlet oil through the pump as it rotates until a zero clearance forces the oil from the discharge port. The principle of operation is that the volume of the missing tooth multiplied by the number of lobes in the outer gear determines the volume of oil pumped per revolution of the outer gear. For this example pump, in one revolution of the driven gear there would be six pockets of oil pumped, because there are six lobes on the driven gear. For one revolution of the idler gear, there would be seven pockets of oil pumped. It should be noted that the idler gear only rotates 6/7 as fast as the driven gear.

Referring to Figure 6-13A, a complete pumping element is shown, one of several which could be mounted on a single shaft within the same pump housing. Figure 6-13B depicts the principle of operation of the gerotor pump. The operation would be as follows:

a) From 0° to 180°, inter-lobe space increases from a minimum to a maximum volume. Most of the 180° it is open to the intake port allowing it to fill with oil.

b) As the space reaches maximum volume, it is closed to the intake port and is in a position to open to the discharge port.

c) At 270°, the space decreases in volume, forcing its oil out the discharge port.

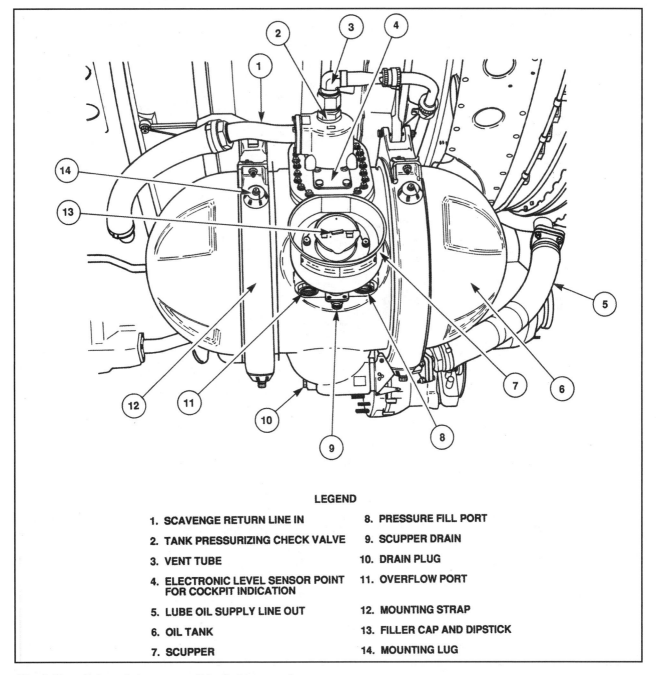

LEGEND

1. SCAVENGE RETURN LINE IN	8. PRESSURE FILL PORT
2. TANK PRESSURIZING CHECK VALVE	9. SCUPPER DRAIN
3. VENT TUBE	10. DRAIN PLUG
4. ELECTRONIC LEVEL SENSOR POINT FOR COCKPIT INDICATION	11. OVERFLOW PORT
5. LUBE OIL SUPPLY LINE OUT	12. MOUNTING STRAP
6. OIL TANK	13. FILLER CAP AND DIPSTICK
7. SCUPPER	14. MOUNTING LUG

Fig. 6-10 — External dry sump oil tank, large engine.

d) As the space reaches minimum volume at 360° it is closed to the discharge port and begins to open to the intake port, repeating the cycle.

This action takes place in each of the seven inter-lobal spaces between the inner six-lobe gerotor and the outer seven-lobe gerotor, giving an essentially continuous oil flow.

3)   Gear Pump

The single element gear type pump Figure 6-14 takes in inlet oil and rotates in a direction which allows oil to move between the gear teeth and the pump inner case until the oil is deposited in the outlet. The idler gear seals the inlet from the outlet preventing fluid backup and also doubles the capacity per revolution. This pump also incorporates a system relief valve in its housing which returns unwanted oil to the pump inlet. Figure 6-15 shows a dual pump with both a pressure and a scavenge element.

c.   Oil Filters

Oil filters are an important part of the lubrication system since they remove contaminant particles that collect in the oil.

1)   Contaminants In Oil

Contaminants found in the oil system filters come primarily from the following sources:
a) Products of decomposition of the oil itself, usually seen as small black specks of carbon;
b) Metallic particles from engine wear and corrosion in oil wetted areas of the engine;
c) Airborne contaminants entering through main bearing seals;
d) Dirt and other foreign matter introduced into the oil supply during servicing.

The contaminants which are seen in filter bowls or on filter screens are always a matter of concern. Usually, the determination as to whether the engine requires maintenance or whether it is airworthy is a matter of professional judgment based on long experience of a person who has seen cases of normal and abnormal levels of contamination. If a spectrometric oil analysis is available, as is the case in most larger aviation companies, a read-out of the various metal particles suspended in the oil can be used in the decision-making process of whether or not there is sufficient cause to perform maintenance on the engine.

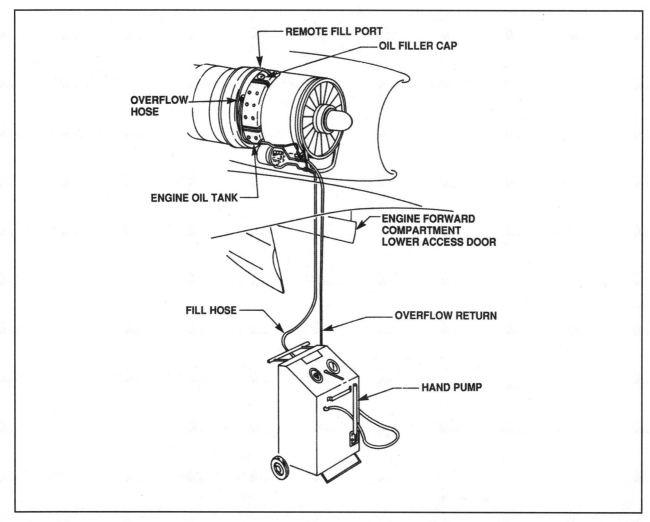

Fig. 6-11 — Pressure oil service cart.

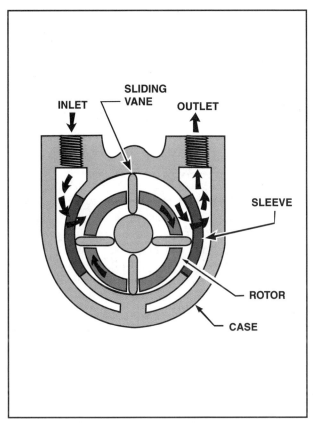

Fig. 6-12 — Sliding vane lubrication pump.

Another common observation of engine oil is to see it turn dark brown, or even blackish, but with little or no contaminants. This is a chemical reaction to excessive oil oxidation. See Paragraph D.1. for an explanation of oil discoloration.

Gas turbine engine oil filters have micronic ratings in that they are designed to prevent passage of micronic-sized contaminant particles into the system.

2) Microns

The term "Micron" is derived from the international system of measurement and represents a size or distance equal to one millionth part of a meter, or approximately .000039 of an inch.

Particles of micronic size are present around us continually, although the unaided human eye cannot readily distinguish objects smaller than about 40 microns. The air we breathe carries many invisible particles, one to five microns in size. Airborne moisture in the form of fog is composed of 5 to 50 micron particles.

Because of this extreme fineness of micronic particle size, it is evident that the prevention of contamination to the oil system by these minute objects must be a closely controlled process (Figure 6-16).

LINEAR EQUIVALENTS

1 Inch	25.4 Millimeters	25,400 Microns
1 Millimeter	0.0394 Inches	1,000 Microns
1 Micron	1/25,400 of an Inch	.001 Millimeters
1 Micron	0.000039 of an Inch	

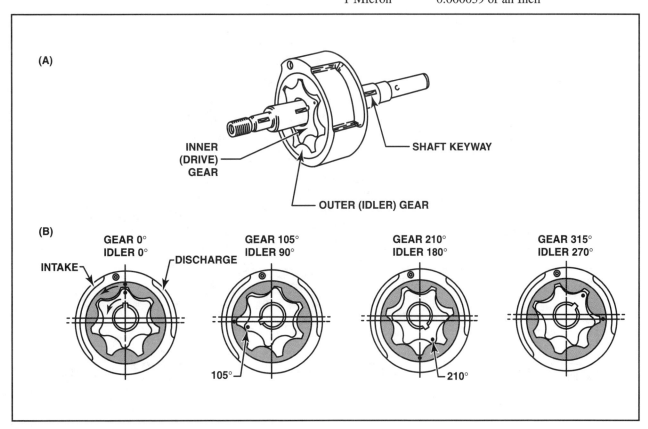

Fig. 6-13A — Gerotor lubrication pumping element.
Fig. 6-13B — Gerotor pump cycle of operation.

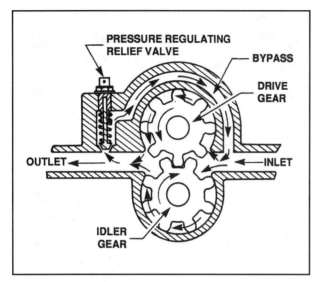

Fig. 6-14 — Side view of gear lubricating pump.

RELATIVE SIZES

Lower Limit of Visibility (Naked Eye)	40 Microns
White Blood Cells	25 Microns
Red Blood Cells	8 Microns
Bacteria (Cocci)	2 Microns

3) Forces Acting On Filters

All types of filters are constructed to withstand high fatigue forces, but they must be in perfect condition to do so. Any damage whatsoever is generally cause for rejection. The forces acting on filters are as follows:

a) Pressure forces which occur when the oil is cold. Cold flowing oil results in high viscosity which can build pressure up to 300 pounds per square inch—gauge in a system normally controlled to 50 pounds per square inch—gauge. This can take place even though the pressure regulating valve and filter bypass valve are open and trying to relieve pressure;

b) Pressure forces from the volume of flow. In the high flow rate, low volume type system used in gas

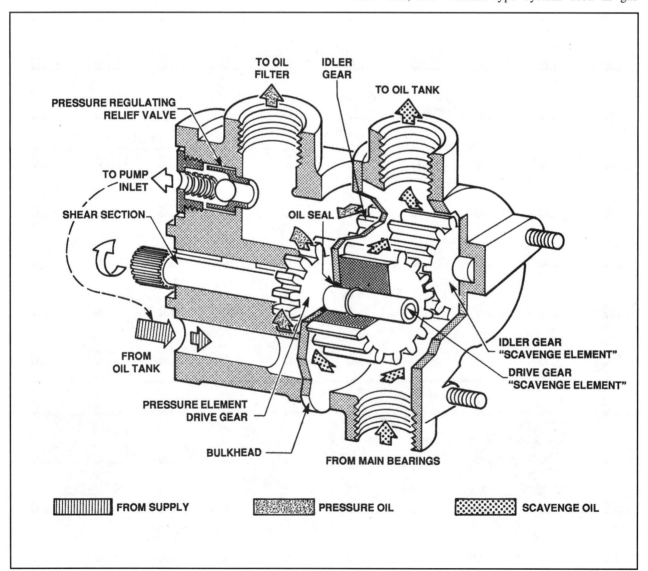

Fig. 6-15 — Cutaway view of combination pressure and scavenge pump.

turbine engines, it is not uncommon to have the entire oil supply pass through the oil filter four to eight times per minute and in large engines as much as 60 gallons per minute;

c) Fatigue forces from high frequency. Oil pump pressure pulsations can emanate from the oil pump gear teeth passing frequency;

d) Fatigue forces from thermal cycling. Temperatures up to 400°F are present in filters located on the scavenge side of the oil system.

4) Filter Types

The most common types of main system filters are the disposable fiber, and the cleanable stainless steel screen. The cleanable screen filter is further broken down into the pleated screen, the wafer screen, and the screen and spacer types. All three metal types are generally cleaned at intervals based on engine cycles.

The difference between cleanable metal screens and disposable fiber filters is as follows:

a)   Woven wire filters will more likely be used in an aircraft where high engine cycles accumulate and frequent filter inspections are required. The cleaning capability then becomes a cost saving measure. Woven wire filters however, cannot generally be made to have a rating below 40 microns. Wire filters also will be physically larger than a disposable filter of the same rating because only about 30 percent of the surface area of the mesh remains as flow area.

b)   The disposable filters in oil systems are capable of filtering down to 15 microns. However, it may not always be possible to use a 15 micron filter with oils of high centistoke values. An advantage of this filter is that it is much smaller in size than a comparable wire mesh

Fig. 6-16 — Filter surface enlarged 250 times.

filter. Because it has no weave, it has an effective flow area of up to 70 percent available.

Filters with low micronic ratings remove all but the smallest pieces, even the small carbon particles, and keep the oil in a relatively "as new" condition. Finer filtration become necessary because of the greater use of labyrinth main bearing oil seals. Labyrinth air-oil seals pass more airborne contaminants into the oil than do carbon seals but are thought to be more durable.

On older aircraft it is common to see metal mesh filters of 175 microns or more. One reason for this is that in earlier years the harmful effect of small particles such as carbon, dust, and dirt were not as fully understood as they are today. Many of the high micronic rated filters have since been changed because filter manufacturers now provide deeper pleated filters with lower micronic ratings which, for a given size, flow equal amounts of oil and provide better filtration.

The tendency today is to change to a lower micron filter if available. The difference in pressure drop across a clean filter is only about three pounds per square inch differential more when changing from a 40 micron filter to a 15 micron filter. The micron rating selected is a compromise between fine filtration, costs, and an acceptable pressure drop the engine can tolerate when the oil is cold. The point here is that the engine might be poorly lubricated under these conditions during a cold weather start.

5) How The Filter Assembly Functions

An observation of the paper disposable and screen mesh filters would reveal that most are heavily pleated or, in the case of stacked filters (wafer or screen and spacer), they consist of many twin screens. This is to provide a maximum surface area for filtration. The screen types have an actual micronic size, measurable in microns. The fiber type filters have an equivalent micronic rating. (Figures 6-18 and 6-19)

Figure 6-17 is an illustration of an in-line bowl type filter which could be either disposable or cleanable. A typical rating for this filter is 40 microns. This means it will filter out particles larger than 40 microns in diameter.

Observe that oil fills the bowl (sump), then forces its way through the filtering element to the core, exiting at the port near the spring side of the bypass relief valve. On a cold morning when oil is highly viscous, or, if filter clogging restricts oil flow through the element, the differential by-pass valve will open, allowing unfiltered oil to flow out to the engine.

During a bypass condition, the amount of oil is reduced from that which would flow normally through the filter screen, but it will provide initial lubrication during starting or sufficient lubrication for at least reduced power operation in flight. Note that the bypass relief valve in Figure 6-17 has a rating of 25 pounds per square inch—differential, often referred to as a differential pressure or delta-p (Δ-p) rating.

If system pressure in which this filter is located is regulated to 45 pounds per square inch gauge (oil-in pressure), and the normal pressure drop across a clean filter is five pounds per square inch gauge, then 40 pounds per square inch gauge oil-out pressure is assisting the 25 pounds per square inch spring in holding the bypass valve closed. As filters become blocked by debris or, if oil is congealed during a cold weather start, the pressure drop across the filtering element will increase. When the pressure drop exceeds the rating of the bypass valve spring, the valve will open bypassing unfiltered oil directly from the inlet to the outlet. When the bypass valve opens, the pressure downstream of the filter does not return to normal. The downstream pressure remains at the same value, lower than the upstream pressure by the psid rating of the bypass valve. If the pressure were to return to normal, the pressure drop would no longer exist which is needed to hold the bypass valve open.

Figure 6-19 shows filters of the cleanable pleated-screen type and the screen and spacer type, which fit into a gearbox annulus and provide the exact same service as the bowl type.

The screen and spacer type filter, also known as an edge-type filter, seen in Figures 6-19 and 6-20, can be disassembled for inspection and cleaning. This filter usually fits into an annulus provided in the main accessory gearbox. The filter configuration is a series of thin screens between spacers which allows oil to flow in the inward direction.

The filters illustrated in Figure 6-19 are more common in the pressure (oil supply) subsystem to the engine. Some engines also provide filtration for the scavenge subsystems which route oil from the engine back to the supply tank. The three different micron ratings shown in the Figure are intended to represent the range of filtration which might be used. The 140 micron filter might be used in an engine that is subject to coking problems, while the 40 and 15 micron filters would be used when coking is not a problem.

6) Filter Cleaning

Traditional methods of hand cleaning filters in solvent are still commonly used and acceptable. However, several cleaning devices that induce high frequency sound waves, called "ultrasonic" cleaning, or high frequency "vibrator cleaners" are also available, and will do a more complete job of removing all the contaminants from the filtering elements (Figure 6-21).

Maintaining a written record of findings during filter inspections is a widely accepted procedure. This provides a trend analysis of contamination build-up during subsequent filter inspections.

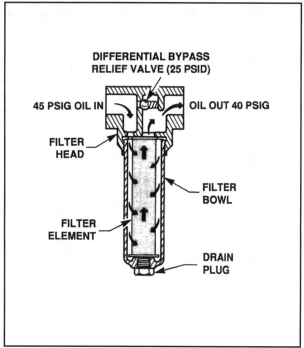

Fig. 6-17 — Bowl type cleanable stainless steel mesh, pleated oil filter.

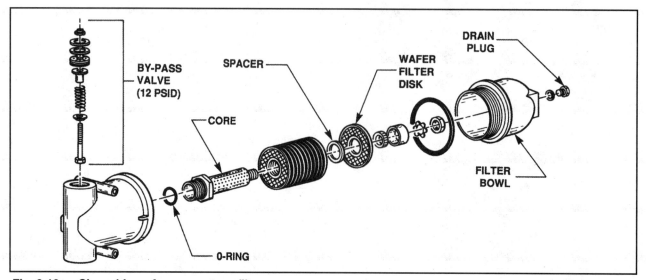

Fig. 6-18 — Cleanable wafer screen type filter.

It is normal to find particles of metal on filter surfaces. If it is found that this contamination level is in excess of the manufacturer's limits, or if any large metal chips are found, the source of the contamination must be located and the problem corrected. Then, the engine should be drained of all oil, re-serviced, and run for a short (prescribed) period of time. Sometimes, several cycles of this procedure are needed to clear the system to the point where the filters remain clean.

d. Pressure Regulating Valves (Relief Valves)

Pressure regulating valves, referred to and talked about in earlier parts of this chapter, are very closely tied to oil filters and oil pumps. For this reason, they will be mentioned again as we finish this section on pumps and filters.

Pressure regulating valves, or relief valves, are designed to either maintain the pressure at a prescribed value or to keep the pressure from going beyond some limit. As such, these valves can be described as either an operating type or a safety type. The operating type is typically off its seat by the time the engine reaches idle, maintaining a set pressure even as the engine is accelerated to takeoff thrust. The safety type is typically on its seat, and would only open and limit the pressure in a circumstance when it would not be safe to let it go any higher.

On engines with operating type relief valves, the location of the valve can be either upstream or downstream of the main oil filter. The location of the valve will play a significant role in what happens during an oil filter bypass condition. For example, if the valve

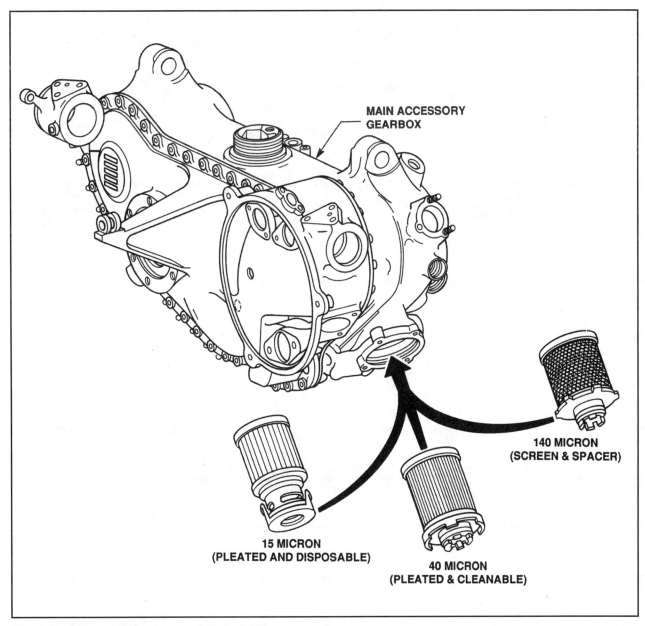

MAIN ACCESSORY
GEARBOX

140 MICRON
(SCREEN & SPACER)

15 MICRON
(PLEATED AND DISPOSABLE)

40 MICRON
(PLEATED & CLEANABLE)

Fig. 6-19 — Types of gearbox mounted oil filters.

is downstream of the filter and the filter clogs, the pressure at this point will not change. The pressure that will change is the value upstream of the filter, and that is what will create the "psid" that causes the filter to bypass. If the relief valve is upstream of the filter, the upstream pressure will remain constant during a bypass condition and the downstream pressure will drop.

The Pratt and Whitney JT-8 engine lube system, shown in Figure 6-34, has an interesting design for its pressure regulating valve. It utilizes a sense line downstream of the oil cooler that connects to the regulating valve. In the event of a clogging oil cooler, which would cause the oil pressure to the engine to drop, the sense line causes the pressure regulating valve to reset the system pressure to a higher value.

The Allison/Rolls Royce AE 3007 turbofan engine, used in aircraft like the Embraer Regional Jets, also has a very interesting design for its pressure regulating valve. It has a valve that senses system pressure and vent pressure, and maintains a constant differential between

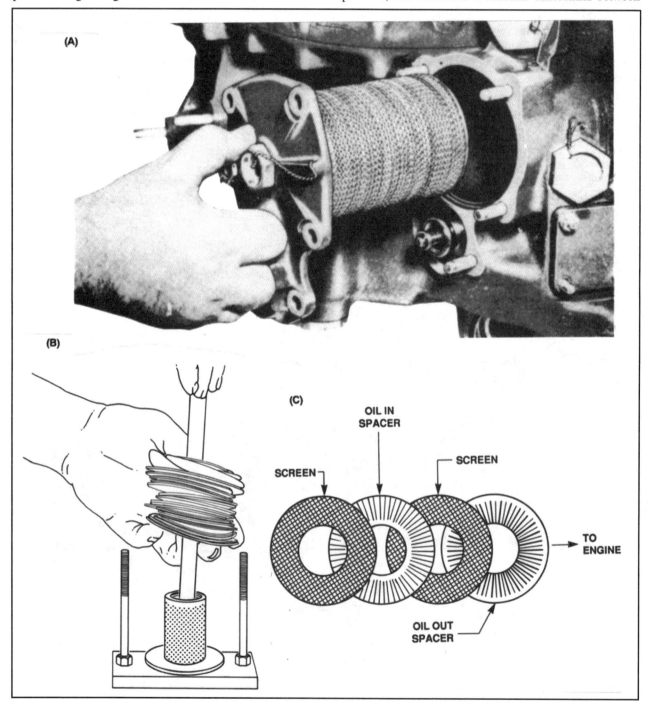

Fig. 6-20A — Screen and spacer oil filter.
Fig. 6-20B — Screen and spacer oil filter being disassembled for cleaning.
Fig. 6-20C — Arrangement of screen and spacers.

the two. Since the amount of oil flow to a bearing is based on the difference between the pressure at the oil jet and the vent pressure in the bearing housing, this valve manages to keep that oil flow constant.

e. Low Pressure Warning Light

All aircraft cockpits have one or more oil pressure gauges. The cockpit pressure gauge will more likely tap into the oil system, downstream (output side) of the main oil filter, to indicate the actual oil pressure being delivered to the engine. Many aircraft are also configured with a low pressure warning light. When power is turned on in the aircraft, this light will illuminate. Then as oil pressure builds in the system during starting, the light will go out at a preset value equal to the low or "red line" limit for the cockpit oil pressure gauge. Figures 6-22 & 6-23A show this warning light.

If the warning light does not go out after start-up or, if it comes back on during operation, the operator will look at the pressure gauge to confirm the extent of the low oil pressure condition and then take the appropriate action by reducing power or by shutting the engine down. Figure 6-23A also shows the low pressure warning light arrangement. If the filter clogs during engine operation, the "low pressure" warning light acts as a bypass warning light. Its microswitch is set so that the cockpit light will come on at the pressure at which the filter will start to bypass oil. This situation is further explained in the following paragraphs with a more detailed illustration of the low oil pressure warning systems.

f. Filter Bypass Warning Lights And Cockpit Gauge

1) Bypass Condition

Oil filter impending bypass warning instrumentation is also installed in many engines to provide flight and maintenance personnel with an indication that the main oil filter is approaching a blocked condition or is completely blocked. Such instrumentation is considered a maintenance aid because timely action in most cases will prolong the life of the engine components. (Figure 6-23B)

Once a filter is obstructed to the point that it bypasses, unfiltered oil will flow to the engine and may clog internal engine oil screens and jets, with a resultant loss of lubrication to the related bearings and seals. Should this occur, the conditions at the bearing and seal locations throughout the engine would be similar to those following loss of main oil pressure.

In a pressure regulated system there might be a change in the oil pressure indication to warn the operator, because the system relief valve would simply return more oil to the pump inlet. In this case it is helpful to have a warning device called an impending bypass light. It is adjusted to actuate at a differential pressure sufficiently less than the Delta-P at which the filter will start bypassing to permit flight crews to take timely action and prevent bypassing of unfiltered oil.

2) Delta-P Light

When a filter is configured with an impending bypass warning light, referred to as a Delta-P (ΔP) light (Figure 6-23B), the light remains off after power is supplied to the instrument panel because no differential pressure exists at this time. The light normally only illuminates at impending filter bypass condition. The light, however, may come on if filter inlet pressure builds rapidly during engine starting. The reason for the rapid pressure rise is generally highly viscous oil, resulting from very cold weather. The light will go out as oil temperature comes up to normal value. Should the light not go out, continued operation above idle with the light on is not usually

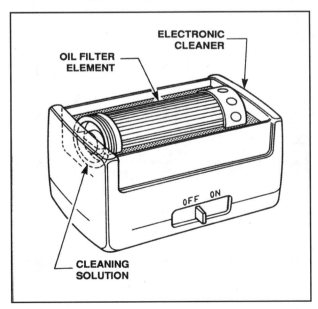

Fig. 6-21 — Fluid vibrator type oil filter cleaner.

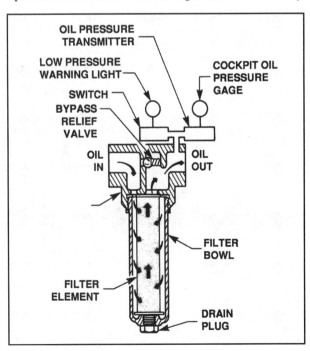

Fig. 6-22 — Oil filter with low oil pressure switch and oil pressure transmitter.

allowed except during in-flight emergencies because there is a good chance that the filter is clogging with solid contaminants.

The operator will carefully access other engine gauge readings such as oil temperature and engine vibration for indications of major engine malfunction during the time the engine is operating in this questionable condition. The differential oil pressure (pressure versus vent) indicating system was developed to provide a reading of the true oil pressure drop across the oil jets, because this is a measure of the quantity of oil flowing to the bearings.

3) Dual Cockpit Gauges

Instead of a Delta-P light, some aircraft are configured with a duel pressure indicating system, which includes two pressure gauges one upstream and one downstream

from the filter. The gauges will be red-lined at the same value as the micro contactor in the warning switch to the light. The difference in the two gauge readings will tell the operator if the bypassing point is imminent or has been reached. For instance, if normal pressure drop across a clean filter is five pounds per square inch—differential and the bypass valve is set to open at 28 pounds per square inch—differential, when the two gauges have a spread of 28 pounds per square inch—differential, bypass is occurring. This situation is further discussed in Paragraph H of this chapter.

4) Procedures During Low Oil Pressure Conditions

The following procedure is recommended for engines on which oil filter pressure drop instrumentation is provided:

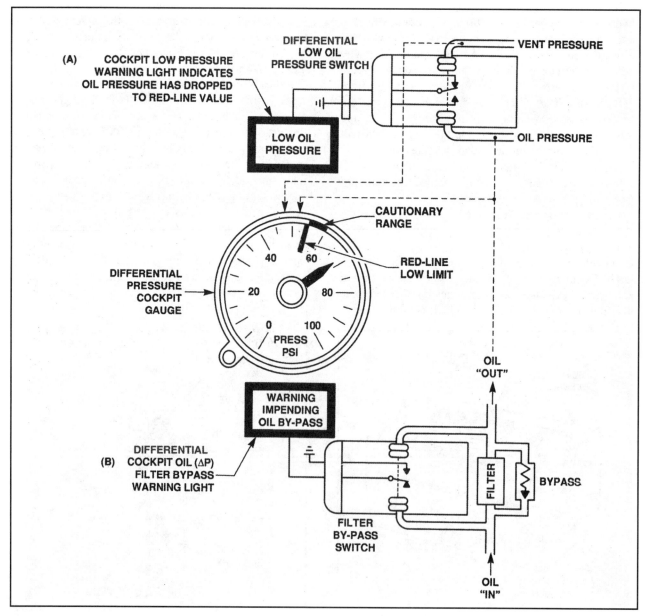

Fig. 6-23A — Cockpit gauge and low oil pressure light.
Fig. 6-23B — Oil filter bypass light.

a) A reduction in power should be made whenever the cockpit pressure indicator reaches the red-line limit and/or its back-up system, the low pressure warning light, illuminates.

b) If the warning light goes out after being on for a short period of time, and all other engine instrument indications remain at acceptable values, engine operation at a reduced throttle setting may be continued at the discretion of the flight crew. If high vent pressure is causing a low oil pressure indication, a reduction in power will often lower the vent pressure and bring the oil pressure back to a more normal value. A high oil temperature indication will often accompany high vent pressure, because more hot gas path air is in contact with the oil.

c) Whenever the oil pressure indicator reading remains at the red-line or the low oil warning light remains on, the engine should be shut down or the throttle setting should be kept at the minimum thrust required to sustain flight until a landing can be made.

d) Whenever the oil pressure indicator reading reaches the red-line limit and/or the warning light illuminates, the incident should be reported as an engine discrepancy and the main oil filter must be inspected by disassembly.

5) Filter Pop-Out Warning

Some filters which do not have pressure drop indicators or warning lights are configured with a warning pop-out button on the filter bowl. Figure 6-24 shows a filter bowl with an impending bypass button. The button will pop out when filter inlet pressure reaches a preset value to provide a visual warning that the filter is about to bypass or that it has already bypassed. Maintenance technicians will see this warning button during routine inspections or during troubleshooting of the oil system and react by examining the filtering element for contamination. Once the problem is resolved, the button is reset by hand.

During cold weather starting, high oil pressure may cause the oil filter differential pressure bypass valve to open. This however will not cause the impending bypass button to pop out. The pop-out assembly contains a thermal low temperature lockout to prevent it from tripping. As the oil warms up to approximately 100°F, the thermal lockout is disengaged and the indicator is ready to warn of filter contamination.

g. Other Components Of Dry Sump Systems:

There are several other components in the dry sump lubricating system, some of which are as follows:

1) System pressure relief valve (Figures 6-25, 6-26);
2) Anti-static leak check valve (Figures 6-26, 6-27);
3) Oil cooler (Figures 6-27, 6-28);
4) Oil jets (Figures 6-27, 6-29);
5) Last chance filters (Figures 6-27, 6-29);
6) Chip detectors (Figures 6-27, 6-30);
7) Rotary air-oil separator (Figures 6-31, 6-33);
8) Pressurizing and vent valve (Figures 6-32, 6-33).

These components will be discussed in the following

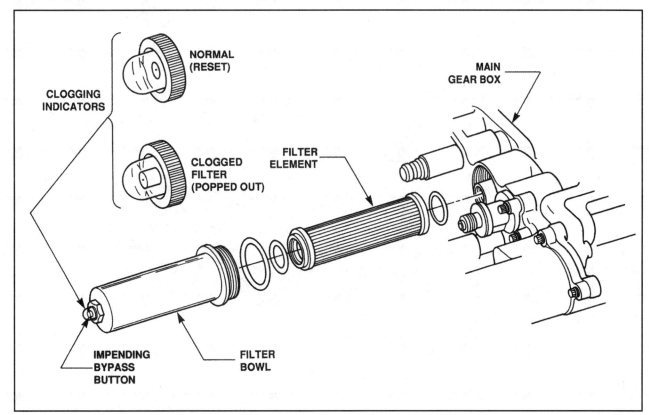

Fig. 6-24 — Main oil filter with bypass warning button.

information concerning the General Electric CJ-610 Turbojet, the Pratt & Whitney PT6 Turboprop, the JT8D turbofan, and the G.E./Snecma CFM56 turbofan lubricating systems.

H. Small Engine Full Flow Lubrication System - General Electric CJ610 Turbojet (Figure 6-27)

1. Oil Pressure Subsystem

a. Pressure Subsystem Oil Flow

In the schematic diagram in Figure 6-27, oil flows from a 0.75 gallon capacity tank to the pressure subsystem pumping element. The pump moves oil at the rate of 2.5 gallons per minute to the relief valve. This valve is adjustable and in this case is set to relieve at 125 pounds per square inch gauge. It relieves the system by routing oil back to the oil tank whenever fluid pressure reaches a preset value, generally called the cracking pressure. In this system, the relief valve is referred to as a cold-start relief valve because it only cracks when back-pressure caused by low ambient temperature and high oil viscosity forces it open. This full flow pressure subsystem operates with varying oil pressure from idle power (five pounds per square inch gauge minimum) to takeoff power (60 pounds per square inch gauge maximum) at normal oil operating temperature.

If an engine does not have a cold-start relief valve, it will have a pressure-regulating relief valve (Figure 6-25). With a regulating relief valve, the oil pressure is held in a much narrower range of operation, for example, 45± five pounds per square inch—gauge. In this case, the relief valve would be cracked open constantly. It will be slightly open at idle speed and opened wider at takeoff power to maintain the preset pressure value. (Figures 6-25, 6-33 and 6-34 have this type relief valve).

After passing the system relief valve in Figure 6-27, oil flows to the fuel-oil cooler. If congealed oil or other restrictions to flow occur, the pressure downstream of the differential pressure bypass valve which is backing up the tensioning spring will diminish. When a differential pressure (Δp) of 26 to 34 pounds per square inch—differential exists, the bypass will open to protect the cooler from over pressurization.

In the illustration, observe an antistatic-leak check valve. It is normally installed at the filter inlet to prevent oil leak-down from the tank to the sump during periods of engine inactivity. This check valve is set to open at minimal pumping pressure, perhaps two to three pounds per square inch—gauge. In addition, this valve helps to keep the oil pump primed for immediate lubrication to the engine on the next start-up (Figure 6-26).

In Figure 6-27, after the oil is cooled, it is filtered. A similar cold starting and filter clogging bypass valve is installed here. It is set to open at a pressure (Δp) of 33 pounds per square inch—differential.

To better understand the way in which this bypass operates, imagine the engine operating at normal oil temperature with a normal five pounds per square inch—differential across a clean filter, oil pressure upstream of the filter at 60 pounds per square inch—gauge, and oil pressure downstream of the filter at 55 pounds per square inch—gauge. Holding the bypass valve closed is 55 pounds per square inch—gauge downstream oil pressure plus a 33 pounds per square inch spring pressure. This value is obviously much higher than the pressure on the upstream side (60 pounds per square inch—gauge). If the filter starts to clog, the pressure upstream starts to rise and the pressure downstream starts to drop. When the differential reaches 33 pounds per square inch, or slightly greater, the bypass will open to maintain sufficient lubrication for operation at low to moderate flight requirements.

In some systems, a differential pressure switch is placed across the filter, inlet to outlet, to activate a warning light in the cockpit if bypass is about to occur. This light is set to illuminate slightly below the bypass pressure value to give an indication of an imminent bypass situation.

Once past the oil filter, oil under pump pressure flows downstream to the oil jets. Oil under pressure also flows to the oil pressure transducer (transmitter). The transducer also receives a vent pressure input.

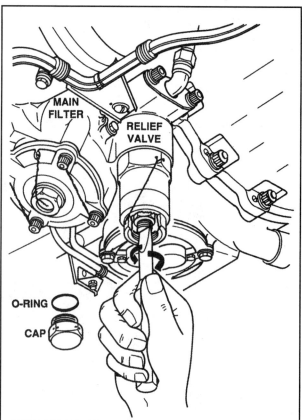

Fig. 6-25 — Engine oil pressure relief valve adjustment.

The transducer is designed so that it sends a corrected oil pressure (fluid pressure minus vent "air" pressure) to the cockpit gauge. This design is used because vent pressure opposes oil flow at the oil jets, and the operator needs to know the flow condition in terms of corrected oil pressure. The vent system is explained in detail later in this chapter. The oil pressure indicating system is explained in detail in Chapter XII.

Note that in this system, the entire oil supply circulates approximately three times per minute. This is typical of most gas turbine engines.

The CJ610 lubrication system is considered a hot tank system because the oil cooler is located in the pressure sub-system and the oil is scavenged (hot) back to the oil tank.

b. System Components

1) Oil Cooler

The oil cooler's main function is to maintain a specific oil temperature under differing oil heat conditions which occur at varying engine speeds. The oil cooler shown in Figure 6-28 is a liquid-to-liquid heat exchanger. It contains numerous soda-straw type passageways for fuel flow on its way to the combustor while the oil circulates around the straws. This allows an exchange of heat to occur between the fuel and the oil.

This fuel-cooled oil cooler contains a combination differential pressure bypass valve and thermostatic bypass valve at the cooler inlet. When the oil is cold, the valve is open, allowing oil to take the path of least

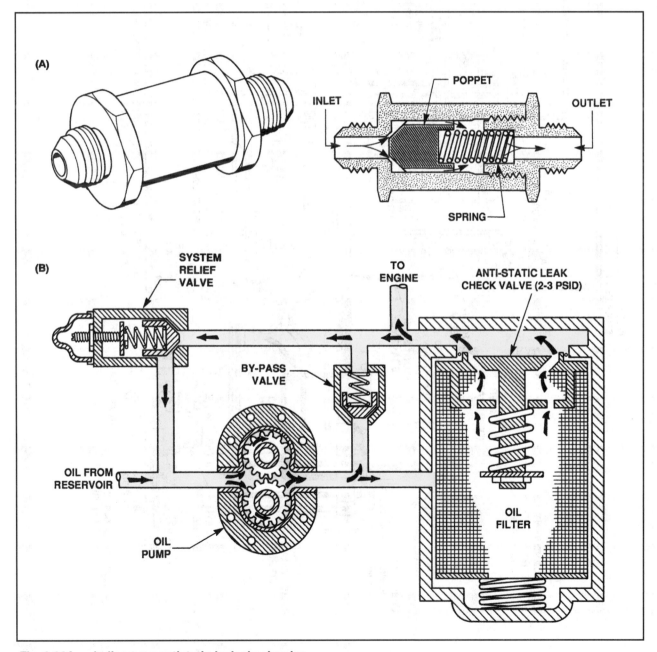

Fig. 6-26A — In-line type antistatic-leak check valve.
Fig. 6-26B — In oil-filter type antistatic-leak check valve.

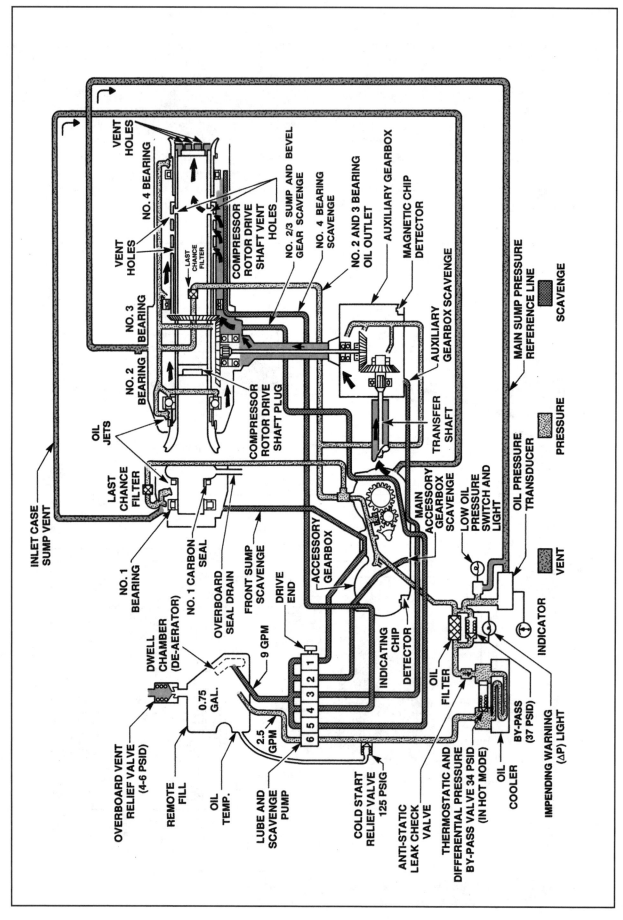

Fig. 6-27 — Full flow lubrication system with hot oil tank for a General Electric CJ610 turbojet engine.

resistance, bypassing the cooling chamber and flowing directly to the system (Figure 6-28B).

When the oil heats up, the thermo-valve expands to close, forcing the oil to flow through the cooler. If a restriction occurs from cooler clogging, pressure buildup off-seats the bypass valve and oil flows uncooled, at a slightly reduced pressure, to the system. The thermostatic valve contains a bi-metallic spring, typically constructed of iron/nickel alloy and brass, which, because of the different coefficient of expansion, produces movement with loss or gain of heat (Figure 6-28C).

A typical oil cooler operational schedule might be as follows: Oil cooler thermostatic valve starts to close at 165°F, and is fully closed at 185°F, with normal engine oil temperature stabilizing at 210°F. From this point, the cooler capacity for fuel flow and oil flow regulate the operational oil temperature rather than the thermo-valve. As the throttle is advanced for the engine to create more power, and therefore more heat for the oil to absorb, the fuel flow through the cooler increases and absorbs this heat. The maximum continuous oil temperature in this system would be 210°F. If the temperature reached a value over 210°F but under 230°F, the red line, the engine would have to be operated at reduced power at the

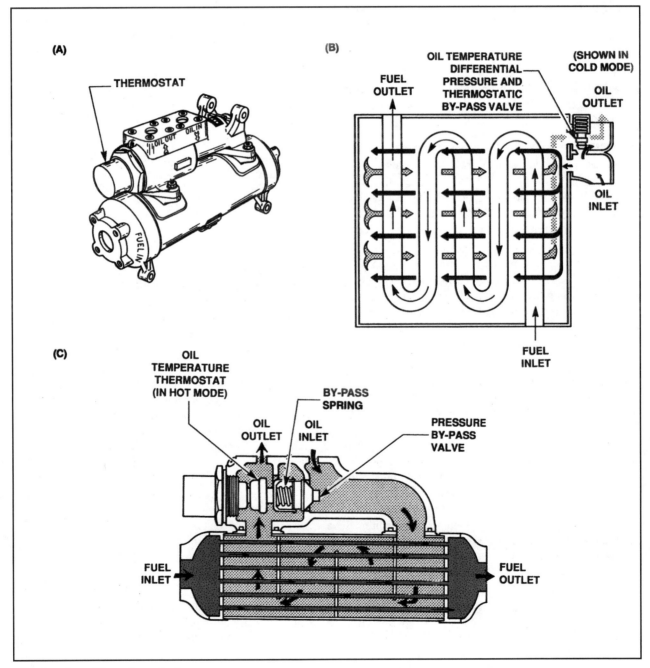

Fig. 6-28A — Oil cooler exterior.
Fig 6-28B — Thermo-valve in transit with oil both cooling and bypassing.
Fig. 6-28C — Thermo-valve closed when oil is hot.

discretion of the pilot. Once an oil temperature of 230°F is reached, the engine would have to be shut down.

The purpose of the thermostatic valve is to quickly bypass oil to the lube points on a cold start. It is not uncommon, however, to see an oil cooler without a thermostatic device if oil can be distributed rapidly enough for quick lubrication when the oil is cold.

One of the checks on an oil cooler is to see a momentary oil temperature rise on engine deceleration, and drop on acceleration as a function of fuel flow. From this, the operator can conclude that the thermo-valve is not stuck in a transient position and is not bypassing.

The fuel-oil cooler is used on most engines and often on larger engines, in combination with an air-oil cooler. The air-oil cooler is also in popular use. The air-oil cooler and thermostatic valve arrangement is quite similar in principle and design to the fuel-oil coolers shown, but the heat exchanger section looks similar to the small radiator type cooler used on reciprocating engines (Figure 6-33).

2) Oil Jets (Figure 6-29A)

Oil jets, or nozzles, as they are sometimes called, are located at the various places within the engine that need to be lubricated. Oil jets are the terminating point of the pressure subsystem. They deliver either an atomized spray or a fluid stream of oil to bearings, oil seals, gears, and other parts.

The fluid stream method is the most common, especially when high loads are present. In most cases this stream of oil is directed onto the bearing surfaces from what is termed a Direct Lubrication Oil Jet (Figure 6-29B).

Another less common method is called a Mist and Vapor Lubrication Oil Jet, where the oil stream (sometimes an air-oil stream) is aimed at a splash pan and slinger ring device. This allows for a wider area of lubrication from a single oil jet and is utilized in some larger engines (Figure 6-29C).

A newer type of oil jet coming into use is called "under-race lubrication", in which oil is routed through rotor shafts and bearing journals, then fed through slots acting as oil jets in the bearing inner races. Manufacturer's information indicates that they are achieving superior cooling when comparing traditional spray-jet lubrication with this method.

Over time, a restriction to flow may occur at the calibrated orifice of the oil jet. An accumulation of carbon (called coking) takes place due to residual engine heat acting on oil coated metal parts. This condition results faster if the prescribed cooling down period prior to engine shutdown is ignored.

Oil jets can be checked for size and cleanliness with a drill pin or the shank end of a new numbered drill bit. It is very important that the drill shank be free from any nicks or burrs. Another method of checking for restrictions to flow

is the smoke check. Smoke or shop air is directed into the oil nozzle inlet port and a check is made of the discharge rate through the orifice. A comparison is usually made to a known good or new oil jet.

A flow tester is also available in most larger repair facilities. This device can measure rate of flow accurately, in gallons per minute, with the oil jet installed in the engine. On some engines, bearing flow checks are part of the 100-hour inspection, or similar inspection requirements.

3) Last Chance Filters

Quite often, last chance filters are installed in oil lines to prevent plugging of the oil jets. Observe in Figure 6-29A the last chance filters. Because of their remote location within the engine, last chance filters are accessible for cleaning only during engine overhaul. To prevent engine damage from clogged last chance screens or plugged oil jets, the main filters are inspected at frequent intervals by ground personnel. Flow testing to detect early signs of filter blockage is also accomplished at periodic intervals.

2. Scavenge Subsystem (CJ610)
(Figure 6-27)

The scavenge subsystem removes oil from the bearing compartments and gearboxes by suction from the lubrication pump scavenge return elements (1 to 5). All five scavenge elements route oil to one return line, which enters the dwell chamber in the oil tank. The dwell chamber acts as an air-oil separator. The total return oil capacity is nine gallons per minute. The entrained air that accumulates in the oil increases oil volume and necessitates the use of a much higher capacity scavenge subsystem than the pressure subsystem.

a. Chip Detectors

Many scavenge systems contain permanent magnet chip detectors which attract and hold ferrous metal particles (Figure 6-30) which would otherwise circulate back to the oil tank and the engine pressure subsystem, possibly causing wear or damage. Chip detectors are a point of frequent inspection to detect early signs of main bearing failure.

As a general rule, the presence of small fuzzy particles or gray metallic paste is considered satisfactory and the result of normal wear. Metallic chips or flakes are an indication of serious internal wear or malfunction. Refer to Figures 6-30A and 6-30B.

Figure 6-33 (insert) shows an indicating-type magnetic chip detector. It has a warning circuit feature. When debris bridges the gap between the magnetic positive electrode in the center and the ground electrode (shell), a warning light is activated in the cockpit. When the light illuminates, the flight crew will take whatever action is warranted, such as in-flight shutdown, continued operation at flight idle, or continued operation at normal cruise, depending on the other engine instruments readings.

b. Pulsed Chip Detector System

A newer type of chip detector is the Electric Pulsed Chip Detector, which can discriminate between small wear-metal particles, both ferrous and non-ferrous, considered non-failure related, and larger particles, which can be an indication of bearing failure, gearbox failure, or other potentially serious engine malfunction (Figure 6-30C).

The Pulsed Chip Detector looks like the Indicating Chip Detector at the gap-end, but its electrical circuit contains a pulsing mechanism which is powered by the aircraft 28 VDC bus.

The pulsed detector is designed with either one or two operating modes: Manual only or manual and automatic.

In the manual mode, each time the gap is sufficiently bridged, regardless of the particle size, the warning light will illuminate in the cockpit. The operator will then initiate the pulse; electrical energy will discharge across the gap-end in an attempt to separate the debris from the hot center electrode. This procedure is called burn-off. If the light goes out and stays out, the operator will consider the bridging a result of a non-failure related cause. If the light does not go out, or repeatedly comes on after being cleared, the operator will take appropriate action, such as reducing engine power or shutting down the engine.

In the automatic mode, if the gap is bridged by small debris, a pulse of electrical energy discharges across the gap. The resulting burn-off prevents a cockpit warning light from illuminating by opening the circuit before a time-delay relay in the circuit activates to complete the current path to ground. If the debris is a large particle, it will remain in place after the burn-off cycle is completed and a warning light will illuminate in the cockpit when the time delay relay closes.

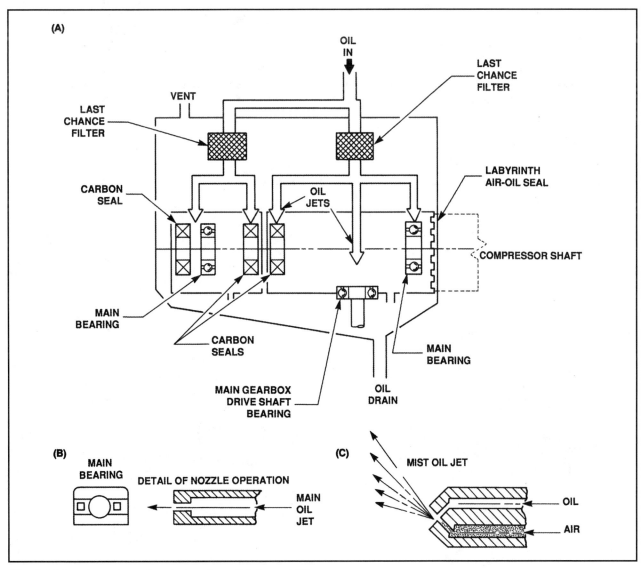

Fig. 6-29A — Location of main bearing oil jets and filters.
Fig. 6-29B — Direct lubrication oil jet.
Fig. 6-29C — Mist and vapor oil jet.

c. Quantitative Debris Monitor (QDM)

The newest development in chip detectors is known as the Quantitative Debris Monitor (QDM). This provides an online system to compute the extent of captured ferrous particles in the oil. It can differentiate between small non-failure related and larger failure related particles and provide a computer readout and analysis of the results.

3. Vent Subsystem (CJ610) (Figure 6-27)

The presence of pressurized air in the bearing cavities is a result of gas path air leaking across carbon and labyrinth type oil seals. This air pressure assists in oil return to the tank by putting a head of pressure on the scavenge oil at the bearing sumps. At the same time, this air is also vented overboard by various methods before an undesirable buildup can occur. On some engines, a separate subsystem is installed to vent this seal leakage air overboard. Other engines have no vent subsystem, as such, but remove seal leakage air, along with the scavenge oil to the oil tank.

Another function of pressurized air in the bearing cavities is to ensure a proper oil spray from the oil jet. By regulating the amount of back-pressure at the oil jet, the quantity of oil flow from the oil jet is also regulated.

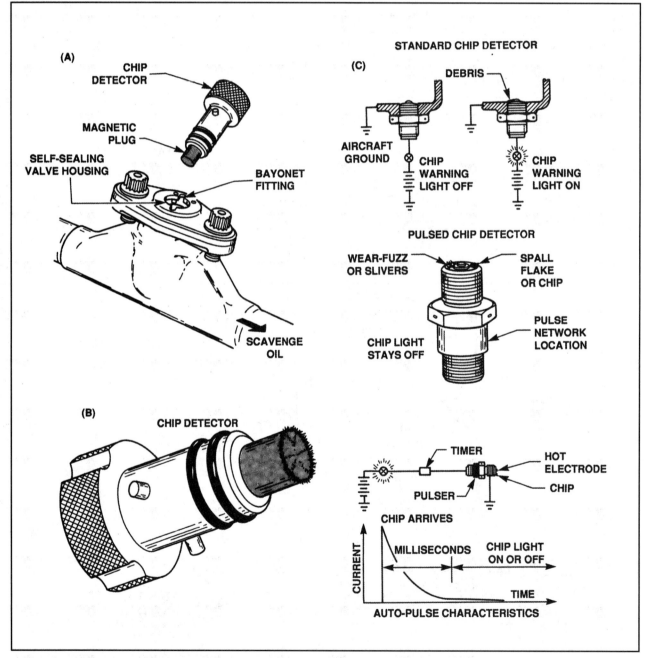

Fig. 6-30A — In-line type scavenge magnetic oil chip detector (non-indicating).
Fig. 6-30B — Chip detector showing accumulation of ferrous particles.
Fig. 6-30C — Comparison between standard, pulsed, and auto-pulse detectors.

A common problem associated with the vent system is coking. Vent air is oil-laden and, over a period of time, the heat to which this mixture is subjected causes some of the oil particles to decompose and turn to a solid form, referred to as coke or carbon. The buildup of coke can slow or even block air flow through some of the smaller passageways so that excessive pressures occur in portions of the vent subsystem.

Problems, such as low oil flow to bearings and high oil temperatures, can result from this restriction to normal venting. The usual procedure when troubleshooting for this malfunction is to isolate the vent system at various points on the engine, measure the pressure, and compare this pressure against the standards in the maintenance manual.

In the CJ610 turbine engine, vent air is deposited in the gearbox along with scavenge oil and then routed to the mid-frame. From there, it is channeled internally down the compressor shaft and out at the turbine into the gas path. A system of seals controls the rate of leakage and prevents turbine section air from backing up into the vent system.

In some large engines, greater vent system airflow results from higher compression and higher gas path pressure. These engines utilize a pressurizing and vent valve and a centrifuge type rotary air-oil separator to assist the vent system.

a. Rotary Air-Oil Separator

The rotary separator in Figures 6-31, 6-33, and 6-34 is an impeller, or centrifuge-like device, located in the main gearbox near the vent outlet. As the oil-laden vent air enters the rotating slinger chamber, centrifugal action throws the oil outward to drain back into the sump, while clean vent air is routed out of the engine or to a pressurizing and vent valve and then overboard.

b. Pressurizing And Vent Valve

The vent pressurizing valve shown in Figure 6-32 consists of an aneroid- bellows with sea level pressure trapped within and typically a three to four pounds per square inch—differential, spring-loaded relief valve located in the overboard line.

At sea level, the bellows valve is open, but it closes with increasing altitude in order to maintain engine vent pressure at a value similar to vent pressure at sea level. Pressure that is similar to sea level assures oil nozzle flow similar to that at sea level.

The vent system operating pressure at sea level is approximately five to seven pounds per square inch—gauge. This means that, even though the P and V valve is wide open in the ground operating condition, volume of flow creates a pressure build-up inside the vent portion of the lubrication system of five to seven pounds per square inch—gauge.

The aneroid shut-off valve will typically start to close at an eight to ten thousand foot altitude and will be completely closed at 20,000 feet. The vent system relief valve then acts as a pressurizing check valve, maintaining five to seven pounds per square inch—gauge within the vent subsystem.

The oil jets in the pressure subsystem, having the same back-pressure across their flow orifices as at sea level, provide the same lubrication in gallons per minute to the engine. Figures 6-33 and 6-34 both show the location of this valve.

I. Small Engine Pressure Relief Valve Lubrication System - Pratt & Whitney PT6 Turboprop (Figure 6-33)

Referring to Figure 6-33, the PT6 turboprop engine contains a "cold tank" lubricating system. Its oil is cooled in the scavenge subsystem. The PT6 gives the appearance of having a wet sump lubrication system, but it has, in actuality, an integral dry sump oil tank. Tank capacity is two gallons, with 1.5 gallons of oil usable and .5 gallon expansion space.

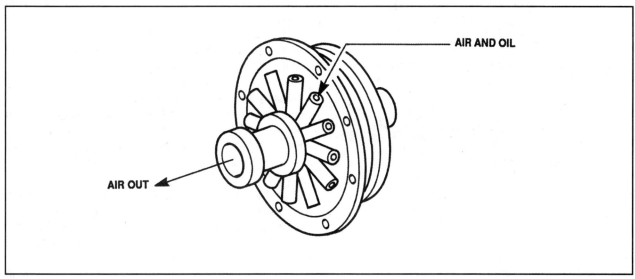

Fig. 6-31 — Rotary air-oil separator.

1. Pressure Subsystem Flow Path

a. Oil tank - Pressurized three to six pounds per square inch-gauge;

b. Oil Pump - A gear type pump, capacity four gallons per minute;

c. Regulating relief valve - Sets oil pressure 80 ±5 pounds per square inch-gauge;

d. Main Oil Filter - Bypass setting 25-30 pounds per square inch-differential;

e. No. 1 bearing and accessory gearbox;

f. Bearings 2, 3, 4 and propeller gearbox - Oil pressure and temperature are taken in this line;

g. Fuel heater - The check valve closes at 40 pounds

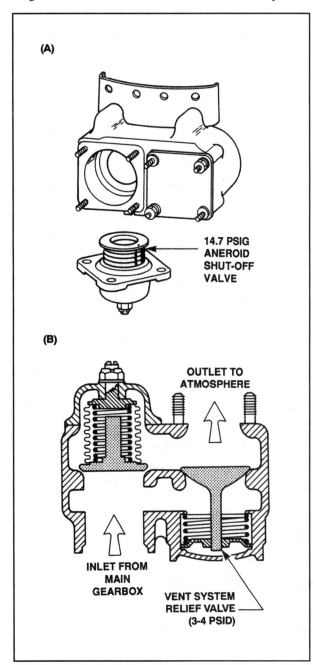

Fig. 6-32A — Pressurizing and vent valve.
Fig. 6-32B — Cutaway view.

per square inch-gauge. If engine is shut down in flight, flow terminates even though engine may be windmilling.

2. Scavenge Subsystem Flow Path

a. No. 1 Bearing sump - Drains directly to accessory gearbox;

b. No. 2 Bearing sump - Pumped to accessory gearbox by No. 2 scavenge pump;

c. No. 3 and 4 bearing sump - Pumped to accessory gearbox by free power turbine scavenge pump;

d. Propeller shaft area - Pumped to supply tank by reduction gearbox scavenge pump through air-oil cooler;

e. Accessory gearbox - Pumped to air-oil cooler by accessory gearbox scavenge pump. A cold-tank system with the oil cooler location in the scavenge subsystem.

3. Vent Subsystem Flow Path

a. Propeller gearbox, bearing sumps 2, 3, 4 - Vent via the scavenge subsystem to the main accessory case and to the oil tank;

b. No. 1 Bearing sump - Vents to accessory gearbox case;

c. Oil tank - Vents to accessory gearbox casing;

d. Accessory case - Vents to atmosphere through rotary air-oil separator.

J. Large Engine Pressure Relief Valve Lubrication System - Pratt and Whitney JT8D Turbofan

(Figure 6-34)

The JT8D is a dry sump hot tank lubricating system. Oil tank capacity is 6.3 gallons, with 4.6 gallons of usable oil and a 27% expansion space. This system contains one gear type pressure pump, one dual gear scavenge pump, and three single gear scavenge pumps.

The JT8D lubricating system does not utilize a thermostatic bypass valve in its fuel-oil cooler, but there is a pressure bypass valve which allows oil to bypass the cooler in the event of high oil viscosity during cold weather starting or in the event of core clogging.

This engine does not need a thermostatic bypass to provide for increased oil to the bearings during starting as some engines do. Oil pressure is regulated to 40 to 55 pounds per square inch—gauge at the fuel-oil cooler outlet by a special pressure regulating relief valve design, and this assures sufficient lubrication during start and warm-up. The regulating valve mechanism is shown on Figure 6-34 at "B", and the sensing oil line can be seen running from the cooler outlet back to the regulating valve.

System pressure is maintained at the cooler outlet regardless of whether the main oil filter or oil cooler are bypassing or whether they are flowing normally. This occurs because this regulating type valve senses pressure downstream of the oil cooler.

If, for instance, oil pressure drops at this point due to high oil viscosity or blockage of some type, the sense line signals the regulating valve to bypass less oil back to the supply side of the oil pump and thus deliver more oil to the system.

The oil pressure in this system is much higher at times in the upstream side of the oil cooler than it is at the downstream side. If the inlet pressure of the main filter is 70 pounds per square inch—gauge higher than the outlet pressure, a bypass condition will exist. Similarly if the fuel-oil cooler inlet pressure is 75 pounds per square inch—gauge more than the cooler outlet pressure, a bypass condition will exist.

1. Pressure Subsystem Flow Path

a. Oil Tank - Pressurized to five pounds per square inch-gauge;

b. Main Oil Pump - A gear type, capacity 35 gallons per minute at takeoff;

c. Main Oil Filter - Bypass setting, 70 pounds per square inch-differential; oil filter check, 150 hours maximum;

d. Regulating Relief Valve - Sets oil pressure 40 to 55 pounds per square inch-gauge downstream of cooler;

e. Fuel Cooled Oil Cooler - Bypass setting, 75 pounds

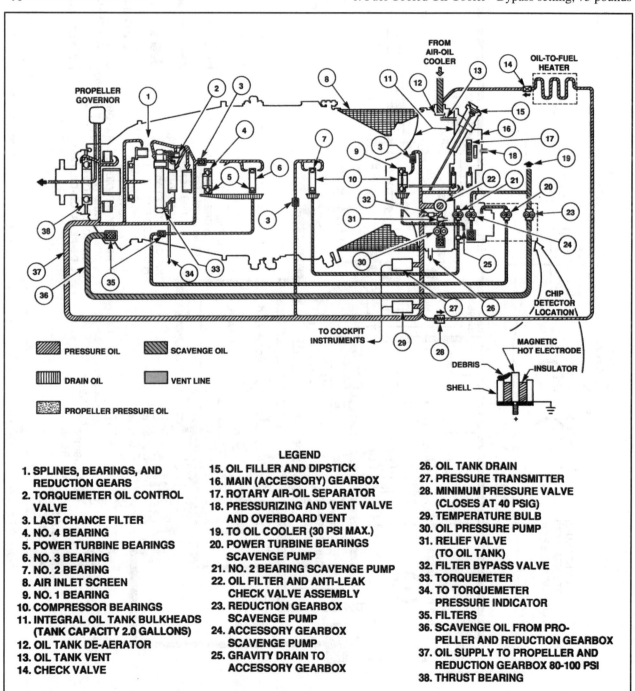

LEGEND

1. SPLINES, BEARINGS, AND REDUCTION GEARS
2. TORQUEMETER OIL CONTROL VALVE
3. LAST CHANCE FILTER
4. NO. 4 BEARING
5. POWER TURBINE BEARINGS
6. NO. 3 BEARING
7. NO. 2 BEARING
8. AIR INLET SCREEN
9. NO. 1 BEARING
10. COMPRESSOR BEARINGS
11. INTEGRAL OIL TANK BULKHEADS (TANK CAPACITY 2.0 GALLONS)
12. OIL TANK DE-AERATOR
13. OIL TANK VENT
14. CHECK VALVE

15. OIL FILLER AND DIPSTICK
16. MAIN (ACCESSORY) GEARBOX
17. ROTARY AIR-OIL SEPARATOR
18. PRESSURIZING AND VENT VALVE AND OVERBOARD VENT
19. TO OIL COOLER (30 PSI MAX.)
20. POWER TURBINE BEARINGS SCAVENGE PUMP
21. NO. 2 BEARING SCAVENGE PUMP
22. OIL FILTER AND ANTI-LEAK CHECK VALVE ASSEMBLY
23. REDUCTION GEARBOX SCAVENGE PUMP
24. ACCESSORY GEARBOX SCAVENGE PUMP
25. GRAVITY DRAIN TO ACCESSORY GEARBOX

26. OIL TANK DRAIN
27. PRESSURE TRANSMITTER
28. MINIMUM PRESSURE VALVE (CLOSES AT 40 PSIG)
29. TEMPERATURE BULB
30. OIL PRESSURE PUMP
31. RELIEF VALVE (TO OIL TANK)
32. FILTER BYPASS VALVE
33. TORQUEMETER
34. TO TORQUEMETER PRESSURE INDICATOR
35. FILTERS
36. SCAVENGE OIL FROM PROPELLER AND REDUCTION GEARBOX
37. OIL SUPPLY TO PROPELLER AND REDUCTION GEARBOX 80-100 PSI
38. THRUST BEARING

Fig. 6-33 — Pratt & Whitney PT6 turboprop engine pressure relief valve lubrication system with cold oil tank.

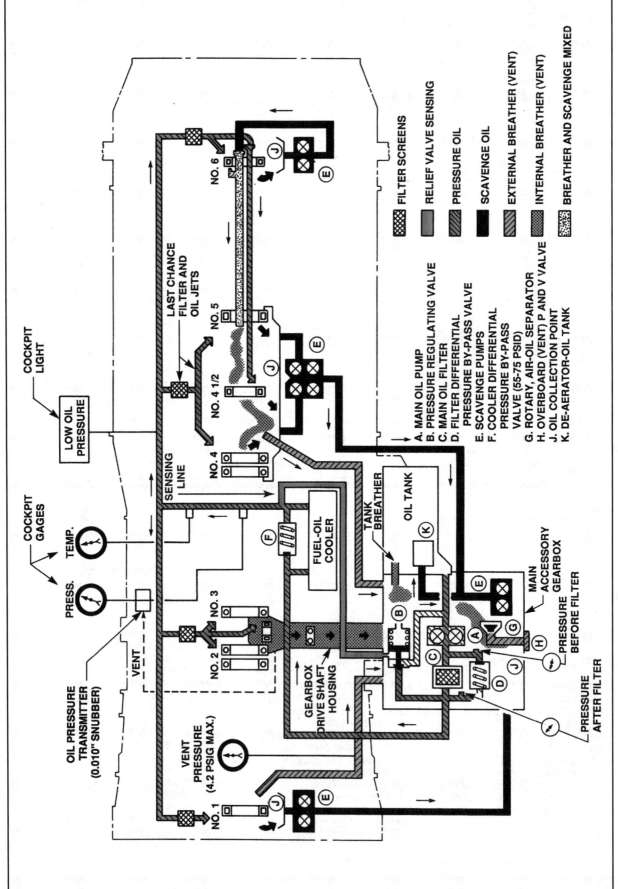

Fig. 6-34 — *Pratt and Whitney JT-8D turbofan pressure relief valve lubrication system with hot oil tank.*

per square inch-differential;

f. Oil pressure connection to transmitter, 40 to 55 pounds per square inch-gauge regulated oil pressure;

g. Oil temperature connection to transmitter, 130°C maximum;

h. Low Oil Pressure Light - During engine start, goes out at 35 pounds per square inch-differential, approximately 28% N2 speed;

i. No. 1 Last Chance Filter, Oil Jet, and Bearing;

j. No. 2 and No. 3 Last Chance Filters, Oil Jets, Bearings, and Bearing of Tower Shaft;

k. No. 4 and No. 5 Last Chance Filters, Oil Jets, and Bearings;

l. No. 6 Last Chance Filter, Oil Jet, and Bearing;

m. No. 4-1/2 Oil Jet and Bearing.

2. Scavenge Subsystem Flow Path

a. No. 1 Bearing Sump - Scavenged by a gear pump located in the No. 1 bearing sump, out through an external line, directly into the main accessory gearbox sump;

b. No. 2 and No. 3 Bearing Sump - Drains down through the gearbox driver shaft housing into the accessory gearbox sump;

c. No. 4 and No. 4-1/2 Bearing Sump - Scavenged by one element of a dual-gear pump, located within the sump, and out through an external line which interconnects the accessory gearbox scavenge pump return line to the oil tank;

d. No. 5 Bearing Sump - Scavenged by the second element of the dual-gear pump within the sump and out through an external line, which also serves to carry No. 4 and No. 4-1/2 bearing oil to the accessory gearbox;

e. No. 6 Bearing Sump - Scavenged by a gear pump located within the sump and out through a combination vent and scavenge tube located within the low pressure turbine shaft. No. 6 scavenge oil then mixes with No. 5 scavenge oil and returns to the accessory gearbox by an external line;

f. Accessory Gearbox Sump - Scavenged by a pump located within the sump. Oil is returned to the oil tank de-aerator via an internal passageway.

3. Vent Subsystem Sequence Of Flow

a. No. 1 Bearing Sump - Vents through an external line into the accessory gearbox;

b. No. 2 and No. 3 Bearing Sumps - Vents down through the gearbox driver shaft housing into the accessory gearbox;

c. No's. 4, 4-1/2, and 5 Bearing Sumps - Vent through an external line into the accessory gearbox;

d. No. 6 Bearing Sump - Vents through a mixed vent/scavenge tube provided within the low pressure turbine shaft, to the vent for Bearings 3, 4, and 5;

e. Oil Tank Expansion Space - Vents through an internal passageway which interconnects the oil tank to the accessory gearbox;

f. Accessory Gearbox - Vents through the rotary air-oil separator and pressurizing and vent valve to the atmosphere.

K. Large Engine Full Flow Lubrication System - CFM56-7B Turbofan (Figure 6-35)

The purpose of the oil system in this engine is to provide lubrication and cooling for gears and bearings located in the engine sumps and gearboxes. The lubrication system includes the following major components:

- An oil tank, located on the right hand side (aft looking forward) of the fan case.
- An anti-leakage valve, in the supply circuit, located at the bottom of the fan case.
- A lubrication unit assembly, installed on the accessory gearbox (AGB). This assembly contains the pressure and scavenge pumps, the pressure relief valve, the supply oil filter, bypass valve, and warning indicator.
- A main oil/fuel heat exchanger and servo fuel heater, through which scavenged oil returns to the oil tank.
- An oil scavenge filter assembly.

The lubrication system for this engine is broken down into three sections, known as the oil supply circuit, the oil scavenge circuit, and the oil venting circuit. On some engines these are referred to as the three subsystems.

1. Oil Supply Circuit (Figure 6-36)

The oil is drawn from the oil tank, through an anti-leakage valve, by a pressure pump (gerotor type) within the lube unit. The oil then passes by the pressure relief valve on its way to the supply oil filter, to be distributed to the engine forward and aft sumps and the accessory and transfer gearboxes.

a. Oil Tank (Figure 6-36, 6-37)

The oil tank is mounted on the fan case, at the 3 o'clock position, and has a maximum capacity of 22 quarts. The tank is made from a machined light alloy and covered with a flame resistant paint. Six inner bulkheads add strength and reduce oil sloshing. The tank has an oil inlet tube coming from the servo fuel heater and the main oil/fuel heat exchanger, an oil outlet to the lubrication unit, and a vent tube.

To replenish the tank, both gravity and remote filling ports are provided, and an overflow port. A scupper at the gravity fill point ducts any oil spillage to a drain line. A plug is provided at the bottom of the tank for draining purposes. There is a sight glass on the side of the tank for checking oil quantity, and an electrical transmitter for sending an oil quantity signal to a gage on the flight deck.

b. Anti-Leakage Valve (Figure 6-36)

The anti-leakage valve prevents oil leakage when the oil tube from the oil tank is removed and upon engine shutdown to counter any siphon effect on the oil tank. It

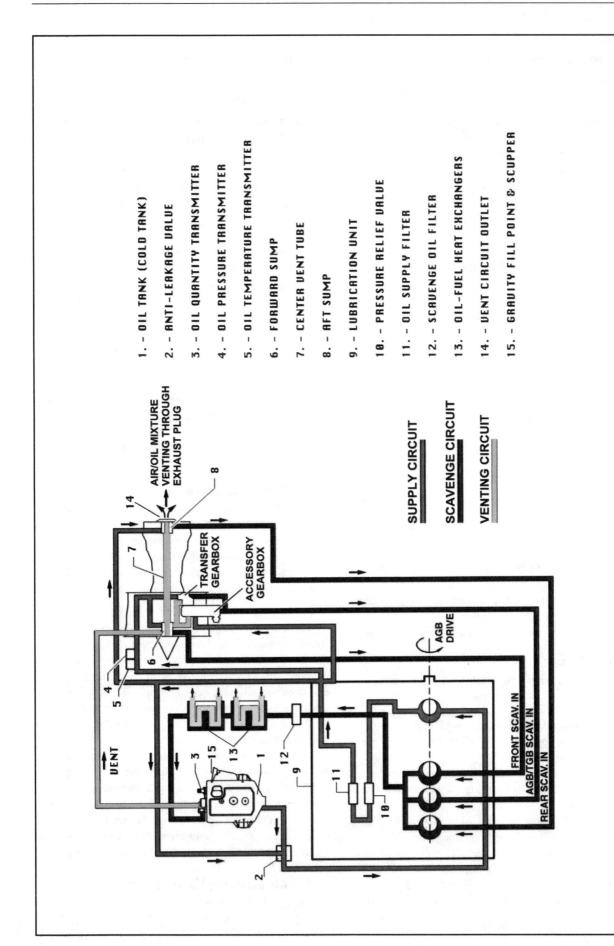

1. – OIL TANK (COLD TANK)
2. – ANTI-LEAKAGE VALVE
3. – OIL QUANTITY TRANSMITTER
4. – OIL PRESSURE TRANSMITTER
5. – OIL TEMPERATURE TRANSMITTER
6. – FORWARD SUMP
7. – CENTER VENT TUBE
8. – AFT SUMP
9. – LUBRICATION UNIT
10. – PRESSURE RELIEF VALVE
11. – OIL SUPPLY FILTER
12. – SCAVENGE OIL FILTER
13. – OIL-FUEL HEAT EXCHANGERS
14. – VENT CIRCUIT OUTLET
15. – GRAVITY FILL POINT & SCUPPER

SUPPLY CIRCUIT

SCAVENGE CIRCUIT

VENTING CIRCUIT

Fig. 6-35 — G.E./Snecma CFM56 full flow lubrication system with cold oil tank

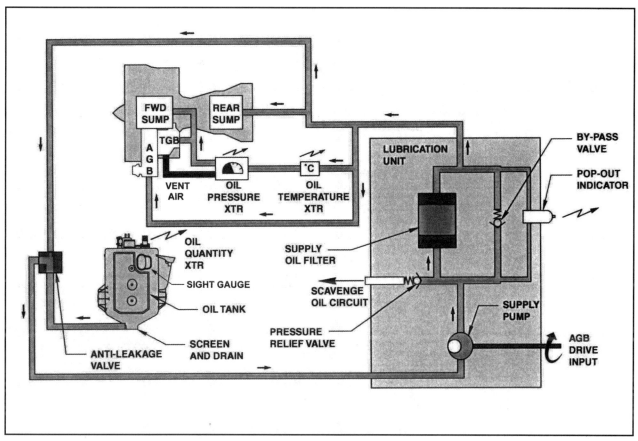

Fig. 6-36 — G.E. / Snecma CFM56 Oil supply circuit

is a pressure actuated, spring-loaded normally closed valve. It is mounted on the fan case, at the 6 o'clock position, in-line with the tube running from the oil tank to the lubrication unit.

During engine operation, oil pressure from the rear sump supply line holds the anti-leakage valve open. When the engine is shut down, spring tension closes the valve.

c. Lubrication Unit

The lubrication unit has two purposes, to pressurize and filter the supply oil for lubrication of the engine bearings and gears, and to pump scavenge oil back to the oil tank. The unit is mounted by a V-band clamp to the rear face of the accessory gearbox.

Externally, the unit has a suction port from the oil tank to the pressure pump, three scavenge ports, three scavenge screens, an oil out port, a supply oil filter, and a differential pressure oil filter clogged indicator. The filter is a 44 micron rated cleanable element. Internally, the unit has four pumps driven by the Accessory Drive Gearbox by way of a single shaft. One of these pumps is dedicated to the supply circuit and the other three are scavenge pumps.

During operation, oil from the oil tank is pressurized through the supply pump and then goes to the supply oil filter. In case of clogging of the supply oil filter, a bypass valve is installed in parallel. It opens when the

differential pressure across the valve is greater than the spring load, which is set to a psid of 17.4 to 20.3. A visual indication of filter clogging is provided by a pop-out indicator. The button pops out at a differential pressure of 11.6 to 14.5, providing an advance warning that a filter bypass condition is approaching. A bimetallic spring prevents the button from popping out at extremely low oil temperatures. A pressure relief valve, installed downstream from the supply pump, redirects the oil to the scavenge circuit when oil pressure reaches a maximum limit value. This maximum limit is 305 psi.

2. Oil Scavenge Circuit (Figure 6-37)

The oil to be scavenged is drawn from the forward sump, from the aft sump, and from the Accessory Drive Gearbox by three scavenge pumps installed within the lube unit. The oil passes through hollow scavenge screens which have threaded inserts inside. The threaded inserts are for the installation of magnetic chip detectors. The oil then goes through a scavenge filter, the servo fuel heater, and finally the main oil/fuel heat exchanger before returning to the oil tank. The scavenge filter is a replaceable cartridge. Scavenge of the Transfer Gearbox occurs by draining into the Accessory Drive Gearbox.

If the scavenge oil filter starts clogging, a light on the flight deck will illuminate at a pressure differential of 25 to 27 psi. If the pressure drop across the filter reaches 28

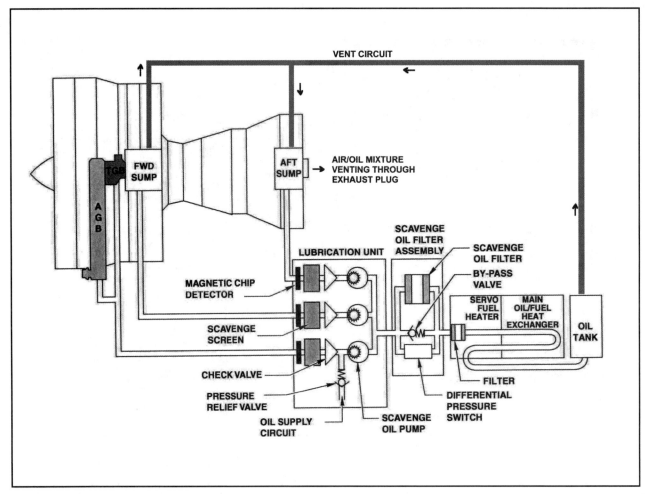

Fig. 6-37 — G.E. / Snecma CFM56 Oil scavenge circuit.

to 34 psi, a pop-out indicator on the filter bowl will become visible, providing a visual warning that a bypass condition is approaching. As with the supply oil filter, a bimetallic spring prevents the button from popping out at extremely low oil temperatures. If no action is taken and the pressure drop across the filter reaches 36.3 to 39.2 psi, the filter bypass will open.

3. Oil Venting Circuit (Figure 6-35, 6-37)

A venting system links the oil tank, the engine sumps, and the engine gearboxes, and its purpose is to vent the air from the scavenge system. A center vent tube connects the forward and aft sumps for oil vapor collection, and to balance the pressure between the sumps. The forward sump and the rear sump vent through the turbine exhaust plug at the rear of the engine.

L. Hot Tank Vs. Cold Tank Systems

An engine has a hot or cold oil tank system, as shown in the three typical lubrication systems, either as a matter of necessity or merely a convenience of location for the manufacturer.

In the classification "hot tank system", the oil cooler is located in the pressure subsystem. An advantage of this is that a maximum heat exchange occurs because oil has less entrained air in the pressure side of the lubrication

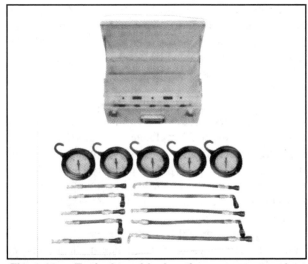

Fig. 6-38 — Typical troubleshooting pressure readout gauge set.

system. This factor allows for a smaller oil-cooler to be used, and a weight savings occurs.

In the cold tank system the oil cooler is located in the scavenge subsystem, which allows the oil to return to the supply tank in a cooled condition. The oil is still aerated from the action of the rotating parts within the engine and a reduced heat exchange is said to occur. This in turn creates a need for the use of a high volume oil cooler.

Also, some engines have normally higher oil temperatures than others. This high oil temperature in the oil tank can affect oil service life, since the bulk oil storage is at a higher temperature for a longer time. If this is the case, a cold tank system will most likely be used.

M. Troubleshooting Procedure

The following information concerning lubrication system problems, the probable causes, the checking procedures, and the remedies are general in nature and intended only to acquaint the reader with the concepts of troubleshooting. This information in no way takes precedence over the manufacturer's recommended procedures. Figure 6-38 shows a direct pressure gauge set, used in many instances to collect troubleshooting data.

The philosophy the technician should adopt in all troubleshooting is to start at the obvious or most likely cause and work toward remote possibilities. To protect the interest of the company or the customer, the troubleshooter should check all possibilities and replace components only when reasonably sure the malfunction has been located.

TROUBLESHOOTING OIL SYSTEMS

NOTE: Chapter V of this text also details general troubleshooting procedures.

PROBLEM/POSSIBLE CAUSE	CHECK PROCEDURE	REMEDY
1. No Engine Oil Pressure (no oil leaks)		
a. Low oil level	Check oil level	Add oil
b. Circuit breaker	Check for location if installed	Reset if tripped. Check circuit wiring
c. Defective indicator	1. Check power input and/or interchange gauge from another engine 2. Slave in another indicator or bench check	Repair circuit or replace indicator
d. Defective transmitter	1. Check power input 2. Slave in another transmitter or bench check	Repair circuit or replace transmitter
e. Obstruction in oil tank	Remove line at pump inlet and check flow rate	Remove obstruction or replace tank
f. Defective oil pump	1. Motor engine with outlet line removed and check flow rate 2. Check for leaks between elements or for sheared drive shaft	Replace pump
2. Low Oil Pressure (no oil leaks)		
a. Same as 1a, 1c, 1d, 1e, 1f	Check as necessary	
b. Improper regulating relief valve setting	1. Check security of valve and install gauges 2. Check for high vent pressure affecting cockpit gauge reading	Reset or replace as necessary

PROBLEM/POSSIBLE CAUSE	CHECK PROCEDURE	REMEDY
c. High vent pressure from P & V valve outlet	Instrument the vent system.	Possible engine teardown for bearing seal replacement
d. Clogging last chance filter (full flow system)	Flow check	Clean or replace

3. High Oil Pressure

a. Same as item 1c, 1d, 2b	Check as necessary	
b. Oil bypass line obstructed	Check line, relief valve to oil supply	Repair or replace
c. Low vent pressure	Check security of vent system	Tighten lines, replace gaskets, etc.

4. Fluctuating Oil Pressure

a. Low oil level	Check oil level in tank	Service as necessary
b. Loose electrical connection	Check circuit	Tighten as necessary
c. Defective indicator	Same as 1c	
d. Defective relief valve	Check for sticking components	Clean or replace
e. Defective transmitter	Bench check or slave in new transmitter	Repair or replace

5. Excessive Oil Consumption

a. External oil leaks	Visually check entire engine	Tighten lines, replace gaskets
b. Gas path oil leaks	1. Check for inop. scavenge pump	Replace/repair pump
	2. Check for restricted scavenge lines or filters	Clear restrictions
	3. Check for high vent pressure forcing oil past seals	Possible teardown
c. Overboard vent discharging oil	1. Rotary breather damage	Possible MGB teardown
	2. Check for high vent subsystem pressure from damaged carbon or labyrinth oil seal	Possible engine teardown
d. Damaged main bearing oil seal	Check overboard vent for oil discharge. Check vent pressure	Usually requires engine teardown
e. Overboard accessory seal drains discharging excessive oil	Check drainage quantity against allowable limits	Isolate the leaking accessory drive and replace gearbox seal
f. Pressurizing and vent valve sticking open at altitude	Check for evidence of oil at cowling vent opening to atmosphere	Bench check P & V valve

PROBLEM/POSSIBLE CAUSE	CHECK PROCEDURE	REMEDY
6. Increasing Oil Quantity		
a. Oil cooler core leak (fuel	Requires bench check	Replace as necessary (intrusion)
7. Excessive Oil in Gas Path		
a. Overservicing	Check servicing procedure, service only during prescribed period after engine shutdown	Remove excess oil and run engine to dry out
b. Inoperative scavenge pump(s)	Check output with direct pressure gauge	Replace if accessible or possible engine teardown
c. High vent pressure	1. Check for inop. scavenge pumps	Replace/repair pumps
	2. Check for restricted scavenge lines or filters, raising sump pressure	Clear restrictions
	3. Check for high vent pressure	Possible teardown
8. Oil in Tailpipe Overnight or Dripping From Gearbox Vent		
a. Pressure subsystem anti-static leak valve	Check for oil migration from contamination or worn check valve seals	Clean or replace seals, run engine & check for leaks
9. Oil Tank Rupture		
a. Oil tank pressurization check	Check for valve sticking closed	Clean or replace valve
10. Oil Pressure Indication Follows Power Lever Movement		
a. Regulating relief valve	Check for sticking valve mechanism	Clean or replace
b. Cold start relief valve	Normal condition	None
11. Oil Temperature High		
a. Vent subsystem coking (carbon build-up)	Check for high vent pressure - overheating of scavenge oil	Clean, or possible engine teardown
b. Oil cooler thermostat	Check for sticking open by performing a pressure drop check	Replace thermostat
c. Main bearing overheating	Flow check for clogged last chance oil filter or oil jet	Possible engine teardown
d. High tamb	Low taxi RPM	Raise RPM or shut down

PROBLEM/POSSIBLE CAUSE	CHECK PROCEDURE	REMEDY
12. Oil Filter Screen Collapsed - Yet Clean		
a. Filter bypass valve	Check for sticking (closed during cold weather starts)	Clean or change
13. Oil Smoke From Exhaust		
a. Clogged vent or scavenge line	Flow check for carbon blockage	Possible engine teardown
14. Low Oil Level (normal consumption)	Check for oil migration at anti-static leak check valve	Clean or replace

QUESTIONS:

1. When heated, an oil of high viscosity index will show which characteristic of viscosity change: Little change or great change?

2. Do synthetic lubricants have a higher or lower flash point than petroleum base oils?

3. What markings do FAR's require near the oil filler opening?

4. Why is fuel to oil dilution not used on turbine engines as it is on reciprocating engines?

5. What device regulates oil tank pressure?

6. Where is the relief valve located in relation to the main oil pressure pump?

7. Why is the scavenge subsystem capacity greater than the pressure subsystem?

8. What are the two basic types of oil coolers?

9. In which of the three lubrication subsystems is the oil cooler located with a hot tank oil system?

Chapter VII
Fuel Systems

A. Principles Of Fuel Systems

The primary function of a fuel system is to supply a precise amount of fuel to the engine in all conditions of ground and air operations. The system must be free of dangerous operational characteristics, such as a vapor lock. This is a condition which restricts fuel flow through units designed to handle liquids rather than gases.

Further, it must be possible to increase and decrease power on command to obtain the thrust required for any operating condition. In a gas turbine engine, this is accomplished by a device called a fuel control which meters fuel to the combustion chamber. The pilot manually selects a fuel flow condition by a power lever which in turn causes the fuel control automatic systems to schedule fuel flow according to prevailing ambient conditions and engine mass airflow conditions. These automatic features prevent rich or lean flameout, and over-temperature or over-speed conditions from occurring.

Lean die-out occurs, as one might expect, from a lessening of fuel in the air-fuel mixture until combustion is no longer supported. A rich blowout occurs when the force of fuel flow during low airflow conditions inter-rupts the normal burning process in close proximity to the fuel distribution nozzle. This momentary instability can cause the flame to blow away from the nozzle. At these points combustion ceases and a relight (restart) procedure is required. It is generally stated that maximum flame speed for supporting combustion using hydrocarbon fuel must be less than 0.4 Mach.

The secondary function of the fuel system is to provide cooling of the engine oil and also to provide hydraulic control for other engine systems, such as variable stator vanes and compressor bleed systems.

1. Gas Turbine Fuels

Jet fuels are liquid hydrocarbons similar to kerosene, some blended with gasoline. Hydrocarbon fuel is a compound of hydrogen and carbon found in coal, natural gas, and crude oil. This mixture is designed to freely mix with oxygen at combustion flow rates and temperatures. The blending of gasoline reduces the fuel's tendency to become too viscous at high altitudes. This is a problem which affects performance of some high altitude aircraft.

The oxides which are formed by combustion in a gas turbine engine are mostly gases. This is another quality designed into jet fuels which keeps solid particles to a minimum, solids that would impinge on turbine nozzle vanes and turbine blades causing erosion.

Jet fuels are not color coded as are reciprocating engine fuels, but they do have a natural straw color.

The following jet fuels are most commonly utilized in commercial and general aviation:

Turbo Fuel A: Commonly called Jet-A or "civil aviation kerosene," it essentially contains no gasoline blend and is the primary fuel for commercial and general aviation use in the United States. Newer military fuel JP-8 is similar to Jet-A.

Turbo Fuel A-1: Commonly called Jet A-1, it is designed as a low temperature fuel with a lower freezing point than Jet-A. It is used by most international airlines.

Specifications	Turbo Fuel A-1	Turbo Fuel A
United States	MIL-T-83133*	———
Great Britain	DERD 2494/2453*	———
Canada	CAN 2-3.23-M80	———
France	AIR 3405*	———
Pratt & Whitney Aircraft	522	522
Allison Div. of GM	EMS-64	EMS-64
ASTM D 1655	Jet A-1	Jet A
IATA Guidance Material	Kerosene*	———
NATO Symbol	F-34*/F35	JP-8
Properties		
Aromatics, % volume	18	18
Mercaptan sulfur, % weight	0.0003	0.0003
Sulfur, % total weight	0.05	0.05
Initial boiling point, °F(°C)	325(163)	325(163)
10% evaporated, °F(°C)	355(179)	364(184)
20% evaporated, °F(°C)	364(184)	372(189)
50% evaporated, °F(°C)	379(203)	411(210)
90% evaporated, °F(°C)	450(232)	474(246)
Final boiling point, °F(°C)	498(259)	520(271)
Flash point, °F(°C)	108(42)	115(46)
Gravity, °API	44.0	42.0
Specific gravity @ 60°F(15.6°C)	0.806	0.816
Freezing point, °F(°C)	- 60(51)	- 48(44)
Viscosity @ 30°F(34.4°C),Cs	7.9	7.9
Heat of combustion, Btu/lb(MJ/Kg)	18,600(43.1)	18,600(43.1)
Existent gum, mg/100 ml	0.2	0.2
Particulate matter, mg/liter	1.0	1.0
Free water, ppm	30	30

Turbo Fuel B: Commonly called Jet-B, it is a blend of approximately 30 percent kerosene and 70 percent gasoline and described as a wide-cut fuel. It has a very low freezing point and low flash point. It is primarily used by the military and similar to military fuel JP-4.

Turbo Fuel 5: A high flash point military fuel for use aboard naval aircraft carriers. Military designation JP-5.

Specifications	Turbo Fuel B	Turbo Fuel 5
United States	MIL-T-5624 *	MIL-T-5624*
Great Britain	DERD 2486/2454*	DERD 2498/2452*
Canada	CAN 2-3.22-M80	3-GP-24M
France	AIR 3407*	AIR 3404*
Pratt & Whitney Aircraft	522	————
ASTM	D 1655	Jet B
NATO Symbol	F-40*	43/F-44*
Properties		
Aromatics, % volume	11.0	18.0
Olefins, % volume	1.0	0.6
Mercaptan sulfur, % weight	0.0005	0.0004
Sulfur, % total weight	0.04	0.02
Initial boiling point, °F(°C)	162(72)	338(170)
10% evaporated, °F(°C)	255(125)	381(194)
20% evaporated, °F(°C)	275(135)	395(202)
50% evaporated, °F(°C)	318(159)	422(217)
90% evaporated, °F(°C)	380(193)	476(247)
Final boiling point, °F(°C)	455(235)	516(269)
Gravity, °API	53.8	41.0
Specific gravity 60°F (15.6°C)	0.764	0.820
Flash point, °F(°C)	0(18)	148(64)
Freezing point, °F(°C)	- 76(60)	- 58(50)
Heat of combustion, Btu/lb(MJ/Kg)	18,700(43.5)	18,500(43.1)
Existent gum, mg/100 ml	0.5	0.8
Particulate matter, mg/liter (max)	1	1
Free water, ppm (max)	30	30

*These specifications require special additives that normal commercial fuels may not contain. If required to meet this specification, the correct additives must be blended into the fuel.

Jet-A, Jet-A1, and Jet-B commercial fuels are interchangeable for use in most gas turbine engines. Military JP-4, JP-5 and JP-8 are generally suitable alternate fuels. Aviation grades 80-145 octane reciprocating engine fuels are often emergency alternate fuels for turbine engines.

For the approved fuel and fuel additives used to service a turbine engine, the technician should check the aircraft operator's manual or the type certificate data sheet file.

When comparing the BTU value of fuels such as Jet-A and Aviation Gasoline, it is interesting to note that Jet-A has more BTU's per gallon, but Aviation Gasoline has more BTU's per pound.   The numbers are as follows:

Jet-A   6.74 lb/gal (18,600 BTU/lb) = 125,364 BTU's per gallon
Av Gas 5.87 lb/gal (18,900 BTU/lb) = 110,943 BTU's per gallon

2. Fuel Handling And Safety

The normal handling cautions exist for jet fuels as for any other flammable or explosive liquid. Especially important is the requirement during refueling that the grounding probe must be in place before the refueling nozzle contacts the filler opening. This must be done to avoid having any static sparks.

Jet fuel in tanks is often more dangerous than gasoline. Gasoline usually maintains a vapor-to-air mixture so rich that ignition is less likely to occur. This is not the case with Jet Fuel, as it is often at its best mixture to ignite.

Personnel handling aviation fuels should observe a number of practical and precautionary measures that reduce the undesirable contact with fuel products. These measures include the following:

a. Avoid all unnecessary contact and use protective equipment to prevent contact.
b. Remove promptly any fuel product that gets on the skin.
c. Do not use fuels or similar solvents to remove oil or grease from the skin.
d. Never wear fuel soaked clothing. Remove immediately and clean before re-use.
e. Avoid breathing fuel vapors. Maintain well ventilated work areas.
f. Clean up spilled products immediately. Keep spills out of sewers, streams, and waterways.
g. Be familiar with proper first-aid techniques for handling unexpected/gross contacts and contact proper medical authorities immediately for assistance.

3. Fuel Additives

The most common fuel additives are the anti-icing and anti-microbiocidal agents. Anti-icing additives keep entrained water from freeze-up without the use of fuel heat, except at very low temperatures. The manufacturer's manual will state the temperature at which fuel heat must be applied. Microbiocidal agents kill microbes, fungi, and bacteria which form a slime, and in some cases a matted waste in fuel systems.

Most often the additives are premixed in the fuel by the fuel distribution company. If it is not, the service person must add the agents when fueling the aircraft. A popular brand of hand-servicing type anti-icing and anti-biocidal mixture is called PRIST®. It is designed to be added during servicing and is capable of reducing the freezing temperature of the fuel by 25°F. The type and amount, however, must be determined to maintain the airworthiness of the fuel system in the existing climatic conditions. Most manufacturers of these products recommend their use year round (Figure 7-1).

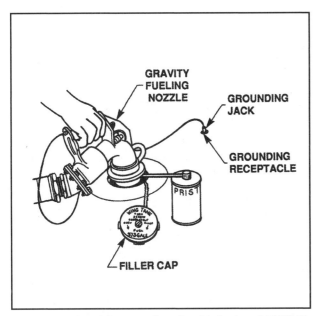

Fig. 7-1 — Servicing an aircraft with fuel and PRIST®

4. Water Detection In Turbine Fuel

All aviation fuels contain some dissolved water and free water. Dissolved water is like humidity in air in that it cannot be seen. It is not a problem as long as it remains dissolved. Free water, also called entrained water, is present in tiny droplets and is visible. It is water in excess of the water that dissolves. Large quantities of free water (over 30 parts per million) can cause engine performance loss or even flame out.

One of the principal concerns during fuel servicing is to deliver fuel into the aircraft that is free of undissolved (free) water. It is desirable, therefore, to test the fuel as it enters the aircraft to ensure that free water has been effectively removed by the clean-up system.

A HYDROKIT (Exxon trade name) is a quick, go/no-go test for detecting the presence of minute quantities of undissolved water in turbine fuel. The HYDROKIT indicator powder, packaged in a ten milliliter evacuated test tube, gives a distinct pink/red color change in the presence of 30 parts per million or more of undissolved water in fuel. An important consideration for fuel handlers is to realize that the Specific Gravity of jet fuel is closer to water than is the Specific Gravity of Avgas. Therefore jet fuel can hold more water in suspension than Avgas without showing it.

5. Thrust Specific Fuel Consumption (TSFC)

a. The Formula

TSFC is a ratio of fuel consumption to engine thrust. This ratio is usually included in any set of engine specifications and affords a means of comparing the fuel consumption or economy of operation of one engine to another regardless of its thrust rating. Specifically, it is the amount of fuel in pounds consumed by an engine while producing one pound of thrust during one hour of operation.

$$TSFC = \frac{\text{Total weight of fuel consumed }(W_f)}{\text{Pounds of thrust (net or gross)}}$$

EXAMPLE: An engine with a TSFC of .49 lb./hr./lbt., has a thrust rating of 3,500 lbs. How many pounds of fuel will it consume per hour?

$$TSFC = \frac{(W_f)}{F_n \text{ or } F_g}$$

$$.49 = \frac{(W_f)}{3,500}$$

$$W_f = .49 \times 3,500$$

$$W_f = 1,715 \text{ lbs./hr.}$$

The comparison of an early model turbojet, the Westinghouse J-34, with a modern turbofan, the Garrett TFE-731, best indicates the current state of the art in engine fuel efficiency.

Engine	Thrust (lbs)(Fg)	TSFC	Wf(pph)
J-34	3,250	1.06	3,445
TFE-731	3,500	0.49	1,715

From the above information, it is clear to see that the TFE-731 turbofan engine is more than twice as efficient in terms of fuel consumption, when compared to the J-34 turbojet engine.

b. Turbofans And TSFC

One of the reasons for turbofan efficiency over the turbojet was discussed previously in terms of Kinetic Energy loss in the hot exhaust (See Chapter II, L).

Another reason for the TSFC advantage of the turbofan lies in the fact that, if more power is required, more fuel flow is required. In the turbofan engine, the turbine wheel can be designed to absorb more energy to drive a larger fan and give the engine more total thrust. In this way, the hot exhaust velocity need not be increased to affect an increase in thrust. In the turbofan, Propulsive Efficiency will remain relatively unchanged, but in the turbojet an increase in exhaust velocity will cause a loss of Propulsive Efficiency.

The following paragraph shows what the gas turbine engine industry is aiming at for the future in terms of TSFC.

By improvements in the way of new materials and designs, mainly in the compressor and turbine, a decrease of ten percent fuel consumption is projected. By a combination of higher turbine inlet temperatures (TIT) and compression ratios, an even more significant reduction of 25 per cent could be achieved. This overall improvement will come about in new designs which result in stall free, higher compressor pressure ratios and higher temperature strength materials for the hot section.

The following statistics on TSFC are for a General Electric CF-6 High-Bypass Turbofan engine, used in the McDonnell-Douglas DC-10 aircraft (ground performance, standard day).

Thrust Setting	Gross Thrust pounds	TSFC lb./hr./lbt.	Fuel Flow lbs./hr
Takeoff (S.L.)	50,200	0.394	19,779
Max. Continuous	46,200	0.385	17,787
75% Takeoff	37,600	0.371	13,579
Flight Idle	5,190	0.450	2,320
Ground Idle	1,740	0.850	1,490

Altitude Performance: Mach 0.85, ISD Temperature (STD TEMP.)

Thrust Setting	Net Thrust pounds	TSFC lb./hr./lbt.	Fuel Flow lbs./hr
Max Climb	11,500	0.664	7,636 Max.
Cruise	10,800	0.654	7,063

EXAMPLE: Using the specifications shown for the CF-6, ground performance, calculate the maximum continuous fuel consumption in pounds per hour.

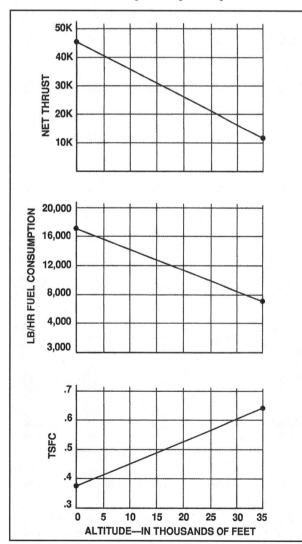

Fig. 7-2 — The effect of altitude on engine performance

$$TSFC = \frac{(Wf)}{Fg}$$

$$0.385 = \frac{(Wf)}{46,200}$$

$$Wf = 0.385 \times 46,200$$
$$Wf = 17,787 \text{ lbs./hr.}$$

EXAMPLE: Using the specifications shown for the CF-6, altitude performance, calculate the maximum cruise fuel consumption in pounds per hour.

$$TSFC = \frac{(Wf)}{Fn}$$

$$0.654 = \frac{(Wf)}{10,800}$$

$$Wf = 0.654 \times 10,800$$
$$Wf = 7,063 \text{ lbs./hr.}$$

If we consider that maximum continuous thrust on the ground and maximum cruise power in flight are the same power setting, note that even though TSFC is higher in flight, actual fuel consumption is only forty percent of fuel used on the ground. This shows the fuel economy a gas turbine engine experiences in flight.

c. TSFC In Flight

The reason TSFC is higher at operating altitude than at ground operating condition is that, in order to keep engine power up when inlet density is dropping, more RPM (by way of increased fuel flow) is needed to maintain correct mass airflow. The increase in fuel flow per pound of thrust results in a higher TSFC. As seen in Figure 7-3A, thrust is remaining fairly constant as airspeed increases, therefore, in terms of the TSFC formula ($TSFC = W_f \div F_n$) as fuel flow increases for a given thrust, the TSFC value increases.

When considering a flight speed increase and an altitude increase, TSFC also increases for a comparable sea level power setting. Refer to Figure 7-3B and consider the following points:
1) W_f decreases to about 40 percent of its sea level value when going to altitude; (A)
2) Flight thrust (F_n) drops to about 20 percent of its sea level value; (B)
3) TSFC increases as a result of the relationship of fuel flow remaining higher than thrust when applied to the TSFC formula. (C)

d. A TSFC Observation

An interesting observation about TSFC can be made between large sized fan engines and small sized fan engines. The TFE-731 is a business jet sized engine, and it has a sea level TSFC of 0.51 lb./hr./lbt. The CF-6 is a commercial sized engine with a much higher bypass ratio and its sea level TSFC is 0.38 lb./hr./lbt. It appears that the smaller engine is very much inferior in terms of fuel consumption per pound of thrust produced. But the smaller engine has in actuality a TSFC improvement when operating at altitude-cruise.

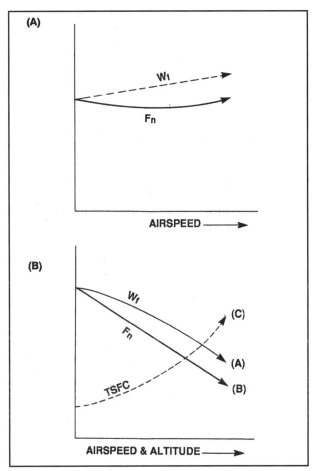

Fig. 7-3A — Effect of airspeed on TSFC.
Fig. 7-3B — Effect of airspeed and altitude on TSFC.

The larger engine is more efficient at sea level (S.L.) because it has a large diameter fan but at altitude-cruise the fan, in the manner of a fixed pitch propeller, loses some of its efficiency. The favorable angle of attack of the fan blades at sea level is diminished at altitude so the core portion of the engine has to make up for it with an increase in fuel flow. In this way, TSFC increases more on a high bypass ratio engine going to altitude than it does on a smaller engine with a lower bypass ratio, as follows:

1) CF-6, TSFC increases from 0.38 at sea level maximum continuous to 0.654 at altitude maximum cruise. Change in TSFC = 72 percent.

2) TFE-731, TSFC increases from 0.51 at sea level maximum continuous to 0.80 at altitude maximum cruise. Change in TSFC = 56 percent.

The high bypass fan engine is still more efficient at 0.654 TSFC, than a low bypass engine operating at 0.8 TSFC, but not by the same degree as seen by sea level figures alone.

e. Thrust Specific Fuel Consumption Versus Thrust-Horsepower Specific Fuel Consumption

Another interesting comparison can be made between engine types designed for subsonic flight and engines designed for supersonic flight. Concorde, for example,

has a cruise TSFC of 1.2. This looks rather high when compared to a DC-10 engine with a cruise TSFC of 0.654, but in actuality the fuel consumed by the Concorde per thrust horsepower is lower. Instead of comparing thrust and fuel flow to form the ratio $SFC(F_n) = W_f \div F_n$, THP can be compared with fuel flow to form the ratio $SFC(T_{HP}) = W_f \div T_{HP}$.

Example: What would the specific fuel consumption (SFC) be for the engine in a DC-10 while operating in cruise? The thrust is 10,800 lbs. per engine, and the fuel consumption per engine is 7,063 lbs. per hour. Initially the thrust horsepower formula from Chapter II will be used, and then the formula for specific fuel consumption.

$$THP = \frac{Net\ Thrust \times A/C\ Speed}{375}$$

$$THP = \frac{10,800 \times 600}{375}$$

THP = 17,280
SFC = Wf ÷ THP
SFC = 7,063 ÷ 17,280
SFC = 0.41

The SFC of the DC-10 engine will be compared to an engine in the Condorde. The Concorde engine is producing 10,500 lbs. of thrust and consuming 12,600 lbs. of fuel per hour. The airplane in cruise is flying at 1,250 Mph. What is the SFC?

$$THP = \frac{Net\ Thrust \times A/C\ Speed}{375}$$

$$THP = \frac{10,500 \times 1,250}{375}$$

THP = 35,000
SFC = Wf ÷ THP
SFC = 12,600 ÷ 35,000
SFC = 0.36

NOTE: Notice the improvement in fuel consumption for Concorde, 0.36 vs. 0.41 for the DC-10, when the comparison is based on thrust horsepower in flight.

B. Fuel Controls

1. The Main Fuel Metering Device.

a. The fuel control is an engine driven accessory which can operate by mechanical, hydraulic, electrical, or pneumatic forces in various combinations. The purpose of the fuel control is to maintain a correct combustion zone air-to-fuel mixture ratio of 15:1 by weight. This ratio represents weight of combustor primary air to weight of fuel. Sometimes this is expressed as a fuel-air ratio of 0.067:1. All fuels require a certain proportion of air for complete burning, but at rich or lean mixtures the fuel will burn but not completely. The ideal proportion for air and jet fuels is 15:1, and it is called the stoichometric (chemically correct) mixture.

Quite often one can see the air-fuel ratio expressed as 60:1. When this occurs, the writer is expressing the air-fuel ratio in terms of the total airflow rather than of primary combustor airflow. If primary airflow is approximately 25 percent of total airflow, then 15:1 is 25 percent of 60:1. A gas turbine engine will experience a rich to lean mixture of about 10:1 during acceleration and 22:1 during deceleration. If the engine is using 25 per cent of its total airflow in the combustion zone, the mixture, when expressed in terms of total airflow, will be 48:1 on acceleration and 80:1 on deceleration.

When the pilot moves the fuel control power lever forward, fuel flow is increased. This increase in fuel flow creates increased gas expansion in the combustor which in turn raises the level of power in the engine. For the turbojet and turbofan, that means a thrust increase. For the turboprop and turboshaft, it means an increase in power to the output drive shaft. This could mean a speed increase at a given propeller load or a stabilized speed at an increasing blade angle and load. Figure 7-4A shows the air-fuel mixture range of a typical gas turbine engine. Air-fuel represents the (mixture) and % N_2 speed (the speed of the engine), as the fuel control sees it at its governor flyweight drive shaft.

Note that at idle about 20 parts of air exists in the mixture on the steady state (S.S.) line and that 15 parts occurs in the 90 to 100 percent N_2 range.

As an engine ages, the air-fuel ratio of 15:1 will change as compression tends to deteriorate with increasing engine service time. But the engine needs its rated compressor pressure ratio (Cr) to remain efficient and stall free. When Cr starts to decrease due to engine aging, contamination, or damage, more power lever, fuel flow and compressor speed will be required to bring Cr back to normal. Thus a richer mixture results for a given Cr. Later, maintenance personnel may be required to take appropriate action to clean, repair, or replace the compressor or turbine as the engine nears its internal temperature limits. All engines are temperature limited, and how these limits come into play will be discussed later in this chapter and in chapter 12.

On a single compressor engine the fuel control is driven directly by the accessory gearbox and indirectly from the compressor. On the dual and triple spool engines, the fuel control is normally driven by the high pressure compressor.

b. Many signals are sent to the fuel control for the automatic control of the air-fuel ratio. How many signals come into play will depend on the engine, and whether or not electronics are involved. The newer engines, with electronic engine controls (EEC), sense many more engine and aircraft parameters than a hydro-mechanical unit will on an older aircraft. A list of the most common signals sent to a hydro-mechanical fuel control are as follows:

1) Engine speed signal (Nc)—given to the fuel control by a direct drive to the engine accessory gearbox through a flyweight governor within the control; used for both steady state fuel scheduling and acceleration/deceleration fuel scheduling (acceleration of most gas turbine engines is in the range of 5-10 seconds from idle to full power).

2) Inlet Pressure (Pt_2)—A total pressure signal transmitted to a fuel control bellows from a probe in the engine inlet, used to give the control a sense of aircraft speed and altitude as ram conditions in the inlet change.

3) Compressor discharge pressure (Ps_4)—A static air pressure signal sent to a bellows within the control, used to give the fuel control an indication of mass airflow at that point in the engine.

4) Burner Can Pressure (P_b)—A static pressure signal sent to the fuel control from within the combustion liner. There is a linear relationship between Burner Pressure and weight of airflow at this point in the engine. If Burner Pressure increases 10 percent, the mass airflow has increased by 10 percent and the burner bellows will schedule 10 percent more fuel to maintain the correct air-fuel ratio. The quick response this signal gives makes it valuable in preventing stalls, flameouts, and over-temperature conditions.

5) Inlet temperature (Tt_2)—A total temperature signal from the engine inlet to the control, a temperature sensor connected by a capillary tube to the fuel control. It is filled with a heat sensitive fluid or gas which expands and contracts as a function of inlet temperature. This signal provides the control with an airflow density value against which a fuel schedule can be established.

2. Simplified Fuel Control Schematic (Hydro-Mechanical Unit)

Figure 7-4B is a simplified schematic of a gas turbine fuel control. It functions to meter fuel as follows:

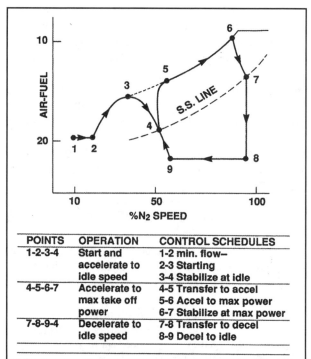

POINTS	OPERATION	CONTROL SCHEDULES
1-2-3-4	Start and accelerate to idle speed	1-2 min. flow— 2-3 Starting 3-4 Stabilize at idle
4-5-6-7	Accelerate to max take off power	4-5 Transfer to accel 5-6 Accel to max power 6-7 Stabilize at max power
7-8-9-4	Decelerate to idle speed	7-8 Transfer to decel 8-9 Decel to idle

Fig. 7-4A — Air-fuel operational diagram.

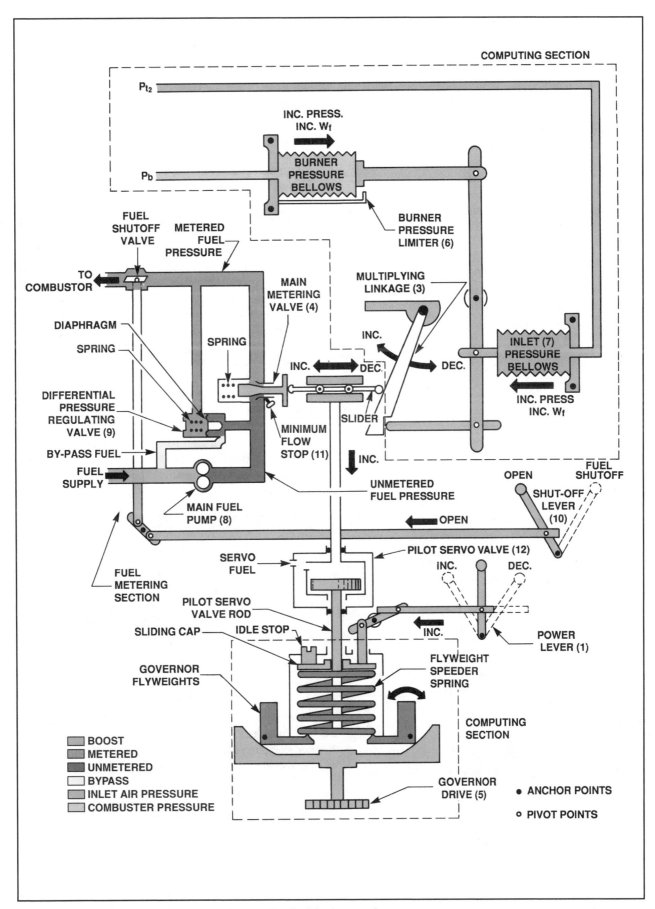

Fig. 7-4B — Simplified diagram of hydro-mechanical fuel control.

a. Fuel Metering Section

1) Movement of the shut-off lever (10) during the engine start cycle allows fuel to flow out to the engine. The manual shut-off lever (10) is needed because the minimum flow stop (11) prevents the main metering valve (4) from ever completely closing. This design is needed in case the speeder spring breaks or if the idle stop is not adjusted correctly. The full rearward position of the power lever is the idle position against the idle stop. This prevents the power lever from becoming a shut-off lever. The shut-off lever in this illustration also provides the function of ensuring the correct working pressure buildup within the control during the starting cycle. This is said to prevent roughly metered fuel from entering the engine before its correct time.

2) Fuel from the supply system is pumped through the main fuel pump (8) to the main metering valve (4). As fuel flows through the orifice created by the taper of the valve, a pressure drop occurs. Fuel, from that point of the metering valve to the fuel nozzles, is referred to as metered fuel. Fuel in this instance is metered by weight rather than volume, because BTU's per pound is constant regardless of fuel temperature, while BTU's per unit volume is not. Fuel now flows in a correctly metered condition to the combustor.

3) The principle involved in metering fuel by weight is mathematically expressed as:

$$W_f = KA \sqrt{\Delta P}$$

Where:

W_f = weight of fuel flow in lbs./hr.

K = constant for a particular fuel control

A = area of orifice of main metering valve

ΔP = pressure differential across the orifice

If only one engine operating condition were needed, only one fuel metering orifice size would be needed, and there would be no variables in this formula because the pressure drop would always be the same value; but, aircraft engines obviously must change power settings. This is accomplished by moving the power lever. When advancing the power lever, the orifice area at (4) will subsequently increase. This action creates a mathematical variable. If it were not for the presence of the differential pressure regulating valve (9), the pressure differential across the metering orifice would change to create a second variable. This arrangement allows for what is referred to as a linear relationship between orifice size and weight of fuel flow. With only one variable, "orifice size", such a relationship exists. That is, if the opening changes, the weight of fuel flow changes proportionally.

A constantly changing fuel bypass is the means by which pressure differential is maintained at a constant value regardless of orifice size. By directing metered fuel to the spring side of the hydraulically-operated differential pressure regulator diaphragm, the pressure differential will always return to the value of the spring tension. Because this spring tension is a constant value,

the pressure differential across the orifice (ΔP) will also become a constant.

To understand this concept more fully, consider that the fuel pump always delivers fuel in excess of the fuel control's needs and the differential pressure regulator valve continually returns excess fuel back to the pump inlet.

EXAMPLE: The un-metered fuel pressure is 500 pounds per square inch—gauge; metered fuel pressure is 420 pounds per square inch—gauge; and, spring tension is 80 pounds per square inch. At this point, there is 500 pounds per square inch—gauge on both sides of the differential pressure regulator diaphragm. The by-pass valve will be in a state of equilibrium and will be bypassing fuel which is surplus to the needs of the engine.

Now, if the pilot moves the power lever forward, the orifice size at the metering valve will increase and the metered pressure downstream will also increase. Let us say that metered pressure increases to 440 pounds per square inch—gauge. This action will create a total pressure of 520 pounds per square inch—gauge on the spring side of the regulator diaphragm, pushing the by-pass valve toward closed. The reduced amount of fuel bypass will cause un-metered pressure to rise until an 80 pounds per square inch—gauge is re-established for the new orifice size. This happens because increased revolutions per minute will cause the positive displacement fuel pump to produce more fuel flow. As previously stated, the ΔP will always come to the setting of the differential pressure regulator valve spring as equilibrium occurs.

b. Computing Section

1) During engine operation, movement of the power lever (1) causes the spring cap to slide down the pilot servo valve rod (2) and compress the flyweight speeder spring. In doing so, the spring base pushes (2) down and forces the flyweights in at the top to an under speed condition. The pilot servo valve functions to prevent sudden movement as its fluid is displaced bottom to top. If we consider that the multiplying linkage (3) remains stationary during this time, the slider will move down the inclined plane and to the left. As it moves left, the slider will force the metering valve (4) to the left against its spring tension, allowing increased fuel to flow to the engine. With increased fuel flow, the engine will speed up and drive the governor shaft (5) faster. The new flyweight force created will come to equilibrium with the speeder spring force as the flyweights return toward an upright position. They are now in position to act at the next speed change.

The flyweights always return toward the upright position so that they can be ready for use at the next load change as follows:

a) Over-speed condition:

(1) Load on the engine decreases and the engine tends to speed up;

(2) The flyweights fly out, closing off some of the fuel;

(3) The engine returns to an on-speed condition. As the flyweights come upright, flyweight force comes into equilibrium with the speeder spring force;

b) Under speed condition:

(1) Load on the engine increases and the engine tends to slow down;

(2) The flyweights move in at the top, adding fuel;

(3) The engine returns to an on-speed condition as the flyweights move outward to the upright position into equilibrium with the speeder spring force.

c) Power lever movement (forward):

(1) The speeder spring is compressed and the flyweights move in at the top in a false under-speed condition;

(2) Fuel is increased and the flyweights start to fly out again to come into equilibrium with the new speeder spring force.

Note: The flyweights will not come completely back to their former position unless the power lever is adjusted because the speeder spring now has a greater force value. This is called droop and defined as the slight loss of RPM due to governing system mechanisms.

2) On many engines, static pressure in the burner can is a useful measure of mass airflow. If mass airflow is known, air-fuel ratio can be more carefully controlled. As burner pressure (P_b) increases, the burner pressure bellows expands to the right. Excessive movement is restricted by the burner limiter (6). If we consider that (2) now remains stationary, the multiplying linkage will force the slider to the left, opening the metering valve to match fuel flow to the increased mass airflow. This condition could occur in an aircraft nose down condition which would increase airspeed, inlet ram air, and engine mass airflow.

3) An increase in inlet pressure would also cause the inlet pressure bellows (7) to expand, forcing the multiplying linkage to the left and the metering valve to open wider.

4) When the engine is shut down, the speeder spring expands in both directions, moving the sliding cap up against the idle stop and pushing the main metering valve off the minimum flow stop. When the engine is started the next time and goes to idle speed, the governor flyweights keep the sliding cap on the idle stop and also moves the main metering valve toward the minimum flow stop.

3. Hydro-Pneumatic Fuel Control System, PT6 Turboprop (Bendix Fuel Control)

The basic fuel system consists of a single, engine-driven pump, a fuel control unit, a starting control, and a dual fuel manifold with 14 simplex (single orifice) fuel nozzles. Two drain valves are provided on the gas generator case to ensure drainage of residual fuel after engine shutdown. Refer to Figure 7-5.

a. Fuel Pump

The fuel pump (1) is a positive displacement gear-type pump driven off the accessory gearbox. Fuel from a booster pump enters the fuel pump through a 74 micron (200 mesh) inlet screen (2) and then on to the pump gear chamber. From there the fuel is delivered at high pressure to the fuel control unit through a ten micron pump outlet filter (3). The inlet screen is spring loaded and, should it become blocked, an increase in fuel pressure differential will overcome the spring, lift the screen from its seat, and allow unfiltered fuel to flow into the system. A bypass valve (4) and cored passages in the pump casing enables unfiltered high pressure fuel to flow from the pump gears to the fuel control unit when the outlet filter is blocked. An internal passage (5), originating at the fuel control unit, returns bypass fuel from the fuel control unit to the pump inlet downstream of the inlet screen.

b. Fuel Control System

The fuel control system consists of three separate units with interdependent functions: The Fuel Control Unit (FCU) (6) determines the proper fuel schedule for engine steady state operation and acceleration. The Starting Flow Control (7) acts as a flow divider, directing Fuel Control Unit metered fuel output to the primary fuel manifold or to both primary and secondary manifolds as required. Full propeller control during forward and reverse thrust operation is provided by a governor package which contains a normal propeller governor section (not shown), and a N_2 power turbine governor (8). The N_2 governor section provides power turbine over-speed protection during normal operation. During reverse thrust operation the propeller governor is inoperative and control of power turbine speed is accomplished by the N_2 governor section.

1) Fuel Control Unit

The Fuel Control Unit (FCU) is mounted on the engine driven fuel pump and is driven at a speed proportional to compressor turbine speed (N_1). The Fuel Control Unit determines the fuel schedule for the engine to provide the required output of the engine and for controlling the speed of the compressor turbine (N_1). Engine power output is directly dependent upon compressor turbine speed. The Fuel Control Unit governs N_1, thereby actually governing the power output of the engine. Control of N_1 is accomplished by regulating the amount of fuel supplied to the combustion section of the engine.

a) Fuel Metering Section

The Fuel Control Unit is supplied with fuel at pump pressure (P_1). Fuel flow is established by a main metering valve (9) and a differential bypass valve (10). Unmetered fuel at P_1 pressure is applied to the entrance of the metering valve. The fuel pressure, immediately after the metering valve, is called metered fuel pressure (P_2). The differential bypass valve maintains an essentially constant fuel pressure differential ($P_1 - P_2$) across the metering valve. The orifice area of the metering valve will change to meet specific engine requirements. Fuel pump output in excess of these requirements will be returned via internal passages in the Fuel Control Unit and fuel pump to the pump inlet downstream of the inlet filter (5). This returned fuel is referred to as P_o. The differential bypass valve consists of a sliding valve working in a ported sleeve. The valve is actuated by means of a diaphragm and spring. In operation, the spring force is balanced by the $(P_1—P_2)$ pressure differential working on the diaphragm. The bypass valve will always be in a position to maintain the $(P_1—P_2)$ differential and to bypass fuel in excess of engine requirements.

A relief valve (11) is incorporated parallel to the bypass valve to prevent a buildup of excessive (P_1) in the Fuel Control Unit. The valve is spring-loaded closed and remains closed unless the inlet fuel pressure (P_1) overcomes the spring force and opens the valve. As soon as the inlet pressure is reduced, the valve closes.

The metering valve (9) consists of a contoured needle working in a sleeve. The metering valve regulates the flow of fuel by changing the orifice area. Fuel flow is a function of metering valve position only, because the differential bypass valve maintains an essentially constant differential fuel pressure across the orifice regardless of variations in inlet or discharge fuel pressures.

Compensation for variations in specific gravity resulting from changes in fuel temperature is accomplished by the bimetallic disks under the differential bypass valve spring.

b) Pneumatic Computing Section (Figure 7-5)

The power lever (12) incorporates a speed scheduling cam which depresses an internal rod when the power is increased. The governor lever is pivoted and one end operates against an orifice to form the governor valve (13). The enrichment lever (14) pivots at the same point as the governor lever and has two extensions which straddle a portion of the governor lever so that after a slight movement, a gap will close and then both levers must move together. The enrichment lever actuates a fluted pin which operates against the enrichment "hat" valve. Another smaller spring connects the enrichment lever to the governor lever.

The speed scheduling cam applies tension to the governor spring (15) through the intermediate lever which applies a force to close the governor valve. The enrichment spring (16), between the enrichment and governor levers, provides a force to open the enrichment valve.

As the drive shaft rotates, it in turn rotates a table (17) on which the governor flyweights are mounted. Small levers on the inside of the flyweights contact the governor spool. As N_1 increases, centrifugal loading causes the flyweights to apply increasing force against the spool. This tends to move the spool outward on the shaft against the enrichment lever. As governor flyweight force overcomes opposing spring force, the governor valve is opened and the enrichment valve is closed.

The enrichment valve will start to close whenever N_1 increases enough to cause the flyweight force to overcome the force of the smaller spring. If N_1 continues to increase, the enrichment lever will continue to move until it contacts the governor lever at which time the enrichment valve will be fully closed. The governor valve will open if N_1 increases sufficiently to cause the weight force to overcome the force of the larger spring. At this point, the governor valve will be open and the enrichment valve closed. The enrichment valves closes down as RPM increases to keep working air pressure fairly constant.

c) Bellows Assembly

The bellows assembly, Figure 7-5, consists of an evacuated (acceleration) bellows (18) and a governor bellows (19) connected by a common rod. The acceleration bellows provides an absolute pressure reference further explained in f)(4) below. The governor bellows is secured in the body cavity and its function is similar to that of a diaphragm. Movement of the bellows is transmitted to the metering valve (9) by the cross shaft and associated levers (20). The cross shaft moves within a torque tube which is attached to the cross shaft near the bellows lever.

The tube is secured in the body casting at the opposite end by means of an adjustment bushing. Therefore, any rotational movement of the cross shaft will result in an increase or decrease in the force of the torque tube. The torque tube forms the seal between the air and fuel sections of the control. The torque tube is positioned during assembly to provide a force in a direction tending to close the metering valve. The bellows act against this force to open the metering valve. P_y pressure is applied to the outside of the governor bellows. P_x pressure is applied to the inside of the governor bellows and to the outside of the acceleration bellows.

For explanation purposes, the governor bellows is illustrated as a diaphragm. Refer to Figure 7-6. P_y pressure is applied to one side of the diaphragm and P_x is applied to the opposite side. P_x is also applied to the evacuated acceleration bellows attached to the diaphragm. The force of P_x applied against the evacuated bellows is cancelled by application of the same pressure on an equal area of the diaphragm as the forces act in opposite directions.

All pressure forces applied to the bellows section can be resolved into forces acting on the diaphragm only. These forces are: P_y pressure acting on the entire surface of the top side; the internal pressure of the evacuated bellows acting on a portion of the under side (within the area of pressure cancellation); and, P_x acting on the remainder of that side. Any change in P_y will have more effect on the diaphragm than an equal change in P_x, due to the difference in effective surface areas.

P_x and P_y vary with changing engine operating conditions. When both pressures increase simultaneously, such as during acceleration, the bellows movement

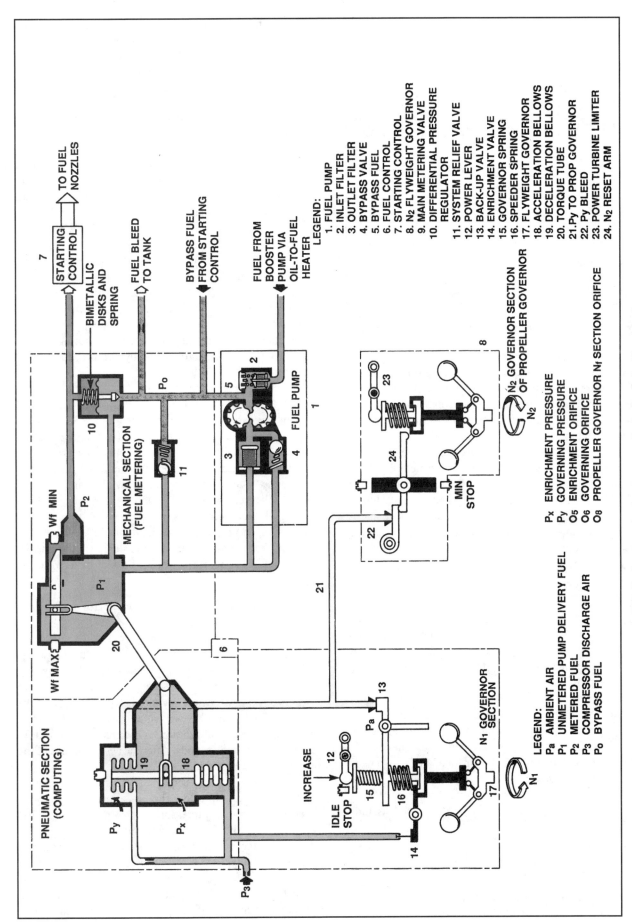

Fig.7-5 — PT6 Turboprop, hydro-pneumatic fuel controlling system

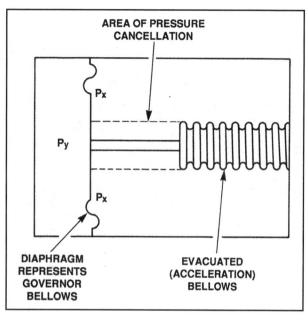

AREA OF PRESSURE CANCELLATION

P_x

P_y

P_x

DIAPHRAGM REPRESENTS GOVERNOR BELLOWS

EVACUATED (ACCELERATION) BELLOWS

Fig. 7-6 — Functional diagram of bellows assembly

downward will cause the metering valve to move to the left in the opening direction. When P_y dumps away at the governor valve as the desired N_1 is approached(for governing after acceleration), the bellows will move upward to reduce the opening of the metering valve.

When both pressures decrease simultaneously, the bellows will travel upward to reduce the metering valve opening because the acceleration bellows is now acting as a spring. This occurs during deceleration as P_y dumps away at the governor valve and P_x dumps away at the enrichment valve causing movement of the metering valve to its minimum flow stop.

d) Power Turbine (N_2) Governor

The N_2 governor section of the propeller governor senses P_y pressure through an external pneumatic line (21) from the body of the Flow Control Unit to the governor. In the event of a power turbine over-speed condition, an air bleed orifice (22) in the N_2 governor section is opened by flyweight action to bleed off P_y pressure through the governor. When this occurs, P_y pressure acting on the Flow Control Unit bellows decreases to move the flow control unit metering valve in a closing direction, thus reducing fuel flow. Reduction in fuel flow decreases N_1 speed and consequently N_2 speed. The speed at which the air bleed orifice opens is dependent on the setting of the propeller governor control lever (23) and the setting of the N_2 reset arm (24). Power turbine (N_2) speed, and hence propeller speed, is thus limited by the N_2 governor.

e) Starting Flow Control

The starting flow control (7) and Figure 7-7 consist of a body assembly incorporating a ported plunger (25) sliding in a ported housing. Rotational movement of the input lever (26) is converted to linear movement of the

plunger through a rack and pinion. Rigging slots are provided at the 45 degree and 72 degree RUN positions. One of these positions, depending on the installation, is used to rig the system to the cockpit lever.

A minimum pressurizing valve (27), located at the inlet to the starting flow control, maintains a minimum pressure in the flow control unit to ensure correct fuel metering. Two connections are provided to the dual manifolds which are interconnected via the transfer valve (28). This valve permits the Number 1 primary manifold to fill initially for light-up and, as pressure increases in the control, the transfer valve opens, allowing fuel into the Number 2 secondary manifold.

When the lever is in the CUT-OFF AND DUMP (zero degree) position (See Figure 7-7A), the fuel supply to both manifolds is blocked off. At the same time, drain ports are aligned (via porting in the plunger) with the "dump" port, allowing the residual fuel in the manifolds to drain overboard. This prevents the fuel from boiling and forming carbon in the system due to heat absorption. Fuel entering the starting flow control during engine rundown is diverted through the bypass port to the fuel pump inlet.

When the lever is placed in the RUN position (Figure 7-7B), the outlet port to Number 1 manifold is uncovered and the bypass port is completely blocked off. As the engine accelerates, both the fuel flow and manifold pressure increase until the transfer valve opens, and the Number 2 manifold fills. When the Number 2 manifold is filled, the total flow is increased by that amount now being delivered through the Number 2 system, and the engine further accelerates to idle. When the lever is moved beyond the RUN (45 degree or 72 degree) position towards the maximum stop (90 degrees), the starting flow control has no further effect on fuel metered to the engine.

f) Operation Of Complete Fuel Control System For A Typical Installation
(1) Engine Starting

The engine starting cycle is initiated with the power control lever placed in the IDLE position and the starting control lever in CUT-OFF. The ignition and starter are switched on and, when required N_1 is attained, the starting flow control lever is advanced to the RUN position. Successful ignition is normally achieved in approximately ten seconds. After successful ignition, the engine accelerates to idle.

During the starting sequence, the fuel control unit metering valve is in a low flow position. As the engine accelerates, the compressor discharge pressure (P_3) increases. P_x and P_y increase simultaneously ($P_x = P_y$) during engine acceleration. The increase in pressure sensed by the bellows (18) causes the metering valve to move in an opening direction. As N_1 approaches idle, the centrifugal effect of the flyweight begins to overcome the governor spring force and opens the governor valve (13).

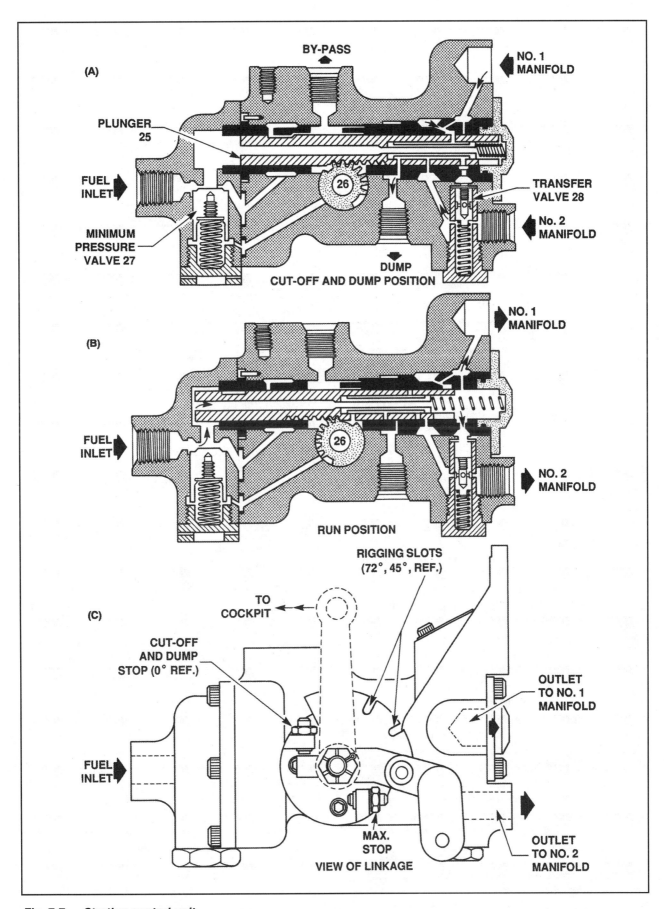

Fig. 7-7 — Starting control unit.

This creates a (P_x-P_y) differential which causes the metering valve to move in a closing direction until the required-to-run idle fuel flow is obtained.

Any variation in engine speed from the selected (idle) speed will be sensed by the governor flyweights and will result in increased or decreased flyweight force. This change in flyweight force will cause movement of the governor valve, which will then be reflected by a change in fuel flow necessary to re-establish the proper speed.

(2) Acceleration

As the power control lever (12) is advanced above idle, it increases the governor spring force. The governor spring then overcomes the flyweight force and moves the lever, closing the governor valve and opening the enrichment valve. P_x and P_y immediately increase and cause the metering valve to move in an opening direction. Acceleration is then a function of increasing ($P_x = P_y$).

With increase in fuel flow, the compressor turbine N_1 will accelerate. When N_1 reaches a predetermined point (approximately 70 to 75 percent), flyweight force overcomes the enrichment spring force and starts to close the enrichment valve. When the enrichment valve starts to close, P_y and P_x pressures increase, causing an increase in the movement rate of the governor bellows and metering valve, thus providing speed enrichment to the acceleration fuel schedule.

Meanwhile as N_1 and hence N_2 increase, the propeller governor increases the pitch of the propeller to control N_2 at the selected speed and to apply the increased power as additional thrust. Acceleration is completed when the centrifugal effect of the flyweights again overcomes the governor spring and opens the governor valve.

(3) Governing

Once the acceleration cycle has been completed, any variation in engine speed from the selected speed will be sensed by the governor flyweights and will result in increased or decreased flyweight force. This change in flyweight force will cause the governor valve to either open or close, which will then be reflected by the change in fuel flow necessary to re-establish the proper speed. When the fuel control unit is governing, the valve will be maintained in a regulating, or "floating" position.

(4) Altitude Compensation

Altitude compensation is automatic with this fuel control system since the acceleration bellows assembly (18) is evacuated and affords an absolute pressure reference. Compressor discharge pressure P_3 is a measurement of engine speed and air density. P_x is proportional to compressor discharge pressure, so it will decrease with a decrease in air density. This is sensed by the acceleration bellows which acts to reduce fuel flow.

(5) Deceleration

When the power control lever is retarded there is a reduction in the governor spring force, allowing the governor valve (13) to move in an opening direction. The resulting drop in Py moves the metering valve in a closing direction until it contacts the minimum flow stop.

This stop assures sufficient fuel to the engine to prevent flameout. The engine will continue to decelerate until the governor flyweight force decreases to balance the governor spring force at the new governing position.

(6) Power Turbine Limiting

The N_2 governor section of the propeller control senses Py pressure through a line from the fuel control. If a power turbine over-speed should occur, the N_2 air bleed orifice will be opened to bleed off P_y pressure through the propeller governor. This decrease in P_y will cause the metering valve in the fuel control unit to move in a closing direction, thus reducing fuel flow and consequently gas generator speed.

(7) Engine Shutdown

The engine is shut down by placing the starting flow control lever in CUT-OFF position. This action moves the manually-operated plunger to the CUT-OFF AND DUMP position, stopping all fuel flow to the engine and dumping the residual fuel contained in the dual manifold overboard.

4. Bendix DP-L2 Fuel Control (Hydro-pneumatic Unit)

This hydro-pneumatic fuel control is installed on the JT15D turbofan (Figure 7-8).

Fuel is supplied to the fuel control unit at pump pressure (P_1), which is applied to the entrance of the metering valve. The metering valve, in conjunction with the by-pass valve system, serves to establish fuel flow. The fuel pressure immediately downstream of the metering valve is known as P_2. The by-pass valve maintains an essentially constant fuel pressure differential (P_1—P_2) across the metering valve, assuring that fuel flow is a function of orifice area only.

a. Components/Functions:

1) Fuel Inlet - From fuel storage tank;
2) Filter - Coarse screen, self relieving type;
3) Gear Pump - Discharge referred to as P_1 fuel;
4) Filter - Fine mesh;
5) Relief Valve - Prevents excessive P1 fuel pump discharge pressure buildup and assists the differential metering head regulator during rapid deceleration;
6) Differential Metering Head Regulator—Hydraulic mechanism which bypasses unwanted (P_0) fuel and establishes a constant fuel pressure differential (P_1—P_2) across the metering valve;
7) Fuel Temperature Bi-Metallic Disks—Automatically compensates for specific gravity changes with fuel temperature changes. Can also be manually adjusted for use of differing specific gravity values of various jet fuels;
8) Metering Valve—Meters P_2 fuel to the fuel nozzles; positioned by the torque tube connecting the bellows unit to the metering valve;
9) Minimum Flow Adjustment—Prevents metering valve from completely closing on deceleration;
10) Maximum Flow Stop Adjustment—Sets maximum rotor speed for limit of engine;

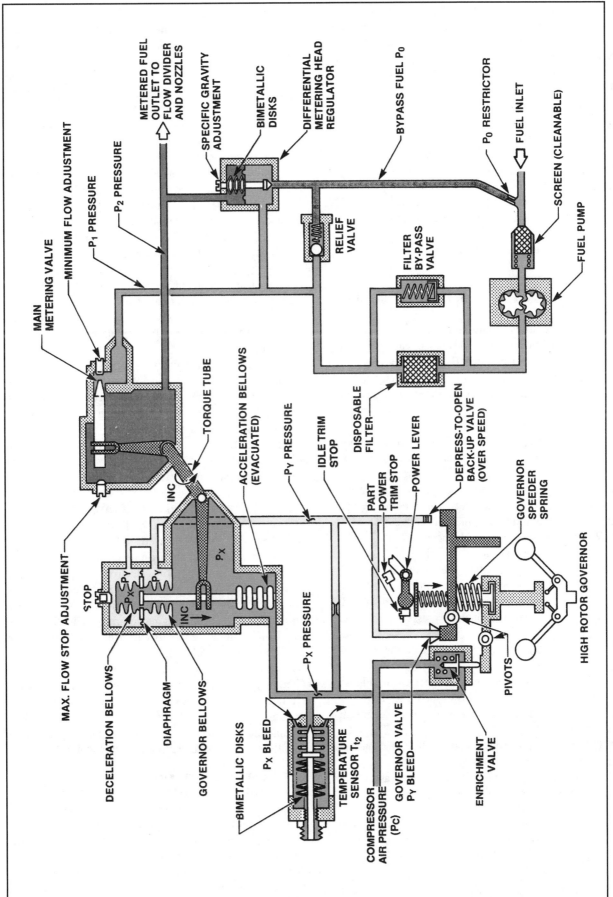

Fig.7-8 — Bendix DP-L® hydro-pneumatic fuel control used on a Pratt and Whitney of Canada JT-15 Turbofan engine.

11) Dual Bellows Units—Governor bellows receives Px and Py air pressure to position the torque tube and change fuel schedule and engine speed. Deceleration bellows expands to its stop when P_y air pressure decreases to cause a reduction in engine speed;

12) Temperature Sensor—Bi-metallic disks sensing engine inlet temperature T_2 to control P_x air pressure to the bellows unit;

13) Enrichment Valve—Receives Pc compressor air pressure and controls P_x and P_y pressure to the dual bellows unit. It closes down as RPM increases to keep approximately the same working pressure;

14) High Rotor Governor—Flyweights throw outward under centrifugal loading of increased engine speed. This action modifies P_y air pressure;

15) Power Lever—Exerts a direct force to position the governor.

b. Operation Of Control

1) Unmetered fuel P_1 is supplied to the fuel control by the fuel pump.

2) P_2 pressure drops across the metering valve orifice in the same manner as was discussed earlier in the simplified fuel control diagram (Figure 7-4B). P_1 then becomes P_2 pressure which flows out to the engine and also influences the operation of the differential pressure regulating valve here referred to as the Differential Metering Head Regulator.

3) The fuel which bypasses back to the fuel pump is labeled P_o. Its pressure is maintained at a higher value than fuel pump inlet pressure via the Po line restrictor.

4) The pneumatic section is operated by compressor discharge air Pc. When modified, this air becomes P_x and P_y air which position the main metering valve.

5) When the power lever is advanced:

a) The flyweights droop in, the force on the speeder spring being greater than the flyweight force;

b) The governor valve closes off the P_y bleed;

c) The enrichment valve moves toward closed, reducing P_c airflow. (Not as much air pressure is required when P_y bleeds are closed);

d) P_x and P_y air pressures equalize on the surfaces of the governor;

e) P_y air becomes the predominant force (Figure 7-6) and the acceleration bellows and the governor bellows rod are both forced downward. The diaphragm allows this movement;

f) The torque tube rotates counterclockwise and the main metering valve moves open;

g) The flyweights move back outward as engine speed increases and the governor valve opens to bleed P_y air;

h) The enrichment valve reopens and P_x air increases over P_y air value;

i) Reduced P_y value allows the governor bellows and rod to move back up;

j) The torque tube rotates clockwise to decrease fuel flow and engine speed stabilizes.

6) When the power lever is retarded to the idle stop:

a) The flyweights move outward, speeder spring force now being less than flyweight force under high engine speed;

b) The governor valve opens dumping P_y air, the backup valve is also depressed, dumping additional P_y air;

c) The enrichment valve opens allowing increased P_x airflow;

d) P_x air expands the governor and deceleration bellows to its stop, the governor rod also moves up, and the main metering valve moves toward closed;

e) P_x air decreases with engine speed decrease, but the acceleration bellows holds the governor rod up;

f) As engine speed slows, the flyweights come back in, closing the P_y bleed at the governor valve and the backup valve;

g) The enrichment valve also moves toward closed out (Py) air increases in relation to P_x value;

h) The deceleration bellows moves downward, the metering valve moves slightly open, and engine speed stabilizes.

7) When ambient temperature goes up for any fixed power lever position:

a) The Tt_2 sensor expands to reduce P_x bleed to keep P_x air pressure stabilized during low Pc pressure conditions. This in turn maintains the acceleration bellows position and the acceleration schedule. Thus the spool up time from idle to take-off power, under hot day conditions is the same as for cold day operations.

5. Electronic Fuel Scheduling Systems

Fuel metering systems with electronic functions had not been as widely used in the past as the hydro-mechanical or hydro-pneumatic controls. In recent years, however, the electronic engine control (EEC) has been incorporated on most newer engines designed for use in both commercial and business size aircraft. The electronic engine control is actually a basic hydro-mechanical control with the addition of an electronic sensor circuit. The electronic circuitry is powered by the aircraft bus, or by its own dedicated alternator, and operates by analyzing engine operating parameters such as exhaust temperatures, gas path pressures, and engine RPM. As a result of these sensed parameters, the electronics portion of the system causes fuel flow to be fine tuned to the correct amount.

a. Example System (Rolls-Royce RB-211)

The RB-211 is a large, three-spool, front turbofan engine. It has a supervisory electronic engine control (EEC) incorporated into its hydro-mechanical fuel scheduling. The electronic control amplifier protects the engine from over temperature conditions when operating at take-off power. In any other operating condition the fuel control operates only on its hydro-mechanical system.

An analysis of Figure 7-9 will show that the control amplifier receives signals from turbine gas temperature (TGT) and two compressor speed signals (N_1 and N_2).

This control operates on a hydro-mechanical schedule until near full engine power, then the electronic control amplifier circuit starts to function as a (part-time) fuel limiting device.

The differential pressure regulator in this installation is similar to the differential pressure regulating valve in the simplified hydro-mechanical fuel control diagram in Figure 7-4B, except that in this system the bypassing of fuel occurs at the fuel pump outlet rather than from within the fuel control. Near full power, when predetermined turbine gas temperature and compressor speed values are reached, the pressure regulator reduces fuel flow to the spray nozzles by returning increased amounts of fuel to the fuel pump inlet. The fuel-flow regulator in this control acts as a hydro-mechanical control, receiving signals from the high pressure compressor (N_3), gas path air pressure (P_1, P_2, P_3), and power lever position.

Referring to Figure 7-9 will reveal that the fuel control receives the following signals from the engine upon which the fuel schedule is established:

1) PLA—Power lever angle;

2) P_1—Compressor inlet total pressure (Fan);

3) P_3—2nd compressor discharge total pressure (Intermediate pressure compressor);

4) P_4—3rd compressor discharge total pressure (High pressure compressor);

5) N_3—3rd compressor rotational speed (High pressure compressor);

6) N_1—1st compressor rotation speed (Fan);

7) N_2—2nd compressor rotation speed (Intermediate pressure compressor);

8) TGT—Turbine gas temperature (Low pressure turbine outlet);

9) OVRD—Override command to block control amplifier functions;

10) Enrichment—Fuel enricher used to start engine below 0°F ambient.

b. Example System (Garrett TFE-731 And ATF-3)

The TFE-731 and ATF-3 are two of the new generation business jet, turbofan engines. They both incorporate a full schedule electronic engine control system (EEC). Analysis of the schematic in Figure 7-10 will reveal that the electronic computer receives the following inputs:

1) N_1—Fan speed;

2) N_2—Intermediate pressure compressor speed;

3) N_3—High pressure compressor speed;

4) Tt_2—inlet total temperature;

5) Tt_8—High pressure turbine inlet temperature;

6) Pt_2—Inlet total pressure;

7) Input power—28 volt DC;

8) PMG—Permanent magnet A.C. generator;

9) PLA—Power lever angle;

10) IGV—Inlet guide vane position;

11) Ps_6—High pressure discharge static pressure.

The electronic portion of the fuel control analyzes the input data and sends a command to position the inlet guide vanes and to schedule fuel flow at the hydro-mechanical portion of the fuel control unit.

Manufacturer's information states that this is a full schedule (full time) system which more accurately schedules fuel flow than a comparable hydro-mechanical unit. From engine starting to takeoff thrust, it also provides the engine with over-temperature protection, over-speed protection, and stall-free rapid acceleration by continually monitoring turbine inlet temperature and several other important engine parameters.

c. Example System (G.E./Snecma CFM56-7B) (Figure 7-11)

The CFM56-7B operates through a system known as FADEC (Full Authority Digital Engine Control). It takes complete control of engine systems in response to command inputs from the aircraft. It also provides information to the aircraft for flight deck indications, engine condition monitoring, maintenance reporting and troubleshooting. The FADEC system accomplishes the following:

- It performs fuel scheduling and provides limit protections for N_1 and N_2.
- It controls the engine parameters during the starting sequence and prevents the engine from exceeding starting EGT limits.
- It manages the thrust according to 2 modes, manual and autothrust.
- It provides optimal engine operation by controlling compressor airflow and turbine clearances.
- It controls the 2 thrust lever interlock solenoids.

1) FADEC Components

The FADEC system consists of:

- An Electronic Engine Control (EEC) containing two identical computers, designated channel A and channel B. The EEC electronically performs engine control calculations and monitors the engine's condition.
- A Hydro-Mechanical Unit (HMU), which converts electrical signals from the EEC into hydraulic pressures to drive the engine's valves and actuators.
- Peripheral components such as valves, actuators and sensors used for control and monitoring.

2) Airplane/EEC Interface (Figure 7-11)

The airplane provides engine thrust and control commands and airplane flight and status information to the EEC as follows:

- Throttle lever position is provided to the EEC in terms of an electrical resolver angle. A dual resolver is mechanically linked to the thrust levers on the flight deck.
- Air Data information and engine-specific commands and data are transmitted to each engine from the airplane Display Electronic Units (DEUs) via an ARINC-429 serial databus.

Aircraft Gas Turbine Powerplants

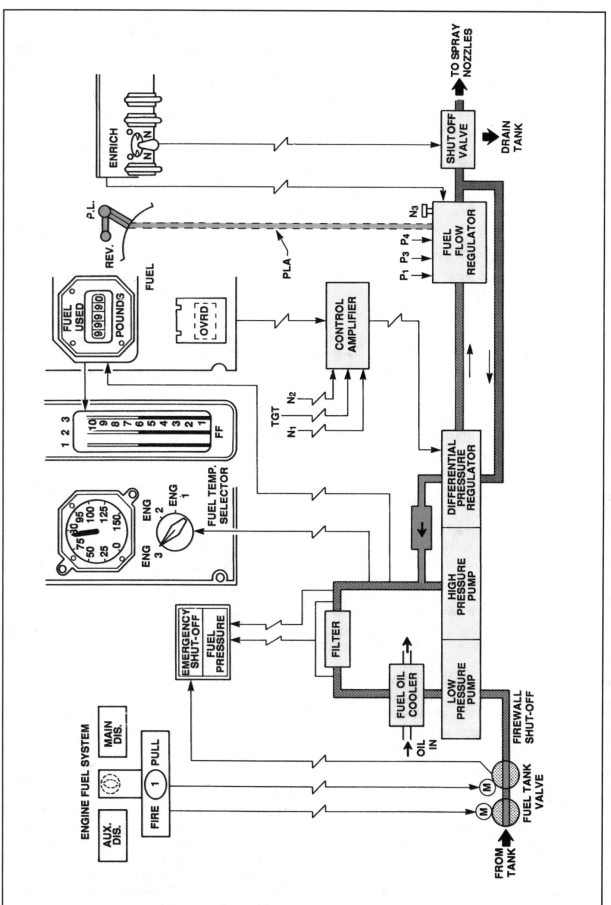

Fig. 7-9 — Fuel System showing Electronic Engine Control (EEC) with supervisory schedule

- Selected airplane discrete command and data signals are hardwired to the EEC.
- Thrust reverser (T/R) position signals from each translating sleeve are wired to the EEC.

The EEC uses bleed-discrete information and flight-configuration data (flight/ground and flap position) from the airplane for thrust setting compensation and for biasing the acceleration fuel topping schedule.

3) FADEC Interfaces

The FADEC system is a Built In Test Equipment (BITE) system. This means it is able to detect its own internal faults and also external faults. To perform all its tasks, the FADEC system communicates with the aircraft computers through the EEC.

The EEC receives operational commands from the Common Display System (CDS) Display Electronic Unit (DEU), which is an interface between the EEC and aircraft systems. Both CDS-DEU 1 and 2 provide the following data from the two Air Data and Inertial Reference Units (ADIRU) and the Flight Management Computer (FMC):

- Air data parameters (altitude, total air temperature, total pressure and Mach number) for thrust calculation.
- The position of the Throttle Resolver Angle (TRA).

4) FADEC Design

The FADEC system is fully redundant and built around the two-channel EEC. The valves and actuators are fitted with dual sensors to provide the EEC with feedback signals. All control inputs are dual, but some parameters, used for monitoring and indicating, are single.

To enhance system reliability, all inputs to one channel are made available to the other, through a Cross Channel Data Link (CCDL). This allows both channels to remain operational even if important inputs to one of them fail.

The two channels, A and B, are identical and permanently operational, but they operate independently from each other. Both channels always receive inputs and process them, but only the channel in control, called the Active channel, delivers output commands. The other is called the Stand-by channel.

Active and Stand-by channel selection is performed at EEC power-up and during operation. The BITE system detects and isolates failures, or combinations of failures, in order to determine the health status of the channels and to transmit maintenance data to the aircraft. Active and Stand-by selection is based upon the health of the channels and each channel determines its own health status. The healthiest is selected as the Active channel.

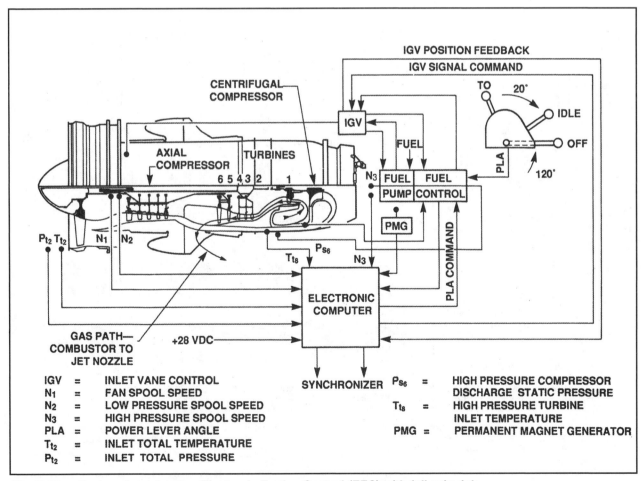

IGV	=	INLET VANE CONTROL
N_1	=	FAN SPOOL SPEED
N_2	=	LOW PRESSURE SPOOL SPEED
N_3	=	HIGH PRESSURE SPOOL SPEED
PLA	=	POWER LEVER ANGLE
T_{t2}	=	INLET TOTAL TEMPERATURE
P_{t2}	=	INLET TOTAL PRESSURE

P_{s6}	=	HIGH PRESSURE COMPRESSOR DISCHARGE STATIC PRESSURE
T_{t8}	=	HIGH PRESSURE TURBINE INLET TEMPERATURE
PMG	=	PERMANENT MAGNET GENERATOR

Fig. 7-10 — Fuel system showing Electronic Engine Control (EEC) with full schedule

When both channels have an equal health status, Active/Stand-by channel selection alternates with every engine start, as soon as N_2 is greater than 10,990 RPM. If a channel is faulty and the Active channel is unable to ensure an engine control function, this function is moved to a position which protects the engine, and is known as the failsafe position.

5) Closed Loop Control Operation

In order to properly control the various engine systems, the EEC uses an operation known as closed loop control. The EEC calculates a position for a system component, known as the Command. The EEC then compares the Command with the actual position of the component, known as the Feedback, and calculates a position difference, which is known as the Demand.

The EEC, through the Electro-Hydraulic Servo Valve (EHSV) of the Hydro-Mechanical Unit (HMU), sends a signal to a component (valve, actuator) which causes it to move. With the movement of the system valve or

actuator, the EEC is provided with a feedback of the component's position. The process is repeated until there is no longer a position difference.

6) Input Parameters

All sensors are dual, except $T_{49.5}$ (exhaust gas temperature), T_5 (low pressure turbine discharge temperature), Ps_{13} (fan outlet static air pressure), P_{25} (high pressure compressor inlet total air temperature), and WF (fuel flow). T_5, Ps_{13}, and P_{25} are optional sensors that are not installed on every engine.

To perform its calculations, each channel of the EEC receives a local value and a cross channel value, through the Cross Channel Data Link (CCDL). Both values pass through a validation test program in each EEC channel. The right value to be used is selected depending on the assessed validity of each reading, or an average of both values might be used.

In case of a dual sensor failure, a model value, computed from other available parameters, is selected. This is the case for the following parameters:

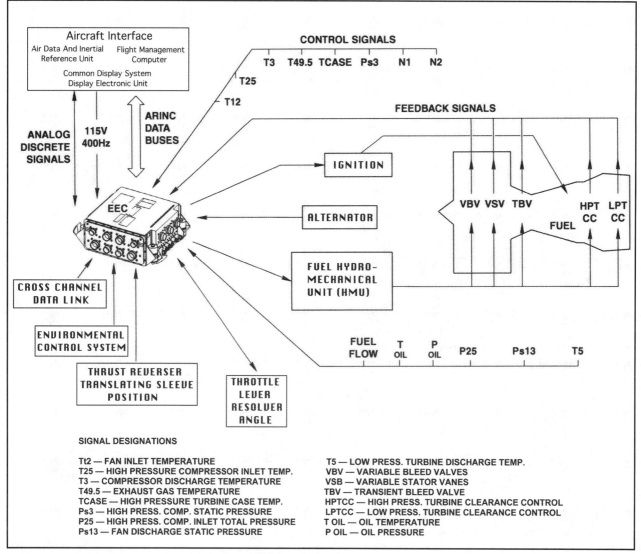

Fig. 7-11 — Fuel system schematic, G.E. / Snecma CFM56-7

• The fan speed (N_1).
• The high pressure compressor speed (N_2).
• Compressor discharge static air pressure (Ps_3).
• The high pressure compressor inlet air temperature (T_{25}).
• The position of the fuel metering valve (FMV).
• The position of the variable bleed valves (VBV).
• The position of the variable stator vanes (VSV).

For all other parameters, if the EEC is not able to select a valid value, failsafe values are selected.

7) EEC Location (Figure 7-12)

The EEC is a dual channel computer housed in an aluminum chassis, which is secured on the right hand side of the fan case at the 2 o'clock position. Four mounting bolts, with shock absorbers, provide isolation from shocks and vibrations.

To operate correctly, the EEC requires cooling to maintain internal temperatures within acceptable limits. Ambient air is picked up by an air scoop, located on the right hand side of the fan inlet cowl. This cooling air is routed up to the EEC internal chamber, around channel A and B compartments, and then exits through a cooling air outlet.

8) EEC Reprogramming

Each EEC can be reprogrammed with a Portable Data Loader (PDL). The PDL connects to the EEC at three of the cannon plug locations, and then both are powered up to allow the latest software to be downloaded. After the download, a display on the PDL will show either "Load Complete" or "Transfer Fail".

9) Engine Rating Identification Plug (Figure 7-13)

The engine rating/identification plug provides the EEC with engine configuration information for proper engine operation. It is plugged into one of the connectors on the EEC and attached to the fan case by a metal strap. It remains with the engine even after EEC replacement. The plug includes a coding circuit, soldered to the plug, which the EEC interprets and uses to determine how much thrust the engine will be able to produce.

The EEC stores schedules, in its non-volatile memory, for all available engine configurations. During initialization, it reads the plug by looking for voltages on certain pins. Depending on the location and voltage present at specific pins, the EEC will select a particular schedule. In case of a missing or invalid ID plug, the EEC uses the value stored in the non-volatile memory for the previous plug configuration.

The ID plug is equipped with fuse and push-pull links. The fuse links provide the EEC with thrust information at power up. They are made by metalization of an area between two contacts on the plug. These links can only be opened by burning them out, thus their reconfiguration is not possible.

By design, all CFM56-7B engines can produce a take-off thrust of 27,300 pounds. Depending on the application, the ID plug changes the take-off thrust to 19,500, 20,600, 22,700, 24,200, or 26,300 pounds.

Bump is an option provided to achieve power levels greater than the normal take-off levels within specific

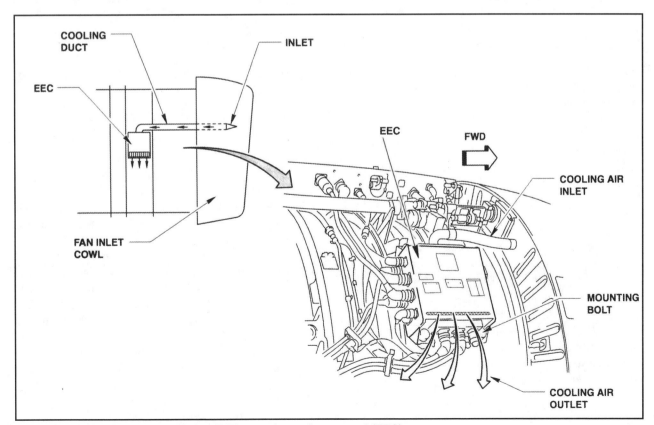

Fig. 7-12 — G.E. / Snecma CFM56-7B Electronic engine control (EEC)

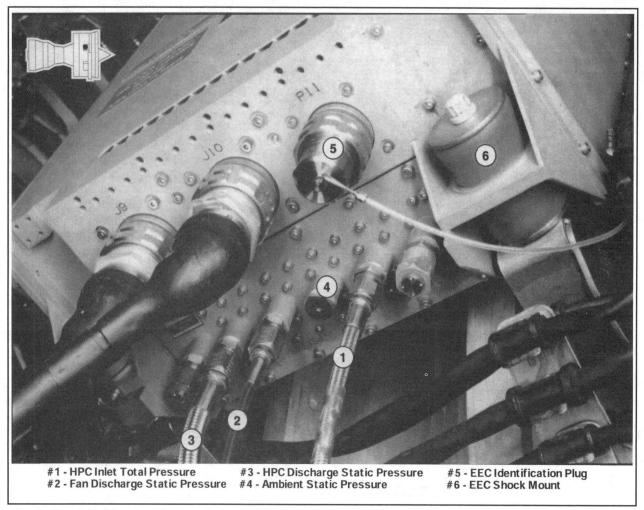

| #1 - HPC Inlet Total Pressure | #3 - HPC Discharge Static Pressure | #5 - EEC Identification Plug |
| #2 - Fan Discharge Static Pressure | #4 - Ambient Static Pressure | #6 - EEC Shock Mount |

Fig. 7-13 — G.E. / Snecma CFM56-7B Electronic Engine Control

limitations. Specific bump rating capabilities may be set by the engine ID plug. The bump rating does not influence power levels which are at, or below Max Continuous Thrust. For any available bump, the redline value for N_1, N_2, and EGT remain identical to the baseline rating.

When new engines are built, a small variation may exist in the amount of thrust they will create at a certain N_1 speed. To account for this, the ID plug may include a modifier to slightly alter the N_1 speed and make an engine identical to what is considered the "norm". Even though the modifier may cause an engine to have a lower N_1 speed, the signal sent to the flight deck gage will not show this reduction. In a twin engine airplane, both N_1 tachometers will show the same RPM.

10) EEC Power Supply

The EEC is provided with redundant power sources to ensure an uninterrupted and failsafe power supply. A logic circuit within the EEC automatically selects the correct power source in the event of a failure. The power sources are as follows:

• The aircraft 115 VAC, 400 Hz normal bus.
• The aircraft 115 VAC, 400 Hz emergency bus.

• The control alternator can provide power from two separate windings, above an engine speed of approximately 12% N_2.

The control alternator is considered the primary source of electrical power for the EEC. If this unit malfunctions, the EEC will automatically switch over to aircraft electrical power.

11) Engine Sensors (Figure 7-14)

The EEC requires information on the engine gas path and operational parameters in order to control the engine during all flight phases. Sensors are installed at aerodynamic stations and various engine locations, to measure engine parameters and provide them to the EEC subsystems. Sensors located at aerodynamic stations have the same number as the station, for example T25. Sensors placed at other engine locations have a particular name, for example T case sensor.

The following engine sensors are used by the EEC.
Speed Sensors:
• Low pressure rotating system speed, N_1.
• High pressure rotating system speed, N_2.
Resistive Thermal Devices (RTD sensors):
• Fan inlet temperature, T_{12}.

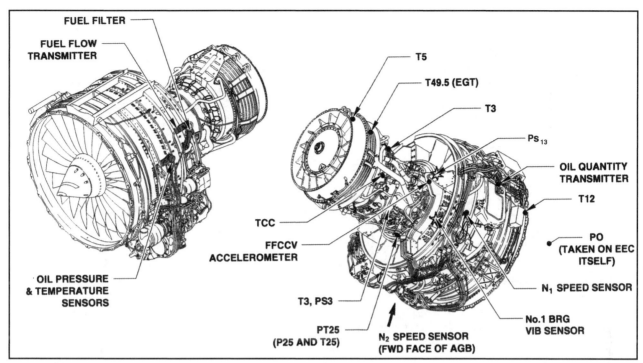

FUEL FILTER
FUEL FLOW TRANSMITTER
T5
T49.5 (EGT)
T3
Ps$_{13}$
OIL QUANTITY TRANSMITTER
T12
PO (TAKEN ON EEC ITSELF)
N$_1$ SPEED SENSOR
No.1 BRG VIB SENSOR
N$_2$ SPEED SENSOR (FWD FACE OF AGB)
PT25 (P25 AND T25)
T3, PS3
FFCCV ACCELEROMETER
TCC
OIL PRESSURE & TEMPERATURE SENSORS

Fig. 7-14 — G.E. / Snecma CFM56-7B Engine Sensors.

- High pressure compressor inlet temperature, T_{25}.

Thermocouples:
- Compressor discharge temperature, T_3.
- Exhaust gas temperature, EGT or $T_{49.5}$.
- Low pressure turbine discharge temperature, T_5.
- High pressure turbine shroud support temperature, TCC.

Pressures:
- Ambient static pressure, P0.
- High pressure compressor discharge static pressure, Ps_3 or CDP.
- Fan discharge static pressure, Ps_{13}.
- High pressure compressor inlet total pressure, P_{25}.

Vibration Sensors:
- Number 1 bearing vibration accelerometer.
- Fan frame compressor case vertical (FFCCV) accelerometer.

6. Power Management And Fuel Scheduling (CFM56-7B) (Figure 7-15)

Power management controls the engine thrust levels by means of throttle lever inputs. It uses fan speed (N_1) as the thrust setting parameter. The EEC calculates five reference fan speeds (corresponding to idle, max climb, max continuous, max take-off/go-around, and max reverse thrust) for the appropriate engine rating (ID plug) and based on ambient conditions and engine bleeds.

a. Throttle Lever

The throttle lever assembly is mechanically connected to a resolver through an adjustable rod. The resolver transforms the mechanical movement into an electrical signal representing the angular position. The electrical signal is transmitted, through hardwire connections, directly to the EEC for use in thrust calculations.

The throttle lever is positioned either by the flight crew or automatically by the autothrottle system. The N_1 command is calculated from the angular position of the throttle lever and other parameters.

b. Ambient Conditions

The power management uses ambient condition parameters, which are static pressure (P_S/P_0), total pressure (P_t), and total air temperature (TAT/T_{12}). Each EEC channel has independent sources of data available for selection. These sources are:
- Static Pressure, as the P0 input from the engine or as the PS input from the Air Data and Inertial Reference Unit (ADIRU).
- Total Pressure, as an input from the ADIRU.
- Total Air Temperature, as the T_{12} input from the engine or as the TAT input from the ADIRU.

c. Bleeds

Engine compressor bleed is used to de-ice the engine nacelles and wings, and to provide high pressure air to the aircraft Environmental Control System (ECS). Each engine provides its own Cowl Thermal Anti-Icing (CTAI) bleed. The EEC controls the compressor bleeds, integrating the needs of the engine and aircraft with the thrust requirements and the appropriate engine limits.

d. Thrust Control Operating Modes

The CFM56-7B engine has three thrust control operating modes, the normal thrust control mode and two alternate thrust control modes which provide fault accommodation for the loss of total pressure data from the ADIRU.

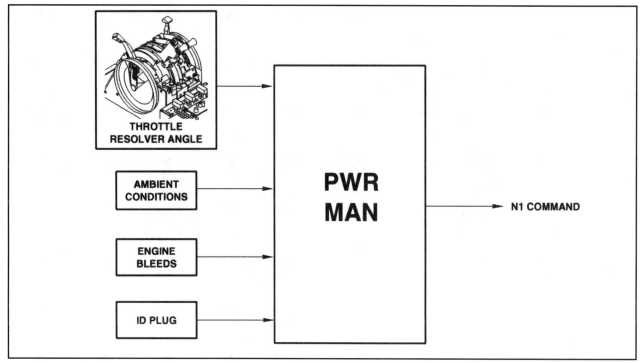

Fig. 7-15 — G.E. / Snecma CFM56-7B Power management.

If the EEC loses ADIRU communication, pressure total data, pressure total probe heat, or there is a disagreement between the data coming from ADIRU 1 and 2, the EEC switches into the soft alternate mode. In soft alternate mode, the EEC no longer calculates a Mach number from PT coming from a single valid input. In this mode, Mach number is calculated with the last valid delta temperature standard day and the current ambient static pressure. Since both engines usually receive the same set of data, the two engines switch into soft mode at the same time. The only time a single engine can be in soft mode is if one engine encounters a data bus failure.

The EEC switches automatically from soft alternate mode into hard alternate mode if the throttle lever is placed below the max climb position. Hard alternate mode can be manually selected by the EEC switch on the flight compartment overhead panel. In this control mode the EEC calculates Mach number with a fixed total air temperature value (30°C) and ambient static pressure.

In the hard alternate mode, the maximum N_1 data provided by the EEC is greater than, or equal to, the maximum N_1 thrust rating in normal mode. During hot day operation, it is possible to significantly exceed engine limits.

e. Auto Throttle (Figure 7-16)

The full range autothrottle system provides automatic positioning of the throttle lever during all flight operations. The system consists of:

- A Flight Management Computer (FMC), with a second FMC being optional.
- A Digital Flight Control System (DFCS).

- An Autothrottle Computer (ATC).
- Two Autothrottle Servo Mechanisms (ASM).

The flight management computer provides a target N_1 power setting or target airspeed to the autothrottle computer. Alternatively, the digital flight control system may provide a target airspeed to the autothrottle computer. When automatic thrust control is engaged, the autothrottle computer positions the throttle lever of both engines using the two autothrottle servo mechanisms, to obtain the target N_1 power setting or target airspeed.

The flight management computer (FMC) and the electronic engine control (EEC) both calculate thrust using information from the ADIRU. But unlike the EEC, the FMC can use parameters from just one ADIRU. This means that when the EEC is missing an ADIRU parameter, it switches to the alternate mode, but the FMC is still able to calculate the correct thrust.

7. Auxiliary Power Unit (APU) Fuel Controlling System

Auxiliary gas turbine engines are widely used for supplying electrical power and pressurized air to the aircraft systems when the main engines are not operating. Similar types of gas turbine engines are used in ground power units (GPU).

a. Example System Garrett Company GTP-30)

Auxiliary gas turbine fuel systems are fully automatic and do not require a power lever. After actuation of a start switch, the fuel system functions to provide the correct amount of fuel for smooth acceleration to the rated speed. Thereafter, the fuel system schedules fuel to maintain a constant engine speed under varying pneumatic bleed and electrical loads. Refer to Figure 7-17.

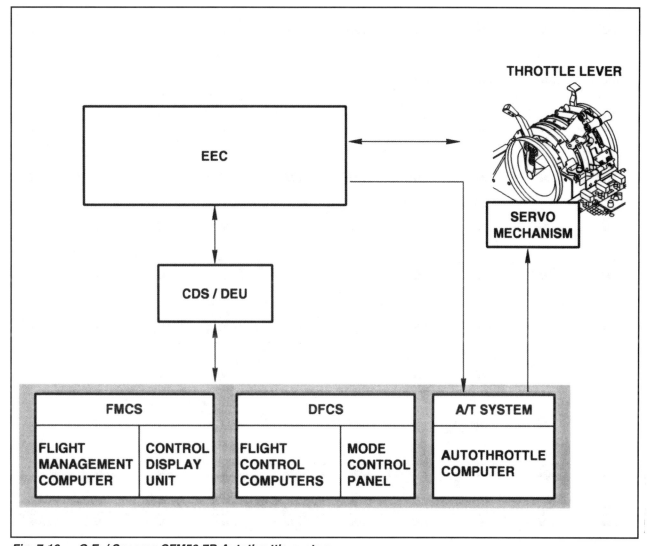

Fig. 7-16 — G.E. / Snecma CFM56-7B Autothrottle system

Observe the controlled-leak type, "acceleration and overload thermostat" located in the exhaust stream. It is a normally closed unit but is open at certain times to dump a portion of the diffuser pressure signal which goes to the top side of the bellows in the acceleration limiter. The thermostat expands acting as a safety device in the presence of excessive exhaust heat and relieves some of the diffuser signal pressure into the exhaust stream. This action prompts the acceleration limiter to function. The acceleration limiter diaphragm functions to control a bypass valve which returns excess fuel to the pump inlet and thus protects against engine over-temperature during acceleration from 0 to 95 percent engine RPM.

A flyweight governor also controls fuel bypass to maintain a steady state speed condition by returning unwanted fuel to the pump inlet. This governor protects against over-speed by overriding the acceleration limiter from 95 to 100 percent engine RPM. As long as the governor flyweight remains loaded or turned by engine rotation, the engine will remain at rated speed.

Sequence of fuel flow:

1) Fuel flows from the aircraft boost pump through the low pressure filter to the main fuel pump under low pressure.

2) Fuel is pumped to the governor under higher pressure and to the fuel (atomizer) nozzle.

3) Fuel bypasses back to the main pump inlet via the acceleration limiter if an overtemperature occurs when the acceleration overload thermostat expands to leak control air overboard into the engine exhaust.

4) Fuel bypasses above 95 percent RPM to control engine speed as per the preset value of the speeder flyweight governor spring.

5) The relief valve limits pump pressure in the event of a malfunction in the bypass portions of the system.

6) The fuel solenoid opens and closes for starting and stopping the engine.

b. Starting And Operation (Figures 7-17 and 7-18)

1) The operator places the door switch to "Auto" to open the air inlet door on the side of the fuselage.

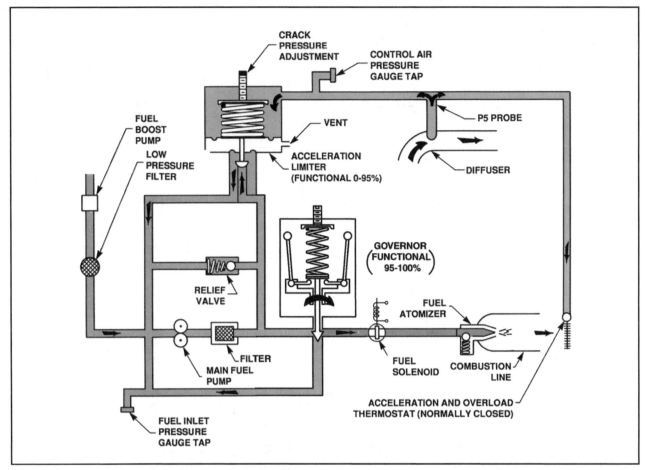

Fig. 7-17 — Small aircraft APU system (a hydromechanical control with pneumatic temperature limiting).

2) The operator places the auxiliary power unit master switch to "Start" and the starter and ignition circuits are energized.

3) The operator moves the start switch to "Run" after rpm and exhaust gas temperature start to read. Termination of starter and ignition occurs automatically at approximately 30 percent engine speed.

4) At approximately 10 percent engine speed, the fuel solenoid automatically opens fuel flow to the combustor, and combustion occurs.

5) The acceleration limiter starts to receive compressor discharge air, and fuel bypass decreases to allow a rapid acceleration.

6) The acceleration thermostat protects against over temperature by dumping compressor discharge air into the exhaust if exhaust gas temperature becomes excessive during engine acceleration from start to 95 percent RPM.

7) At 95 percent RPM, the governor overrides the acceleration limiter and bypasses fuel to cause a steady state operation at 100 percent RPM.

8) When the generator is turned on, or when air is drawn away from the unit, the governor flyweights will droop in at the top and deliver more fuel to keep the engine on-speed.

9) After takeoff, during climb-out, the auxiliary power unit is generally shut down.

8. Fuel Control Adjustments

Fuel control maintenance on the flight line is usually limited to removal and replacement of the fuel control unit and resetting of the control adjustments. The adjustments include specific gravity, idle RPM and maximum power on hydro-mechanical or hydro-pneumatic controls. On engines with full schedule electronic engine controls, or with FADECs, few if any adjustments are necessary because the system adjusts and compensates on its own.

a. Specific Gravity Adjustment

When a run-up is to be made for gas turbine engine performance checks, the normal fuel prescribed by the manufacturer should be used because the Btu value, as well as specific gravity, may be different in an alternate fuel and the validity of the check could be compromised.

Otherwise a specific gravity adjustment can be made (Figure 7-19A). It is a means of resetting tension on the Differential Pressure Regulating Valve Spring within the fuel control when an alternate fuel is being used and the engine is undergoing performance testing. Refer to Figure 7-8.

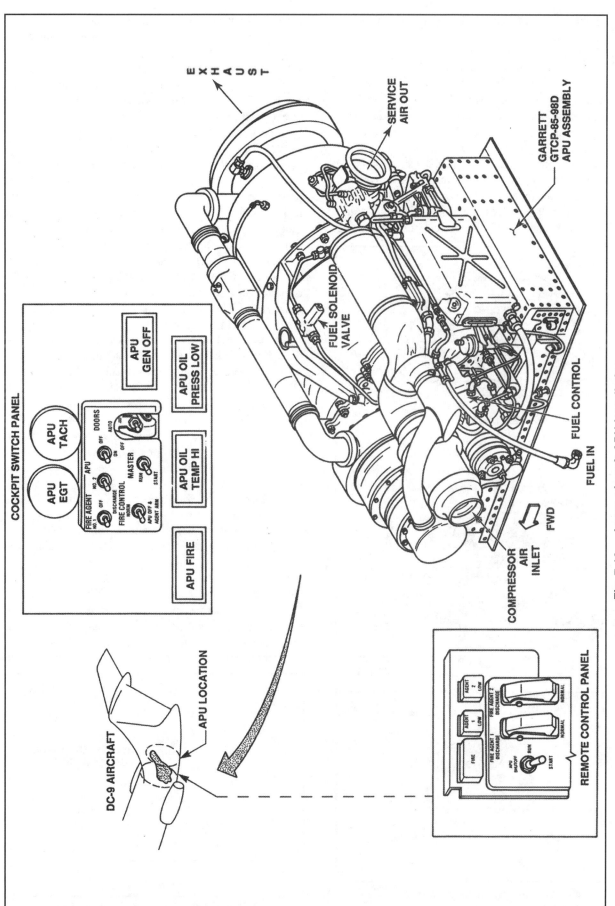

Fig. 7-18 — Large aircraft APU installation.

b. Performance Checks (Turbojet And Turbofan Engines)

1) Trimming (Figure 7-19B)

Trimming is a term applied to idle speed and maximum thrust adjustment during performance testing. Trimming is accomplished with the engine installed in the airplane or with the engine in a test cell. Idle speed adjustment is very similar from one engine to the next in that it sets engine idling speed to the manufacturer's best economy and performance range. Idle speed is used during periods of operation when thrust is not required. Depending on the particular engine, a maximum percent RPM adjustment, or maximum Engine Pressure Ratio (EPR) adjustment assures the correct thrust is being

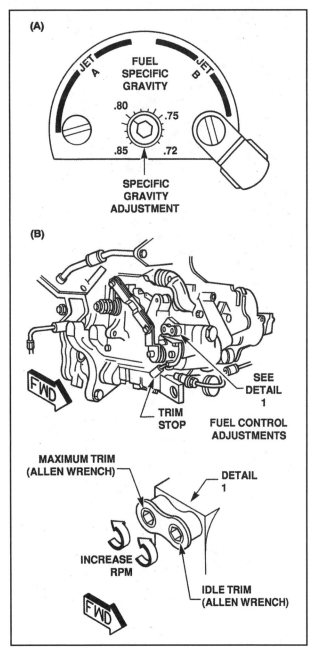

Fig. 7-19A — Specific gravity adjustment.
Fig. 7-19B — Trim adjustment.

produced by the engine. This thrust value is referred to as manufacturer's guaranteed rated thrust, sometimes shortened to rated thrust.

Most manufacturer's recommend that, in order to stabilize cams, springs, and linkages within the fuel control, all final trim adjustments be made in the increase direction. If over adjustment occurs, the procedure would be repeated by decreasing trim to below target values then increase trim back to the desired values.

The trim check is accomplished whenever engine thrust is suspect and after such maintenance tasks as prescribed by the manufacturer. A few of these might include trimming after engine change, module change, or fuel control change. Trimming is otherwise required from time to time due to deterioration of engine performance as engine service time takes its toll. Aircraft linkage systems stretch with age, causing misalignment in the cockpit to engine control systems or loss of cushion in the power lever. This condition may require a trim check.

2) Acceleration Check

In conjunction with the trim procedure, an acceleration check is usually accomplished as an additional test of engine performance. After the trim check is completed, a mark is placed on the cockpit power lever quadrant at the takeoff position. The power lever is then advanced from idle position to takeoff position, and the time is measured against a published tolerance. The time, even for a large gas turbine engine, is quite low, in the range of five to ten seconds (Figure 7-20A).

3) Throttle Spring-back and Cushion Checks (Figure 7-20B)

Another important part of the trim procedure is to check for power lever spring-back and cushion. The operator, before and after the trim run, moves the power lever full forward and releases it. The distance the lever springs back is measured against prescribed tolerances. On an airliner for instance, this distance might measure one-quarter inch or more. When spring-back is correct, the fuel control will reach its internal stops before the cockpit quadrant reaches its forward stop. If out of limits,

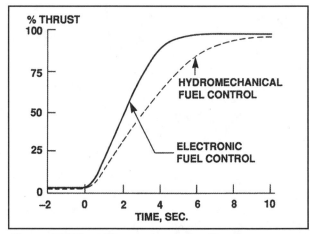

Figure. 7-20A — Thrust vs. acceleration time.

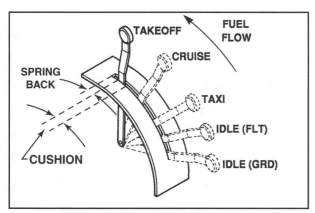

Fig. 7-20B — Spring back and cushion checks.

an adjustment of the aircraft control system which attaches to the fuel control is required by the technician.

Cushion is the distance in inches from the power lever at take-off setting to full power lever travel.

The cushion check insures that the pilot will not only be able to obtain takeoff power but also additional power lever travel in case of emergencies.

c. Part Power Trim

In order to save wear on the engine and also to save fuel, both engine pressure ratio rated engines and speed rated engines are generally trimmed at less than takeoff power. This procedure involves closing all service bleeds to avoid compression loss and placing a physical obstruction in the path of the fuel control lever linkage called a part power trim stop. The power lever is advanced to hit the stop during trimming and the trimming adjustment is made at this position with the engine operating at approximately the "maximum continuous" thrust rating. To stabilize internal fuel control linkages, trim adjustments are made in the increase direction. After trimming, the stop is removed in order to perform a takeoff power check.

d. Two Types Of Trim Procedures—Engine Pressure Ratio Trim And Speed Trim

Thrust producing turbine engines utilize either the engine pressure ratio trim or the fan speed trim procedure. If the engine is configured with an engine pressure ratio system, the pilot will use a cockpit engine pressure ratio gauge to set engine power. In terms of trimming, the engine is referred to as an engine pressure ratio rated engine. If the engine does not have an engine pressure ratio system, it is trimmed in accordance with fan speed and the pilot in this case uses a tachometer indicator to set engine power. In terms of trimming, this engine is referred to as a fan speed rated engine. NOTE: Power checks for turboprop and turboshaft engines are discussed later in this Chapter.

1) Engine Pressure Ratio (EPR)

The aircraft utilizes an engine pressure ratio gauge for thrust indication. This gauge conveniently reads the ratio of turbine discharge pressure divided by compressor inlet pressure and automatically corrects for changing ambient

conditions. The engine pressure ratio system is discussed in more detail later in this chapter and in Chapter XI.

EXAMPLE: If turbine discharge pressure is measured to be 58.2 inches of mercury when the engine is correctly trimmed and engine inlet pressure reads 30.0 inches of mercury, the engine pressure ratio is calculated as follows:

$$EPR = \frac{\text{Turbine Discharge Pressure}}{\text{Compressor Inlet Pressure}} = \frac{58.2}{30.0} = 1.94$$

If the cockpit indicator reads within the accepted tolerance of 1.94, both the engine pressure ratio indicating system and the engine are performing satisfactorily.

2) Trimming Procedure For Engine Pressure Ratio Rated Engines

On many axial flow engines, there exists a better relationship between internal engine pressures and thrust than engine RPM and thrust. In fact, on some dual-spool engines the last ten percent of the RPM range can increase thrust by as much as 30 percent. On these engines, engine pressure ratio is a quicker measure of thrust than by use of RPM/thrust charts.

By turning the maximum trim adjustment (Figure 7-19B), fuel flow and thrust will be increased or decreased. This in turn will affect the relationship between compressor inlet pressure and turbine discharge pressure. That is, as the latter goes up with fuel flow increase, engine pressure ratio will also go up for a given compressor inlet condition.

The trim procedure is as follows:

With finely calibrated gauges, maintenance personnel measure inlet conditions of barometric pressure and ambient temperature before running the engine. They will insert the part power trim stop, and install the necessary fittings to measure turbine discharge pressure. Finally, with the engine running on the part power stop, they will trim the engine to a value prescribed by a manufacturer's graph (Figure 7-21).

Cautions to be observed at this time are: Do not use the temperature given at the control tower; there could be a measurable difference between that reading and the on-site reading. Also, do not use the aircraft Outside Air Temperature (OAT) gauge; it could be heat soaked from the sun and again be significantly different from a thermometer reading taken at the engine. An industry wide procedure is to hang the thermometer in the shade of the nose wheel-well until the temperature stabilizes.

Manufacturers also commonly recommend that two or more accelerations be made to a high power setting to properly pre-load the internal mechanisms within the fuel control and ensure a higher degree of repeatability before the actual acceleration to trim power setting is made.

Figure 7-21 shows a typical engine pressure ratio-rated business jet's part-power engine trim curve. After calculating the necessary turbine discharge for an outside air temperature of 75°F and inlet pressure of 30 inches of mercury, if the engine is not producing 58.20 inches of mercury turbine discharge pressure, maintenance personnel will up-trim the engine to this value.

At that time, maintenance personnel will mathematically compute 58.2 inches of mercury turbine discharge pressure divided by 30.0 inches of mercury compressor inlet pressure, to be an engine pressure ratio of 1.94. The cockpit gauge must at that time read 1.94, plus or minus a typical tolerance value. If it does not, the engine pressure ratio indicating system must be checked.

Note that Figure 7-21 utilizes barometric pressure (Pam) rather than compressor inlet pressure (Pt$_2$). This is common practice because there is no convenient way to

measure Pt$_2$ on most aircraft, and total pressure is only slightly different than ambient pressure. The graph, of course, is corrected for this, and the engine is in actuality trimmed to an engine pressure ratio of Pt$_5$ divided by Pt$_2$.

a) Full Power Check After Trimming

After the part power trim is completed, the part power stop is removed and the power lever is advanced toward the full power Turbine Discharge Pressure value of 67.0 inches of mercury (Figure 7-21). If this value can be achieved without exceeding the limits of engine condition instruments, such as engine speed, exhaust gas temperature, and fuel-flow, the engine full power check is satisfactory. This check is further discussed in the following paragraphs on trimming of speed rated engines.

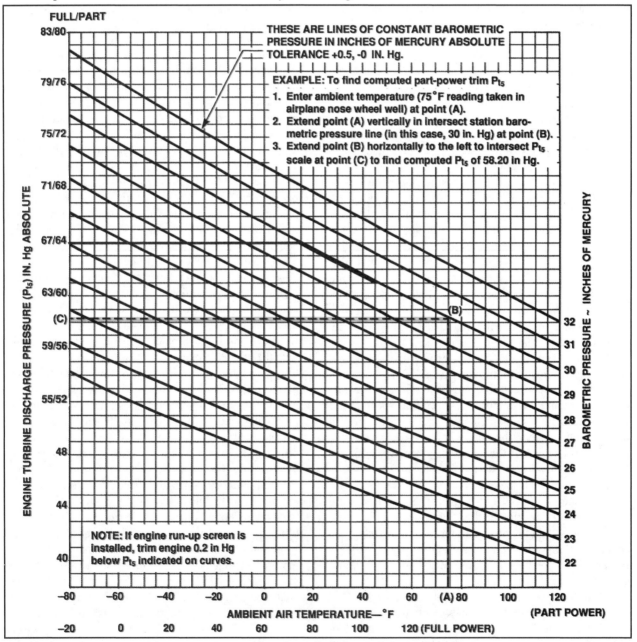

Fig. 7-21 — Part power trim and full power check chart (EPR-rated turbofan engine).

3) Trimming Procedure For Speed-rated Engine

A fan speed trim is generally performed on turbofans of the dual-spool configuration where there exists a direct relationship between fan speed (N_1) and thrust. Counterclockwise rotation of the maximum adjustment (Figure 7-19B) will increase fuel flow to the engine, increase fan speed, and, consequently, engine thrust output. Adjusting the idle set screw will reset idle speed to the manufacturer's recommended percent RPM value. The amount of adjustment will depend on the parameters of an engine performance curve, such as the one in Figure 7-22.

The fan speed trim determination in this case is dependent on ambient temperatures. The example engine is speed rated. That is, its thrust is determined by a comparison to fan speed. High pressure compressor speed, turbine temperature, and other engine operational parameters must fall within an allowable range when rated fan speed is obtained. If they do not, one of two conditions probably exists, a turbo-machinery malfunction or a fuel scheduling malfunction as follows:

a) Dirty compressors and damaged compressors can cause aerodynamic problems. Damaged hot sections can cause thermodynamic problems.

b) Poor fuel scheduling can cause compressor stalls, over temperatures, and flameout.

In order to obtain required thrust, some part of the engine is being over-taxed, and this shows up on one of the condition-monitoring instruments in the cockpit, i.e., RPM, exhaust gas temperature, fuel flow, etc. The cause of the high indicator reading must then be determined by troubleshooting procedures and corrected before the engine is released for service.

To ensure accuracy of readings, many operators utilize a portable precision tachometer slaved into the aircraft percent rpm indicating system. This gives the trim crew personnel an immediate indication of condition of the cockpit instrument and more information with which to completely assess the condition of the engine.

The trim procedure is as follows:

(1) With a precision thermometer reading taken at the aircraft, plot the fan (N_1) speed for the ambient temperature on Figure 7-22.

(2) Deploy trim part power stop;

(3) Run aircraft, advancing power lever until linkage hits trim stop;

(4) Adjust maximum setting and record gauge readings check against manufacturer's limits;

(5) Retract trim stop and advance power lever to N_1 value on Figure 7-23. Check N_2 speed and T_5 to be within limits.

EXAMPLE:

1. With ambient temperature at the aircraft of 65°F, operate the engine with the power lever advanced to the part power stop (Figure 7-24A). The engine should be operating at 83 percent fan (N_1) speed in accordance with Figure 7-22.

2. If the N_1 speed is not 83 percent, a max-trim adjustment must be made.

3. Reduce power and check idle speed to be 50 ± 1 percent.

4. Remove part power stop and advance power lever toward 99 percent, N_1 speed, in accordance with Figure 7-23. Exhaust gas temperature (T_5) must remain under 700°C and the high pressure compressor (N_2) speed must remain under 96 percent; otherwise, do not advance the power lever further. Shut the engine down and perform troubleshooting procedures.

Note that Figure 7-21 is biased for both ambient pressure and ambient temperature, compared to Figure 7-22 that is biased for only ambient temperature. The reason for this is the fuel control used on the engine in question has an acceleration bellows which compensates for changes in ambient pressure (see Figure 7-8).

e. Data Plate Speed Check (Figure 7-24B)

A performance check that is quite often completed along with the trim check is the data plate speed check. On many gas turbine engines a small metal plate is attached at time of manufacture during final performance testing.

The plate is stamped with the engine speed at which required thrust value at part power trim was obtained. No two engines would necessarily be stamped with the same speed because production tolerances of engine parts vary the speed to thrust relationship on nearly every engine in some measurable way. However, all engines produced will probably be within 2 to 3 percent RPM of each other.

The purpose of this check is to compare future engine performance against the "as new" performance data. For example, consider a hypothetical data plate is stamped (87.25 percent N_2 Speed at 1.61 engine pressure ratio, 59°F). As a ground performance check on engine condition when the engine accumulates service time (cycles and hours), the data plate speed check can be accomplished. The procedure in this instance would be to operate the engine at 1.61 engine pressure ratio and observe the N_2 tachometer indication, then, compare that indication to the "as new" speed on the data plate. If the tolerance is (+2.0 percent) and the engine being tested goes to 89.5 percent N_2 speed, the engine is out of limits for the data plate speed check because the limit is 89.25 percent.

This check is an assessment of engine performance and not necessarily a pass or fail type check. If the engine is otherwise performing satisfactorily, the operator might decide to keep the engine in service, even though it is no doubt consuming more fuel to give the required 1.61 engine pressure ratio than when new.

It might also tell the operator that the compressor is contaminated and requires field cleaning or that the hot section is deteriorating and should be scheduled for repair at the next inspection interval. The test run will seldom, if ever, be accomplished on a Standard Day 59°F, so the observed speed on the tachometer indicator will have to

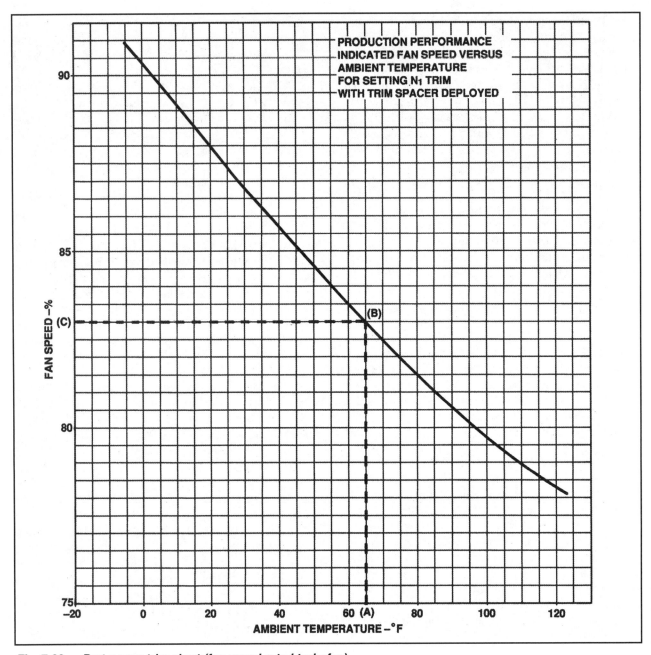

Fig. 7-22 — Part power trim chart (fan speed-rated turbofan).

be corrected as per manufacturers charts before comparison to the data plate speed. (See Chapter V, paragraph H.)

The discussion above described an engine pressure ratio rated engine. But the data plate speed check is equally applicable to the turbofan speed rated engine, or the turboprop engine, which is rated in torque units or horsepower units.

f. Trim Restrictions

There are always ambient condition restrictions on trimming which must be closely followed. Typical wind direction and velocity restrictions are shown in Figure 7-25. Excessive wind in the direction of the tailpipe will cause a false high turbine discharge pressure and subsequent low trim when the wind is later within limits.

Excessive wind in the inlet will cause a false high compression and turbine discharge pressure and a subsequent low trim when wind conditions drop within the limits.

These situations occur as follows:

1) Wind up the tailpipe causes a back pressure and a false high turbine discharge pressure for which the technician would compensate by down-trimming. Then, later, in calm air, turbine discharge pressure would be low and, consequently, engine pressure ratio would be low;

2) Wind into the inlet causes a false high compressor inlet pressure which generally affects compression to a greater degree than it affects the cockpit engine pressure ratio reading.

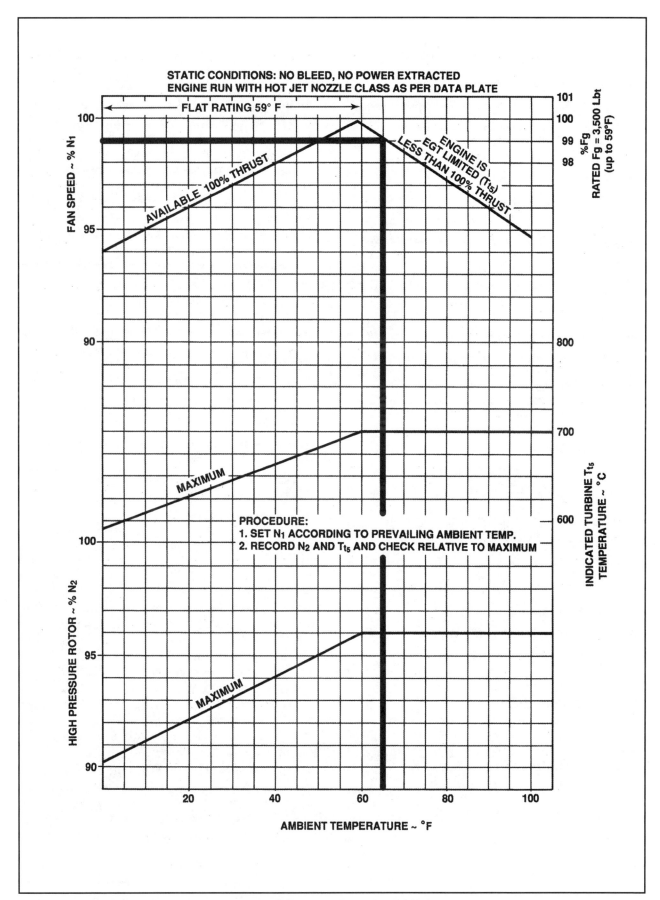

Fig. 7-23 — Full power check chart — sea level (fan speed-rated turbofan).

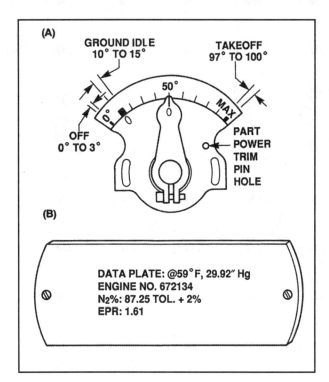

Fig. 7-24A — Power lever protractor —
approximately 90° power lever angle (PLA).
Fig. 7-24B — Data plate example.

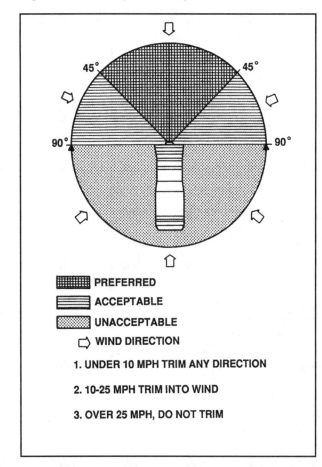

Fig. 7-25 — Wind direction, and velocity limits, Pratt
& Whitney JT12.

The compressor magnifies the false high inlet pressure by increased compression which affects a rise in turbine discharge pressure. This causes what appears to be a higher engine pressure ratio reading or over-trimmed engine. The trim crew will compensate for this by down-trimming and then later in calm air the engine will be under-trimmed. Wind is also seldom steady and, when gusting, it causes erratic gauge readings which make trimming calculations difficult to obtain.

Other trim restrictions such as moisture content (rain) and moisture (icing) will also be found in the aircraft operations manual and must be followed or a false trim will result.

The same restrictions apply to the speed rated engines. Even though the trim instrumentation is not as directly affected, the engine performance will be affected, and an incorrect trim could result.

g. Trim Danger Zones (Figures 7-26 A and B)

An inherent danger to personnel and equipment exists in the area of operating gas turbine engines. All flight line personnel must be constantly alert to keep out of the danger areas when approaching or leaving the proximity of an operating engine. Loose articles of clothing, microphone chords, mechanic wipe rags, tools, etc., must be carefully secured so they will not be ingested by the engine. For maximum safety, use an intercom system between the cockpit and the ground crew to minimize or use hand signals (included in Appendix 5 of this book).

h. Ear Protection From Noise (Figure 7-27)

A large turbojet or turbofan engine operating at full power settings can generate sound levels up to 160 decibels at the aircraft. Smaller engines of all types can generate sound levels up to approximately 130 decibels. This noise intensity is sufficient to cause either temporary or permanent hearing loss if adequate ear protection is not used by ground personnel.

The most effective ear protection device is the muff type, which fits over the entire ear and defends against noise to the ear opening and also to the bone structure behind the ear. Ear plugs provide minimal hearing loss protection and are generally only recommended for use in lower noise areas or for low time exposure to higher noise areas.

The Federal Standard for noise protection is outlined in the Occupational Safety and Health Administration Standard, 36th Federal Register, 105, Section 19-10.95.

i. Flat Rating

Today, most gas turbine engines are characterized as flat-rated. This refers to the flat shape of the full power curve and the point on the ambient temperature scale at which the power starts to drop below 100 percent. Figure 7-28 shows this concept on a fan speed-rated engine. Analysis of the curve will reveal that a fan speed of 96 percent RPM corresponds to 100 percent thrust on this engine, and that this value can be obtained at any ambient temperature up to 90°F. That is, by moving the power lever more and more forward, the pilot can obtain rated

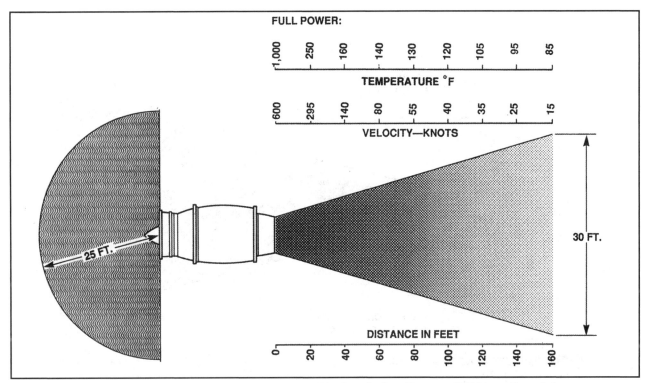

Fig.7-26A — Inlet and exhaust jet wake danger areas, JT15D turbofan (Pratt and Whitney, Canada).

thrust at any temperature up to 90°F. After 90°F, more forward movement of the power lever is not permitted because it most likely will result in an engine over temperature.

When ambient temperature exceeds the flat rating of the engine, 100 percent thrust can no longer be obtained. This being the case, the aircraft's gross weight might need to be adjusted, or, at the very least, runway takeoff roll will increase and the flight crew will need to account for this in their take-off procedures.

Some engines are flat rated to only 59°F, others over 100°F. This consideration depends largely on the needs of the aircraft manufacturer. Generally, flat rating is believed to enable the engine to produce a constant rated thrust over a wide range of ambient temperatures without working the engine harder than necessary, in the interest of prolonging engine service life.

For example, an engine rated at 3,500 pounds thrust at 59°F might be re-rated to 3,350 pounds thrust at 90°F. The aircraft user might not need to utilize 3,500 pounds thrust, nor the maximum gross weight of the aircraft, and he would like to benefit from increased engine service life and lower fuel consumption by operating at 3,350 pounds thrust maximum. Flat rating is an engine manufacturer's way of re-rating an engine to a lower rated thrust than it would have at Standard Day temperature. The engine will be able to use that lower rated thrust over a wider ambient temperature range. Flat-rating is equally applicable to all types of gas turbine engines, both thrust producing engines and torque producing engines. The aircraft manufacturer will

probably use the following process, or one very similar, when selecting the flat-rating that best suits his needs.

1) The user decides the take-off power needed for his aircraft configuration, route requirements, runway lengths, runway altitudes, etc.

2) The user calculates the highest ambient temperature at which required takeoff power can be obtained.

3) The engine and aircraft manufacturer print all of the flight manuals, operational instructions, etc., to reflect the selected takeoff power as the maximum usable for normal operation.

From this example, it can be seen that if an engine is re-rated to a lower power level than it is capable of producing, the engine still retains its full capability of power as a reserve for emergencies. It can also be seen that no mechanical changes are needed to the engine or fuel scheduling system, merely changes in the printed operational data.

j. Turboprop And Turboshaft Engine Performance Checks

Turboprop and turboshaft engines are torque producers rather than thrust producers. Performance calculations of torque producing engines are very different from that of turbofan and turbojet engines which use engine pressure ratio or fan speed as power indicators in the cockpit.

The turboprop and turboshaft aircraft cockpit contains a torque indicator that reads out in either torque (psi) oil pressure, torque (ft.lbs.), or torque (%). The gauge reading is produced most often by either a "phased shift" electronic torquemeter system or a "balanced piston" torquemeter oil system.

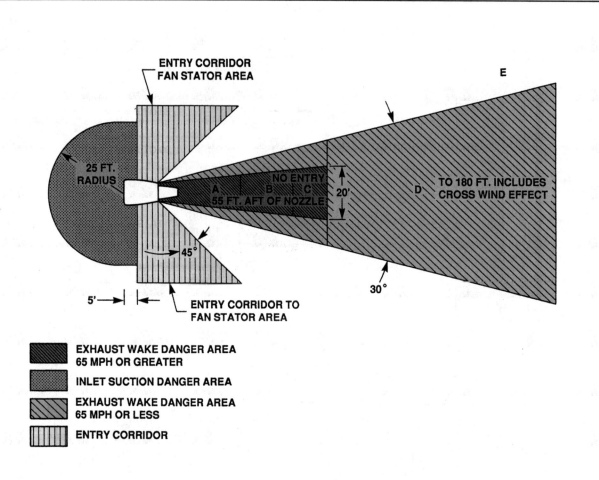

IDLE SPEED:

AREA	APPROX. WIND VELOCITY (MPH)	
A	210 TO 145	A MAN STANDING WILL BE PICKED UP AND THROWN; AIRCRAFT WILL BE COMPLETELY DESTROYED OR DAMAGED BEYOND ECONOMICAL REPAIR; COMPLETE DESTRUCTION OF FRAME OR BRICK HOMES.
B	145 TO 105	A MAN STANDING FACE-ON WILL BE PICKED UP AND THROWN; DAMAGE NEARING TOTAL DESTRUCTION TO LIGHT INDUSTRIAL BUILDINGS OR RIGID STEEL FRAMING; CORRUGATED STEEL STRUCTURES LESS SEVERELY
C	105 TO 65	MODERATE DAMAGE TO LIGHT INDUSTRIAL BUILDINGS AND TRANSPORT-TYPE AIRCRAFT
D	65 TO 20	LIGHT TO MODERATE DAMAGE TO TRANSPORT-TYPE AIRCRAFT
E	20	BEYOND DANGER AREA.

NOTE: AT TAKE-OFF POWER: 700MPH WIND VELOCITY AT AREA "A"

Fig. 7-26B — Inlet and exhaust wake areas, General Electric CF6 High Bypass Turbofan.

ALLOWABLE NOISE EXPOSURE SOUND LEVEL IN dB							
TYPE EAR PROTECTIVE DEVICES	EXPOSURE TIME, HOURS*						
	1/4	1/2	1	2	4	6	8
NO PROTECTION	115	110	105	100	95	92	90
EAR PLUGS WITH AVERAGE SEAL	127	122	117	112	107	104	102
EAR PLUGS AND EARMUFFS	135	130	125	120	115	112	110

*DURATION OF EXPOSURE PER DAY

EAR PROTECTIVE DEVICES

UNIVERSAL FIT EARPLUG	EAR PLUG V-51-R TYPE OR SIMILAR	TYPICAL EARMUFF

Fig. 7-27 — Ear protection guidelines.

Example 1: When a turboprop engine's power output is indicated in the cockpit by a "Torque Gauge" that reads in foot pounds. To the pilot, this is representative of a certain shaft horsepower value. The process by which the foot-pound reading of the cockpit gauge is produced and by which the actual shaft horsepower within the engine is being produced is as follows:

$$\text{Shaft Hp} = \text{Torque (lb. ft.)} \times \text{Rpm} \times K$$

Where:

Torque = A flight deck gauge reading

Rpm = Turbine speed going to prop

K = A derived constant

Recall from Chapter II that: $\text{Power} = \dfrac{\text{Force x Distance}}{\text{Time}}$

$$Hp = \frac{\text{Power (ft. lbs./min.)}}{33,000}$$

Where:

Force = pounds

Distance = feet

Time = minutes

In the previous formula, when Horsepower is applied to a turboprop or turboshaft engine, "time" and "distance" become a function of RPM of the free Power Turbine, and "force" is the turning force called torque. Torque is measured in pound-feet, and is created as a result of a force of one pound acting through a moment arm, or radius, of one foot. Torque is often expressed in units of foot-pounds, but the correct units are pound-feet.

The Power Turbine generates power to drive the propeller through a reduction gearbox. As an example,

the PT6A-34 power turbine speed is 33,000 RPM at rated power and its propeller reduction gearbox has a 15:1 ratio. This results in a 2,200 RPM drive shaft speed at the propeller. The torque produced when the propeller is under load is therefore an indication of the engine shaft horsepower being produced.

The torque (T) produced by the Power Turbine in the illustration (Figure 7-29) is the force developed in the plane of the turbine rotor times the moment arm (radius). As a formula, it would be expressed as follows:

Torque = Force x Moment Arm

To calculate horsepower, the Torque, RPM, and Distance around the mean circumference of the rotor blades is used. This is the distance through which the force acts during each revolution of the turbine wheel (Figure 7-29).

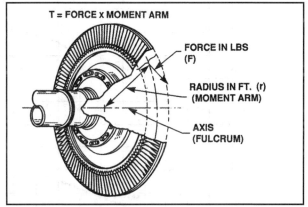

Fig. 7-29 — Power turbine torque, moment arm and force.

The force value "F" can be arrived at by direct measurement during factory testing or by calculations involving British thermal units of fuel energy available at the power turbine. One British thermal unit equals 778 foot pounds of work. For our discussion here, we will merely use the term "F" for force and will not actually work out its value because that will be done automatically within the engine by the torque meter and the gauge in the cockpit which reads out in pound-feet (or foot-pounds).

Example 2: To calculate shaft horsepower, we can proceed by changing Time and Distance in the horsepower formula to RPM multiplied by circumference, as follows:

$$Hp = \frac{F \times Np \times 2\pi r}{33,000}$$

Where:

F = Force in lbs.

Np = Propeller Rpm

r = Mean radius in feet

33,000 = Conversion to Hp

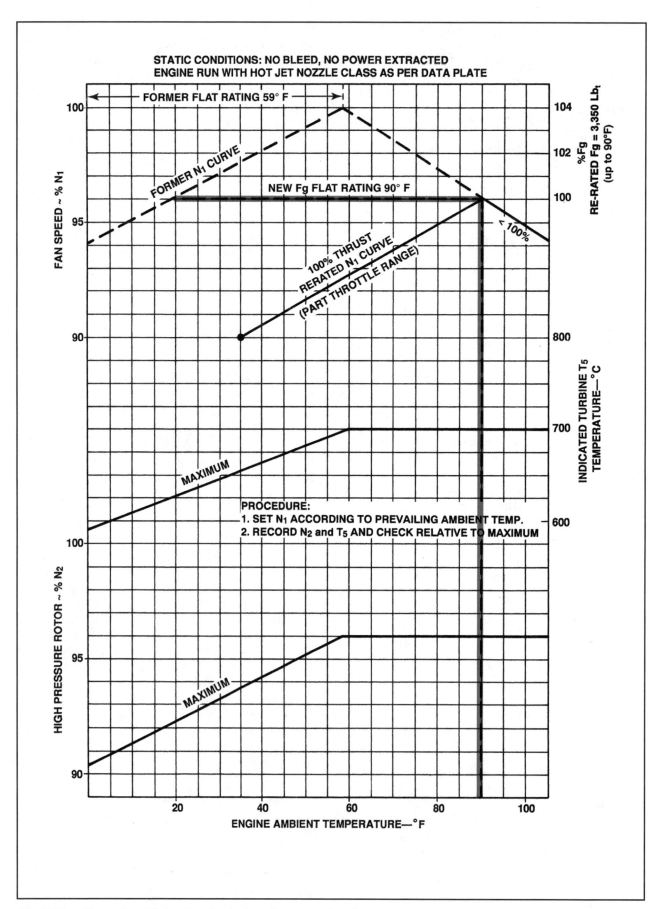

Fig. 7-28 — Example of flat rating (typical engine at sea level).

The horsepower formula shown in previous example can be rearranged as follows:

$$Hp = \frac{(F \times r) \times Np \times 2\pi}{33,000}$$

$$Hp = \frac{Torque \times Np \times 2\pi}{33,000}$$

$$Hp = \frac{Torque \times Rpm}{5252}$$

Where:

F = Force in lbs.
Np = Propeller Rpm
r = Mean radius in feet
33,000 = Conversion to Hp
Torque = F × r
$\frac{1}{5252}$ = 2π ÷ 33,000

The formula shows that the actual shaft horsepower that the engine is producing can be obtained by the use of the cockpit torque gauge reading in pound-feet and the prop RPM gauge. The torque reading may be in pounds per square inch (psi) and must be converted to pound-feet by a math conversion. The prop RPM reading may be in percent RPM, and must be converted to actual RPM.

k. Converting Torque (psi) To Torque In Pound-Feet

If the gauge on the flight deck shows the engine torque as a psi value, this can be converted to a pound-feet value by using a conversion factor. Each engine and model will use a different conversion factor. The Pratt and Whitney PT6A-34 turboprop, for example, uses a conversion of 30.57 when the engine is at 100% RPM. The formula would be as follows:

Torque (pound-feet) = Torque Psi x 30.57

EXAMPLE: If the torque gauge on the flight deck of a PT6A-34 powered airplane shows a value of 42.05 psi, what would be the engine's torque in pound-feet?

Torque lbs. ft. = 42.05 x 30.37
Torque lbs. ft. = 1,285

l. Converting Percent RPM To Actual Revolutions Per Minute

With regard to actual revolutions per minute and percent RPM, if 100 percent is equal to 2,200 revolutions of the propeller per minute, then a gauge reading of 98% would represent 98% of 2,200. As a formula, the relationship would be expressed as follows:

Actual RPM = % RPM (100% value)

m. Calculating Torque Pound-Feet From Take-Off Graph

Using a typical takeoff Power Setting curve (Figure 7-30), when the ambient temperature is 77°F and the field barometric pressure is 29.92 inches of mercury, the takeoff torque value is 1,285 pound-feet.

The operator will start the engine and accelerate to this value for takeoff or during a maintenance power check. The operator will also ensure that, when obtaining the correct takeoff power, all of the other gauges in the cockpit pertaining to engine conditions are reading satisfactorily. This being the case, it indicates that the engine is performing as designed and is airworthy in terms of this check.

n. Computing Shaft Horsepower From Cockpit Reading

From the previous example, the Shaft Horsepower can now be computed if the RPM of the propeller (Np) is known. In this instance, all of the PT6 turboprop engines that drive propellers through reduction gearing use 2,200 RPM as 100 percent Np speed.

EXAMPLE:

$$Shp = \frac{Torque \times Np}{5252}$$

$$Shp = \frac{1,285 \times 2,200}{5252}$$

$$Shp = 537$$

After cruise RPM is set, the propeller governor and fuel control will keep the power turbine (N_2) on speed even though ambient conditions and load conditions change at the propeller and engine. Fuel flow will be varied and N_1 speed will vary by action of sensors within the prop and fuel scheduling systems, but the power turbine, and thus propeller speed, will be held constant.

The torque and the resulting shaft horsepower will vary with the load applied, in accordance with Newton's first law which states: "Objects at rest tend to remain at rest, (resisting increase in motion). Objects in motion tend to remain in motion, (resisting decrease in motion)." If, for instance, flight conditions cause an increase in fuel flow and N_1 speed, the N_2 speed will try to increase; but, the propeller governor will select a higher blade angle, and the propeller will stay on-speed. The increase in blade angle will create more resistance to movement, and torque and shaft horsepower will increase in the absence of an RPM change.

C. Water Injection Thrust Augmentation

1. Principles Of Operation

Some gas turbine engines require the use of a water injection type, power augmentation system, particularly when operating under high ambient temperatures or high altitude runway conditions. Water, in a fine spray, is introduced into the compressor inlet, the combustion inlet, or both in an attempt to recover lagging thrust created by these poor ambient conditions (Figure 7-31).

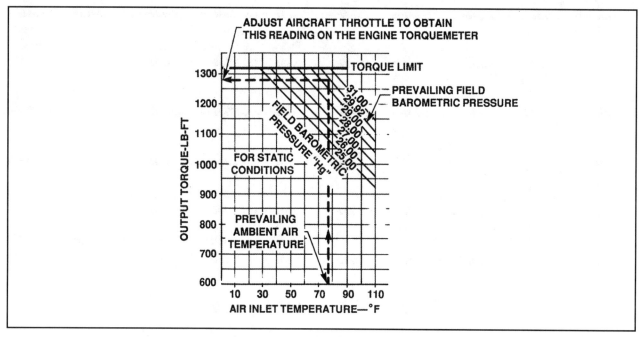

Fig. 7-30 — *Typical takeoff power setting chart for turboprop engine.*

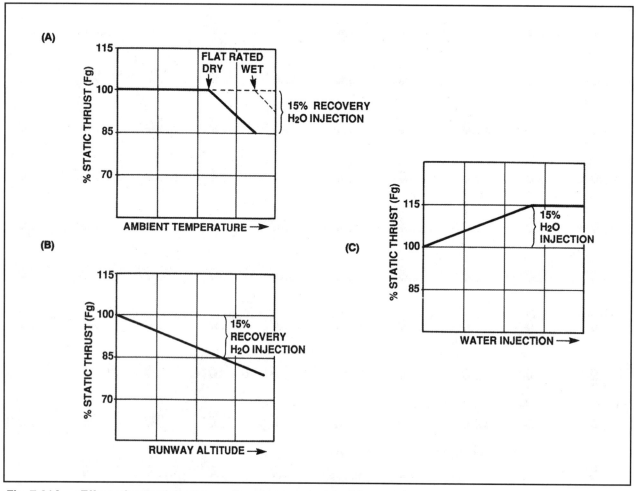

Fig. 7-31A — *Effect of water injection on thrust versus ambient temperature.*
Fig. 7-31B — *Effect of water injection on thrust versus runway altitude.*
Fig. 7-31C — *Added thrust with water injection.*

The principle of latent heat of vaporization applies to the water injection process in the gas turbine engine; that is, injection of fluid into the gas path causes a heat transfer. When the fluid evaporates, heat in the air will be transferred into the fluid droplets, cooling the air and making the gas flow more dense. When water is vaporized within the engine, it absorbs heat from the air at the rate of approximately 1000 British thermal units per pound of water.

Water injection in a gas turbine engine is then a means of augmenting engine thrust. Augmentation can be thought of as occurring in two ways. First, addition of water to air in the compressor increases compression and mass flow. Second, water cools the combustion gases which allows additional fuel to be used without exceeding maximum temperature limits during takeoff. Increases in these three engine parameters results in a thrust increase in the range of 10 to 15 per cent.

Inlet water injection is designed for use at ambient temperature above 40°F. Below this temperature, icing is likely to occur in the water injection system and in the engine inlet. There is no temperature restriction concerning combustor inlet water injection.

When the latent heat of evaporation principle is applied here, it is apparent the compressor inlet temperatures will be lowered during water injection. Water injection is only used at takeoff power settings because the combination of cooling effect of high velocity airflow and absorption of heat by water molecules sets up conditions for icing well above 32°F ambient.

When the temperature approaches 40°F and water injection is required, heated water is serviced into the aircraft tanks. The tanks are also configured with heating elements to keep the water at the required temperature until use. A more detailed discussion of this icing phenomena can be found in Chapter IX.

2. Water Injection Fluids

Pure demineralized or distilled water is the most common water injection fluid. Ordinary tap water is not used because it has high mineral solid content which can cause severe turbine distress when the minerals impinge on the turbine blades. Pure water is also widely used because it produces a greater cooling effect than a mixture of water and methyl or ethyl alcohol. Airliners can take advantage of this and not worry about altitude freeze up by using the complete supply of water at takeoff. Aircraft, such as helicopters and turboprops, which make frequent takeoffs and landings, are forced to use a water-alcohol mixture to protect against freeze up.

Typical fluid properties are as follows:

a. Demineralized water or distilled water must have less than 10 parts per million (ppm) of solids.

b. Methyl/ethyl mixtures will generally be a blend of 35 to 50 percent alcohol in either demineralized or distilled water.

The following table shows the heat absorption or vaporization effect of the most common injection fluids.

Fluid Type	BTU/lb. Absorbed	Temp.	Heating Value BTU/lb.
Water	970	212°F	0
Methyl alcohol	481	148°F	9,000 approx.
Ethyl alcohol	396	173°F	12,000 approx.

Even though water does not contain the heating value of alcohol, it has been determined that because of its heat absorption capability, more thrust can be obtained by injecting a given volume of water into the engine than an equal mixture of water and alcohol. Another way to think about this is that, although alcohol can be used as fuel after it is used as a coolant, the thrust augmentation factor per unit volume in a water/alcohol mixture is less than that of pure water.

3. Water Injection Systems

Not many large aircraft today use water injection because the modern turbofan engine generally has enough thrust capability to offset the negative effect that high ambient temperatures and high runway altitudes have on thrust. Many commuter-sized and other smaller aircraft, however, do need water injection to meet performance requirements. An advantage here is that, when the water is all used, the aircraft is lighter. If a larger engine were to be used, the added engine and subsequent aircraft weight would still be present.

a. Water Injection System (Large Engine)

Since available thrust quite often determines allowable aircraft takeoff weight, water injection is used almost exclusively at takeoff power settings. For instance, the Boeing 707 and DC-8 aircraft carry approximately 300 gallons of water injection fluid per engine, using up the entire supply in a three minute takeoff and climb. This would equal an air-water ratio of approximately 12 to 1, based on a mass airflow of 160 pounds per second and a water injection rate of 100 gallons per minute (13.6 lb./sec.).

In terms of fuel flow, this engine has a takeoff fuel flow of 9,000 pounds per hour (22 gallons per minute). Therefore, with a 100 gallons per minute water flow, a 4.5:1 water to fuel ratio exists.

A typical water injection system is shown in Figure 7-32. Notice that it contains two independent injection nozzles, one to spray water into the compressor inlet and the other to spray into the diffuser/combustor area. Compressor injection increases mass air flow and also cools the combustion air-fuel mixture, allowing increased fuel flow. The addition of fuel increases acceleration of gases exiting the tailpipe. Both of these factors increase the thrust output of the engine.

In the system shown, full thrust augmentation, when required, will necessitate the use of both compressor and diffuser injection. In other installations it is common to see injection at only one location, either the compressor

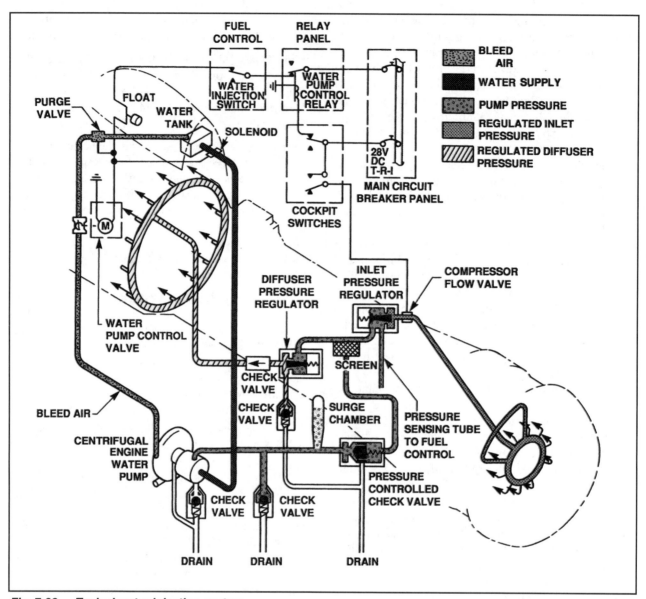

Fig. 7-32 — Typical water injection system.

or diffuser. Although diffuser injection alone will be less effective for a given water flow rate.

When the ambient temperature is low, only the diffuser injection system can be used. Below 40°F, at takeoff revolutions per minute, there is a danger of ice formation. At low ambient temperatures, thrust is usually high enough without water injection for almost any aircraft gross takeoff weight.

This water-injection system is controlled by a cockpit switch which arms the circuit and makes flow into both manifolds possible. When closed, the cockpit switch allows electrical current to flow to the fuel control microswitch. As the power lever reaches takeoff power, the microswitch is depressed and the water pump valve will be powered to open. This allows compressor bleed air to flow through the air-driven water pump, which supplies water under a pressure of 200 to 300 pounds per square inch—gauge to the dual manifold.

If compressor flow is not needed, a cockpit switch deactivates the flow valve. The pressure sensing tube to the fuel control is present to alert the control to reset fuel flow higher when water is flowing. This system is not generally needed if water/alcohol is used because combustion of the alcohol keeps turbine inlet temperature at its required value.

A tank float level circuit will cut off power to the pump when the tank is empty and will also prevent the system from operating if the circuit is activated when the water supply is low or unserviced. When the water injection system is not in use, the check valve at the diffuser prevents high temperature air from backing up into the water system.

Drains are present to drain the lines when the system is not in use, preventing freeze-up. The surge chambers are present to alleviate water pressure peaks by providing an air cushioning effect to the system. A bleed air system allows the pilot, in some installations, to purge the system of water after terminating water injection. In this system it will occur automatically when the water supply is depleted, and the water pump control valve redirects bleed air through the purge valve.

b. Water Injection System (Small Engine)

In the system shown in Figure 7-33, only compressor inlet injection is utilized, and compressor discharge air pressure is used as the motive force for pumping the fluid to the engine. The water line restrictor shown creates a predictable pressure drop and establishes the correct water schedule at takeoff power setting. System water flow is between 1.2 and 1.3 gallons per minute at a discharge pressure of approximately 40 pounds per square inch gauge. The duration time for this system is three minutes.

In the example schematic, the following sequence of events occur when selecting water injection:

1) Push in Warning Light circuit breaker. Water/Alcohol Low Level light will not illuminate because the circuit is open at the System Switch;

2) Push in System circuit breaker. Circuit is open at the System Switch;

3) Turn on System Switch;

• Low Fluid Warning Relay coil circuit is completed to Low Level Float switch;

• Low Fluid Warning Relay coil is energized and contactors move down if water/alcohol tank is serviced to cause the float switch to be closed;

• Circuit is now open to Water/Alcohol Low Level Light. This light will only illuminate if fluid level is low in the tank, keeping the warning relay contractor closed;

• Injection Switch is powered but circuit is open;

• Water/Alcohol Injection Light is powered but circuit is open at the Pressure Switch;

4) Turn on Injection Switch;

• Solenoid Valve opens and water flows to engine;

• Pressure Switch expands to complete Water/Alcohol Injection Light circuit through the Differential Pressure Switch. Equal pressure on both sides of the diaphragm results in contactor closing;

• Water/Alcohol Injection Light illuminates to show "Normal" water flow condition exists. The light will not illuminate if the water tank is not pressurized correctly due to system air leak, loose filler cap, etc., because weak air pressure on the contactor side of the diaphragm will allow contactor to open. This is a safety feature because low air pressure could result in a low Water/Alcohol flow and could cause low engine power to result;

• Low water level in the fluid tank will cause Water/Alcohol Low Level Light to illuminate. When tank has 30 seconds of water remaining, the float contactor will open, de-energizing the low fluid warning relay;

• Water/Alcohol Injection Light will go out when the tank is empty and contactor side of the Differential Pressure Switch diaphragm experiences a pressure drop in excess of 4.5 to 7.0 pressure per square inch—differential; as would occure with a poor seal or a loose filler cap.

• Loss of water pressure will also cause the Pressure Switch to open the circuit to Water/Alcohol Injection Light;

5) Turn off Injection Switch;

For normal termination of water injection with some water remaining in the tank, turning off the Injection Switch will cause the Solenoid valve to close and the Pressure Switch to open the Water/Alcohol Injection light circuit.

In reference to Figure 7-34, at standard conditions, an engine of this type will produce 310 shaft horsepower dry and 335 shaft horsepower wet. This engine would also be capable of attaining its dry rated power of 310 shaft horsepower, in water injection, up to 95° F.

D. FAA Engine Power Ratings

Refer to Chapter XIV for FAA approved power ratings of take off, maximum continuous, maximum cruise, etc.

E. Fuel System Components And Accessories

1. Main Fuel Pump

The main fuel pump is an engine driven component. As such, when the engine speeds up, the pump also speeds up and delivers more fuel. The pump is designed to deliver a continuous supply of fuel to the fuel control at a quantity which is in excess of engine needs. After metering the required amount of fuel to the combustor, the fuel control returns the surplus fuel to the pump inlet via the differential pressure regulating valve. See Figure 7-4B.

Main fuel pumps are self-lubricating, are generally spur-gear types with single or dual elements, and often include a centrifugal boost element. The gear pump is classed as a positive displacement type because it delivers a fixed quantity of fluid per revolution. In this respect, it is very similar to a gear-type oil pump.

In a few cases, the main fuel pump is a sliding vane type, but this is not common. A typical positive displacement pump is shown in Figure 7-35A. The boost element is geared to produce the required inlet pressure to the dual high pressure gear elements. Dual primary and secondary elements, with shear sections on the drive shaft, are designed so that, if one section fails, the other will continue to function and provide sufficient fuel for cruise and landing operation. Both elements have the same flow capacity.

Check valves are present in the outlet to prevent fuel re-circulation into an inoperative element, and a further loss of fuel to the fuel control. A relief valve is incorporated to provide protection to the fuel system if overspeeding or restrictions cause high pressures.

Pumps of this type produce the high pressure needed for atomization of fuel in the combustor. Many large gear pumps can produce up to 1,500 pounds per square inch and a volume up to 30,000 pounds per hour.

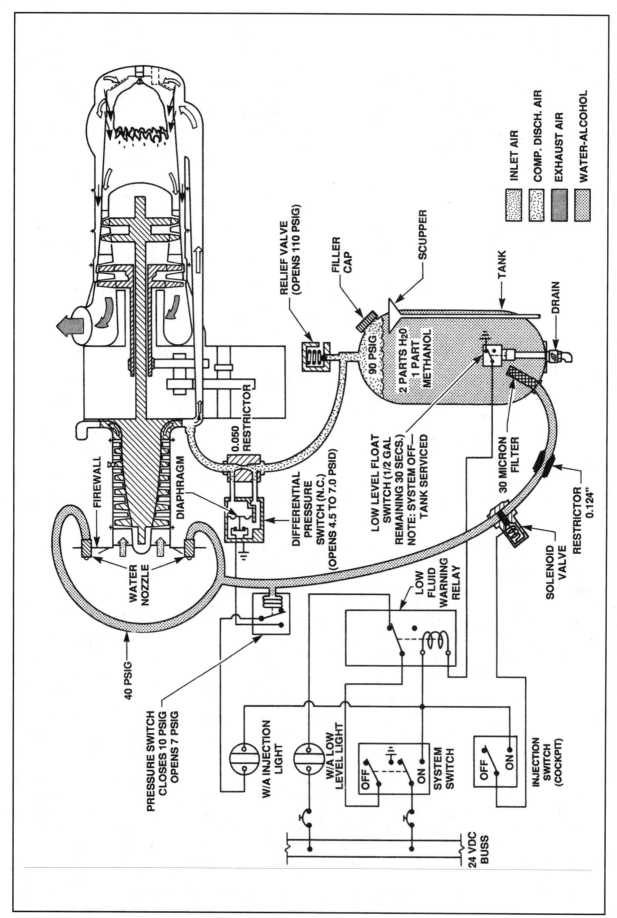

Fig. 7-33 — *Small engine water-alcohol injection system, Allison 250 Turboshaft.*

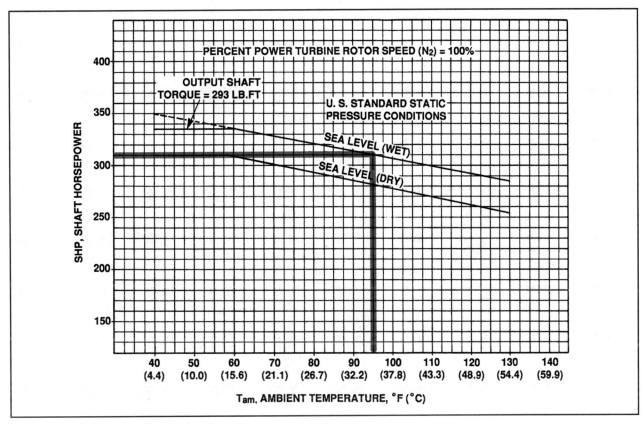

Fig. 7-34 — Effect of water-alcohol injection on shaft horsepower.

On some engines the fuel pump provides a mounting base for the fuel control (Figure 7-35B), on others the fuel pump is not a separate unit at all but rather the pump housing is integral in the base of the fuel control (Figure 7-36).

In another pump illustration (Figure 7-37), a coarse screen, low pressure fuel filter is added to the head end of the pump. In this pump, fuel enters the boost impeller stage and is directed to the outer portion of the low pressure filter bowl. From there it flows into the core of the filtering element, through an external line and into the bypass and boost cavity inlet of the main gear pump (A). The bypass referred to here is the fuel control differential bypass regulator valve return line. After the fuel leaves the pump outlet it will pass through a fine mesh filter and to the fuel control.

2. Fuel Heater (De-Icer) (Figure 7-38)

Some engines use only the lubrication system oil cooler for heat transfer to the fuel, while others incorporate a separate fuel heater. The fuel-oil cooler or fuel heater is often positioned between the engine fuel boost pump and the engine main fuel pump filter inlet to prevent icing of the filter screen. (Refer to Figures 7-53 and 7-54)

Fuel heat is supplied to prevent ice crystal formation by entrained water in the fuel supply. When ice forms, fuel filter clogging occurs, which can cause the filter to bypass. This condition allows unfiltered fuel to flow to

downstream components. In severe cases, icing can cause flow interruption and engine flameout as ice re-forms in components downstream of the filter.

On engines where icing presents critical operational problems, a differential pressure switch is often installed in the fuel filter outlet line. If the filter ices over, a resulting pressure drop will cause a warning light to illuminate in the cockpit. Refer to Figure 7-41.

Fuel heat is designed to be used when the fuel temperature approaches 32°F. Fuel heat is either automatically activated three to five degrees Fahrenheit above the freezing point of water, or it is selected by a toggle switch in the cockpit, as shown in Figure 7-38. In this system, fuel on its way to the engine low pressure filter passes through the cores of the heater assembly. When the solenoid switch is open, it allows bleed air to pass through the air shut-off valve and over the cores to warm the fuel.

a. Typical operational restrictions of fuel heat are as follows:

1) Operate for one minute prior to takeoff. Note: excessive heating can cause vapor lock or heat damage to fuel control.

2) Operate as needed should fuel filter bypass light illuminate.

3) Do not operate during takeoff, approach, or go around because of the flameout possibilities from vaporization during these critical flight regimes.

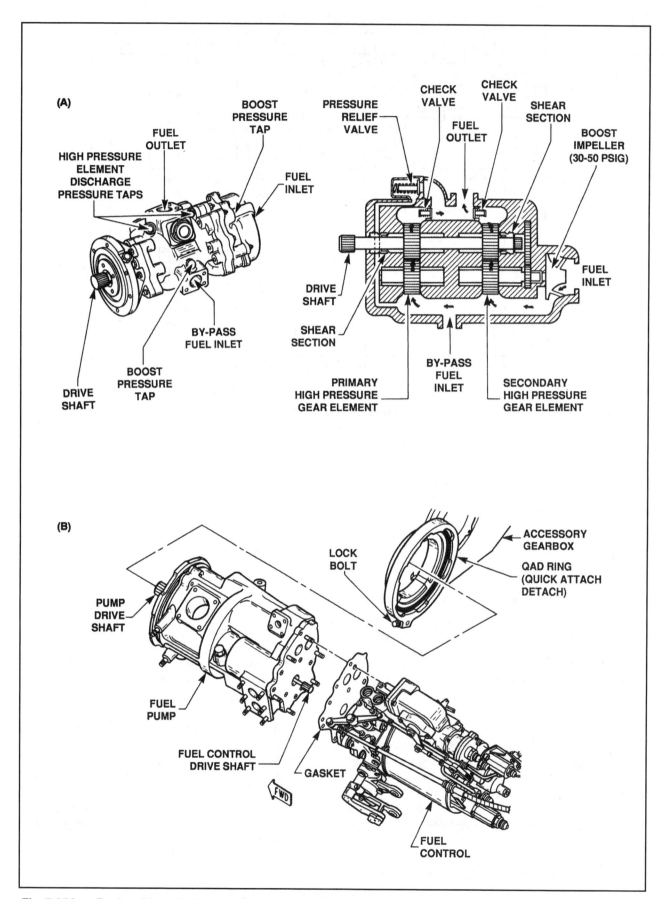

Fig. 7-35A — Engine-driven fuel pump, dual element with boost stage.
Fig. 7-35B — Engine-driven fuel pump with fuel control in tandem.

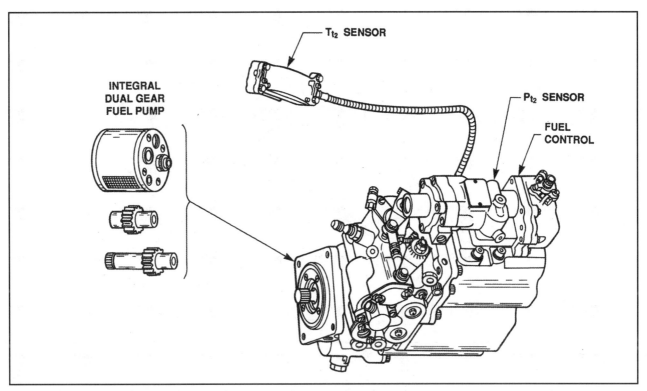

Fig. 7-36 — Small engine combination fuel pump and fuel control.

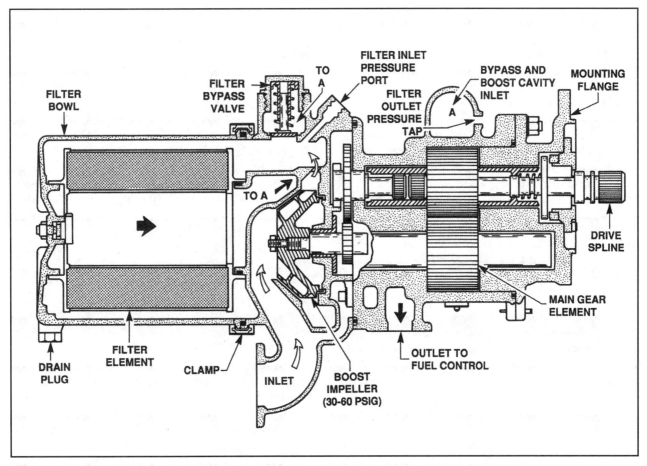

Fig. 7-37 — Engine-driven fuel pump, single element with low pressure filter.

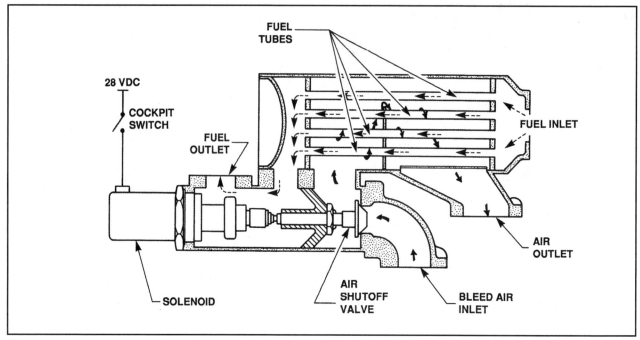

Fig. 7-38 — Fuel heater.

b. On some installations, the cycle time is automatically controlled by an electric timer and gate valve arrangement. To check on the operation, as the system cycles on, the operator can observe cockpit indications such as engine pressure ratio, oil temperature, and the fuel filter light as follows:

1) Engine Pressure Ratio will usually drop a slight but noticeable amount, due to compression loss as bleed air flows;

2) Oil temperature will usually rise slightly as fuel temperature rises within the oil cooler;

3) If a filter bypass light is illuminated due to filter icing, the light should extinguish as the fuel heat system cycles on and ice dissipates.

NOTE: If the fuel bypass light remains on, the operator would suspect a solid contamination at the fuel filter rather than icing.

In some aircraft, a separate fuel heat system is not installed because the fuel-oil cooler, plus additives in the fuel, gives sufficient protection against fuel icing. If an air-oil cooler is used in place of a fuel-oil cooler, a fuel heat system is generally used.

3. Fuel Filters

Two levels of filtration are generally required in turbine engine fuel systems. A low pressure, coarse-mesh filter is installed between the supply tank and the engine, and a fine-mesh filter between the fuel pump and the fuel control. The fine filter is necessary because the fuel control is a device with many minute passageways and fine tolerances.

Filters for this application have a micronic rating of 10 to 500 microns, depending on the amount of contamination protection needed. A micron is a metric

linear measurement of one millionth of a meter, equal to 39.4/1,000,000 of an inch (39.4 millionths of an inch).

Several varieties of filtering elements are used in fuel systems. The most common are: The wafer screen, the steel mesh pleated screen, the steel mesh cylindrical screen, and the cellulose fiber. The cellulose fiber filter has an equivalent micron rating. By way of explanation, a 35 micron filter of the wafer screen type will have square openings with a size of 35 microns (side to side) and will prevent particles larger than 35 microns in diameter from passing through to the system. The cellulose element with its over-lapping fiber design will filter out particles relatively the same size.

Fuel filter checks are frequent inspection card items for the maintenance personnel. If water or metal contaminants are present in the filter element or in the filter bowl, the source of the problem must be determined before returning the aircraft to service.

In Figure 7-39A, a wafer screen, bowl type filter is illustrated containing a bypass valve. This bypass valve will open at 12 pounds per square inch differential. In other words, it will open if the downstream pressure is less than the upstream pressure by 12 pounds per square inch, as would occur if the filter starts to accumulate ice crystals or solid contaminants.

In Figure 7-39B, notice that one filter contains two elements. The pleated mesh element filters main system fuel on its way to the combustor and has a filtration rating of 40 microns. A bypass valve relieves at 32 pounds per square inch differential if this element clogs. The cylindrical mesh element is rated at 10 microns and filters fuel being routed to the fuel control. The minimal flow in this part of the fuel system permits the use of a

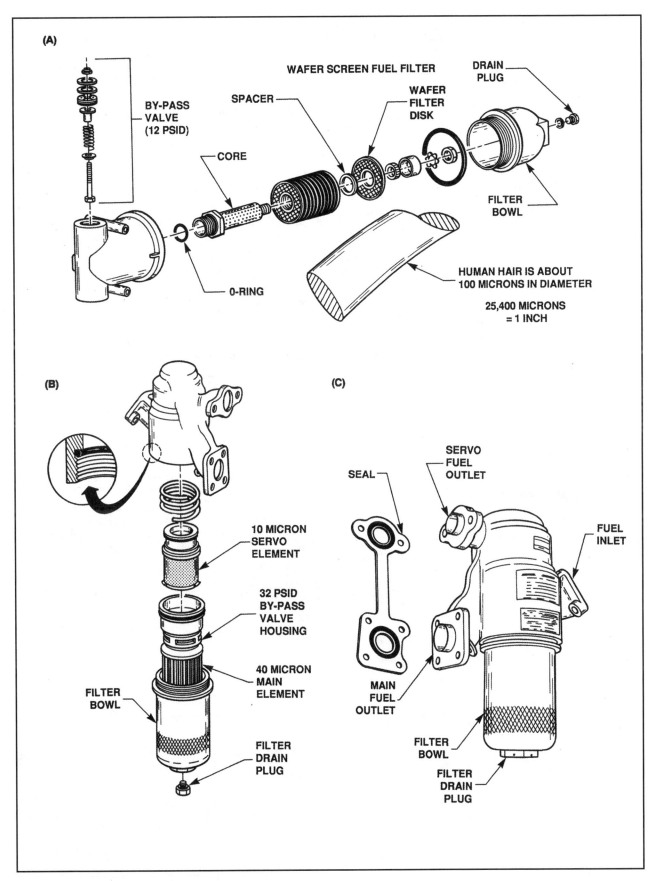

Fig. 7-39A — Cleanable wafer screen fuel filter.
Fig. 7-39B — Dual cleanable steel mesh and pleated filter, exploded view.
Fig. 7-39C — Dual cleanable steel mesh filter, assembled.

very fine filter. This fine filter is needed to protect the highly machined parts of the fuel control, and protect against clogging of the numerous small fluid passageways.

a. Fuel Filter Warning Switches (Bypass And Low Pressure)

Fuel filters have warning systems similar to those found in oil systems. In Figures 7-40 and 7-41, the differential pressure switch is present to detect a partial blockage of the filter screen and indicate that an impending bypass condition exists by illuminating an Impending Bypass warning light in the cockpit.

If the filter continues to clog and fuel boost pressure becomes low enough to actuate the low pressure switch at the outlet of the filter, a Low Fuel Pressure warning light will come on in the cockpit indicating a filter bypass condition exists. The operator will try to clear the blockage with fuel heat, and, if unsuccessful, he will most likely reduce power to what he feels is a safe level, or he may elect to shut down the engine.

In the illustration also notice the fuel temperature transmitter. It is placed in the filter outlet to send an impulse to a cockpit temperature gauge. If the gauge reading drops close to 32°F, the pilot will turn on fuel heat to prevent ice formation on the surface of the filtering element in the event that there is a high level of water entrained in the fuel.

b. Micron Rating Versus Mesh Size

Some fuel filters, rather than having a micron rating, are described in technical literature as having a U.S. sieve number, also called mesh number. An analysis of the screen size chart of common filter sizes will show that there is a relationship between a micron rating and the mesh openings per linear inch. The mesh size is very close to, or in some cases exactly the same as, the U.S. sieve number. For example, a 44 micron filter indicates that the opening size or the square mesh is 44 microns in diameter, or in English measurement equivalents, 0.0017 inches. Also, there are 323 square meshes per linear inch.

The difference in the two ratings then, is that the micron rating deals with the diameter of the filter screen openings and the U.S. sieve number deals with the number of openings per linear inch.

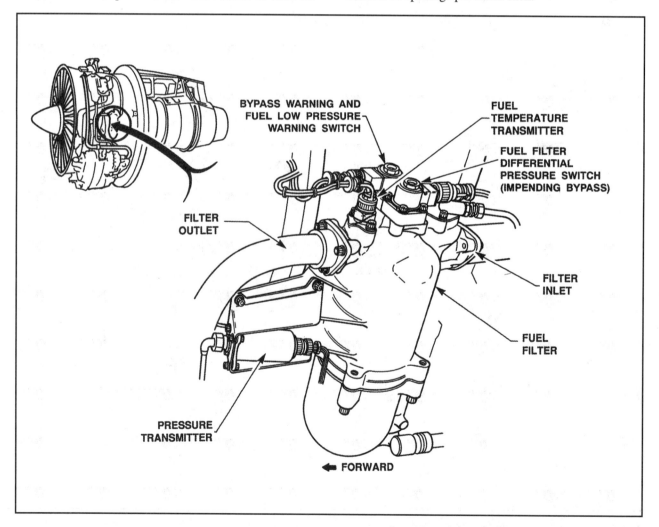

Fig. 7-40 — Typical fuel filter installation with warning switches — large engine.

SCREEN SIZE CHART

Opening in Microns	US Sieve #	Opening in Inches	Meshes per Linear Inch
10	—	.00039	1407.94
20	—	.00078	768.07
44	323	.0017	323.00
53	270	.0021	270.26
74	200	.0029	200.00
105	140	.0041	140.86
149	100	.0059	101.01
210	70	.0083	72.45
297	50	.017	52.36

4. Fuel Nozzles

Fuel nozzles, also called fuel distributors, are the terminating point of the fuel system. They are located in the inlet of the combustion liner to deliver fuel in a defined quantity. Fuel cannot be burned in a liquid state. It must first be mixed with air in correct proportions by atomization or vaporization.

a. Fuel Nozzles (Pressure-Atomizing Type)

The pressure-atomizing type of nozzle receives fuel under high pressure from a manifold and delivers it to the combustor in a highly atomized, precisely patterned spray. The cone shaped, atomized spray pattern provides a large fuel surface area of very fine fuel droplets. This optimizes fuel-air mixing and ensures the highest heat release from the fuel. The most desirable flame pattern occurs at higher compressor pressure ratios.

Consequently, during starting and other off-design speeds, the lack of compression allows the flame length to increase.

If the spray pattern is also slightly distorted, the flame, rather than being held centered in the liner, can touch the liner surface and cause a hot spot, or even burn through. Another problem that distorts the spray pattern is contaminant particles within the nozzle, or carbon buildup outside the nozzle orifice. This can cause hot streaking, which is an un-atomized stream of fuel which forms and tends to cut through the cooling air blanket and impinge on the liner or on downstream components such as the turbine nozzle (Figure 7-42).

Fuel pressures sufficient for good atomization are very high. Small to medium sized engines will have a fuel pressure at the fuel nozzle of 800 to 900 pounds per square inch—gauge and large engines up to 1,500 pounds per square inch—gauge.

Some fuel nozzles are mounted on pads external to the engine to facilitate removal for inspection. Others are mounted internally and are only accessible when the combustion outer case is removed. The duplex nozzle shown in Figure 7-44 is an externally mounted design. The duplex nozzle shown in Figure 7-45 is an integrally-mounted type.

b. Simplex Fuel Nozzles

The simplex design is basically a small round orifice which provides a single spray pattern and incorporates an internally fluted spin chamber to impart a swirling

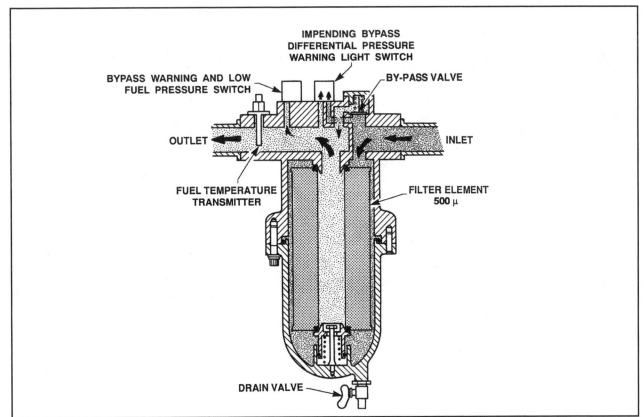

Fig. 7-41 — Low pressure filter with bypass warning switches.

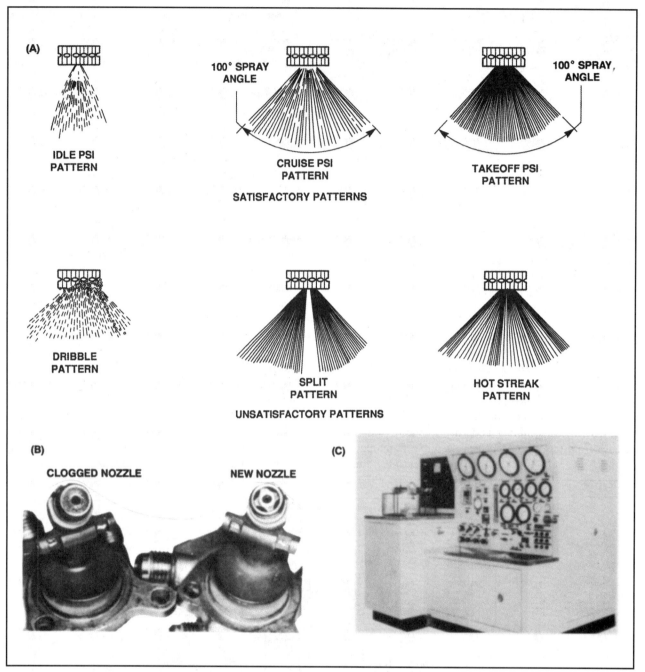

Fig. 7-42A — Examples of good and bad simplex nozzle spray patterns of an atomizing type nozzle.
Fig. 7-42B — Example of carbon build-up on fuel nozzles.
Fig. 7-42C — Fuel nozzle test stand.

motion and reduce axial velocity of the fuel to provide atomization as it exits the orifice. The internal check valve, present in the simplex nozzle shown, is there to prevent dribbling of fuel from the fuel manifold into the combustor after shutdown. Refer to Figure 7-43.

Some fuel systems with simplex nozzles as their main fuel distributors incorporate a second smaller simplex nozzle, called a primer or starting nozzle, which sprays a very fine atomized mist for improved light-off. After light-off, start/primer systems are generally turned off.

Another configuration with simplex nozzles is called "sector burning". The engine is started on one-half or more of the fuel nozzles and operated in that manner up to ground idle speed. Then, at approximately flight idle speed, fuel pressure is sufficiently high to overcome a check valve, which allows the remaining fuel nozzles to flow.

c. Duplex Fuel Nozzles

There are two common types of duplex fuel nozzles, the single-line and the dual-line type.

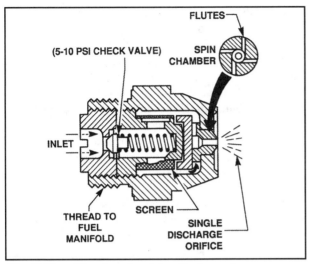

Fig. 7-43 — Simplex atomizing fuel nozzle.

1) Single-Line Duplex Fuel Nozzles

The duplex nozzle (Figure 7-44A, B, C) referred to as a single-line duplex type, receives its fuel at one inlet port and becomes a flow divider to distribute fuel through two spray orifices. Often, as shown, the round center orifice, called the pilot, or primary fuel, sprays at a wide angle during engine start and acceleration to idle. The annular outer orifice, referred to as main or secondary fuel, opens at a preset fuel pressure to flow along with the pilot fuel. Fuel of much higher volume and pressure flowing from this outer orifice causes the spray pattern to narrow so that the fuel will not impinge on the combustion liner at higher power settings (Figure 7-44D).

There are engines with single-line (or dual-line) duplex nozzles that have flow angles which are different from what is identified in the preceding parpgraph. The CFM56 turbofan has single-line duplex nozzles which

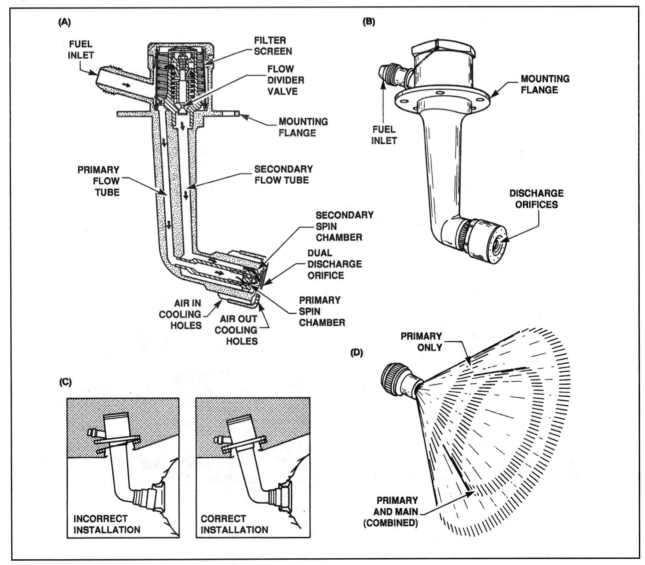

Fig. 7-44A — Single line duplex atomizing fuel nozzle.
Fig. 7-44B — Exterior view of duplex nozzle.
Fig. 7-44C — Installation of an externally mounted fuel nozzle.
Fig. 7-44D — Duplex fuel nozzle spray pattern.

have the widest flow angle coming from the secondary, and a narrower angle from the primary. With advancements that have taken place in combustor design, to include better control of airflow and the flame zone within the combustor, engines today are able to have secondary fuel flow at a wider angle and still keep the flame away from the metal.

The duplex nozzles also utilize a spin chamber for each orifice. This arrangement provides an efficient fuel atomization and fuel-air mixture residence time, as it is called, over a wide range of fuel pressures. The high pressure supplied to create the spray pattern, generally 800-1500 pounds per square inch—gauge, also gives good resistance to fouling of the orifices from entrained contaminants.

The head of the fuel nozzle is generally also configured with air holes which provide some primary air for combustion but are mainly used for cooling and cleaning the nozzle head and spray orifices. At times of starting fuel flow only, the cooling airflow is also designed to prevent primary fuel from backflowing into the secondary orifice and carbonizing.

Airflow in the direction of the fuel nozzle orifice results from the pressure differential that exists between high pressure secondary air outside the liner and the lower pressure primary air within the liner. These cooling air holes must be kept clean, or carbon build-up and heat erosion will be accelerated.

A distortion of the orifice flow area by carbon buildup around the head of the nozzle can distort the spray pattern. This buildup can be seen on a borescope check on some engines and, if severe enough, could require removal of the nozzles for cleaning. This could, in some installations, even require an engine tear-down to remove the carbon build-up. However, a recent development in decarbonizing allows the engine to be flushed with a special solution through the fuel manifolds. This purging under pressure loosens and removes the carbon and is a routine line maintenance procedure on some newer aircraft.

2) Dual-Line Duplex Fuel Nozzles (Figure 7-45)

A second type of duplex nozzle, called a dual line duplex type is quite similar to the single line except that it contains no flow divider check valve to separate primary and secondary fuel. The check valve in this system is located in the Pressurizing and Dump Valve (Figure 7-49) and is labeled "Pressurizing Valve". The pressurizing valve acts as a single, main flow divider for all of the fuel nozzles, whereas in the single-line duplex nozzle, each has its own flow divider in the form of its check valve.

d. Air Blast Fuel Nozzles (Figure 7-46)

The air blast fuel nozzle is a newer design and is being more widely used in various sized engines because it enhances the atomization process and produces finer fuel droplets. This nozzle is said to be more effective during

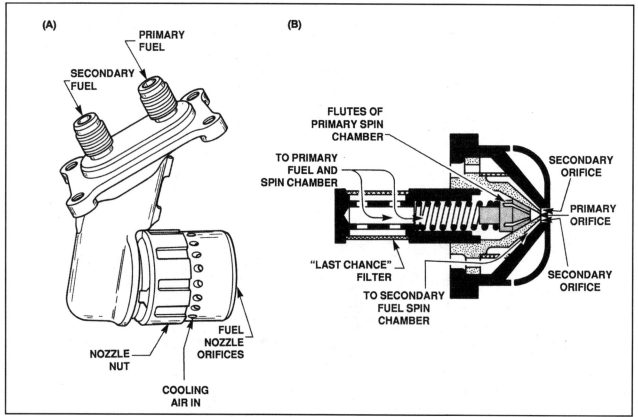

Fig. 7-45A — Dual line duplex atomizing fuel nozzle assembly.
Fig. 7-45B — Duplex fuel nozzle, cutaway veiw.

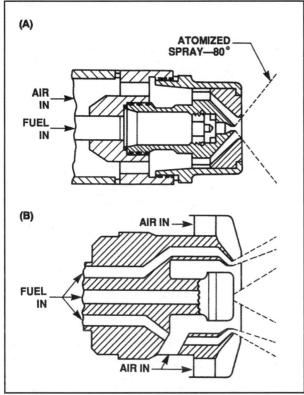

Fig. 7-46A — Air-blast fuel nozzle, simplex type.
Fig. 7-46B — Air-blast fuel nozzle, duplex type.

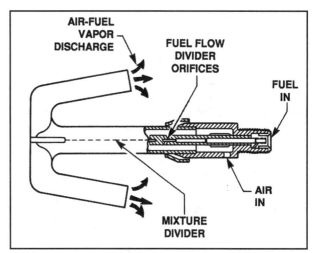

Fig. 7-47 — Heat-vaporizing type fuel nozzle.

starting when low fuel pressure causes atomization problems. By using a high velocity airflow, air blast nozzles more completely atomize the fuel than can be accomplished with fuel under pressure alone. This nozzle also has an advantage in that it utilizes a lower system working pressure than the basic atomizing types of nozzles.

5. Fuel Nozzles (Vaporizing Type)

The vaporizing fuel nozzle shown in Figure 7-47 connects to a fuel manifold in an arrangement similar to the atomizing type. Instead of delivering the fuel directly into the primary air of the combustor, as the atomizing type does, the vaporizing tube premixes the primary air and fuel. Combustor heat surrounding the nozzle causes the mixture to vaporize before exiting into the combustor flame zone (Figure 7-48).

Whereas the atomizer nozzle discharges in the downstream direction, the vaporizer discharges in the upstream direction and the mixture then makes a 180° turn to move downstream. This arrangement provides a slow moving, fine spray over a wide range of fuel flows and is said to produce more stable combustion in some engines than can be achieved by atomizing nozzles, especially at low revolutions per minute. Some vaporizers

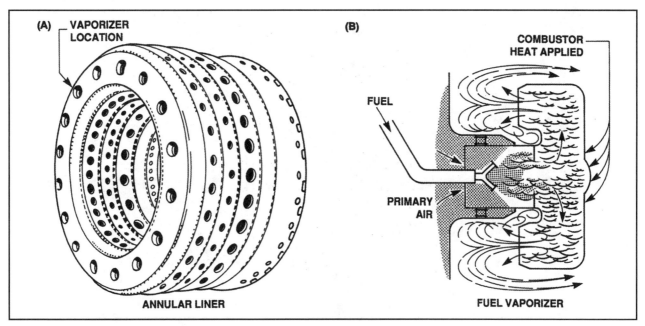

Fig. 7-48A — Vaporizer tube location in combustor.
Fig. 7-48B — Vaporizer tube in operation.

have only one outlet and are referred to as cane-shaped vaporizers.

The tee-shaped vaporizer, shown in Figure 7-47, is one of a set of eleven utilized in some models of the Lycoming T-53 turboshaft engine. Because vaporizing nozzles do not provide an effective spray pattern for starting, the T-53 incorporates an additional set of small atomizing type spray nozzles which spray into the combustor during starting. After light-off, start fuel is terminated on spool-up to idle. This system is generally referred to as a primer or starting fuel system. The Rolls Royce Olympus engine in the Concorde SST, and several other engines, utilize the vaporizing fuel nozzle and primer fuel nozzle systems, but these systems are not in wide use throughout the industry.

6. Fuel Pressurizing And Dump Valve

A pressurizing and dump valve (P and D valve) is used along with a duplex fuel nozzle of the dual inlet line type. Rather than providing a flow divider in each nozzle, as with the single line duplex fuel nozzle, this arrangement allows for one central flow divider, called a pressurizing and dump valve. The term "pressurizing" refers to the fact that at a pre-set pressure, a pressurizing valve within the P and D valve opens and fuel flows into the main manifold as well as through the pilot manifold.

The term dump refers to a second internal valve which has the capability of dumping the entire fuel manifold after shut-down. Manifold dumping is a procedure which sharply cuts off combustion and also prevents fuel boiling as a result of residual engine heat. This boiling would tend to leave solid deposits in the manifold which could clog the finely calibrated passageways.

In Figure 7-49 a pressure signal from the fuel control arrives at the P and D valve when the power lever is opened for engine start. This pressure signal shifts the dump valve to the left, closing the dump port and opening the passageway to the manifolds. Metered fuel pressure builds at the inlet check valve until the spring tension is overcome and fuel is allowed to flow through the filter to the pilot manifold. At a speed slightly above ground idle, fuel pressure will be sufficient to overcome the pressurizing valve spring force, and fuel will also flow to the main manifold.

The tension on the pressurizing valve spring is normally adjustable as a line maintenance task. A valve opening too early can give an improper fuel spray pattern and create hot starts or off-idle stalls. A late opening valve can cause slow-acceleration problems. To delay the opening of the secondary manifold and eliminate hot start or off-idle stalls, the adjusting screw would be turned in

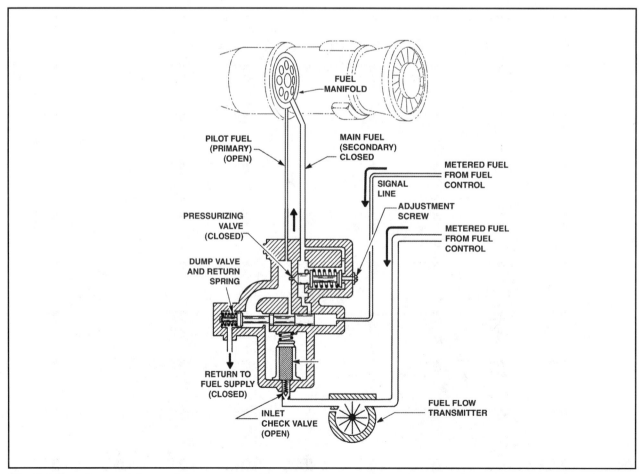

Fig. 7-49A — Pressurizing and dump valve with the engine operating at idle (primary manifold flowing fuel-only), dump valve closed.

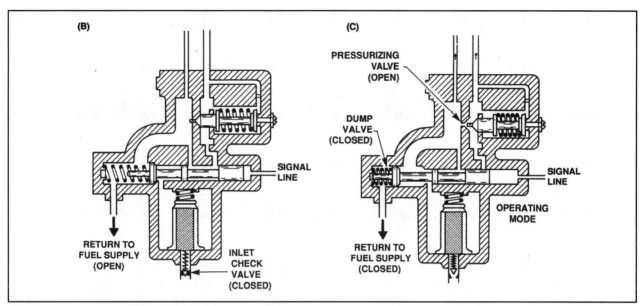

Fig. 7-49B — Dump valve open, engine not operating.
Fig. 7-49C — Pressurizing valve open, engine operating above flight idle speed.

to increase tension on the pressurizing valve spring. Conversely, to cause early fuel flow to the secondary manifold and enhance acceleration, the adjuster would be turned outward.

To shut off the engine, the fuel lever in the cockpit is moved to off. The fuel control pressure signal is then lost, and spring pressure will shift the dump valve back to the right, opening the dump valve port. At the same time, the inlet check valve will close, keeping the metered line flooded and ready for use on the next engine start.

a. Drain Tanks

Dump fuel, in years past, had been allowed to spill onto the ground or siphon from a drain tank in flight. Current FAA regulations, however, prohibit this form of environmental pollution, and now the drain tank fuel must be captured, perhaps by hand draining. Figure 7-53 shows this drain. To prevent hand-draining, several types of recycling systems have recently evolved. One such system returns fuel to the aircraft fuel supply. Another type of system pushes fuel, which formerly would have

been dumped, out of the fuel nozzles by introducing bleed air into the dump port. This prolongs combustion slightly until fuel starvation occurs. In the system shown in Figure 7-50, a full tank causes a float valve to actuate and drain the tank via an eductor type flow system.

7. Dump Valve (Figure 7-51)

The dump valve, sometimes called a drip valve, is incorporated in the low point of fuel manifolds which

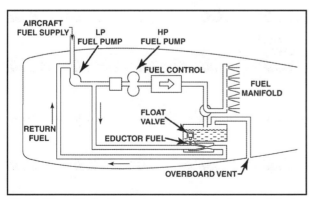

Fig. 7-50 — Rolls Royce Tay - recirculating fuel drain system

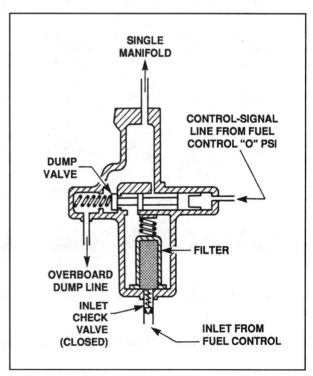

Fig. 7-51 — Dump valve, shown with dump valve open - engine not operating.

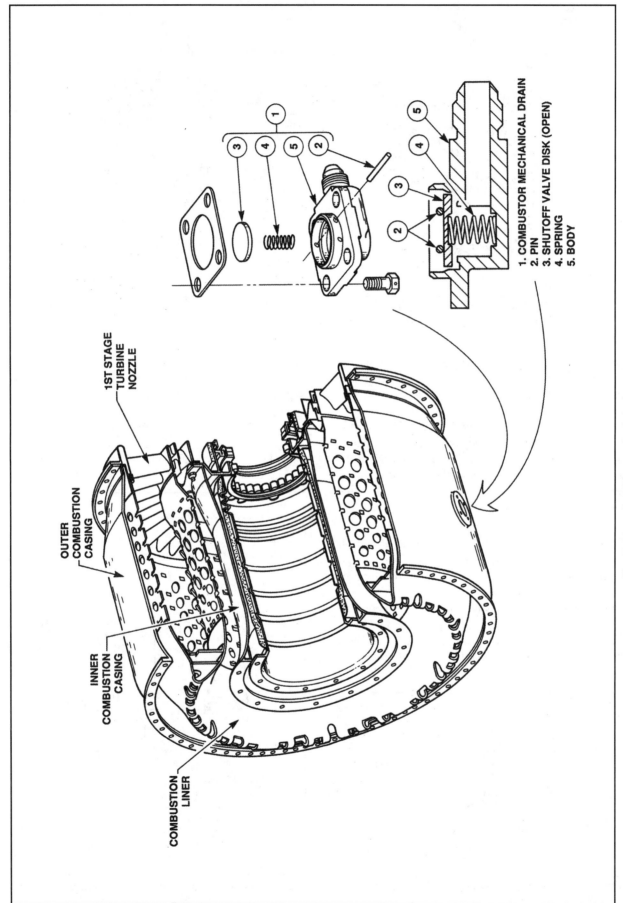

1. COMBUSTOR MECHANICAL DRAIN
2. PIN
3. SHUTOFF VALVE DISK (OPEN)
4. SPRING
5. BODY

1ST STAGE TURBINE NOZZLE

OUTER COMBUSTION CASING

INNER COMBUSTION CASING

COMBUSTION LINER

Fig. 7-52 — Combustor fuel drain valve.

utilize the simplex and the single line duplex types of fuel nozzles. Its sole purpose is to drain the fuel manifold after engine shutdown. It is subject to the same environmental restrictions discussed for the P and D valve. The function of its dump valve is identical to the dump valve in the P and D valve.

8. Combustor Drain Valve

The combustor drain valve shown in Figure 7-52 is a mechanical device located in the low point of a combustion case. It is closed by gas pressure within the combustor during engine operation and is opened by spring pressure when the engine is not in operation. This valve prevents fuel accumulation in the combustor after a false start or any other time fuel might tend to puddle at the low point.

A false start in this case is a no-start condition or hung-start condition which results in a fuel soaked combustor and tailpipe. Draining of fuel in this manner prevents such safety hazards as after-fires and hot starts. This drain also removes un-atomized fuel which could ignite near the lower turbine stator vanes causing serious local overheating during starting, when cooling airflow is at the lowest flow rate.

As mentioned in the P and D valve discussion, if the dump line is capped off as an ecology control, the fuel manifolds will drain through the lower nozzles and fuel will evaporate in the combustor or exit the combustor via the mechanical drain valve into an aircraft drain receptacle. Maintenance personnel will periodically drain this tank as a pollution control measure before it spills over onto the ramp. (See Figure 7-54 for drain tank location).

F. Example of Corporate Engine Fuel System (Pratt & Whitney JT-12)

The following is a complete fuel system schematic, in that it shows the relationship of component parts, one to another. This configuration is typical of the Rockwell Sabreliner aircraft (Figure 7-53).

1. Fuel Flow Sequence:
   a. Fuel storage tank;
   b. Boost Pump—Present to help eliminate vapor lock;
   c. Shut-off Valve—FAA regulation requires its presence;
   d. Fuel Screen—Coarse mesh (200 micron);
   e. Vapor Vent—Present to help eliminate vapor lock;
   f. Centrifugal Stage—Incorporated in the main fuel pump;
   g. Fuel Heater;
   h. Fine Filter—(20 micron);
   i. Gear Stage main fuel pump—Operating range 100-800 pounds per square inch—gauge;

   j. Fuel Control—Hydro-mechanical unit;
   k. Fuel Flow meter;
   l. Heat Exchanger—(Fuel cooled oil cooler);
   m. P and D valve;
   n. Pilot Fuel Manifold and Fuel Nozzles;
   o. Main Fuel Manifold and Fuel Nozzles.

The 24V differential pressure switch is present to illuminate a cockpit warning light if the fuel pump filter is clogged and approaching a bypass condition.

The bleed actuator is a fuel operated, compressor air "bleed system", which will be covered in a subsequent Chapter VIII of this text.

G. Example of Commercial Engine Fuel System (Pratt & Whitney JT8D)

The following is a complete fuel system schematic showing the relationship of all the components, one to the other, on a typical commercial sized engine. This configuration is typical of a Boeing 727 aircraft (Figure 7-54).

1. Fuel Flow Sequence:
   a. Aircraft fuel tank and boost pump;
   b. Engine Centrifugal Boost Pump—Bypass set 0.5 to 1.0 pounds per square inch—differential;
   c. Air-Fuel Heater—Bypass set to 20 ± 3 pounds per square inch—differential;
   d. Low Pressure Fuel Filter—(40 micron disposable) bypass set to 8-12 pounds per square inch—differential;
   e. Main Gear-Type Fuel Pump—Operating range 150 to 900 pounds per square inch—gauge;
   f. Fuel Control—Fuel flows via high pressure filter (20 micron cleanable) bypass set to 27-30 pounds per square inch—differential;
   g. Fuel Flowmeter Transmitter;
   h. Fuel-Oil Cooler;
   i. Pressurizing and Dump Valve;
   j. Primary Fuel Manifold and Primary Fuel Nozzles;
   k. Secondary Fuel Manifold and Secondary Fuel Nozzles.

H. Example of Commercial Engine Fuel System (G.E./Snecma CFM56)

The schematic shown in Figure 7-55 is for the fuel system in the CFM56 engine, as used on the Boeing 737-800 aircraft.

1. The fuel flow sequence is as follows:
   a. Aircraft boost pumps provide fuel to the engine driven centrifugal boost pump.
   b. The engine driven boost pump provides fuel to the Integrated Drive Generator (IDG) fuel/oil cooler. The cooler incorporates a bypass valve, in case the cooler becomes clogged.

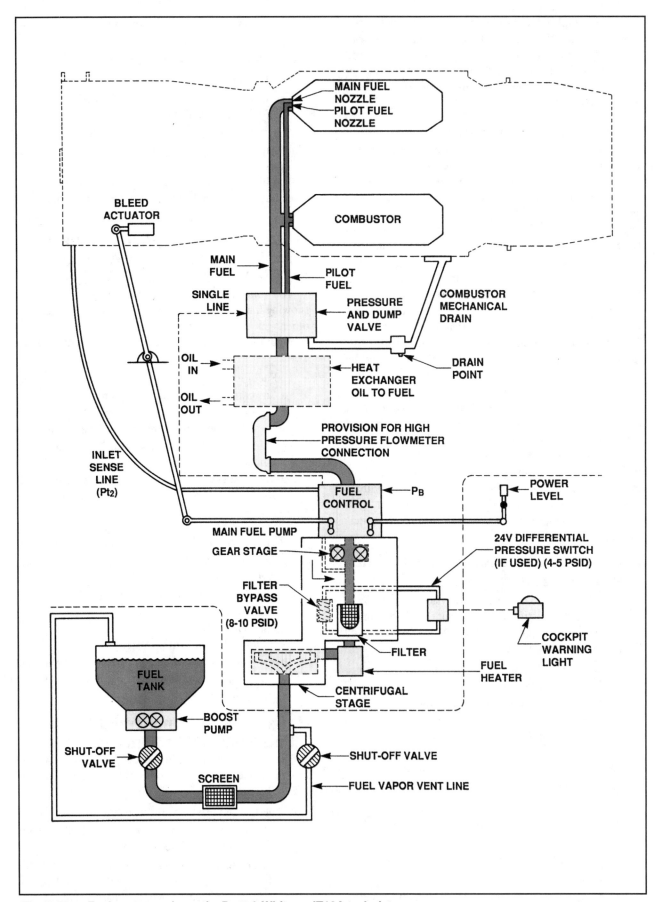

Fig. 7-53 — Fuel system schematic, Pratt & Whitney JT12A turbojet.

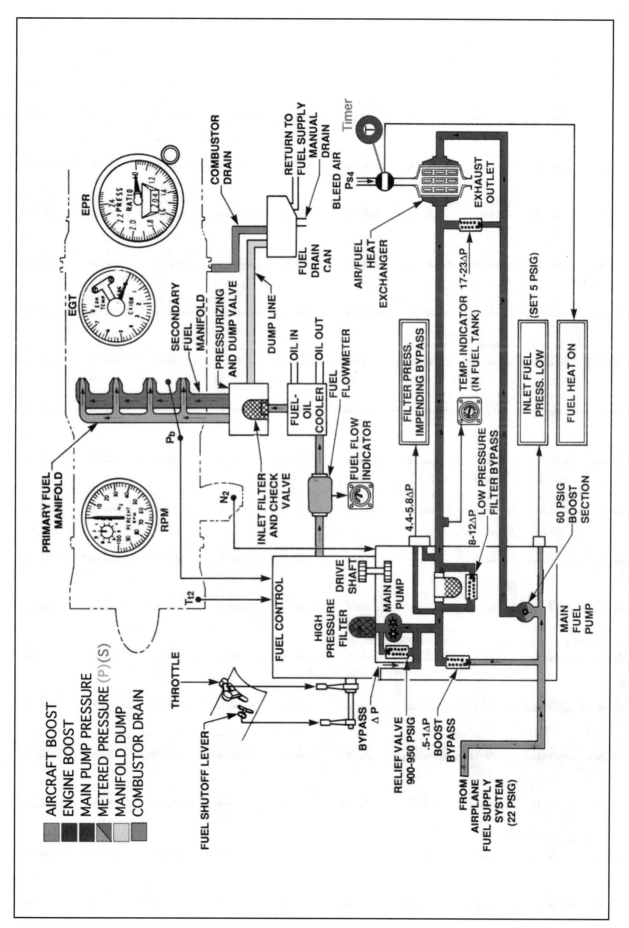

Fig. 7-54 — Fuel system schematic, Pratt & Whitney JT8D Turbofan.

c. From the IDG cooler, fuel flows to the engine fuel/oil heat exchanger. The heat exchanger incorporates a bypass valve, should the cooler become clogged.

d. From the Fuel/oil heat exchanger, fuel flows to the low pressure fuel filter. The filter incorporates a bypass valve, should the filter become clogged. If it does clog, an advisory light is illuminated on the flight deck.

e. Low pressure filter fuel flows to the gear type high pressure pump.

f. From the high pressure pump, fuel flows to the servo wash filter. This filter ensures the fuel is clean enough to be used inside the hydro mechanical unit (HMU) as servo fuel. The servo fuel is used to power the actuators for the variable vane system and the compressor bleed system.

g. From the servo wash filter, the fuel flows to two locations. It flows through the servo fuel heater and into the servo actuation portion of the HMU. It also flows to the fuel metering portion of the HMU.

h. Within the metering portion of the HMU, the fuel flows to the Fuel Metering Valve (FMV), the high pressure shutoff valve (HPSOV), and then exits the HMU. The position of the metering valve is controlled by the Electronic Engine Control (EEC). The high pressure shutoff valve is controlled by the start levers on the flight deck and also the fire switches. In the event of a fire, the fire switches will cause the shutoff valve to close.

i. After exiting the HMU, the fuel flows through a fuel flow transmitter and an inline fuel filter (last chance filter).

j. From the inline fuel filter, fuel flows to the unstaged fuel nozzles (10 single-line duplex), and to the burner staging valve (BSV).

k. The burner staging valve provides fuel to the staged fuel nozzles (10 single-line duplex). At low fuel/air ratios (a lot of air and not so much fuel), the burner staging valve shuts off the flow of fuel to the 10 staged nozzles. This is done to richen the mixture at the ten unstaged fuel nozzles to help prevent engine flameout. At high fuel/air ratios, the burner staging valve is open and sends fuel to the 10 staged nozzles.

l. The burner staging valve is controlled by the Electronic Engine Control (EEC) on the engine.

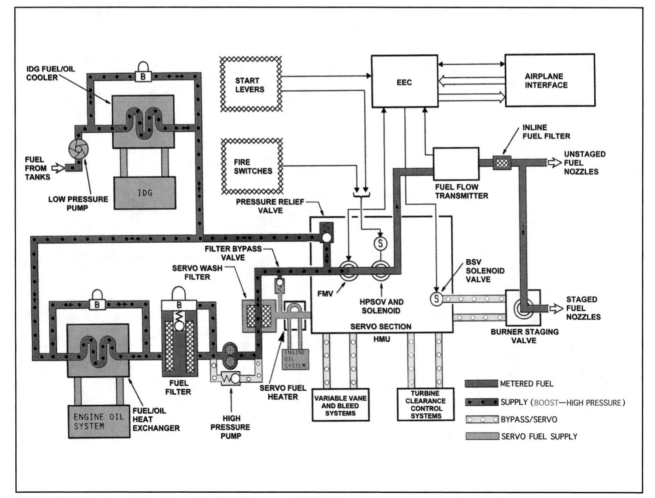

Fig. 7-55 — Fuel system schematic, G.E./Snecma CFM56-7

TROUBLESHOOTING FUEL SYSTEMS

PROBLEM/POSSIBLE CAUSE	CHECK FOR	REMEDY
1. Engine motors over but does not start—No or low fuel when fuel control shutoff valve is opened.		
a. No fuel to engine	Correct fuel tank level	Service
b. Improper rigging of shut-off valve (aircraft and engine)	Full travel	Re-rig linkage
c. Engine filters	Clogging or icing, degrading spray pattern	Clean
d. Malfunctioning fuel pump	Correct output pressure	Adjust relief valve or
e. Malfunctioning fuel control	Correct output pressure	Replace control
2. Engine motors over but does not start—Good fuel flow indication but no exhaust gas temperature.		
a. Ignition system	Weak or no spark	See ignition troubleshooting
b. P and D valve	1. Dump valve stuck open	Replace valve
	2. Pressurizing valve stuck open (both affect working pressure and atomization at fuel nozzles)	Adjust or replace valve
3. Engine starts but hangs up and will not self-accelerate to idle.		
a. Starter	Cut-out speed—too early	See starter troubleshooting
b. Fuel control	Entrapped air preventing proper operation	Bleed unit as per manual
c. Fuel control sensing lines	Looseness causing loss of signal	Tighten.
d. P and D valve	Pressurization valve stuck open, degrading spray pattern	Adjust or replace valve
4. Engine hot starts.		
a. Fuel control	High fuel flow indication	Replace control
b. P and D valve	1. Partially open dump valve affecting fuel schedule and atomization at fuel nozzles causing late hot start.	Replace P and D valve
	2. Partially open pressurizing valve-it should not be pressurized on start (causes late hot start)	Replane P and D valve
5. Engine unable to attain takeoff power.		
a. Improper fuel control setting	Trim adjustment or linkage problem	Re-trim or re-rig

PROBLEM/POSSIBLE CAUSE	CHECK FOR	REMEDY
b. Fuel filters	Partial clogging, degrading spray pattern	Clean
c. Fuel pump	1. Correct output pressure 2. One pumping element sheared	Adjust relief valve Replace pump
d. Fuel control	Correct output pressure and fuel flow	Replace fuel control

6. Engine unable to attain full power without exceeding limits of EGT or RPM.

a. Compressor or turbine	Contamination or damage	Possible teardown
b. Bleed air	Engine or customer service bleed air flowing when it shouldn't	Replace air valve or correct electrical fault

7. Flame-out—When applying take-off power.

a. Fuel pump — one element sheared shaft or relief valve open	Low pressure at high RPM	Replace pump
b. Fuel control	Correct fuel flow indication	Replace control

8. Engine is slow to accelerate/engine off idle stalls.

a. Same as 5 and 6		
b. P and D valve	Correct pressurizing valve adjustment	Adjust spring tension or replace P and D valve

9. Transitory combustor rumble on acceleration.

a. P and D valve	Correct cracking point of pressurizing valve	Reset to decrease cracking point
b. Fuel control	Proper output pressure	Replace fuel control

Note 1: FADEC System Failure and troubleshooting is beyond the scope of this text; it requires special test equipment procedures by trained personnel.

Note 2: Clogging filters and many other flow restricting conditions cause degrading of fuel nozzle spray patterns and poor heat release within the combustor.

QUESTIONS:

1. What is the name of the fuel scheduling device most widely used on gas turbine engines?

2. By what name is the control lever on the fuel control known?

3. Is a mixture control lever utilized on a turbine engine fuel control?

4. Name the fuel control input signal that is a measure of mass airflow through a gas turbine engine.

5. What type of fluid is used in water injection systems?

6. At what power setting is water injection used?

7. What term refers to making fuel control idle speed and maximum power adjustments during performance running?

8. What is the purpose of the engine trim check?

9. What does the EPR gauge indicate to the pilot?

10. What are the two best ambient conditions for trimming?

11. Of the two types of fuel pumps, spur gear and centrifugal, which is positive displacement?

12. Where is fuel system icing most prevalent?

13. Pilot fuel by itself is used during which engine operational mode?

14. What are the two purposes of a pressurizing and dump valve?

15. What force closes the combustion case drain?

Chapter VIII
Compressor Anti-Stall Systems

A. Variable Angle Compressor Vane System (Large Engine)

The variable vane actuating system is incorporated on many gas turbine engines, especially on engines with high compression, or those in which the compressor may have inherent compressor stall problems during acceleration or deceleration at low or intermediate speeds. The variable vane system automatically varies the geometry (area and shape) of the compressor gas path to exclude unwanted air and maintain the proper relationship between compressor speed and airflow in the front compressor stages. At low compressor speeds the variable stator vanes are partially closed.

As compressor rotor speed increases, the vanes open to allow more and more air to flow through the compressor. In effect, varying the vane angle schedules the correct angle-of-attack relationship between the angle of airflow approaching the rotor blades and the rotor blade leading edges. A correct angle-of-attack allows for a smooth and rapid engine acceleration.

Another way of viewing this situation is that the deflection of airflow imposed on the airstream by varying vane angles slows the airstream's axial velocity before it reaches the rotor blades. Thus the low RPM of the rotor blade and the low axial velocity of the airstream are matched.

For example, if we look at angle of attack of compressor blades as it was discussed in Chapter III, the vector diagram would look like Figures 8-1A, and 8-1B. Illustration A represents a normal condition of approximately 15 degrees effective angle-of-attack with the variable vanes at their normal 30- degree closed position as shown in Illustration C. Illustration B shows that if the variable vane system malfunctioned in the 40-degree closed position, as shown in Illustration C, the velocity in the axial direction would decrease, even though idle speed remains the same. As an example, inlet velocity in this case decreased from 200 feet per second to 100 feet per second, and the effective angle-of-attack increased from 15 degrees to 25 degrees. The result of this change would be a loss of compression and a good possibility of a stall upon acceleration off idle, as the front stage airflow becomes out of match with the rear stages.

1. System Operation (General Electric CF-6 Turbofan)

The example system in Figure 8-2 shows the inlet guide vanes and the six stator stages of the N2 compressor as being variable. To permit movement, the vanes are fitted with Teflon® type sockets at both ends. The remaining vane stages are conventionally installed stationary vanes.

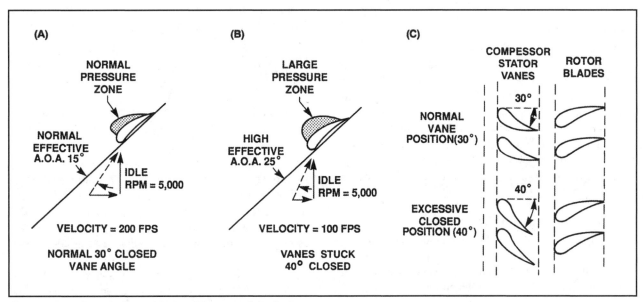

Fig. 8-1A — Compressor blade with normal A. O. A.
Fig. 8-1B — Compressor blade with high A. O. A.
Fig. 8-1C — Stator vane positions.

This system utilizes fuel control discharge pressure as a motive force to position hydraulic actuators located on the compressor case. The actuators move the vanes open by a beam arrangement. The beam attaches to vane actuating rings that connect to the variable stator vanes.

As the power lever is moved forward, fuel pressure increases at the head end of the actuator to open the vanes. The mechanical feedback cable signals the fuel control to cut off fuel pressure and allows the vane position to stabilize at the correct angle.

The Tt_2 sensor shown in the illustration is a heat sensitive, gas filled bulb which receives a fuel signal at constant pressure. The sensor also regulates return pressure of a regulated value as per the temperature in the engine inlet. The Tt_2 sensor contains a fuel metering orifice to accomplish this. The fuel control receives the return signal and uses it to schedule vane position through the rod end and head end fuel actuating lines. Even when the power lever is in a fixed position, the Tt_2 sensor will function to control compressor vane angles.

The compressor inlet temperature (CIT) sensor (Tt_2) is installed to reset the vane-open schedule to match ambient temperature changes, which affects mass airflow. At low Tt_2 values the air will have increased density and the vane system will start to open at a lower compressor speed to increase airflow. This is necessary because cool air has a tendency to move more slowly than warm air. In this way, the air velocity and compressor speed will remain in the proper relationship, maintaining a correct angle-of-attack.

Another way to view this situation is that if compressor inlet temperature decreases, compression increases in the rear stages, which do not have variable vanes. Added compression in the rear stages starts to slow airflow. When the Tt_2 sensor schedules the vanes to open earlier, increased airflow (mass and velocity) occurs in the front stages to push air in the rear stages back up to its former velocity.

Again this keeps the compressor speed versus compressor air velocity in proper relationship to maintain the angle-of-attack. If a temperature shift downward occurs when the variable vanes are fully open, they obviously cannot open wider. In this case, other sensors in the fuel control function to force a reduction in fuel flow and compressor speed. This in turn brings compressor speed back down into match with air velocity.

2. Variable Vane Schedule

The operational aspects of the variable system can best be seen in its operating schedule. In Figure 8-3 observe that when on normal schedule, the vanes will remain closed up to 65% N_2 speed, at which time they will start to open, and by 95% N_2 they will be fully open.

When inlet temperature increases or decreases from Standard Day conditions, the vane schedule also changes.

If, for instance, ambient temperature drops to 30°F, the vanes will start to open at approximately 60% N_2 speed instead of 65%, and they would be fully opened at 92% instead of 95%. This of course accomplishes the same compressor versus air velocity change as in the previous discussion about temperature shifts and angle-of-attack. If the CIT sensor fails or the linkages to the variable vanes are maladjusted, the correct vane schedule will not be met and a compressor stall is likely to occur.

The engine mounted protractor (Figure 8-2) is present to give the technician a means of checking the vane position while the engine is being operated in order to plot the vane schedule of operation against a standard curve.

3. Why Variable Vanes Are Needed On High Compression Engines

a. Stall Curve With Fixed Vanes — Low Compression Engines

A further explanation of the function of variable vanes can be made by use of stall line curves, which compare engines with and without variable angle vane systems.

Compressors are designed such that for any given mass airflow/RPM, a certain compressor pressure ratio (Cr) exists. In Figure 8-4, the line A-B represents the results of factory testing to establish the maximum mass airflow to compressor pressure ratio relationship that can exist without a compressor stall. This curve is similar to the stall margin curve discussed in Chapter III, except that it is simplified to only two plots, compressor pressure ratio and mass airflow and with Compressor Speed (RPM) lines removed.

Any compression ratio above the stall line A-B indicates a compressor ratio too high for existing mass airflow and a resulting stall. Operating line C-D indicates a normal compressor ratio to mass airflow relationship. However, if too much fuel flow is applied during acceleration, excessive combustor pressure can result, causing a blockage of mass airflow and a rise in compressor ratio. Then line A-B can be exceeded with a resulting compressor stall.

b. Stall Curve With Variable Vanes — High Compression Engines

Variable vanes control compressor pressure ratio (Cr) and mass airflow (ms) to give the compressor the correct relationship of compressor pressure ratio and mass airflow during acceleration and deceleration. The variable vanes as shown in Figure 8-3 operate on an RPM schedule biased to compressor inlet temperature (Tt2). Figure 8-5 shows the relationship between compressor pressure ratio and mass airflow (Ms)/(RPM).

This curve shows that by the use of variable vanes, the operating line (C-D) can be raised. This means the engine will be able to operate at higher compressor pressure ratio for a given RPM and not have tendencies to stall.

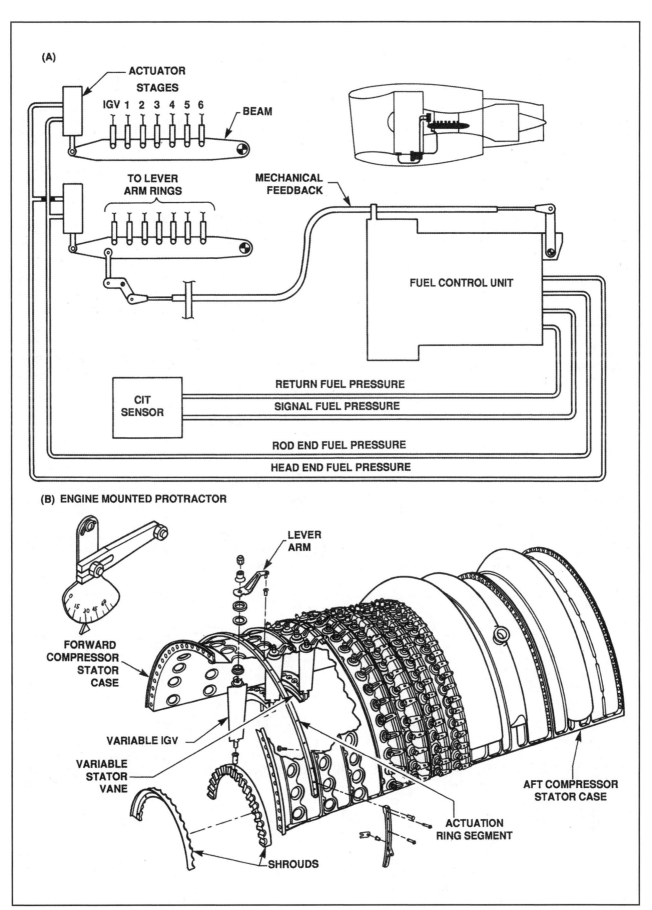

Fig. 8-2 — *Typical variable IGV and Stator vane system.*

Line C-D represents a normal compressor pressure ratio to RPM relationship of an engine with fixed stator vanes, as discussed in Figure 8-4. At this safe low line position, maximum compression of the engine will also be low. With variable vanes installed, the compression can also be raised in the engine and the operating line can also be safely raised to position E-F. The reasons for the higher operating line is that for any given RPM, where the variable vane system regulates airflow, the vane system will automatically schedule the correct compressor pressure ratio and mass airflow.

In other words, if the operating line (C-D) of a fixed stator engine is determined by factory testing, then a second operating line (E-F) can be determined for a variable vane engine by the same methods. It is now the function of the variable vane system to keep the engine from stalling during normal acceleration and deceleration.

From this discussion, it can be seen that designing a high compression engine is not possible without incorporating some form of air regulating system because the compressor will stall if it does not receive some help in managing its airflow. The compressor stator airfoils are made to have variable angles to accomplish this airflow management.

B. Variable Angle Inlet Guide Vane System (Small Engine)

The system shown in Figure 8-7 is typical of many smaller gas turbine engine anti-stall systems, wherein only the inlet guide vanes have a variable angle capability. The compressor stator vanes are all of the fixed angle type.

The inlet guide vanes in this system, as seen in Figure 8-6, have a 45 degree range of movement, from 51.5 degrees closed at low compressor speed to 6.5 degrees closed at high compressor speed.

This system is fuel pressure operated by command of the power lever. It is controlled by fuel signals from the fuel control for its operating schedule in the manner of the large engine anti-stall system mentioned in the first part of this chapter.

At idle speed, the vanes are scheduled 51.5 degrees closed, and, to provide a stall free rapid acceleration of the engine, the vanes move toward their 6.5 degree position as engine speed increases. This action maintains the correct angle-of-attack relationship between inlet airflow and compressor speed.

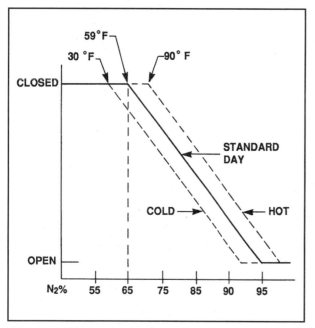

Fig. 8-3 — Example of vane operating schedule.

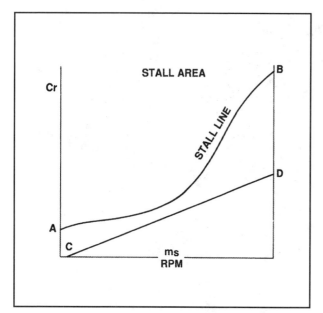

Fig. 8-4 — Typical stall line chart, engine with fixed compressor stator vanes.

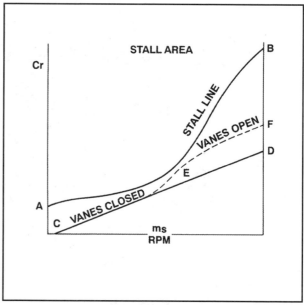

Fig. 8-5 — Typical stall line chart, engine with variable angle compressor stator vanes.

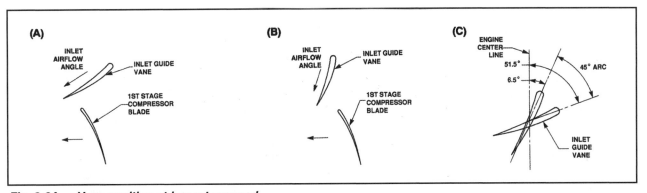

Fig. 8-6A — Vane position at low rotor speed.
Fig. 8-6B — Vane position at high rotor speed.
Fig. 8-6C — Inlet guide vane angular range.

C. Troubleshooting The Variable Vane System

NOTE: Refer to Chapter VI for general troubleshooting procedures.

PROBLEM/POSSIBLE CAUSE	CHECK FOR	REMEDY
1. Compressor stall on acceleration or deceleration.		
a. Variable Vane System	1. Out of track condition or binding	Re-rig system
	2. Feedback cable out of adjustment or binding	Adjust or clean
b. Compressor Inlet Sensor (Tt2)	Sensor malfunction	Replace sensor
c. Fuel Control	Correct fuel pressure to vane system	Replace control
2. Engine unable to attain full power (without exceeding EGT limit).		
a. Variable Vane System	Vanes not fully open (observe vanes and protractor)	Re-rig system

D. Compressor Anti-Stall Bleed Systems

The compressor anti-stall bleed system, as with the variable vane system, is installed on some gas turbine engines to minimize compressor acceleration and deceleration stall problems at low and intermediate speeds. Rather than exclude unwanted air, as is the case with the variable vane system, the compressor bleed system automatically dumps away unwanted air.

Except at cruise rpm and higher, some compressors cannot handle the amount of air passing through the engine without an air bleed system. For example, in a compressor with a 30:1 compressor pressure ratio, during starting a compression ratio of only approximately 2:1 exists. In this condition, the flow outlet area of the compressor would have to be about 80% of its inlet area in order to move the air without a drastic slow down in its velocity. The average outlet area being only about 25% of the inlet area necessitates the use of a compressor bleed air system.

Another way of describing this situation is that in

some engines at low and intermediate speeds, a relationship between compressor rotor RPM and airflow cannot be maintained to give the rotating airfoils the correct effective angle-of-attack to the oncoming airstream unless some of the compressor air is being bled away. At high rotational speeds, the compressor is designed to handle maximum airflow without aerodynamic disturbance so the bleed system is scheduled closed.

1. A Comparison Of The Variable Vane System And The Compressor Bleed System.

a. At the low end of the compressor speed range the variable vane system allows less air to enter. This in turn keeps compression low and prevents piling up of air molecules in the rear stages which tend to block airflow.

b. At the low end of the compressor speed range the compressor bleed system bleeds away the excess of air molecules in the rear stages, which in effect accomplishes the very same results.

On larger engines, one or more bleed valves fitted to the compressor's outer case are used to dump unwanted air either into the fan duct or directly overboard. On smaller engines, it is more convenient to use a sliding band which uncovers bleed ports to bleed away unwanted air.

On large engines, a combination of bleed valves and variable vanes may be used. The higher the compression ratio, the greater the need for systems which control the stall margin.

2. Small Engine Bleed Band System
(Figure 8-8)

The bleed band system is incorporated on many small engines to control the stall margin of the engine. The band is positioned so that it will dump air from a selected rearward stage of compression that will result in the best operating condition of that engine. In the system shown, the band bleeds air away from the last axial stage of compression in an engine, which contains a combination axial-centrifugal compressor. At low and intermediate speeds, the band is fully open. In the cruise

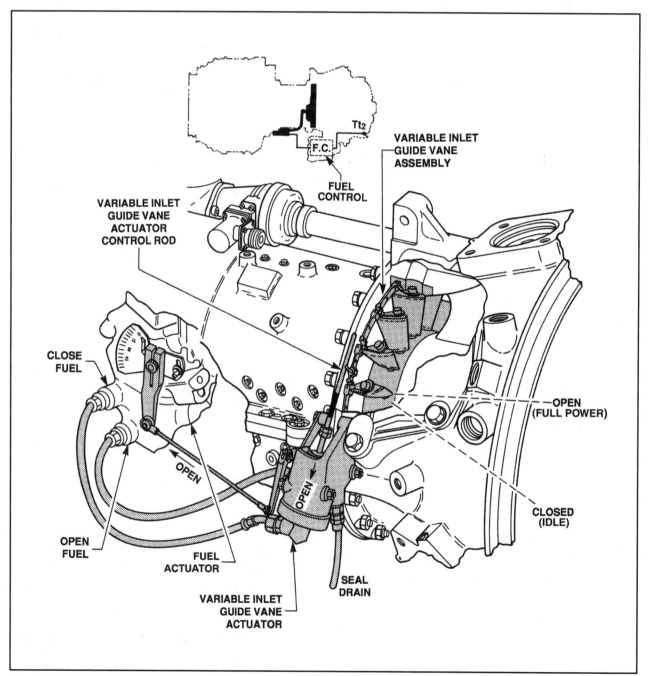

Fig. 8-7 — Variable inlet guide vane system.

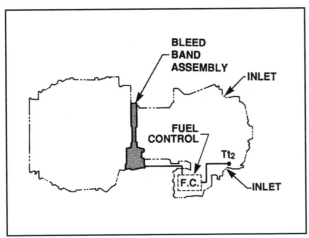

Fig. 8-8 — Location of bleed band assembly, T53 turboshaft, Honeywell-Lycoming.

to takeoff power range, the band is fully closed. This system does not meter bleed air, it is either fully open or fully closed.

In the schematic view (Figure 8-9), observe that P3 air which is tapped from the last stage of compression, pressurizes the actuator cavity, holding the piston up. Observe also that Pm air is locked in by the slider, and with the same pressure on both sides of the Pm diaphragm the actuator valve is designed to close. This operational mode occurs when the fuel control is set at some predetermined high power setting and after the engine has had a stall free acceleration from a lower power setting. When the power lever is moved rearward, the fuel control will schedule the control valve slider to the right uncovering the Pa port, and Pm control air will bleed to atmospheric.

This causes a pressure drop on the Pm side of the diaphragm and an oil-canning type movement upwards takes place which opens the actuator valve. This action allows P3 air to dump from the actuator cavity and the open-spring to push the piston downward. This in turn slackens the band, uncovering the bleed ports. In this operational mode, the bleeds remove a portion of the pressurized air in the compressor to the atmosphere and cause the axial compressor velocity of flow in the front stages to increase to match compressor speed for angle-of-attack controlling purposes. This system is needed on many engines because at lower compressor speeds the high pressure ratio in the rear stages tends to slow airflow in the front stages.

Operationally, when the bleed band opens and closes, cockpit instruments such as Engine Pressure Ratio and engine rpm will make a noticeable shift that can be observed by the operator.

To bias system operation to ambient temperature, the slider will open and close at the direction of a Tt_2 sensor in the fuel control (F.C.). At cooler ambient temperatures the slider closes earlier upon engine acceleration so that the heavier, slower moving airflow will be speeded up

during the compression process. This maintains the correct angle-of-attack relationships within the compressor.

3. Bleed Band Schedule

The accompanying chart (Figure 8-10) illustrates a typical anti-surge bleed band schedule. For example, at 60°F, if the engine is accelerated from idle to a high power setting, the bleed band must close no earlier than 66% N_1 speed and no later than 72% N_1 speed. Then, in deceleration, the bleed band must open below 72% and no lower than 66%. If the bleed band closes for example at 69% on acceleration, it must open at 67% minimum and within the limits of the band schedule.

From the chart it can be seen that the bleed band is scheduled open longer on acceleration, meaning to a higher N_1 speed, as ambient temperature goes higher. As ambient temperature increases, airflow velocity tends to increase. The bleed is kept open longer to prevent a pile up of molecules in the rear stages. After bleed closing speed is reached, the compressor by its design will handle the additional airflow and maintain the correct angle-of-attack relationships without compressor stall.

The reader should note that the words "compressor bleed air" are used to describe several air bleed systems, both engine and non-engine. The bleed band is not a compressor air bleed source for aircraft air conditioning or fuel tank pressurization, which is more properly referred to as customer bleed air.

4. Large Engine Bleed Valve System, (Pratt & Whitney, JT8D Turbofan)

Description: The Pratt & Whitney JT8D turbofan engine utilizes a bleed valve system described as a Pressure Ratio Bleed Control System to provide its compressor with anti-stall protection.

The system consists of three-bleed valves, two to bleed 13th stage air, the last stage of compression, and one to bleed 8th stage air. There is no metering of bleed air in this system. The valves are either in the fully open or fully closed position.

This system utilizes three air pressures from the engine to operate the valves: Low pressure compressor discharge static pressure (Ps_3), compressor inlet total pressure (Pt_2), and high pressure discharge pressure (Ps_4). Ps_3 and Pt_2 are sensing pressures and Ps_4 is used as the "control" air pressure to operate the mechanisms.

System Operation: This system schedules the bleed valve operation as a function of the pressure ratio across the low pressure compressor.

The three-bleed valves are scheduled to be open when the engine is operating at low power and closed at slightly below cruise power.

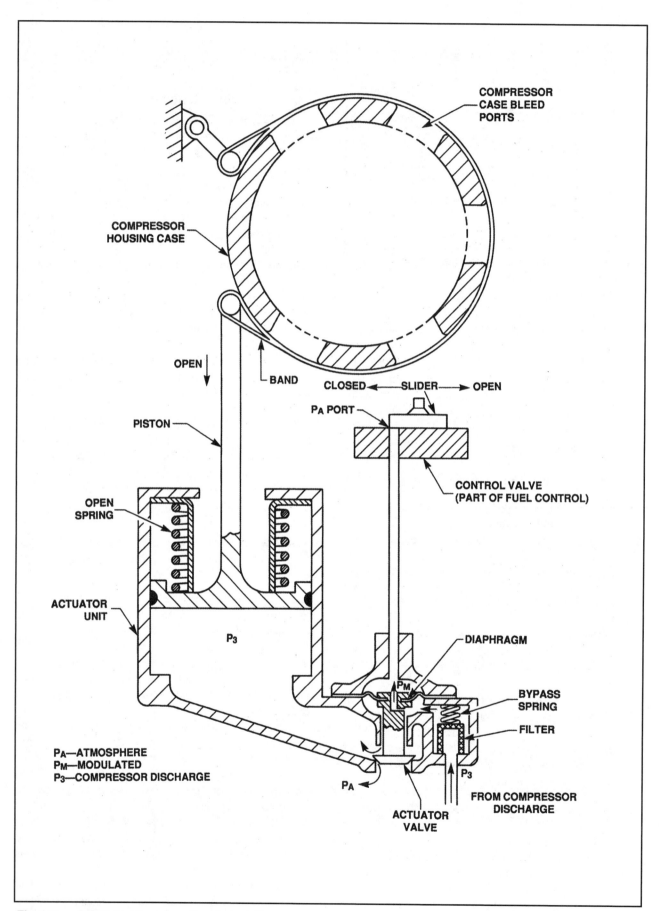

Fig. 8-9. — Bleed band system (band closed).

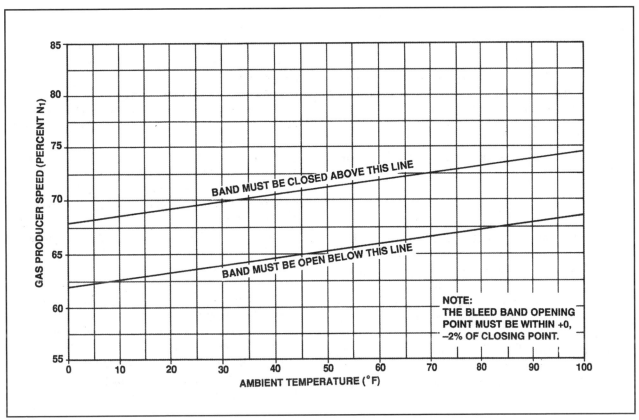

Fig. 8-10 — Anti-stall bleed band operational schedule.

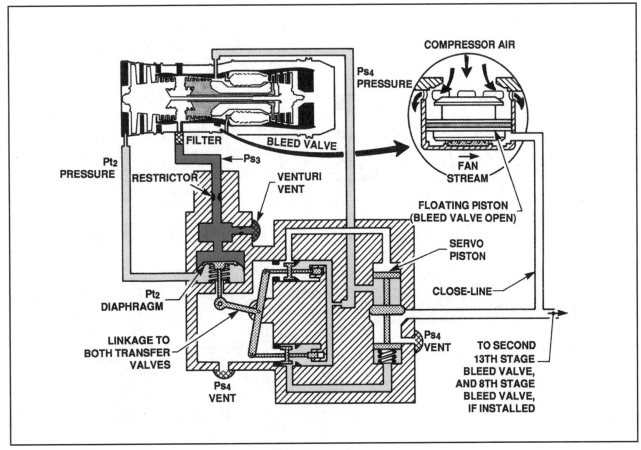

Fig. 8-11 — JT8D anti-stall bleed valve system (bleeds open).

When the engine is not operating, the Pt$_2$ diaphragm in Figure 8-11 is in the upward position in response to Pt$_2$ pressure and spring pressure. This correctly positions the linkage to the two transfer valves.

During engine starting, Ps$_3$ pressure enters the cavity above the diaphragm through a filter and a pressure control restrictor. It is also vented overboard through a venturi fitting. The venturi allows Ps$_3$ to have a modified value less than actual Ps$_3$ value. The venturi will "choke" as the engine comes up to idle speed and provide a steady back-pressure on the diaphragm to act against Pt$_2$ pressure and spring pressure. At this time, Pt$_2$ plus spring pressure is greater than Ps$_3$ pressure.

When the engine is at idle speed up to valve closing speed, the top of the servo piston is vented overboard by way of the top transfer valve and the Ps$_4$ vent. Control pressure, Ps$_4$, is blocked at the servo piston center section but routed to the bottom side through the lower transfer valve. This pressure plus the spring pressure holds the servo piston in the upward position. The bleed valve close-line is vented overboard at this time, and, at the same time, pressure within the compressor is forcing the bleed valves open.

As engine speed increases, modified Ps$_3$ pressure becomes greater than Pt$_2$ pressure plus the spring pressure and the diaphragm (Figure 8-12) is forced to move downward to reverse the position of the transfer valves.

When the transfer valves change position, Ps4 is routed to the top surface of the servo piston applying downward pressure. Ps$_4$ is also routed to the center surface of the servo piston, which has a larger area than the top surface. The pressure differential causes a downward movement of the servo piston.

With the servo piston down, Ps$_4$ is directed to the bleed valve close-line, and all three bleed valves close simultaneously because the area under the floating pistons is greater than the cone-shaped area at the close-off point at the compressor case.

If this engine had no bleed air system, the fuel schedule would have to be lowered to allow the heavier low pressure compressor time to speed up and stay in step with the high pressure compressor, and the acceleration schedule of the engine would suffer. In the same way, if the bleed valves close too early, the acceleration time will increase.

Deceleration is also aided by the compressor bleed valves. By having the valve open at a point just below cruise speed, it is possible to relieve some of the airflow and the compressor slows down more quickly.

Notice that this pressure ratio system does not have an inlet temperature sensor, to change the opening and closing schedule according to temperature. It doesn't need one, because at lower inlet air temperatures, the air is more dense and Ps$_3$ will overpower Pt$_2$ sooner. When this happens, the bleed valves will close early.

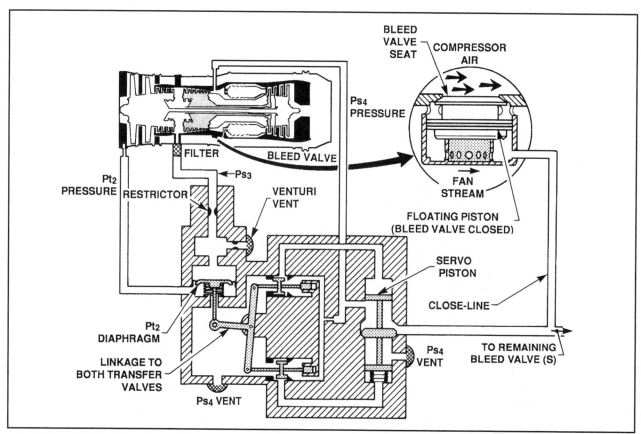

Fig. 8-12— JT8D anti-stall bleed valve system (valves closed).

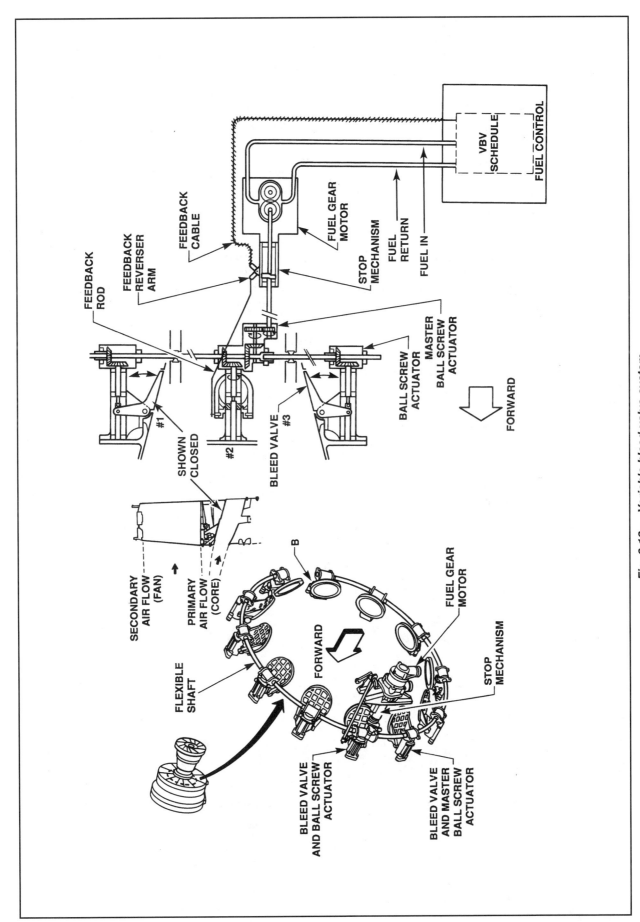

Fig. 8-13 — Variable bleed valve system.

Newer systems of this type have been modified so that the bleed valves can be scheduled closed electronically during the start cycle, to initially provide better starting air flow. As the engine accelerates toward idle, the valves open to aid in acceleration.

5. Variable Bleed Valve System (G.E. Snecma, CFM56 Turbofan)

The variable bleed valve system (Figure 8-13) is similar in function to the JT8D turbofan bleed valve system previously mentioned, which is to optimize the performance of the high pressure compressor. The difference in the CFM56 bleed system is that the bleed valve position can be varied to bleed the required amount of air according to the needs of the engine. The JT8D, like many other engines today, has only two bleed valve positions, full open and full closed.

The CFM56 utilizes a low compressor discharge bleed air system containing 12 variable position bleed valves, which are operated by a hydro-mechanical controlling system.

The bleed valves are located around the low pressure N_1 compressor outer case and release some of N_1 discharge air pressure into the fan duct. They are fully open at idle speed and slowly close on a schedule controlled by a computer and by mechanisms within the fuel control. Full closing occurs at approximately 85 to 88% N_2 speed, which is slightly below cruise speed.

The valves are operated by a mechanical actuator and a flexible shaft mechanism which is powered by a fuel driven motor. The bleed valves operate in response to two principle controls. The first control is the movement of the power lever (throttle) on the flight deck. Advancing the power lever causes the valves to move toward closed, and retarding the power lever moves them toward open. The valves also move in response to changes in operational parameters of N_2 Speed and Fan Discharge Temperature that are received by the fuel control. The feedback cable in the illustration gives the fuel control a continual mechanical signal of bleed valve position against which the automatic signals of speed and temperature can be compared.

This system is stated to better control compressor blade angle of attack and the stall margin during acceleration and deceleration than the two-position systems. It also contributes to the low fuel consumption rate of this advanced technology engine.

E. Troubleshooting Compressor Bleed Systems

NOTE: Refer to Chapter VI for general troubleshooting procedures.

PROBLEM/POSSIBLE CAUSE	CHECK FOR	REMEDY
1. Compressor stall on acceleration from low or intermediate speeds.		
a. Bleed Systems	1. Early closing of bleed ports	Reset schedule or replace control device
	2. Binding mechanism	Adjust
2. Compressor stall on deceleration from high speeds.		
a. Bleed System	Late opening of bleed ports	Adjust
3. Engine unable to attain full power (without exceeding EGT limit).		
a. Bleed System	1. Air bleed ports not fully closed	Re-rig system
	2. Binding mechanism	Adjust
4. Fluctuating RPM and EGT.		
a. Bleed System	Modulating bleed	Adjust or replace as necessary

QUESTIONS:

1. Why is a variable stator vane system installed on some gas turbine engines?

2. How many vanes in a single stage have controllable angles?

3. An angle of attack relationship occurs at the compressor blade leading edge from inlet airflow and what other factor within the engine?

4. Is the compressor bleed system closed at takeoff power?

5. Whes the compressor bleed system air directed to?

6. If an engine with a compressor bleed system experiences compressor stalls, what is a probable cause?

Chapter IX
Anti-Icing Systems

On many aircraft the flight cowling, the fan, fan spinner, compressor inlet case, inlet guide vanes, nose dome, and nose cowling are configured with internal passages which allow the circulation of hot air for anti-icing purposes.

On some aircraft, icing is not a problem for the engine because ice does not form in sufficient quantity, and no engine anti-icing provisions are necessary. On some turboprops, the oil reservoir is located within the propeller reduction gearbox, providing some anti-ice capability, and only a minimum of hot air flow is required to anti-ice the inlet area.

When an anti-ice system is required to provide protection against ice formation in the inlet, engine service bleed air is extracted from the compressor or diffuser of the engine being anti-iced and routed to the inlet area through external piping and control valves.

The air is extracted from the point in the engine which will provide the correct pressure and temperature to satisfy the needs of the engine during both ground and flight operations. If only the flight cowl is anti-iced, electrical heat strips are often used.

Anti-ice air is directed radially inward at the engine inlet case to heat all the surfaces upon which ice might form. Unlike certain de-ice systems on wing leading edges and propellers, this system does not allow ice to form. If the anti-ice system is inadvertently used to de-ice the inlet area by being turned on after compressor stalls occur from ice formation, the impact forces of ice on compressor blades and vanes can severely damage the engine or even cause the engine to fail completely.

Icing conditions are most prevalent when operating the engine at high speeds on the ground. Ice can form in the inlet up to 40°F ambient temperature in relatively dry air and up to 45°F in visibly moist air, due to the cooling effect of high inlet airflow velocities (Figure 9-1).

The inlet super cooling effect was discussed in Chapter VII concerning the use of water injection in the inlet below 40°F, which can also result in inlet icing. Another comparison which can be made is the use of carburetor heat to prevent icing at the venturi in the carburetor throat. The combination of high velocity and high volume of atomized fuel create a condition where ice can form up to 70°F.

In the flight inlet of a gas turbine engine, the large flow area would not support a 70°F freeze up condition, but the same processes by which ice can form are present. They are:

1. Increased velocity of air causes a pressure drop and increases the cooling effect on the air;

2. Evaporation of water at low pressure increases the cooling effect;

3. Freezing of condensed water vapor occurs in air because of the effect low pressure has on air temperature;

4. Water suspended in air comes into contact with metal surfaces of 32°F or below.

Consider the following example using Formula 7, Appendix 8, by which we can calculate the temperature drop in the inlet when inlet velocity is Mach 0.5 and ambient temperature is 40°F.

$$\frac{Tt}{Ts} = 1 + \left[\frac{\gamma - 1}{2}\right] \times M^2$$

$$\frac{500}{Ts} = 1 + \left[\frac{1.4 - 1}{2}\right] 0.5^2$$

$$\frac{500}{Ts} = 1 + (0.2 \times 0.25)$$

$$\frac{500}{Ts} = 1.05$$

$$Ts = 476°R \ (16°F)$$

Where: $\gamma = 1.4$ (specific heat ratio)
           $40°F = 500°R$
           M = Mach No.

This indicates that the temperature is between 16°F and 40°F in different parts of the inlet. Molecular motion is a function of temperature. When velocity is high, pressure is low. When pressure is low, molecular motion is down and thus temperature is down.

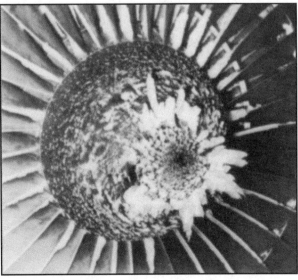

Fig. 9-1 — Fan icing tests showing ice formation on the fan spinner and fan blades.

It might appear that anti-ice should be used at much higher temperatures than 40 to 45 degrees to prevent freeze up, but industry testing has proven that it is a safe limit. It takes time for water suspended in air passing through the inlet to turn to ice, and if the temperature in the inlet is no lower than 45°F, ice will not form.

During flight the anti-icing system is turned on before entering the icing condition. Anti-icing heat is required when visible moisture is present in the form of clouds or precipitation and the true air temperature (ambient plus ram effect) in the inlet is typically between 40°F and 5°F. Below 5°F ambient air is dry, ice is not likely to form, and anti-ice will be used at the discretion of the pilot.

The ambient temperature is well below 5°F at all cruise altitudes for a gas turbine powered aircraft, and ram pressure will not raise inlet temperature sufficiently above freezing. However, most of the flight time will be above cloud level and anti-icing will not be required. When required, the usual method of initiating anti-icing is to select one engine, then watch the engine parameters stabilize, after which the remaining engine(s) are selected in a similar manner.

On takeoff, climb-out, descent, and landing, the pilot will have to carefully assess the need for anti-icing according to the prevailing weather conditions. To prevent engine malfunction or damage, the operator will have to make the same assessment when running the engine on the ground.

A. System Operation

The system illustrated in Figure 9-2 contains two electric motor driven air shutoff valves which are opened simultaneously by actuation of a cockpit switch. Once the valves are opened, bimetallic coils inside the air regulator valves control the amount of airflow by the temperature of the air. Air that is too hot can affect the material strength of inlet components and can also affect engine performance as the anti-ice air is ingested into the compressor.

The idea is that in some engines increase in temperature of compressor bleed air at high power settings may adversely affect engine performance, so the flow is regulated. Some aircraft have no need for regulator valves because the change in temperature has a

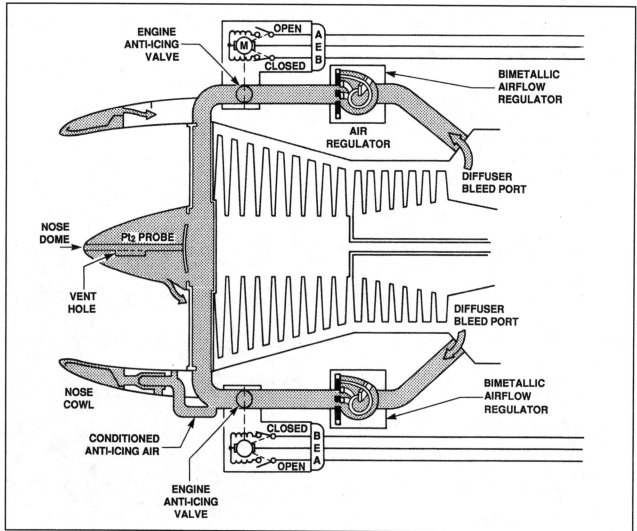

Fig. 9-2 — Typical engine inlet anti-icing system.

negligible effect on performance and material strength. In this case, they contain only the electric shutoff valves. On some large fan engines only the flight inlet is anti-iced because the absence of inlet guide vanes and the slinging action of the fan eliminates engine inlet ice formation.

When anti-ice is selected, an indicator light illuminates in the cockpit and a slight rise in exhaust gas temperature (approximately 10°C) occurs to indicate proper operation of the anti-icing system. Other engine instruments such as Engine Pressure Ratio and tachometer indicators might also shift noticeably at this time due to the momentary change in compression delivered to the combustor.

The vent hole in the Pt_2 probe (Figure 9-2) is present to act as a water drain and also as an ice detector. If the probe ices up at the nose dome opening, the influence of ram pressure is lost to the Engine Pressure Ratio System and the probe acts as a Ps_2 probe. This will result in a rise in the engine pressure ratio indication in the cockpit. A dangerous false high engine pressure ratio for takeoff will result because Ps_2 is always less than Pt_2 when the engine is moving forward.

If anti-icing air is turned on at the time of the icing, the anti-ice air will pressurize the nose dome and the vent hole to the engine pressure ratio system, causing a sharp drop in engine pressure ratio. This occurs because the resultant increase in Pt_2 will drive the engine pressure ratio system into a false low indication. The operator will be able to notice engine pressure ratio returning to normal when the Pt_2 probe ice blockage is cleared. The engine pressure ratio system is discussed in detail in Chapter XII.

B. Regulator Valve

The regulator valve shown in Figure 9-3 is set to automatically provide 500°F air at its maximum flow position at idle engine power settings and provide 650°F air at its minimum flow position near takeoff power.

The bimetallic spring, when cool, holds the valve disk open. Then, as air delivered to the system increases in flow and temperature with engine power increase, the disk moves toward closed until it hits the stop. This restriction to flow prevents overheating of the inlet, which could result in loss of engine power, compressor stalls, or heat damage to the inlet structure.

C. Cockpit Controls And Anti-Ice Valve Operation

The following is the sequence of operation of the anti-ice valves and the cockpit indicator lights when the cockpit on/off switch is actuated as seen in Figure 9-4.

1. Anti-Ice Switch "On"

a. When the anti-ice switch is first turned on, the four limit switches are in a position opposite to that which is shown on the diagram, and AC power will actuate the two motors and valves open through Limit Switches No. 2 and No. 4. As the valves reach their open limit, the limit switches are forced to move into their present position. They are now in the correct position for a later command to actuate the motors closed.

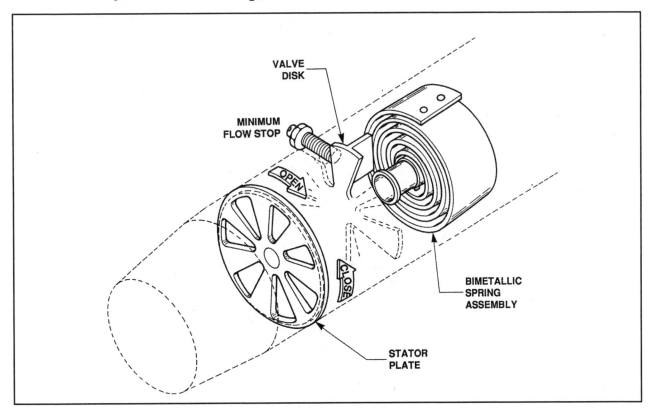

Fig. 9-3 — Anti-ice bi-metallic regulator valve.

b. Before the limit switches changed position, the amber light was illuminated in the cockpit through Limit Switches No. 1 and No. 3. After the limit switches reached their present position the amber light is out and the blue light illuminated.

c. If the blue light does not illuminate, it warns the operator that neither motor has fully actuated its airflow valve fully opened.

d. If one of the motors does not actuate fully, the amber light will remain on along with the blue light to warn the operator of the malfunction.

2. Anti-Ice Switch "Off"

a. When the cockpit switch is later turned off, the blue light will remain on and the amber light will again come on.

b. At that time the 115 VAC circuit will power the two motors to the closed position, and the four limit switches will cycle back to the position opposite the diagram to await the next open command.

c. As the motor limit switches move off their open contactors, both lights will go out.

3. Electro-Thermal Anti-Icing System

Some smaller turboprop and turboshaft engines use electric heat strip systems classed as electro-thermal anti-icing systems. They are constructed of electrical resistance wire embedded in layers of reinforced neoprene materials and located primarily at the lip of the nacelle flight inlet. Other possible locations are the engine inlet case and the engine inlet struts.

Like the hot air anti-ice systems, the electro-thermal systems are cycled on and off as required by ambient conditions. They are designed to operate only when the engine is running, since operating the strip without air passing over it would tend to overheat the strip and the part of the engine it is attached to.

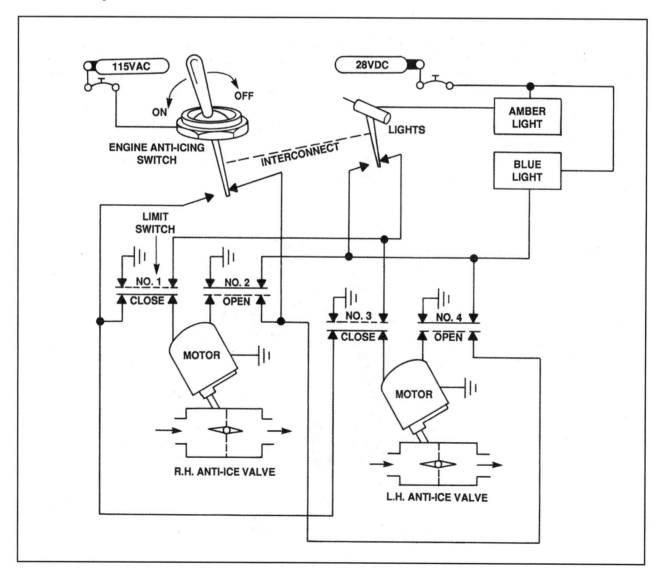

Fig. 9-4 — Cockpit switch, cockpit indicator lights and anti-ice valves shown in system "on".

E. Troubleshooting The Anti-Icing System
NOTE: Refer to Chapter VI for general troubleshooting procedures.

PROBLEM/POSSIBLE CAUSE	CHECK FOR	REMEDY
1. Ice forms in the inlet with the anti-icing system turned on.		
a. Anti-ice Valves (not open)	1. Correct input voltage 2. Proper operation of valves	Correct as necessary Replace valve(s)
2. Compressor stalls at high power setting with anti-icing system off.		
a. Inlet-icing (Ground)	Adverse ambient conditions	Shut down and remove ice. Continue run with anti-ice on
b. Inlet-icing (Flight)	Adverse ambient conditions	Pilot's discretion
3. Engine unable to attain full power (at EGT limit).		
a. Anti-ice Shut Off Valves (system off, but valve stuck open)	Leak through - Carefully feel forward side of valve with hand for heat from air leak.	Replace valve
b. Air regulator stuck full open	Malfunctioning bi-metallic coil	Replace or bench check
4. Fluctuating EGT and RPM.		
a. Anti-icing valves (system off)	Modulating valve motor	Adjust micro-switch or replace motor
5. EPR Rise (Flight)		
a. Inlet Probe	Ice buildup causing decrease in inlet pressure	Pilot's discretion

QUESTIONS:

1. Is the anti-icing system designed to remove ice from the engine inlet?

2. Is the anti-icing regulator electrically controlled?

3. How does inlet ice cause compressor stall?

Chapter X
Starter Systems

Gas turbine engines are generally started by starter power input to the main accessory gearbox which in turn rotates the compressor (Figure 10-1). On the dual-compressor gas turbine, the starter rotates the high pressure compressor system only. On free turbine, turboprop, and turboshaft engines with single compressors, only the compressor is rotated by the starter through the accessory gearbox. The free turbine is not coupled to the starter drive.

Compressor rotation by the starter provides an engine with sufficient air for combustion and also aids the engine in self-accelerating to idle speed after combustion occurs. Neither the starter nor the turbine wheel have sufficient power on their own to bring the engine from rest to idle speed but, when used in combination, the process takes place smoothly in approximately 30 seconds (on the typical engine). The starter is normally initiated by a cockpit toggle switch, but it is often automatically terminated by a speed sensor device, at five to ten percent RPM after self-accelerating speed is reached. At this point turbine power alone is sufficient to take the engine up to idle.

If the engine is not assisted to the correct speed, a hung (stagnated) start may occur. That is, the engine stabilizes at or near the point of starter cutoff. To remedy this situation, the engine must be shut down for investigation of the problem. Any attempt to accelerate by adding fuel will quite often result in a hot start, as well as a hung start, because the engine is operating with insufficient airflow to support further combustion.

Turboprop and turboshaft engines are started either in low pitch to reduce drag on the rotor and provide more speed and airflow or they are configured with a free-turbine driving the propeller. This allows for low drag acceleration in that the compressor rotor system only is being turned by the starter.

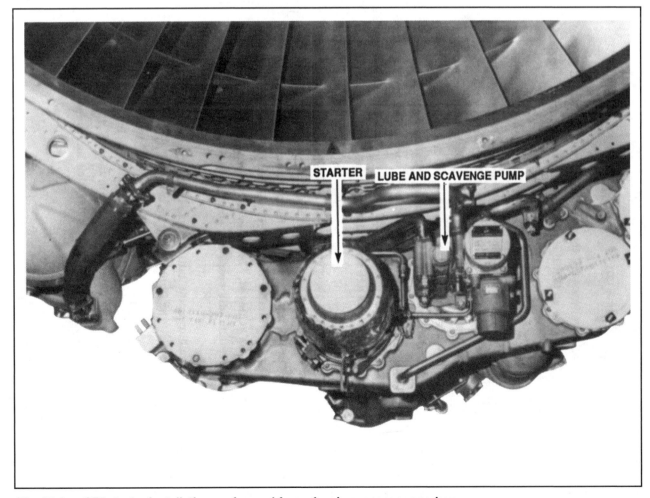

Fig. 10-1 — CF6 starter installation on forward face of main accessory gearbox.

The usual starting sequence is to energize the starter, then at five to ten percent rpm to energize ignition and open the fuel lever. A normal light-off will occur in 20 seconds or less. If light-off does not occur within the prescribed time limit, the start will generally be aborted to investigate the malfunction. Problems such as low starting power, weak ignition, or air in the fuel lines can degrade the starting process and cause a slow or no light-off condition.

The following charts (Figure 10-2) show the typical starting events of starter-on, ignition-on, and fuel-on in relationship to time, compressor speed, and exhaust gas

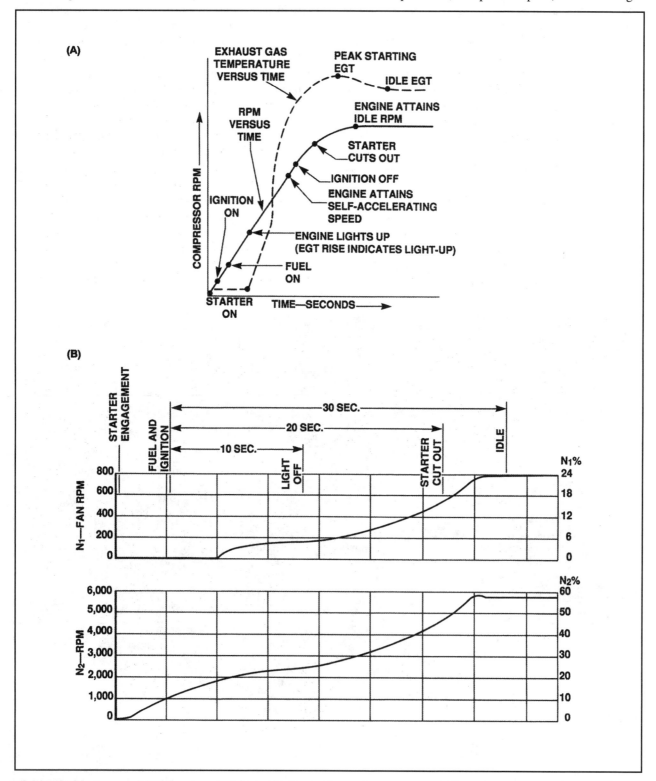

Fig. 10-2A — Rpm and EGT curves during start of a single compressor engine.
Fig. 10-2B — RPM and percent RPM curves during start of a dual compressor engine.

temperature. Recall that in Chapter VII, "Fuel Systems", it was mentioned that a rich fuel mixture is scheduled for the starting cycle so that time from start to idle is reduced. When idle RPM is reached, the flyweights in the fuel control governor move outward to cause the main metering valve to move slightly toward closed. You can observe this in Figure 10-2(A) at the top of the exhaust gas temperature curve and the top of the RPM curve, at which points the curves peak and start to turn horizontally to a stabilized compressor speed and engine gas temperature.

In Illustration (B), we can observe a dual-compressor relationship of N_1 and N_2 speeds during the start cycle. Note that, because the N_2 compressor is powered directly by the starter, it starts to rotate immediately after starter engagement, and N_1 fan speed starts to rotate only after air pressure within the engine builds sufficiently to cause it to rotate.

This curve is typical of a high bypass fan engine. When the starter cuts out at approximately 4,800 rpm, this represents 48 percent N_2 speed. The engine then stabilizes at idle N_2 speed of 58 percent (5,800 rpm) after

a slight overshoot where the fuel control governor flyweights start to control the fuel schedule. At idle, the N_1 compressor and fan are at 24 percent N_1 speed, and its speed curve stabilizes when N_2 speed stabilizes.

Newer aircraft with engines that utilize an electronic engine control (EEC), may be capable of starting in an automatic mode. When the start sequence is initiated in this mode, ignition and fuel come on line automatically, the starter and ignition turn off at the appropriate time. Overtemperature protection system is also present.

A. Electric Starters

Electric starters are not in wide use on flight engines because they are heavy, and the combination starter-generator provides a weight saving that makes it more feasible for small engines. However, electric starters are widely used on auxiliary and ground power units and some small flight engines.

Most electric starters contain an automatic release clutch mechanism to disengage the starter drive from the engine drive. Figure 10-3 shows a clutch assembly that

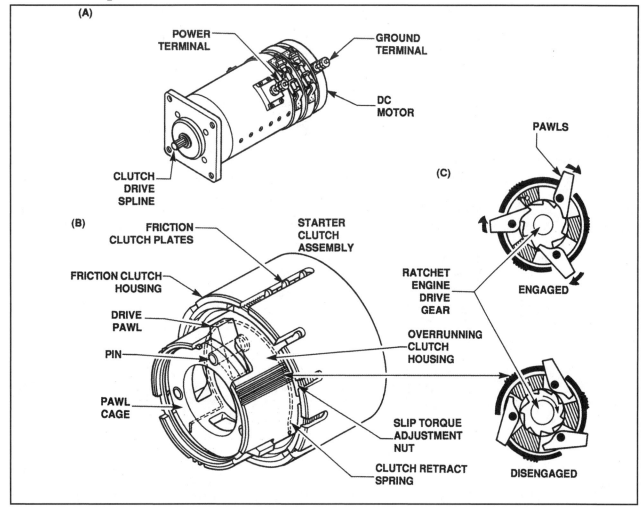

Fig.10-3A — Electrical Starter, 28VDC.
Fig. 10-3B — Starter clutch assembly.
Fig. 10-3C — Overrunning clutch.

performs this function and two additional functions. Its second function is to prevent the starter from applying excessive torque to the engine drive. At approximately 130 inch pounds of torque, small clutch plates within the clutch housing slip and act as a friction clutch. This setting is adjustable via the slip torque adjustment nut.

During starting, the friction clutch is designed to slip until engine speed and starter speed increase and develop less than the slip torque setting. It is important that the clutch tension is correct. If the tension is set too high, the engine drive point (ratchet) can be damaged. If the tension is too low, the engine could experience a slow or hot start.

The third function of the clutch assembly is to act as an overrunning clutch. This pawl and ratchet type mechanism contains three pawls which are spring loaded to the disengaged position (Figure 10-3C). When the starter is rotated, inertia causes the pawls to move inward to engage a ratchet type engine drive gear. This occurs because the pawl cage assembly, which floats within the overrunning clutch housing, tries to remain stationary when the armature starts to drive the clutch housing around.

The overrunning clutch housing, however, quickly forces the pawls inward by a bumping action, overcoming the disengage spring force. When engine speed approaches idle, its speed exceeds that of the starter and the pawls slip out of the tapered slots of the engine drive gear and throw outward via force of the disengage spring. This overrunning feature prevents the engine from driving the starter.

B. Starter-Generator (Figure 10-4)

The starter-generator is the most widely used starting unit on small gas turbine engines, to include turbojets, turbofans, turboprops and turboshafts. On very large engines the starter-generator is not practical, because the starting power requirements would be too great. Some auxiliary power units on commercial aircraft are using starter-generators, to avoid the need for two separate accessories. In this case, the starter-generator is quite large, in order to provide the aircraft's electrical needs. The starter-generator used on the Boeing 737-800 APU weighs 60 pounds and is rated at 90 KVA.

An analysis of the schematic in Figure 10-4 will be made easier by tracing the circuit in the following steps.

1. D.C. Bus is powered by External Power via Wire #6.

2. Engine Master Switch closed "on," allows power to reach the following:

a) Fuel valve via DC bus and wire #2.

b) Power lever relay coil via DC bus, wires #2 and #12 and the power lever switch.

c) Fuel pumps via DC bus, wire #3 and power lever relay.

d) Ignition solenoid coil via DC bus, wire #2, start switch, and wire #10.

e) Ignition exciters via DC bus, wire #3, power lever relay, wires #11, #14, and ignition solenoid contacts.

Note: The test switch will also activate the ignition exciters via wire #15 when the ignition solenoid contacts are "open." Operation of the ignition exciters and igniter plugs are checked by listening to a sharp snapping sound.

f) Start solenoid coil via DC bus, wire #2, master switch contacts, start switch, and wire #8. Wire #8 also supplies power to the contact of the under current solenoid.

g) Starter circuit via DC bus, wire #4, starter solenoid contacts, under current solenoid coil, and wire #9.

3. As long as the under current solenoid contacts are closed, the starter will remain energized; even when the spring loaded start switch is released. This is possible because the starter solenoid coil is now being powered via the DC bus, wire #5, and the under current solenoid.

4. Under current solenoid will re-open as engine speed increases or when less than 200 amperes of current is flowing.

5. Stop relay allows a pilot to terminate the start cycle by moving the start switch to the "stop" position; thus opening the circuit to the starter solenoid coil via wire #5.

6. A microswitch on the external power door prevents both external and battery power on the bus simultaneously.

7. The generator circuit activates via terminals "B" and "ground" after the engine approaches idle speed. Voltage regulating is accomplished via terminal "A."

C. Pneumatic (Air Turbine) Starter

The pneumatic (air turbine) starter (Figure 10-5), a type of low pressure air motor, was developed as a high power to weight ratio device. It has approximately one-fifth the weight of a comparable electric starter. This starter is used on almost every large commercial aircraft and is becoming a more widely used accessory on many corporate jets.

A low pressure, high volume air source of approximately 45 pounds per square inch—gauge, at 50-100 pounds per minute, is supplied to this starter from an onboard auxiliary power unit (APU), a ground power unit, or from the cross-bleed air source of another operating main engine.

Referring to Figure 10-6, observe that air enters the starter inlet and passes through a set of turbine nozzle vanes to change pressure to velocity and impinge at high kinetic energy levels on the turbine blades. The exhaust air exits overboard through a cowl fairing. In some installations, starting is terminated by shutting off the air supply manually with a cockpit toggle switch connected to the starter pressure-regulating and shut-off valve (Figure 10-8). In the illustration shown, the air supply is terminated automatically by a centrifugal flyweight cutout switch which causes the inlet air supply shut-off valve to close. The cutout switch in the starter provides the path to ground for the solenoid valve in the air supply shut-off valve. At the proper RPM, the path to ground is taken away and the shut-off valve closes.

Engines equipped with an electronic engine control (EEC) or with a full authority digital engine control (FADEC), often control the operation of the starter through these electronic systems. The activation of the starter circuit takes place through the EEC, and when the RPM sensing devices on the engine tell the EEC that the proper RPM has been reached, the start signal is removed. The system on the Boeing 737-800 is

sophisticated enough to sense a possible hot start and shut off fuel, yet leave the starter engaged to rotate the engine and cool things off. It will also sense what is termed a "wet start" (fuel introduced but no ignition), and keep the engine rotating to purge the fuel out of the combustor. This sophisticated type of system is becoming common in the new generation of electronic airplanes.

The turbine in this starter rotates up to 60 to 80 thousand rotations per minute and is geared down 20 to 30 times to achieve its high torque rating. A large unit for

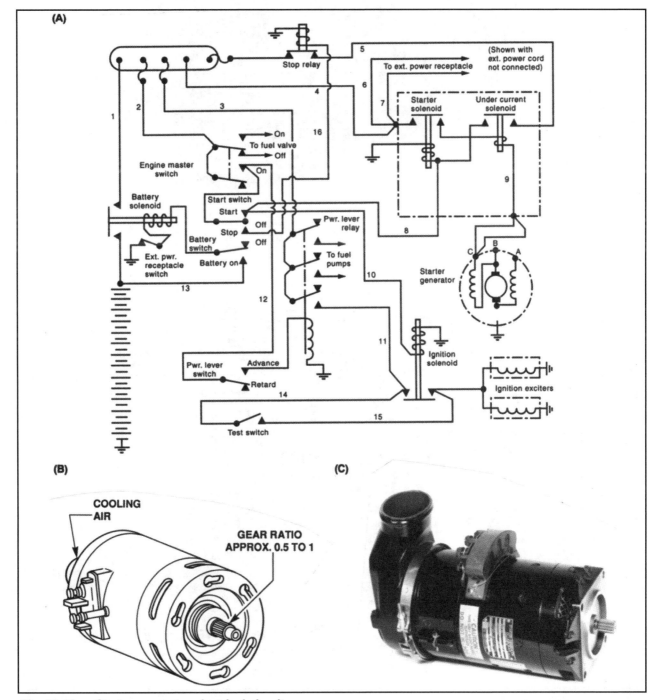

Fig. 10-4A — Starter-generator electrical circuit.
Fig. 10-4B — Starter-generator gear ratio.
Fig. 10-4C — Starter-generator unit.

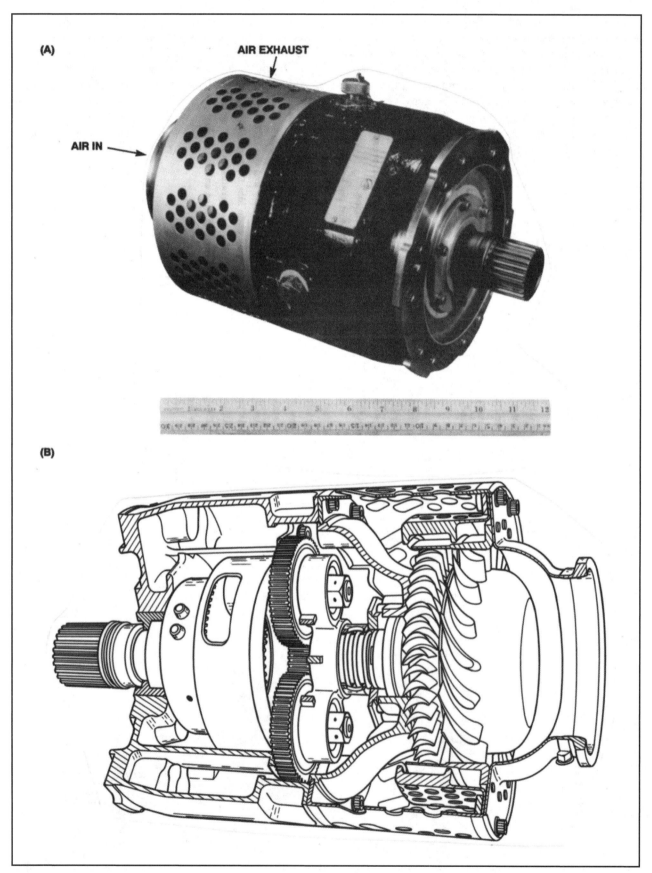

***Fig. 10-5A** — Large engine pneumatic (air turbine) starter, showing its relatively small size. Physical weight is approximately 30 lbs.*

***Fig. 10-5B** — Cutaway view of large engine pneumatic starter.*

the Boeing-747 aircraft will develop 200 horsepower, with approximately 30 pounds of physical weight. Smaller units, down to approximately 20 horsepower, are available.

The starter contains an integral oil supply of the same type oil used by the engine. Approximately four ounces of oil in small units, up to 12 ounces in large units, provide lubrication of the gear train. The oil level and

magnetic drain plug are frequent inspection items for maintenance personnel. On some engines, the starter gets it's lubricating oil from the engine's accessory gearbox, rather than having its own self-contained oil supply. For example, the CFM56-7 engine utilizes this technique.

On shutdown, at approximately 20 percent engine speed, the pawls of the overrunning clutch on this starter re-engage sufficiently for restarting, if it should be

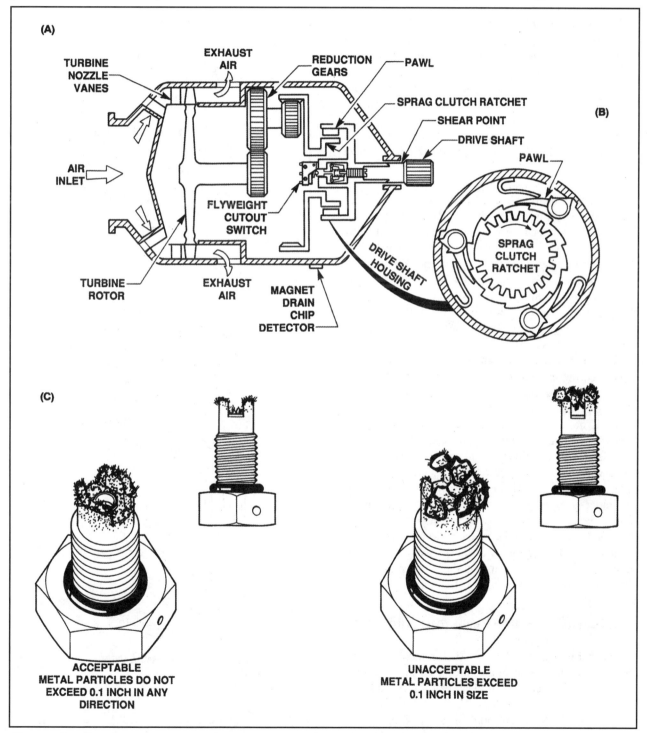

Fig. 10-6A — Pneumatic (air turbine) starter assembly, cutaway view.
Fig. 10-6B — Overrunning or sprag clutch.
Fig. 10-6C — Examples of magnetic chip detector contamination found during a special inspection.

required (Figure 10-6B). This procedure can damage some starters and must only be accomplished within the manufacturer's recommended limits. The only conditions under which starter engagement on a rotating engine are likely to be necessary are: 1) engine tail pipe fires during ground shut-down to purge the engine gas path of fuel vapors, 2) during starter assisted air-starts when wind-milling speed is too low to obtain a relight.

Safety features usually incorporated in this starter include a drive shaft shear point, which will break at a predetermined gear train induced torque force preventing damage to the engine. Another safety feature to prevent the starter from reaching burst speed if inlet air does not terminate on schedule is that airflow at the turbine nozzle vanes becomes choked and the turbine wheel speed will stabilize in a controlled over speed condition. After either of these malfunctions occur, a special inspection of the magnetic drain chip detector is generally required (Figure 10-6C).

The illustration in Figure 10-6B shows the overrunning clutch, called a sprag or sprague clutch assembly, is configured differently than the one previously mentioned for electric starters. The clutch in this installation is in a drive shaft housing which stays permanently engaged to the engine gearbox drive.

The pawls are forced inward by small leaf springs to engage the sprag clutch ratchet. At a preset engine speed, the pawls experience sufficient G-force to be thrown outward, disengaging the drive shaft assembly from the sprag clutch ratchet.

The sprag clutch ratchet and starter gear train coast to a halt and the drive shaft housing containing the pawls will continue to rotate at engine gearbox speed. A clicking sound heard during coast down on this type starter is not a malfunction, but rather the result of the pawls re-engaging and riding on the ratchet.

A dangerous situation to avoid with pneumatic starters fitted with pawl and ratchet drives is what is called a "crash engagement". This can occur if the air supply to the starter is turned on after the engine is running. In this case, the ratchet gear in the starter will be turning at an extremely high RPM. If the engine RPM is reduced to the speed at which the pawls try to engage the ratchet gear, a violent clash will occur between these two pieces. This can cause serious damage to the starter and possibly the accessory gearbox.

1. Starter Pressure-Regulating And Shut-Off Valve (Figure 10-7)

The starter "air valve" is installed in the inlet air line to the starter. It consists of a control head and a butterfly valve and is powered open electrically by means of a cockpit switch (Figure 10-9).

In Figure 10-8, the solenoid is energized upward by the cockpit start switch, and the following events occur.

a. The control crank rotates counterclockwise, pushing the control rod to the right and extending the bellows

fully. The butterfly type regulating valve, being closed at this time, permits this movement because no pressure is present in the sensing line.

b. The control crank also forces the pilot valve rod and cap to the right against a spring tension.

c. Air that had been blocked in the filtered inlet line flows past the cap to the servo piston and opens the butterfly valve.

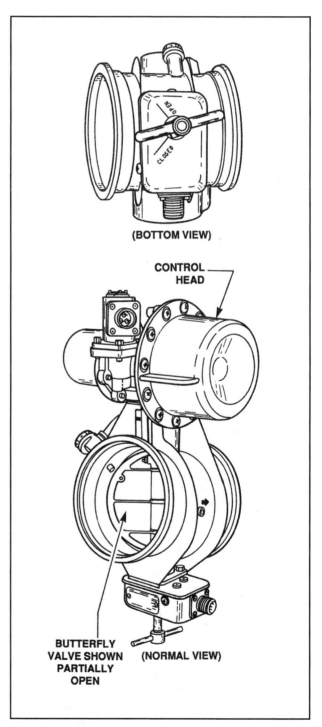

Fig. 10-7 — Starter pressure-regulating and shut-off valve with manual override handle in partially open position.

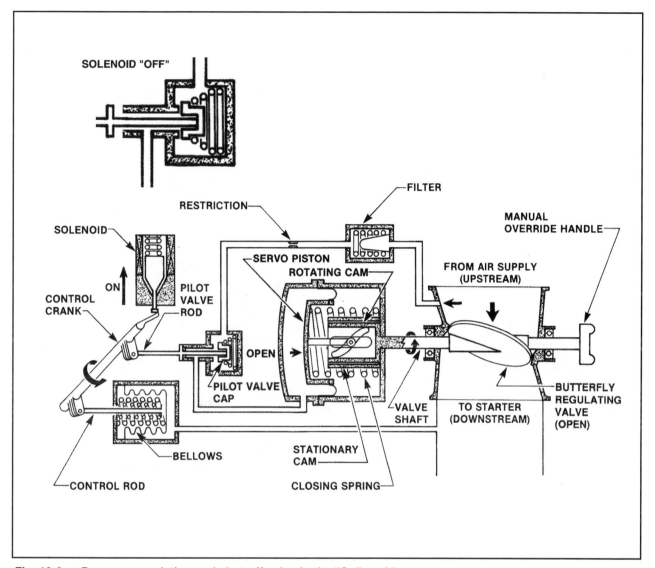

Fig. 10-8 — Pressure-regulating and shut-off valve in the "On" position.

d. As pressure builds in the downstream supply line, the sensing line takeoff directs air to partially compress the bellows. As this occurs, the pilot valve rod off-seats, allowing some of the servo piston air to vent to the atmosphere and the butterfly valve to reset slightly closed.

e. When downstream air pressure reaches a preset value, the amount of air flowing to the servo piston through the restrictor equals the amount of air being bled to the atmosphere, and the system is in a state of equilibrium. This feature is present to protect the starter if inlet air pressure is set too high.

f. When a predetermined starter drive speed is reached, the centrifugal cutout flyweight switch in this starter de-energizes the solenoid and the butterfly returns to a closed position.

g. The manual override handle is present to manually rotate the butterfly open and closed if an electrical failure has occurred or if corrosion or icing is causing excessive friction within the system. After freeing the restriction to

movement, the valve must operate normally or be replaced.

2. Manual Operation By The T-Handle

A three-step procedure which must be done with caution because the handle can move suddenly and injure the hand. It may also be hot enough to burn the hand if gloves are not used.

The typical procedure to use is as follows:

a. Pull out on the T-handle using a hook or a light hand grip. CAUTION! THE HANDLE MAY TURN QUICKLY. This pulling action vents the Servo Piston Chamber;

b. Turn the T-handle to "open" and hold throughout the starting period. This overcomes the close spring in the servo piston;

c. At 35 percent N_2 speed, turn the T-handle to "close" and push the handle in until it seats. (CAUTION—At 40 percent N_2, the starter will over-speed).

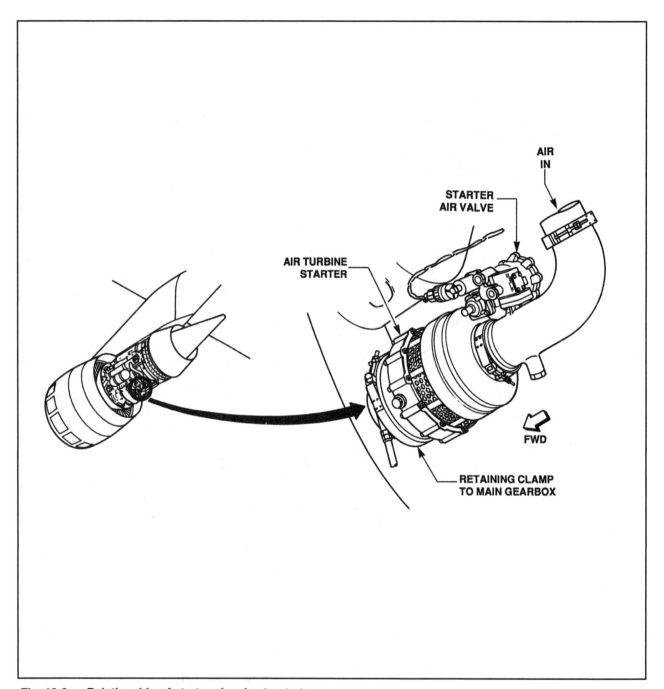

Fig. 10-9 — Relationship of starter air valve to starter.

3. Pneumatic (Air Turbine) Starting System

The auxiliary power unit is generally mounted in the rear of the airplane or in a lower fuselage compartment and an air manifold which runs through the entire ship interconnects the auxiliary power unit, the ground service connection, the engine bleed air ports, and the starter inlets. It is possible with this system to start one engine from a ground or onboard starting unit and then to start the remaining engine(s) from the cross-bleed air source of the operating engine.

a. Starting Procedure

The starting procedure of a typical dual-spool engine is as follows: (Refer to Figure 10-10).

1) Start auxiliary power unit (Figure 10-11) or ground power unit and watch for 45 pounds per square inch—gauge on Start Air Manifold gauge in the cockpit;

CAUTION: Because of the very high forces present within the air supply, procedures must be in place to ensure personnel and equipment safety. For example, a ground unit air hose must be free of foreign objects and free of kinks, and complete engagement of the hose adapter is critical.

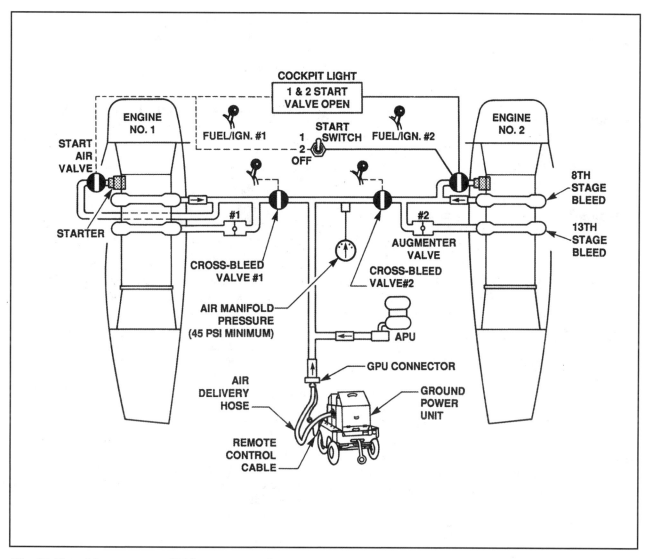

Fig. 10-10 — Air sources available to pneumatic starters.

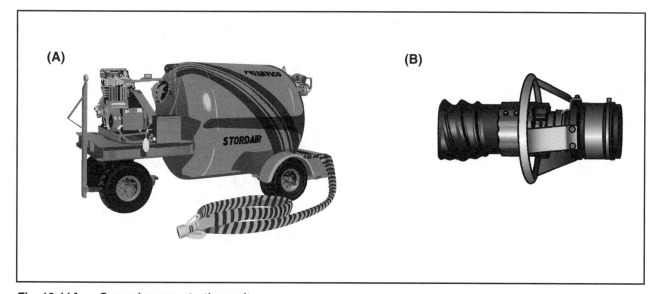

Fig. 10-11A — Ground power starting unit.
Fig. 10-11B — Hose to aircraft adapter.

2) Open Cross-Bleed valve #2;

3) Place Start Switch to "No. 2" (energizes solenoid Figure 10-8) and observe cockpit light "on;"

4) Watch for slight drop in starter air manifold pressure;

5) See N_2 speed begin to increase on cockpit tachometer indicator;

6) See N_1 speed begin to increase within five to ten seconds of N_2 indication;

7) Place start Fuel/Ignition lever to "On";

8) Watch for exhaust gas temperature rise and oil pressure indication;

9) Watch for cockpit light to go out and a slight rise in air manifold pressure as #2 start air valve and ignition de-energize, approximately ten percent rpm below idle speed;

10) Monitor all engine instruments as engine spools up to idle speed. (Close cross bleed valve No. 2.);

11) Start the remaining engine(s) from the auxiliary power unit or ground power unit;

12) Follow prescribed checklist for remainder of run as suggested in Chapter XIV, "Engine Operation".

b. Cross-Bleed Starting

After one engine is started, the remaining engine(s) can be started with cross-bleed air, but this is not desirable under normal circumstances. It requires approximately 80 percent N_2 speed to obtain the necessary air pressure, and this presents a problem of noise and jet blast on the ramp as well as a waste of fuel.

1) To start #1 engine from cross-bleed air, open cross-bleed valves No. 1 and No. 2.

2) Open #2 Augmenter Valve if air manifold pressure is low on a hot day or if customer bleed air is being used.

3) Place Start Switch to "No. 1" and follow procedure as for No. 2 engine.

c. Air Starter Duty Cycle

The air starter has a prescribed duty cycle, typically:

1) During engine starting, 5 minutes "On", 2 minutes "Off" to cool.

2) During motor over checks, 5 minutes "On", due to additional loading 5 minutes "Off" to cool.

The reason for this restricted operating cycle time is that this unit contains a ring gear type reduction system which builds up friction heat very readily, and the low volume splash type wet sump oil system contained in the gear section has a limited cooling capability.

D. Other Starting Systems

Many other starting systems have been developed in the past for military and commercial engines. They are not in common use in either general or commercial aviation today.

1. High-Low Pressure Pneumatic Starter

An accessory gearbox mounted starter (Figure 10-12), which is a type of air turbine starter that can utilize either conventional low pressure starting or a high pressure, 3,000 pounds per square inch, air source from an aircraft mounted storage bottle.

High pressure air starting (usually only on one engine) gives the aircraft a self-starting capability without the assistance of an auxiliary power unit or ground power unit.

2. Cartridge-Pneumatic Starter

An accessory gearbox mounted starter which can use either an explosive solid propellant charge or a low pressure, high volume air source similar to the pneumatic (air turbine) starter. The charge is ignited electrically from the aircraft battery, giving the aircraft a self-starting capability without auxiliary power unit or ground power unit (Figure 10-13).

3. Fuel-Air Combustion Starter

An accessory gearbox mounted starter which utilizes a high pressure, 3,000 pounds per square inch, air source and a combustion process. It is very similar to a small gas turbine engine. Combustion is initiated electrically from the aircraft battery giving the aircraft a self-starting capability (Figure 10-14).

4. Turbine Impingement Starting

A low pressure, high volume air source of 45 pounds per square inch—gauge at 200 to 300 pounds per minute is directed onto the engine turbine wheel. The air source terminates after self- accelerating speed is reached. No accessory is required in this system, only an inlet air port (Figure 10-15).

5. Hydraulic Starter

An accessory gearbox mounted hydraulic starter motor. It is driven by fluid from an auxiliary power unit mounted hydraulic pump, or a hand pump and accumulator arrangement.

Additional starting procedures are discussed in detail in Chapter XIV.

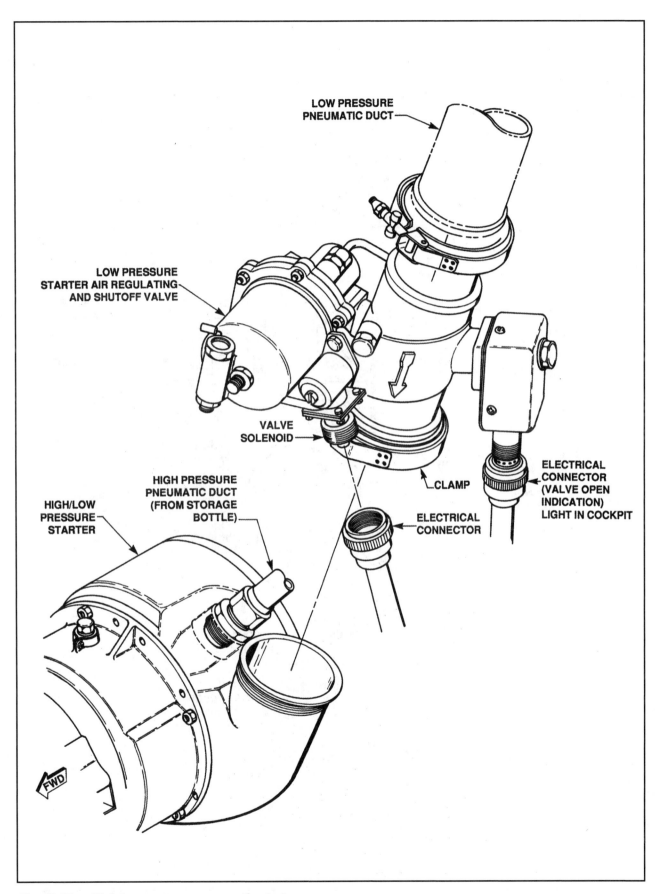

Fig. 10-12 — High-low pressure pneumatic starter.

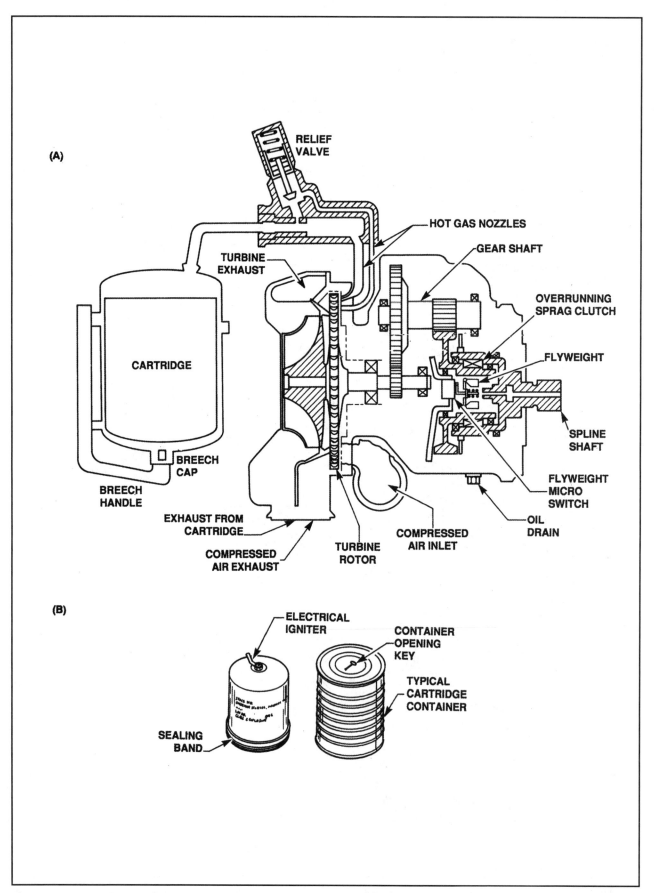

Fig. 10-13A — Cartridge/pneumatic starter cutaway view.
Fig. 10-13B — Solid propellant cartridge.

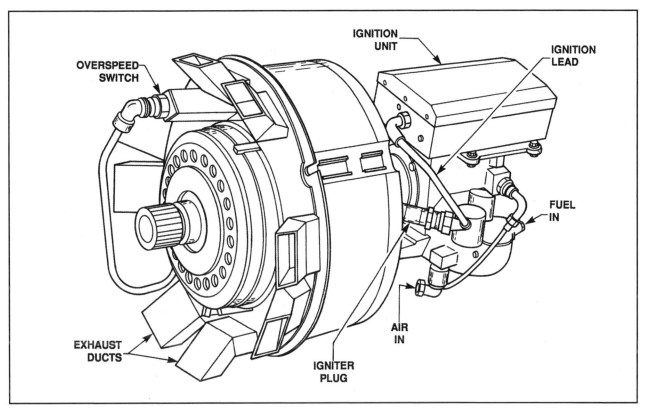

Fig. 10-14 — Fuel/air combustion starter.

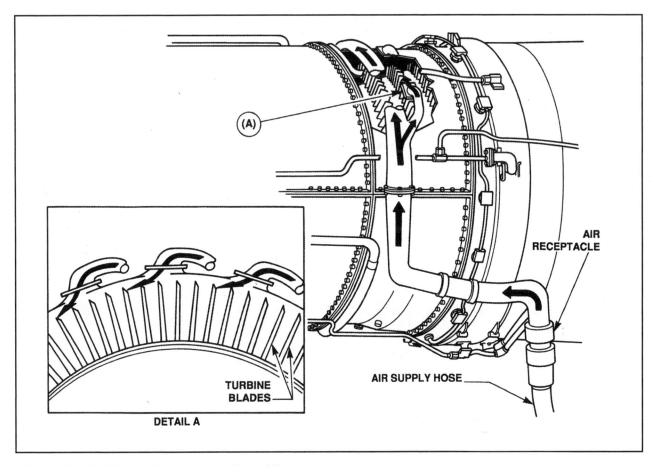

Fig. 10-15 — Turbine impingement starting airflow.

E. Troubleshooting Starter Systems

NOTE: Refer to Chapter VI for general troubleshooting procedures.

PROBLEM/POSSIBLE CAUSE	CHECK FOR	REMEDY

1.Starter-Generator

a. Engine does not rotate when the starter switch is closed during a battery start.

1) External Power Receptacle Door	Door open or faulty microswitch	Close door or repair switch
2) Battery Relay	Power at DC start bus	Repair as necessary
3) Motor Relay	Proper closing	Repair or replace
4) Starter-Generator	a) Correct input voltage b) Sheared shaft	Change battery Replace starter

b. Engine does not rotate when the start switch is closed during external power start.

1) External Power Source	Correct connection to aircraft	Make connection
2) a. 1), a. 2), a. 3), a. 4), above		

c. Starting terminates when start switch is released.

1) Undercurrent Relay	Proper closing	Replace as necessary

d. Engine starts but will not self-accelerate (hung start).

1) Power Supply	Low voltage	Charge or change battery
2) Starter-Generator	Internal malfunction	Change unit

2. Air Turbine Starter

a. Engine does not rotate when the start switch is closed.

1) APU or GPU	Presence of air in starting manifold (Look at cockpit gauge)	Correct as necessary
2) Starter Air Valve	a) Solenoid operation b) Ice or corrosion preventing valve operationor apply heat	Repair or replace Cycle with manual override
3) Starter	Shaft sheared	Replace shaft and/or starter

b. Starter does not rotate to normal cutoff speed.

1) APU or GPU	Low air supply	Repair or replace air unit

PROBLEM/POSSIBLE CAUSE	CHECK FOR	REMEDY
2) Starter	Centrifugal flyweight switch cutout setting	Adjust setting or replace starter
3) Starter Air Valve	Internal malfunction	Replace valve

c. Starter does not cut off.

1) b. 2) above (flyweight switch inoperative) or b. 3) above

d. Metal particles on magnetic drain plug.

1) Internal Starter Malfunction	a) Small fuzzy particles	Normal
	b) Chips or slivers	Replace starter

QUESTIONS:

1. Where is a turbine engine starter normally mounted?

2. What starter clutch feature prevents the engine from driving the starter to burst speed?

3. Which type starter remains completely engaged to the engine during engine operation?

4. Which unit controls airflow to the pneumatic (air turbine) starter?

5. From which three sources does the pneumatic (air turbine) starter receive its air supply?

Chapter XI
Ignition Systems

A gas turbine engine ignition system contains three major components: a high voltage exciter, a high voltage transmission lead, and an igniter plug. The exciter is powered by the aircraft electrical system, either D.C. or A.C., or a dedicated permanent magnet alternator (PMA) and produces a high voltage pulse through the igniter lead to the plug. The igniter plug then arcs (spark jumps a gap) to ignite the fuel/air mixture in the combustion chamber.

Modern gas turbine engine ignition systems are of the high intensity capacitor discharge type with either Intermittent Duty or Extended Duty cycles. Intermittent Duty types are of sufficiently high current draw to cause overheat damage to their units, so they have a restricted duty cycle based on operating time, followed by a cooling off period. Extended Duty types have long duty cycles, or in some cases are rated for continuous duty, meaning they have no time limits at all.

After a normal start, ignition is no longer needed and the ignition system is deactivated. At this time, the flame within the combustor acts as the ignition source for continuous combustion.

There are two common classifications of the capacitor discharge ignition systems, the high tension system and the low tension system. With either the high or the low tension system, two igniter plugs are usually incorporated in the engine combustor at approximately the four o'clock and eight o'clock positions. The typical system also consists of two exciter units or channels and two high tension leads which attach to the igniter plugs. The two exciter channels may be housed separately or as one unit (Figure 11-1).

A. Main Ignition System

The main ignition system is used primarily during ground starting and is then turned off. A secondary function of this system is to provide a standby protection against in-flight flameout which might occur at takeoff, landing, bad weather operation, or when operating in anti-ice bleed air mode.

If an extended duty main system is installed, the pilot can select full ignition to either plug, or both plugs, at his discretion and in consideration of the service life of the igniter plug.

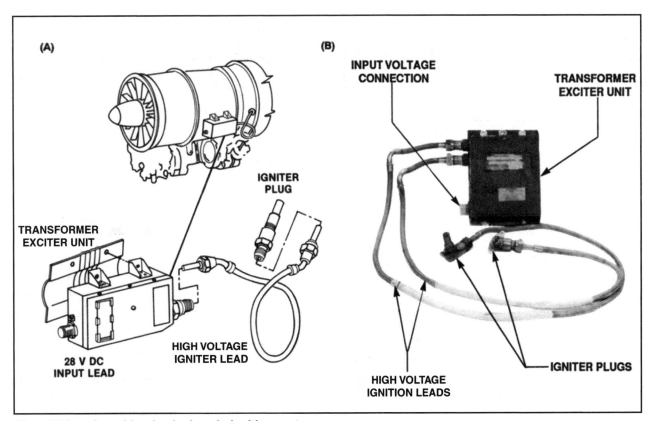

Fig. 11-1A — *One side of a dual, main ignition system.*
Fig. 11-1B — *Dual, main ignition system.*

In the Figure 11-2 shown, the Ground Start position will cause engine ignition to occur at both igniter plugs. After start up, the switch will be turned to the "Off" position. The Ground Start position also powers the engine starter and will be indicated by the start valve light.

During takeoff, landing, and other critical flight times, the switch will generally be placed in either the left or right positions to protect against flameout. The Flight position is mainly used after a flameout occurs. It provides full ignition to both igniter plugs but does not power the engine starter. Engine rotation in flight for starting is normally accomplished by engine wind-milling, created by ram air within the engine inlet.

If the main system is on an older aircraft, it may be of the intermittent duty type with an operation time limit. This occurs more often in High Tension Type systems in

which heat buildup can damage the exciter units. A typical time limit is two minutes on, three minutes off.

If a second two minutes on is needed, a 20 minute cooling off period is required.

1. Continuous Duty Circuit

In recent years, the majority of new ignition exciter designs have incorporated extended or continuous duty circuits. This has driven the designs to store lower energies and incorporate as many system efficiency improvements as possible in the exciter circuitry, ignition leads, and plug firing tips.

When the main system is of the intermittent duty type, there is often a low energy (low joule) system called a "continuous duty circuit" incorporated within the ignition exciter to give stand-by protection against flameout at critical operating times, such as takeoff and landing, etc. This unit is considered to have no time limit. Figure 11-3 shows a dual unit that can be operated on either the intermittent or the continuous duty circuit. If an engine relight in flight becomes necessary and continuous ignition does not create sufficient spark energy to cause combustion to occur, the main system will be used within its time limits.

2. Auto-Ignition

Many turbine powered aircraft have an auto-ignition circuit installed. It is designed primarily to ensure instantaneous ignition if an engine begins to lose power from inlet icing and is in danger of flaming out. When the auto-ignition arming switch is "On" in the cockpit, electrical power is supplied to a sensor on the engine which is alerted if the engine experiences a sudden reduction in power. The two most common sensing systems utilize either loss of torque oil pressure or loss of compressor discharge pressure to actuate the auto-ignition system and to illuminate a cockpit warning light.

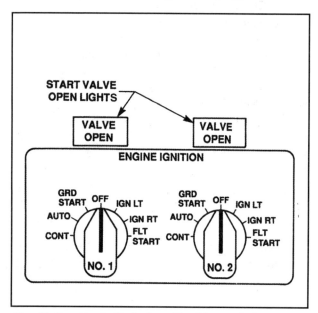

Fig. 11-2 — Cockpit start and ignition switch.

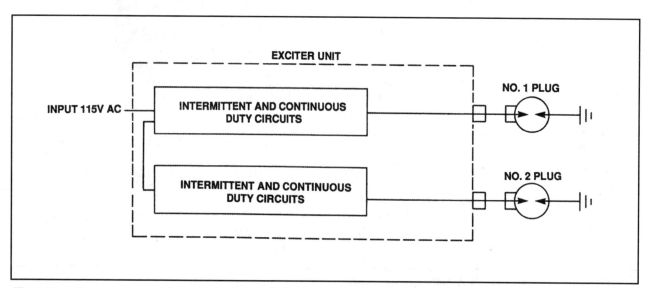

Fig. 11-3 — Transformer exciter with both intermittent and continuous duty circuits.

The next generation Boeing 737, like the 737-800, has an automatic ignition feature. On this airplane, auto ignition is enabled when the engine start switch is in the "off" position, versus having a separate switch position labeled automatic. The ignition system will be automatically activated by the electronic engine control (EEC) when the following conditions are met:

- The start lever is in the idle position;
- The EEC sees an engine deceleration (without command) greater than normal schedule or the core speed is below 57% N_2;
- The core speed is greater than 40% N_2.

B. Special Handling

In ignition systems, the term high intensity infers that a lethal charge is present and this system requires special maintenance and handling as prescribed by the manufacturer. Typical of these procedures are as follows:

1. Ensure that the ignition switch is turned off before performing any maintenance on the system;

2. To remove an igniter plug, disconnect the exciter input lead and wait the time prescribed by the manufacturer, usually one to five minutes. Waiting for this period of time allows any residual stored energy to bleed off through the internal safety resistors. Then disconnect the igniter lead and ground the center electrode to the engine, to ensure the capacitor is not charged. The igniter plug is now safe to remove;

3. Exercise great caution in handling damaged hermetically sealed exciter units. Some contain small amounts of radioactive material, (cesium-barium 137 or krypton-85), within the air gap tubes. This material is used to calibrate and stabilize the discharge point to a preset voltage;

4. Ensure proper disposal of unserviceable igniter plugs. If they are the types that contain aluminum oxide or the higher heat range beryllium oxide, care must be exercised because both materials are toxic;

5. Before a firing test of igniters is performed, the technician must ensure that the combustor is not fuel-wetted or a fire or explosion could occur;

6. Do not energize the system for troubleshooting if the igniter plugs are removed, since high voltage would be present at the igniter leads;

7. If an igniter plug is dropped it should be discarded since internal damage, such as cracked ceramic insulators, can occur that possibly may not be detectable by testing or examination;

8. Always use a new gasket where the plug is reinstalled. The gasket is essential in providing a good conductive current path to ground.

C. Joule Ratings

Turbine ignition systems carry a joule rating. A joule is defined as power (watts) multiplied by time (seconds),

whereby one joule per second equals one watt. The time factor for plug firing is very short, in the millionths of a second. Ignition of atomized fuel occurs very rapidly, also in milliseconds, so a long term spark is not necessary. A mathematical explanation of why turbine ignition systems are considered lethal is as follows:

EXAMPLE: A turbine engine ignition system with a stored voltage of 2,000 VDC has an ionizing voltage at the plug of 500 VDC. The current in the system is 200 amps, and the spark jumps the igniter plug gap in 40 millionths of a second (0.000040 sec.). What would be the joule rating on this ignition system?

$$
\begin{aligned}
\text{Watts} &= \text{Volts x Amps} \\
\text{Watts} &= 500 \text{ x } 200 \\
\text{Watts} &= 100,000 \\
\text{Joules} &= \text{Watts x Time} \\
\text{Joules} &= 100,000 \text{ x } 0.00040 \\
\text{Joules} &= 4
\end{aligned}
$$

NOTE: The higher stored voltage ensures the ionizing voltage at the igniter plug is sufficient, recognizing that there may be long igniter leads creating a voltage drop and that the igniter plug gap will increase with time.

Some ignition systems of the high energy type are rated as high as 20 joules, with 2,000 amps output. This power is possible from the physically small generating system described because of the very short duration of time required to cause flash-over at the igniter plug gap.

As a general rule of thumb, the stored energy of large main engine turbine ignition exciters is between 4 and 20 joules. Stored energy for small main engine exciters may be 1 to 4 joules, and APU's may employ exciters storing between .75 and 4 joules. The actual energy delivered to the spark event at the end of the plug is typically on the order of 20 to 30 % of the stored energy, and is typically delivered a minimum of 1 to 2 spark events per second.

The output voltage of the ignition exciter can be completely independent of the stored energy. That is, a 1 joule ignition exciter could be a high tension unit capable of 24 kilovolt output.

D. Types Of Ignition Systems

Both low tension (voltage) and high tension (voltage) ignition systems are in general use, and they are designed to use either direct current or alternating current as input power.

DC operated systems receive their power from the battery bus, and AC systems are powered from the aircraft AC bus or by a dedicated permanent magnet alternator (PMA). These PMA's can serve as a power supply to an ignition system which stores between 1 and

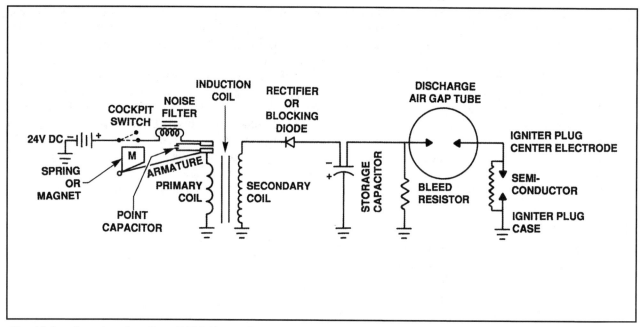

Fig. 11-4 — Low tension (2 to 7 KV) "Intermittent Duty" ignition system—one side of a dual system.

4 joules of energy. Each PMA is designed to produce sufficient current during the low cranking speeds associated with starting.

1. Intermittent Duty Low Tension Ignition System—With D.C. Voltage Input

The output voltage of low tension ignition system is in the range of two to ten kilo volts. Figure 11-4 depicts a low tension, DC input system. These systems, which are typical of business jet applications, typically store from 1 to 4 joules of energy. Note that only one igniter plug is fired by each exciter channel. Therefore, the engine will have either two identical circuits in a single exciter unit or two separate exciter units to supply power to its two igniter plugs.

Leading particulars of ignition system in Figure 11-4:

      Input Voltage — 24 to 28 VDC
      Operational Limit — 10 to 30 Volts
      Input Current — 3 Amps
      Stored Energy — 4.0 Joules
      Output Voltage — 3,000 to 7,000 Volts
      Output Current — 200 Amps
      Output Power — 400,000 watts
      Spark Rate (sparks per second)
            4 per sec at 14 volts
            8 per sec at 30 volts
      Time for Spark to Jump Gap — 0.00001 secs

a. Sequence Of Operations

1) With the cockpit switch open, the permanent magnet will hold the points closed by attraction of the point armature;

2) When the switch is closed, current will flow from the battery negative side, up through the primary coil, across the points, and to the battery positive terminal;

3) As electromagnetic force builds, the points are pulled open, stopping current flow. This action is repeated approximately 200 times per second. As the points open, there is a tendency for the current to jump the points gap. A capacitor across the points prevents arcing by offering a path of least resistance for this current flow;

4) When the current first flows through the closed points, bottom to top of the primary coil, a pulse is produced in the secondary coil. This pulse attempts to flow in the opposite direction, from the bottom of the secondary coil out of the ground, and up through the capacitor to the top side of the secondary coil, but the rectifier blocks current flow in this direction. The current path is also blocked by the discharge tube which is open at this time;

5) A second stronger pulse occurs when the points open and the primary field collapses into the secondary, creating a voltage of greatly increased value. Secondary current flows in the opposite direction, from the top of the coil and through the rectifier, to allow electrons to store on the top plate of the storage capacitor. The current path is completed as free electrons are pushed from the bottom plate of the capacitor, out of the ground, to the bottom side of the secondary coil. The half-wave rectifier or blocking diode is present to change secondary coil induced alternating current to pulsating direct current;

6) After repeated cycles, a charge will build on the negative (top) side of the storage capacitor which is sufficient to overcome the gap in the discharge tube. The initial current surge ionizes the air gap (makes conductive) and allows the capacitor to discharge fully to the igniter plug;

7) In a low tension system, the igniter plug is referred to as a self-ionizing or shunted-gap type plug. The firing end of the plug contains a semi-conductor material which initially provides a highly conductive path by bridging the gap between the center electrode and the ground electrode (provided by the igniter plug outer casing). The plug fires when the current flows from the storage capacitor through the center electrode, the semi-conductor, the outer casing, and then back to the lower positive plate of the capacitor;

As current flows initially through the semi-conductor, heat builds up creating an increased resistance to current flow. When the semi-conductor reaches an incandescent state, the air gap becomes heated sufficiently to ionize and the current takes the path of least resistance across the ionized gap, fully discharging the capacitor and creating a high energy capacitive discharge spark;

8) The Bleed Resistor is present in the circuit to act as a safety device in accomplishing the following:

a) Dissipate the excess voltage that may be available at each plug firing. Plugs fire at the minimum required voltage, and the bleed resistor releases the remainder;

b) Dissipate the capacitor discharge if the voltage required to fire a worn plug is greater than the voltage available;

c) Provide a discharge path for capacitor energy if the system is fired when no igniter plug is installed;

d) Bleed off the capacitor when the system is de-energized.

2. High Tension, Intermittent Duty, AC Input System

The following electrical circuit is of the type found on some modern large gas turbine engines. It is a high tension system, typically of 14 to 28 kilovolts, with an alternating current input voltage.

Some combustors need a higher intensity flashover at the igniter plug and utilize this type system for that reason (Figure 11-5).

Leading particulars for ignition system in Figure 11-5:

Input Voltages	105V to 122V at
Frequency	380Hz to 420Hz
Input Power/Current	0.65 Amps Max at 115V 400Hz
Stored Energy	16.0 Joules
Output Voltage	20 KV (at lead output coductor)
Output Current	200 Amps Peak Min.
Spark Rate	1.0 at 105V-380 Hertz
(sparks per second)	2.0 +0.75 at 115V-400 Hertz
	5.0 at 122V-420 Hertz
Time for Spark to Jump Gap	0.000004 sec

a. Sequence Of Events:

1) Alternating current at 115 volts, 400 cycles is supplied to the primary coil of the power transformer. Note the absence of the vibrator point system, which is not needed with an AC input system. In some DC systems, the points were a constant source of malfunction and the AC system was developed to counteract this problem.

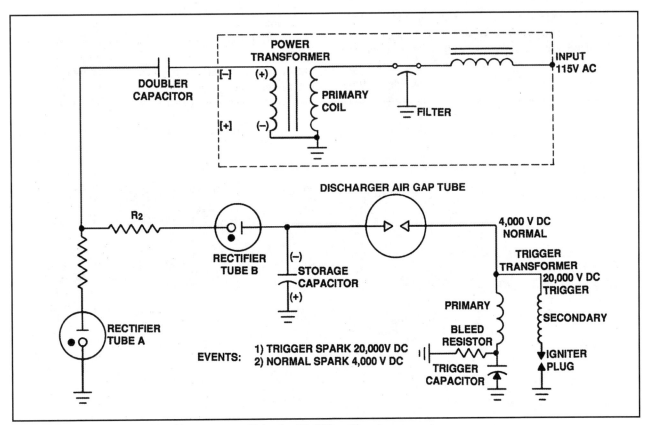

Fig. 11-5 — High tension ignition system 20 joule, 28,000 volt system.

2) During the first half cycle, the primary coil produces approximately 2,000 volts in the secondary coil and current flows from the bottom (-) side of the coil and out at the ground. Current then flows into the ground at Rectifier Tube "A" through resistor (R1), through the doubler capacitor, and back to the top (+) side of the secondary coil. This leaves the left side of the doubler capacitor charged at 2,000 volts. Rectifier Tube "B" blocks any other current path during the first half cycle current flow.

3) During the second half cycle the primary coil produces another 2,000 volts in the secondary coil and current flows from the top side of the coil, through the doubler capacitor where it now has a total of 4000 volts, through resistor R2, through Rectifier Tube B, through the storage capacitor, out of the ground, and returning to the bottom (+) side of the secondary coil. Note that the presence of resistor R1 and the gas discharge tube cause current to seek the path of least resistance, which is straight back to the secondary coil. Rectifier Tube A also blocks current flow from the doubler capacitor and R1 to ground ensuring current flow to the storage capacitor.

4) Repeated pulses charge the storage capacitor top (-) side at 4,000 volts to a point where the air gap in the discharge tube ionizes. When this occurs, current flows through the trigger transformer primary coil, the trigger capacitor, the ground, and back to the bottom (+) side of the storage capacitor.

This action induces voltage into the secondary coil of the trigger transformer, at approximately 20,000 volts, sufficient to ionize the igniter plug air gap and complete a path back to the storage capacitor. The trigger spark which occurs by action of the trigger transformer and capacitor, creates a low resistance path and allows both the trigger capacitor and storage capacitor to fully

discharge at the igniter plug, creating a second high intensity spark.

The high tension spark created by this type system is needed to blast carbon deposits from the igniter plug electrodes, also to vaporize fuel globules at the firing end sufficiently to ignite the air-fuel mixture in the combustor either on the ground or in flight.

3. Solid State Low and High Tension Ignition Systems

The most recent development in gas turbine engine ignition systems is the solid state circuit. Solid state circuitry produces less heat, is lighter in weight, and is also designed so that the igniter plug firing interval is constant regardless of input voltage. This adds to safety in engine relight capability and in extended service life of the unit.

Newer solid state low tension systems have little or no duty cycle restrictions and can be operated with full rated power supplied to both igniter plugs. Transistors have replaced the mechanical points in the primary circuit, and other new low heat generating circuit designs account for the change in duty cycle times.

Most low tension, extended duty units which fire at 4 Joules or less have no duty cycle restrictions; meaning they can be in operation for any length of time required. Low tension systems rated higher than 4 Joules will probably have a restricted duty cycle.

The exciter unit has an expected service life of thousands of hours, but the expected service life of the typical igniter plug is much less.

Some extended duty systems on very large aircraft have as high as 16 Joules of stored energy available in their capacitors, but they are still considered to be of low tension because the energy needed by a new igniter plug to fire correctly is only approximately two Joules. If the

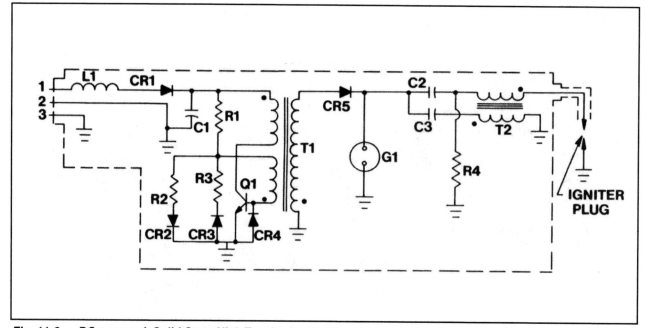

Fig. 11-6 — DC powered, Solid State High Tension Ignition System.

plug is wearing out, however, the full stored energy is available to continue to fire the plug until the transformer capacity is exceeded.

The extended duty systems are designed for either DC input or AC input voltage and use the semi-conductor (shunted-gap) type of igniter plugs previously mentioned in the discussion of the intermittent duty ignition system.

Figure 11-6 shows a schematic of a solid state High Tension circuit ignition system which uses 24 volts DC as its input.

This system was designed for an Auxiliary Power Unit which requires aircraft battery input voltage for starting. The circuit shown includes an Exciter Unit to step up 24 VDC to 21,000 VDC, a High Tension Lead and an Igniter Plug.

The particulars of this ignition system are as follows:

Input Voltage	14 to 32 VDC (24 VDC nominal)
Input Current	4.0 Amps DC Maximum
Stored Energy	4.0 Joules
Spark Rate (sparks per sec.)	1 at 14 VDC, 10 at 32 VDC
Output Voltage	21,000 Volts Nominal

A simplified description of the Exciter operation and the manufacturer's complete description are as follows:

a. Sequence of Events (simplified description) Figure 11-6

1) 24 VDC is supplied to the input terminals at position 1 and 2.

2) The current flows through the transistorized Primary Circuit of the internal transformer T1 which peaks and then collapses as if a switch had opened the circuit. This was seen in the Primary Point Armature operation of Fig. 11-4.

3) Repeated peaking and subsequent collapse of the T1 Primary Coil into the Secondary Coil creates a highly stepped-up voltage.

4) At approximately 3000 volts, the Air Gap Tube G1 becomes ionized and completes a path to the Primary windings of the Trigger Transformer T2.

5) At this time, the circuit design is producing a high frequency, oscillating current which steps up to 21,000 volts in the Secondary winding of transformer T2.

6) The High Tension Lead then carries the current to the Igniter Plug gap, which is ionized (made conductive) to ground in what is referred to as a trigger spark.

7) The Storage Capacitors C2 and C3, at approximately 3000 volts, now discharge through T2 and across the Igniter Plug gap in a second spark. Because of the very short spark interval, the two sparks appear as one and create a very visible flashover with a plume of up to three-fourths inch. This occurs due to the very wide gap of per-

haps .180" when new and up to .300" before replacement is required.

b. Sequence of Events (Unison Corporation's Expanded Description), Figure 11-6

The explanation of events below will follow conventional current flow theory, from positive to negative.

1) When 24 VDC power is applied across input terminal pins 1 and 2 of the exciter, current initially flows through coil L1, reverse polarity protection diode CR1, starting resistor R1, base resistor R2 and diode CR2 to the negative side of the power supply. The current parameters, the value of resistors and the characteristics of the diodes are such that the voltage developed at the junction of R1 and R2 is always greater than the base to emitter voltage of transistor Q1. This voltage causes transistor Q1 to turn "on".

2) Current flows through the primary winding of transformer T1 and the collector-emitter junction of the transistor to ground. Current through the primary winding induces a tertiary voltage of a polarity which increases the forward-bias on transistor Q1. The tertiary voltage causes the transistor to conduct even more current. Due to this regenerative action, transistor Q1 quickly goes into saturation.

3) During the "on" period of the cycle, a relatively constant voltage (approximately equal to the supply voltage) appears across the primary of transformer T1. Since the polarity of the secondary voltage does not allow high voltage rectifier CR5 to conduct during the transistor's "on" period, the secondary circuit is open circuited with no energy being transferred at this instant of the cycle.

4) The relatively constant voltage induced on the tertiary winding produces a constant base current, which will determine the maximum (peak) collector current. The linearly rising collector (primary) current reaches a maximum value determined by beta XI_b, where beta is the current gain of the transistor and I_b is the base current. The path for the base current during the conduction period is from base to emitter junction of the transistor, diode CR3, base resistor R3 and back to the base of the transistor through the tertiary winding. The amplitude of the base current is controlled by the base resistor R3. When the maximum current point is reached, transistor Q1 moves out of saturation. At this instant, the induced voltage in the tertiary of transformer T1 drops toward zero. This drop in induced voltage starts a regenerative action which drives the transistor into the cut-off region. As the primary current drops, the induced voltage in the secondary winding is reversed allowing high voltage rectifier CR5 to conduct and the energy in the core of the transformer will be transferred to storage capacitor C2 and high frequency capacitor C3. As long as the voltages across capacitors C2 and C3 and rectifier CR5 anode cause CR5 to be forward biased, energy will be transferred to C2 and C3.

5) As the current flowing through the primary winding of transformer T1 decreases, the voltage induced in the

tertiary winding is also reversed. Such reversal of voltage in the tertiary winding holds the transistor in the non-conducting (off) state. This reverse voltage condition in the tertiary winding remains until the energy in the core of transformer T1 is transferred to capacitors C2 and C3.

6) When all the energy is transferred to storage capacitor C2 and high frequency capacitor C3, the current in the secondary winding of transformer T1 goes to zero. The voltages induced in the secondary and tertiary winding are reversed, preventing high voltage on rectifier CR5 from conducting. The polarity of induced voltages on primary and tertiary windings are such that the switching transistor is forward-biased and turns "on". The converted circuit is restored to its initial condition and the "on/off" cycle is repeated.

7) The gap between the electrodes of air gap tube G1 is set to break down (ionize) between 2900 and 3200 volts. When the charge across capacitor C2 reaches this value, the spark gap ionizes. This completes a path from capacitor C3 through the primary of the trigger transformer T2 to ground and back to C3 through the spark gap G1. The current flow through this path is a high frequency oscillating current caused by the combination of capacitor C3 and the primary winding of transformer T2. This high frequency current induces a high voltage in the secondary winding of transformer T2.

8) With the high voltage pulse present, the igniter plug is ionized and the current starts to flow from the storage capacitor C2 through transformer T2 and the igniter plug.

Safety resistor R4, in parallel with the igniter plug, provides an alternate path for discharging capacitor C2 whenever the ignition exciter is operated open circuited or whenever the igniter plug becomes open circuited.

4. AC Versus DC Input Systems

a. The AC input system is said to have a better extreme climate reliability than the DC input system which depends on the aircraft battery for its input. The AC system receives its power from the aircraft auxiliary power unit.

b. The operational cycle of a typical intermittent duty cycle, the AC main system is 10 minutes on, 10 to 20 minutes off (for cooling). The DC main system heats up more rapidly, and a typical operational cycle of a system with the same Joule rating as the AC system mentioned earlier might be two minutes on, three minutes to 20 minutes off.

NOTE: This time frame is considered adequate in most circumstances for the pilot to fly clear of bad weather. If not, the pilot will operate the system over the time limit and then have the ignition system repaired or replaced after landing.

c. In flight, both AC and DC main systems can be switched from one igniter plug to the other. This

procedure could be repeated as long as in-flight ignition is required.

d. If a low joule AC continuous ignition system is installed to supplement an intermittent duty system, there is usually no time limit.

e. The DC system remains in popular use, especially when no auxiliary power unit is installed and a battery input voltage is all that is available for starting.

f. On larger aircraft, the APU has a battery DC input ignition, and the main engines use the APU's alternator output to power their AC input systems.

5. High Tension Versus Low Tension Systems

a. There is a need for the high tension system in some engines to counteract a tendency of carbon accumulation on the firing tip of the igniter plug. Also some engines need a high blast effect to better vaporize fuel droplets during starting. This may be especially needed for reliable high altitude relight capability. The low voltage tension might be less effective from this standpoint in a particular combustor.

b. The low tension system is typically less expensive, and represents a simpler design due to the absence of a trigger transformer and capacitor circuit.

E. Igniter Plug Types

1. Spark Igniters

Igniter plugs for gas turbine engines differ considerably from spark plugs for reciprocating engines. The gap at the igniter plug tip is much wider and the electrode is designed to withstand a much higher intensity spark. The igniter plug is also less susceptible to fouling because the high energy spark removes carbon and other deposits each time the plug fires. The construction material is also different because the igniter plug shell is made of a very high quality, nickel-chromium alloy and the center electrode is of tungsten or iridium, all highly wear resistant materials. The threads in many cases are also silver plated to prevent seizing. For this reason, it is many times more expensive than a spark plug (Figures 11-7 and 11-8).

The shell at the hot end of the igniter plug may be air cooled to keep it 500°F to 600°F cooler than the surrounding gas temperature. This helps to prevent hot corrosion and erosion. Cooling air is pulled inward through the cooling holes by the pressure differential, which exists between combustor primary and secondary airflow.

Many varieties of igniter plugs are available, but, usually, only one will suit the needs of a particular engine. The igniter plug tip must protrude properly into the combustor in each installation and on some fully ducted fan engines, especially, must be long enough to

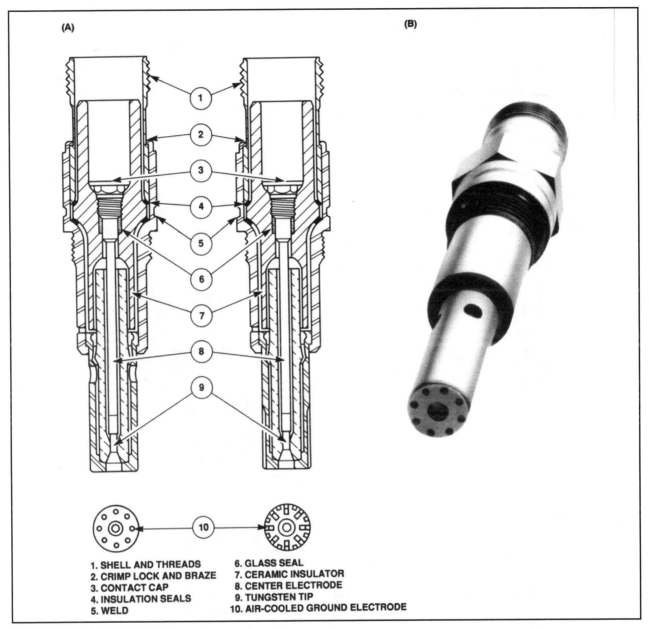

Fig. 11-7A — High tension igniter plug—cutaway view.
Fig. 11-7B — Photo of high tension igniter

mount on the outer case, pass through the fan duct, and penetrate the combustor.

Igniters for high and low tension systems are not interchangeable, and care should be taken to ensure the manufacturer's recommended igniter plug is used.

1. Igniter Plug Gaskets

It is very important to select the correct gasket to ensure the position of the firing tip in the combustion liner. If the tip penetrates too deeply into the liner, the resulting increase in tip temperature can cause the plug to fail. (Figure 11-8B)

2. Glow Plug Igniters (Figure 11-9)

Some smaller engines incorporate a glow plug type

igniter rather than a spark igniter. This glow plug is a resistance coil of very high heat value, and is said to be designed for extreme low temperature starting. A typical system is seen in some models of the Pratt & Whitney PT6 turboprop engine.

The glow plug is supplied with 28VDC at approximately 10 amps to heat the coil to a yellow hot condition. The coil is very similar in appearance to an automobile cigarette lighter. Air directed up through the coil mixes with fuel running down from the main fuel nozzle. This is designed to occur when the main nozzle is not completely atomizing its discharge at low flow conditions during engine starting. The influence of the airflow on the fuel acts to create a hot streak or blow torch type ignition. After fuel is terminated the air source

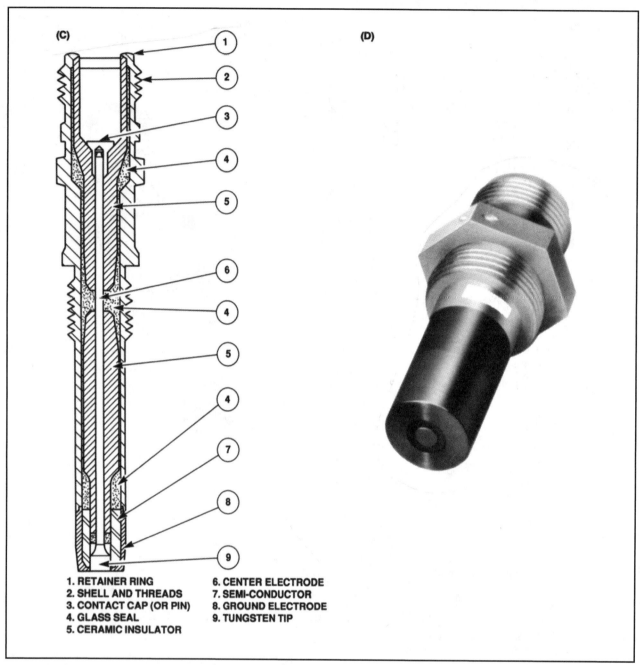

1. RETAINER RING   6. CENTER ELECTRODE
2. SHELL AND THREADS   7. SEMI-CONDUCTOR
3. CONTACT CAP (OR PIN)   8. GROUND ELECTRODE
4. GLASS SEAL   9. TUNGSTEN TIP
5. CERAMIC INSULATOR

Fig. 11-7C — Low tension igniter plug—cutaway view.
Fig. 11-7D — Photo of low tension igniter.

serves to cool the igniter coil during the time the engine is being operated.

3. Cleaning And Inspection Of Igniter Plugs

a. High Tension Igniter Plug Checks

As mentioned earlier in this chapter, turbine ignition systems contain a possible lethal shock if contacted at the high voltage end of the circuit. To remove an igniter plug, first remove the power input lead to the exciter. Next disconnect the high tension lead from the output of the ignition exciter. The last step is to disconnect the high tension lead from the igniter plug and remove the plug.

The high tension igniter plug shown in Figure 11-10 is cleaned on the outer case with a soft brush and solvent and the ceramic portion is cleaned with a felt swab and solvent. Black flashover marks, caused by air gaps or contaminants, are completely removed because they can later cause misfiring of the plug. The lead and connector are also inspected and cleaned to prevent recurrence of flashover. The electrode tip usually may be cleaned with solvent and a soft non-metallic brush. Abrasive grit-blast cleaning is never permitted because the ceramic insulator

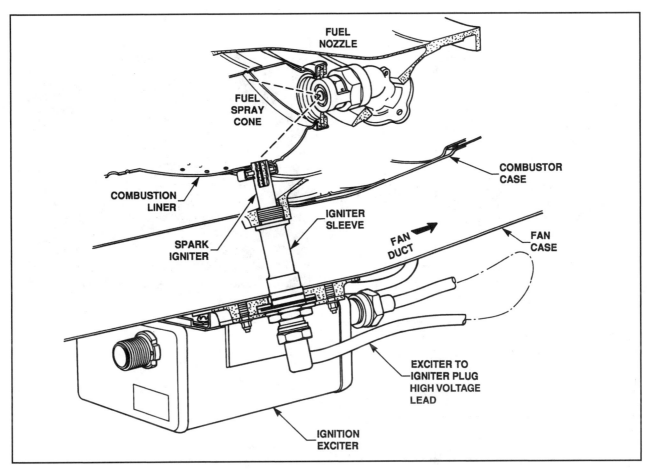

Fig. 11-8A — Igniter plug installation on turbofan engine.

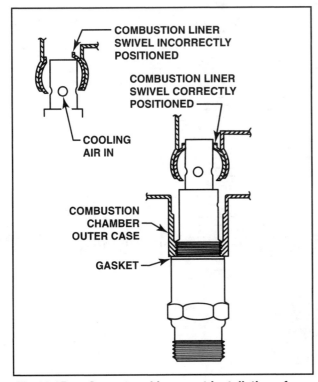

Fig.11-8B — Correct and incorrect installation of igniter into liner.

between the electrode and the case would be damaged. After cleaning, air is used to blow off the remaining solvent and the plug is ready for inspection.

1) Inspection

Igniter plug inspection of high voltage plugs generally consists of a visual inspection and a gap measurement check with a special measuring tool (Figure 11-11C) and a mechanics scale and suitable depth micrometer.

After visual inspection an operational check is performed. A typical operational check might include connecting the conditioned plug to its circuit lead, with the plug positioned outside of the engine and firing it for 20 to 30 seconds to compare its spark intensity with that of a new plug. During this check, extreme care must be taken to completely dissipate the capacitor's charge before handling the center electrode.

Another check typical of installed igniters, is to fire the plugs one at a time, using the aircraft cockpit switches and listening near the tailpipe for the sharp snapping noise associated with good ignition spark. The spark rate can also be timed during this check. The maintenance manual will specify the exact rate for each particular system. Caution must again be exercised to ensure no fuel vapors are present in the combustor during the check or a serious fire could result.

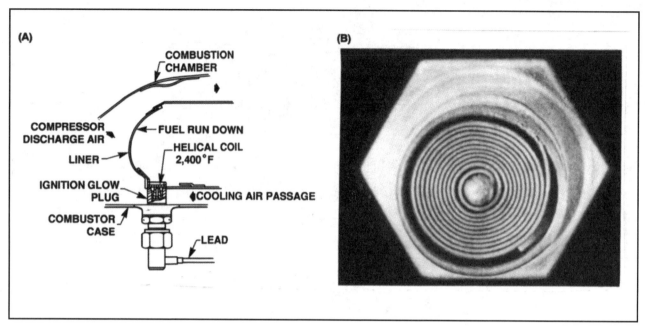

Fig. 11-9A — Glow plug igniter installation.
Fig. 11-9B — Glow plug coil.

GAP DESCRIPTION	TYPICAL FIRING END CONFIGURATION	CLEAN FIRING END
HIGH VOLTAGE AIR SURFACE GAP	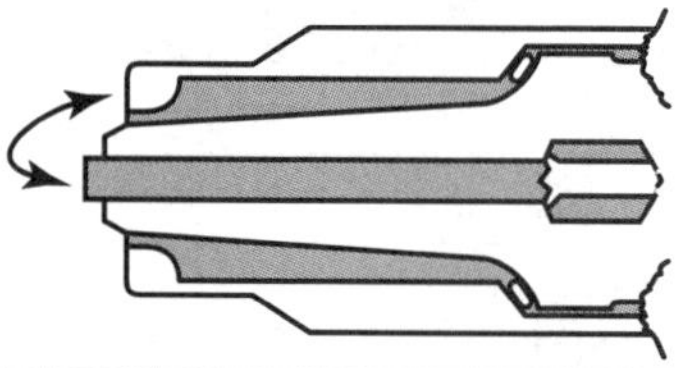	YES
HIGH VOLTAGE SURFACE GAP	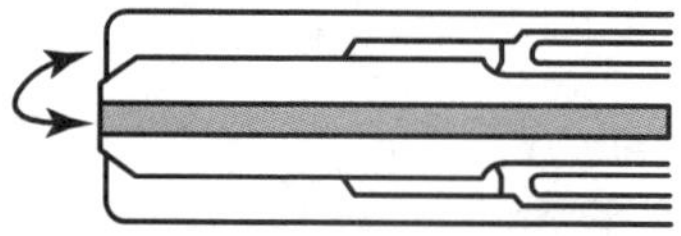	YES
HIGH VOLTAGE RECESSED SURFACE GAP	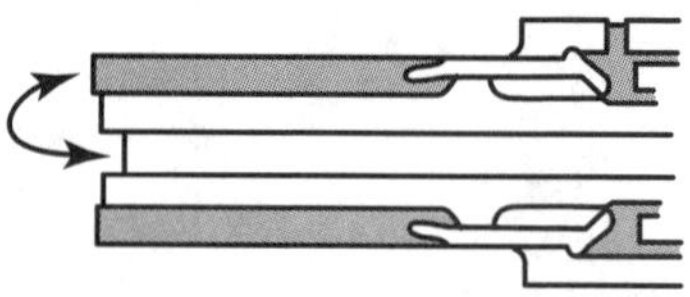	YES
LOW VOLTAGE SHUNTED SURFACE GAP (SELF IONIZING)	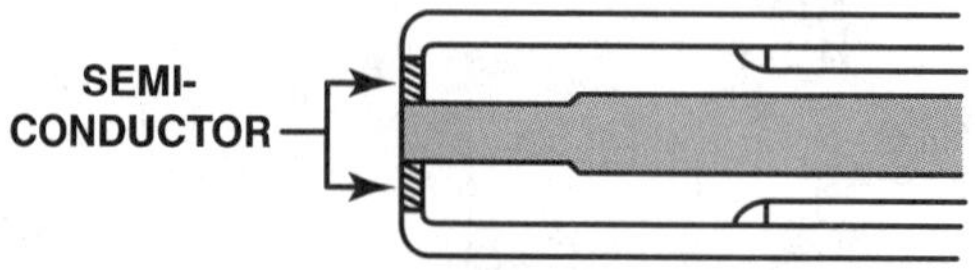 SEMI-CONDUCTOR	SELDEM
LOW VOLTAGE GLOW COIL ELEMENT		YES

Fig. 11-10 — Common types of ignition plug firing ends.

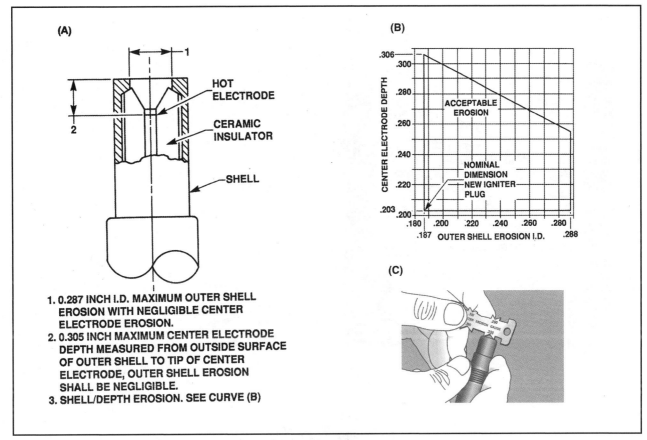

Fig. 11-11A — High voltage igniter plug wear check measurements.
Fig. 11-11B — Typical high tension igniter plug wear check chart.
Fig. 11-11C — Special tool for wear measurement checks.

2) Changing Igniter Plugs

Most operators establish a trend analysis of igniter usage and arrive at a suitable time change interval for igniter plugs. An aircraft on a long route schedule with little igniter use may establish an 800 to 1,200 engine operating hour time change based on estimated igniter use during that engine operating time, whereas, a short haul operator might have a 200 to 300 hour time change in a similar type aircraft because he requires more igniter operation with more frequent takeoffs and landings.

b. Low Tension Igniter Plug Checks
1) Cleaning

The self-ionizing, or shunted gap igniter plug, as it is called, is often cleaned only on its outer casing. The semi-conductor material at the firing end is easily damaged, and manufacturers may not permit cleaning, regardless of the carbon buildup, except during reconditioning at the factory. (Fig. 11-10) If cleaning is permitted, it is generally recommended that it be done with a soft brush or soft cloth and an approved solvent.

2) Measurement Checks (Figure 11-11)

Measurement checks are not usually accomplished on the firing end of low tension plugs because they cannot be cleaned, and this makes it difficult to measure effective-ly. Generally, visual inspection and then comparison of the plug condition to a drawing provided by the manufacturer (see Figure 11-12) is the accepted method. The operational checks similar to those mentioned for high voltage plugs are also applicable inspection criteria.

3) Changing Igniter Plugs

Low tension igniter plugs are changed on an interval system similar to high tension plugs mentioned earlier. The older style tungsten center electrode plugs, with a semi-conductor coating on a base material, will typically have a 400 to 500 hour change interval. The newer iridium center electrode plugs, with what is called a solid pellet semi-conductor, have an 800 to 1200 hour service life. Iridium, a metallic element found in platinum, is one of the few materials that can withstand the high temperature environment at the tip of the igniter plug in a modern day engine.

c. Glow Plug Checks
1) Cleaning

If glow plug heater coils have carbon build up which appears to fuse the coils together, the coil end can be immersed in carbon remover to soften the carbon. Brushing off with a soft nylon brush or fiber brush then generally removes the loosened carbon. (A metal brush of

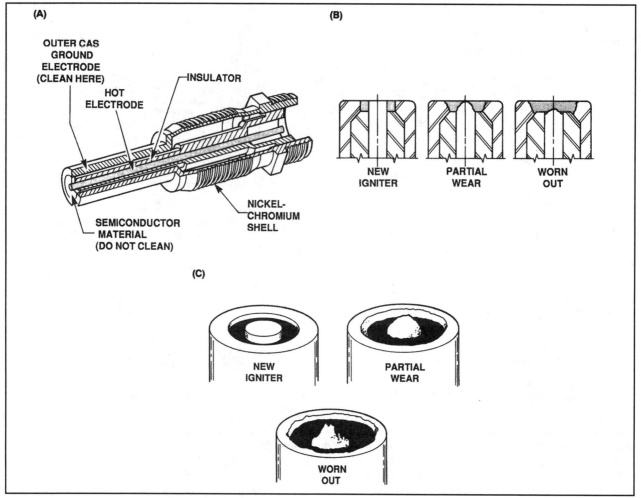

Fig. 11-12A — Low voltage igniter plug, cutaway view.
Fig. 11-12B — Side view of erosion of firing end seen during visual inspection.
Fig. 11-12C — End view of firing tip erosion.

any kind is not acceptable because it may damage the insulation on the coils). Finally the coil is rinsed in warm water and blown dry with an air blast. The maximum remaining fusing of coils that is acceptable is very small, usually one coil fused to another no more than one-eighth inch in length.

The reasons for early build-up are as follows:
a) The pilot initiates fuel flow before the coil heats up correctly;
b) Low voltage to the coil prevents it from heating up correctly;
c) Loose connections prevent the coil from heating up correctly.

2) Inspection

If the plug passes the visual test, an operational check is performed by attaching the plug to its engine ignition lead and observing a bright yellow glow within a prescribed time limit, generally 20 to 30 seconds.

d. Special Test Equipment

If the ignition system fails the operational checks, it can be checked for opens and shorts with the traditional volt-ohmmeter. There are also special test units which

can perform other tests on the system, such as input voltage, output voltage, insulation breakdown, input amperage, output amperage, and spark rate per input voltage. Figure 11-13 shows this type of test unit.

F. Complete Engine Ignition System – GE/Snecma CFM56 (Figure 11-14)

The engine's ignition system is located on the right-hand side of the fan case at the five o'clock position. The ignition system has two independent high tension circuits consisting of:
• 2 high energy ignition exciters.
• 2 ignition lead assemblies.
• 2 igniter plugs.

1. Power Supply

The ignition system receives its electrical power from the aircraft AC bus by way of the two separate channels (A and B) of the electronic engine control (EEC). The ignition exciters are powered by 115 VAC, 400 Hz. Each channel of the EEC is able to control both ignition exciters, thereby providing redundancy in the system.

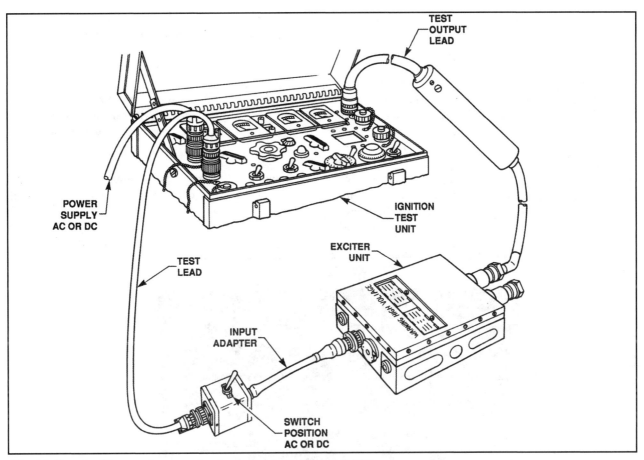

Fig. 11-13 — Ignition system spark rate and output voltage tester.

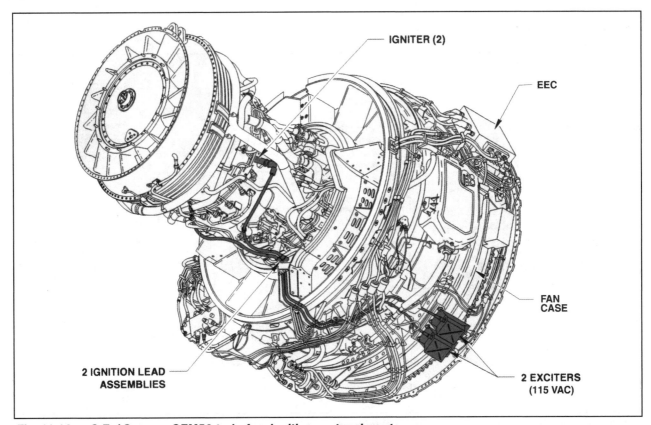

Fig. 11-14 — G.E. / Snecma CFM56 turbofan, ignition system layout.

2. Igniter Selection

The EEC selects (or enables) the left, right or both igniter plug(s) based on the position of the flight-compartment ignition selector switch. The standard operating procedure calls for the flight crew to manually change the ignition selection on successive engine starts from ignition left to ignition right. This procedure allows each igniter plug to receive approximately the same operating time, and a faulty ignition system is detectable once every two ground engine starts.

The engine start panel, as used on a Boeing 737-800, has two engine start switches and one ignition selector switch. The engine start switches (engine 1 and 2) have four positions, as follows (Figure 11-15):

Off — The starter is de-energized and ignition is de-energized, unless an engine flame-out is sensed, in which case the ignition turns on automatically.

Ground — The starter is energized and ignition is energized, with one plug or both plugs firing depending on the ignition selector switch position.

Continuous — The starter is de-energized and ignition is energized, with one plug or both plugs firing depending on the ignition selector switch position.

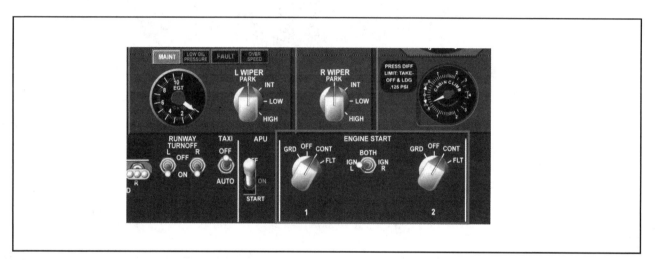

Fig. 11-15 — Boeing 737-800 ignition and start panel.

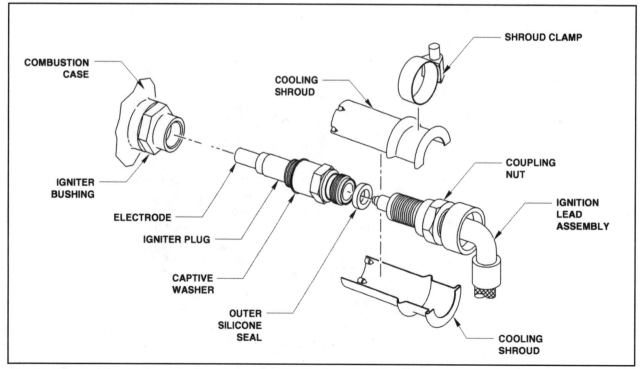

Fig. 11-16 — Ignition lead and igniter plug assembly, Boeing 737-800.

Flight The starter is de-energized and both igniter plugs are energized, regardless of the ignition selector switch position.

The ignition selector switch has three positions, as follows (Figure 11-15):
• Ignition Left.
• Ignition Right.
• Both.

3. System Operation

The ignition exciters use 115 VAC to produce a 14,000 to 18,000 volt DC output at the rate of approximately one pulse per second to the igniter plugs. The exciters transform, rectify and store energy in a capacitor at an energy level of 14.5 to 16 joules. The exciter housings are hermetically sealed, and the interior components are secured mechanically or with silicon cement for protection against engine vibration.

From the ignition exciters, two ignition leads carry the electrical energy to the two igniter plugs located at four and eight o'clock in the combustor. The ignition leads on this engine are identical and interchangeable. The portion of the igniter lead that passes along the core engine, as well as the outer portion of the igniter, is cooled by fan discharge air. The igniter leads consist of 14-gauge stranded copper conductors with silicone rubber insulation within a tinned copper braid and nickel outer braid.

The igniter plugs utilize a recessed surface gap, similar to the plug shown in Figure 11-10. Their center electrode is insulated from the outer shell by aluminum oxide. The plugs thread into an igniter bushing, which threads into the combustion case. The ignition lead and igniter plug arrangement can be seen in Figure 11-16.

G. Troubleshooting Ignition System

Refer to Chapter VI for general troubleshooting procedures. Ignition System troubleshooting of the exciter is beyond the scope of this text. It is very hazardous due to the high voltages involved, and requires special test equipment and procedures by trained personnel.

PROBLEM/POSSIBLE CAUSE	CHECK FOR	REMEDY
1. No igniter spark with the system turned on.		
a. Ignition Relay	Correct power input to transformer unit	Correct relay problems, refer to starter-generator circuit
b. Exciter Unit	Correct power output	Test with special equipment, observing ignition system cautions
c. High Tension Lead	Continuity or highresistance shorts with ohmmeter and megger test unit	Replace lead
d. Igniter Plug	1. Damaged insulator ordamaged semi-conductor	Replace plug
	2. Hot electrode erosion	Replace plug
2. Long interval between sparks.		
a. Power supply	Weak battery	Recharge battery
3. Weak (low intensity) spark.		
a. Igniter Plug	Cracked ceramic insulation	Replace plug

QUESTIONS:

1. Why is a half-wave rectifier needed in a turbine ignition system?

2. What is the main difference between the spark of a reciprocating and turbine engine ignition system?

3. Is the high voltage present in the primary or the secondary circuit of a turbine ignition system?

4. What type construction material makes the turbine igniter more expensive than a spark plug?

CHAPTER XII
Engine Instrument Systems

Engine instruments in the cockpit (flight deck in larger aircraft) are referred to as being in two different categories, Performance Indicators or Engine Condition Indicators. Thrust indicating instruments such as Engine Pressure Ratio (EPR) and Fan Speed (N_1) are described as Performance Indicators. Exhaust Gas Temperature (EGT), Fuel Flow, Compressor Speed, Oil Pressure, and Temperature Gauges are described as Engine Condition monitoring instruments.

Condition indicators, in effect, show the pilot how hard the engine is working to produce the power seen on the performance indicator. If some portion of the engine is working too hard, it will show up as high exhaust gas temperature, high RPM, etc. The pilot must then take the necessary action to reduce power, shut down the engine, or whatever action is appropriate for safe operation of the aircraft.

The two photographs of instrument panels in Figure 12-1 show the conventional panel with typical gauge displays and the newer "glass cockpit" with cathode ray tube (CRT) and light emitting diode (LED) displays. Both provide essentially the same information to the pilot. The newer flight decks, however, are capable of displaying a greater amount of fault isolation information about the instrument package and the engine. For example, most CRT readouts turn "red" when the maximum engine operating limits are reached. At that time, the instrument values and the duration times are recorded automatically.

The following is a brief description of the gauges included in Figure 12-2. Most of these indicating systems will be discussed in detail later in this chapter.

1. Engine Pressure Ratio (EPR)—Receives inputs from two pressure sources, one located in the engine inlet at Station-2 (Pt_2), and one located at the low pressure (LP) Turbine discharge at Station 5.4. ($Pt_{5.4}$). The gauge has both numerical and pointer readout and a reminder display (See EPR System).

2. Oil Pressure—Taken from an external oil line at the accessories gearbox.

3. Oil Temperature—Taken by a sensor in an external line at the accessories gearbox.

4. Oil Quantity—Taken at the oil tank.

5. Fuel Pressure—Taken at the fuel control metered pressure line.

6. N_1 Tach—Receives a signal from a fan case electronic generating device as an indication of fan (LP Compressor) speed and turbine speed. The gauge has both numerical and pointer readouts.

7. ITT Gauge—Receives electrical impulses from a set of averaging thermocouple probes located in the HP Turbine discharge airflow. The gauge has both numerical and pointer readouts.

8. N_2 Tach—Receives a signal from an Accessories Gearbox Electric Tachometer Generator to indicate HP Compressor and Turbine Speed. The gauge has both numerical and pointer readouts.

9. FF Gauge—Receives signal from a fuel flow transmitter located in the fuel control metered line to the combustor. The gauge has both numerical and pointer readouts.

10. Engine Vibration—Shows the vibration level, often given in mils (thousandths) of inches at four locations, two on the LP system at the fan and turbine and two on the HP system at the N_2 compressor and turbine. Four mils is the approximate allowable maximum vibration at any location.

Fig. 12-1A — Conventional flight deck.
Fig. 12-1B — Newer "glass cockpit".

11. Engine Indicator Maximum Pointer Reset—Resets the maximum indicator pointer when actuated. Three critical gauges are configured with a second pointer which locks in overshoot values of N_1, N_2, and exhaust gas temperature.

The following is a brief description of the CRT display of engine gauges shown in Figure 12-3. The display includes what would typically be described as primary and secondary engine instruments. These instruments would generally be displayed on two separate screens. The readings shown on this screen would not be expected to exist at the same time, since the left engine is shown in reverse thrust and the right engine in forward thrust. There are many other indications that would not exist at the same time.

Left Side of Display:

1. A/T LIM — Indicates that the auto throttle is in control.

2. CRZ — Indicates that the thrust mode for the engines is "cruise".

3. TAT - 12c — Indicates that the total air temperature is 12 degrees Centigrade.

4. REV — Indicates that the left engine is in reverse thrust.

5. 96.0 — Indicates that the N_1 reference is 96% (fan speed).

6. N1 — Both engines have an N_1 (fan speed) of 87.7%.

7. TAI — Indicates that thermal anti-ice is turned on.

8. EGT — Both engines show an EGT of 663 degrees, and the left engine has failed.

9. X-BLD START — Indicates that a cross bleed engine start is taking place.

10. N_2 — Both engines have an N2 (high speed compressor) of 87.7%.

11. FF/FU — The fuel flow for both engines is 11,270 lbs./hr. The fuel used (FU) would be displayed by moving a switch to select it.

12. FUEL LB — The digital reading shows the fuel in three separate tanks, in pounds.

Right Side of Display:

1. The top advisory lights are for the left and right engine start valves, oil filter bypass, and low oil pressure.

2. OIL P — Oil pressure on the left engine is approximately 40 psi.

3. OIL T — Oil temperature on the left engine is approximately 120° Centigrade.

4. OIL Q% — The left engine oil tank is 75% full.

5. VIB — The vibration on the left engine is approximately 1.6 mils (.0016").

6. HYD P — The hydraulic pressure in System A is approximately 2800 psi.

7. HYD Q% — The System A hydraulic tank is 70% full.

A. Exhaust Temperature Indicating Systems

The temperature of the exhaust gases is always monitored closely during engine operation, especially during the starting cycle when overheat damage is most prevalent. Hot section temperature is considered the most critical of all the engine operating parameters because an out of limits condition can render an engine unairworthy in a matter of seconds.

The temperature gauge in the cockpit, when labeled "Turbine Inlet Temperature" (TIT), indicates the temperature is being monitored forward of the turbine wheel(s). When it is labeled "Interstage Turbine Temperature" (ITT), it indicates the temperature is being taken at some intermediate position between multiple turbine wheels. When labeled "Exhaust Gas Temperature" (EGT), sometimes "Turbine Outlet Temperature" (TOT), it indicates that temperature is being taken aft of the turbine wheel(s).

Regardless of the actual monitoring position, the important consideration is the temperature at the turbine inlet (TIT) just forward of the first stage turbine nozzle. However, it is not always possible to monitor temperature at this point in the engine because the high heat sometimes degrades the service life of the temperature sensing probe.

The manufacturer, therefore, provides a comparison value between TIT temperature and temperature at other points within the engine where the actual monitoring takes place. Although the temperature is lower at these points, it still provides the necessary surveillance over the engine's internal condition.

Several total temperature probes, or thermocouples, as they are called, are positioned around the engine on pads which allow one end, referred to as the hot junction, to penetrate into the hot gas path. When connected in a parallel electrical circuit, the system indicates the average of all the thermocouple temperatures on a gauge in the cockpit (Figure 12-4).

This system, more so than any other engine instrument system, indicates the integrity of the turbine components. For instance, an inefficiency occurring from damaged or missing turbine blades will result in a high temperature indication, because the hot gases will more quickly reach the temperature sensing probes. This is one of the reasons that the exhaust gas temperature system is the most popular of the three systems. Another is that the exhaust gas temperature thermocouple may have a greater service life when located at the turbine discharge area.

When turbine inlet temperature is an essential value for fuel scheduling, such as with an electronic engine control (EEC), a photo electric cell might be used to provide a TIT value to the system.

1. System Components

Figure 12-5 shows a typical exhaust gas temperature circuit made up of eight thermocouples with each

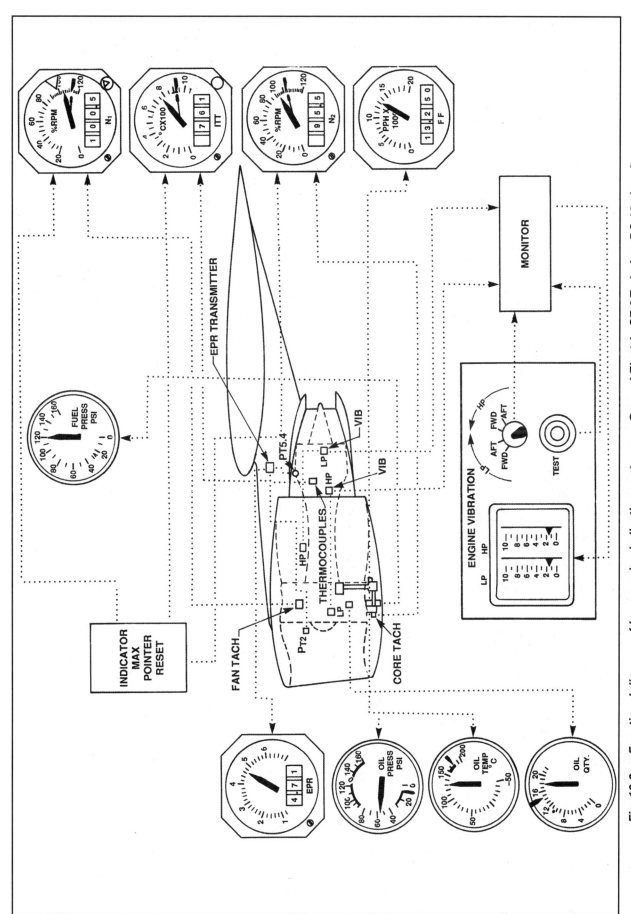

Fig. 12-2 — Functional diagram of large engine indicating systems — General Electric CF-6 Turbofan, DC-10 aircraft.

containing chromel and alumel conductor wires. The other components are: The circuit leads, a variable calibrating resistor, and an indicator. Thermocouples are placed in what is referred to as a thermo-electric circuit, the principle of which is the generating of an electric current that is proportional to the heat applied.

Chromel is a nonferrous nickel chromium alloy. It is non-magnetic, has positive electrical potential, and is color coded white. Its terminal connector is often the smaller of the two and Size 8-32. Alumel is a ferrous alloy of nickel aluminum. It is magnetic, has negative potential, and is color coded green. Its terminal connector is often the larger of the two and Size 10-32. These characteristics allow for identification of leads which sometimes become discolored from extended use in heated areas outside of the engine.

Gas turbine engine temperature systems contain thermocouples known as K-type. The chromel and alumel materials they utilize are suitable for temperatures up to 1,200°C. Copper and constantan wire are used in portions of the thermocouple circuit where no more than 300°C will be experienced (Figure 12-5).

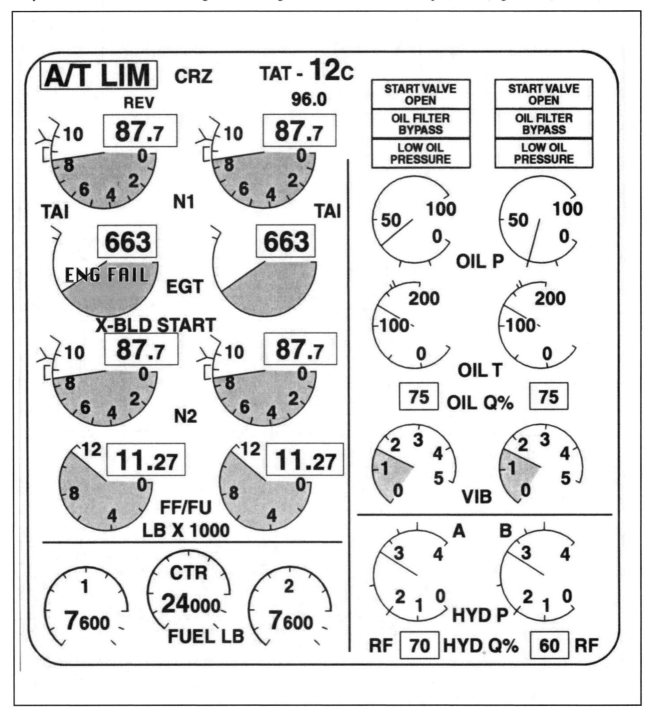

Fig. 12-3 — Primary and secondary engine instruments displayed on a CRT.

The K-type thermocouple generates a known 40 millionths of a volt per degree Centigrade of heat applied. Because chromel-alumel wire has a relatively high resistance per foot, it is only used from the thermocouple harness to the engine terminal block. From the terminal block, copper-constantan wire completes the circuit to the gauge on the flight deck.

The indicator is a d'Arsonval meter, and it serves as a cold junction in this circuit.

The calibrating resistor provides a means of adjustment to calibrate the system to the specific total resistance required. A typical circuit is either 8, 15, or 22 ohms, depending on the distance from the thermocouple harness on the engine to the indicator in the cockpit; the

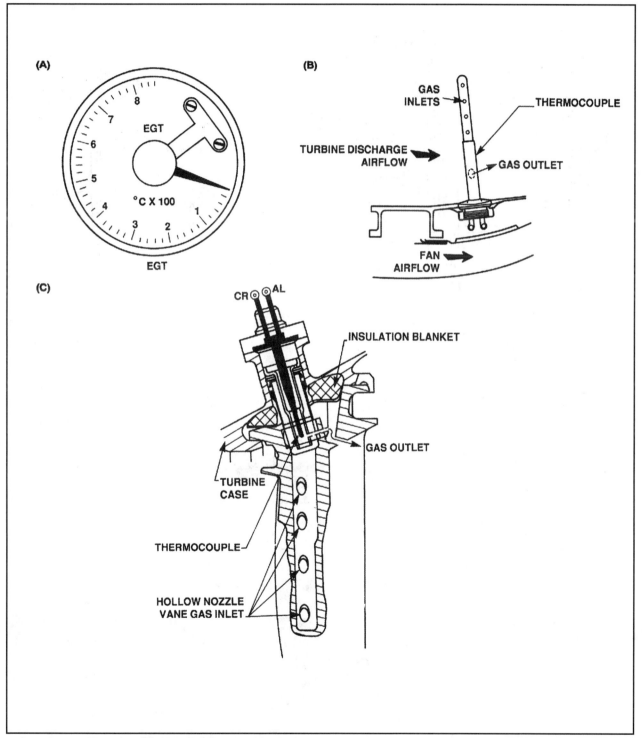

Fig. 12-4A — Cockpit exhaust gas temperature gauge.
Fig. 12-4B — Thermocouple in a fully ducted turbofan.
Fig. 12-4C — ITT thermocouple located in a hollow turbine nozzle vane.

longer the length, the higher the resistance. Otherwise, use of larger wire diameter would cause weight problems in trying to keep resistance low.

Some newer systems are alternating or direct current powered and differ from the traditional self-generating system mentioned here. One type uses a non-intrusive pyrometer to monitor optical and infrared emissions. The interested reader can consult manufacturer's manuals of specific engines for details concerning these systems.

a. Thermocouples

Themocouple may be either single or dual, meaning having one or two hot junctions.

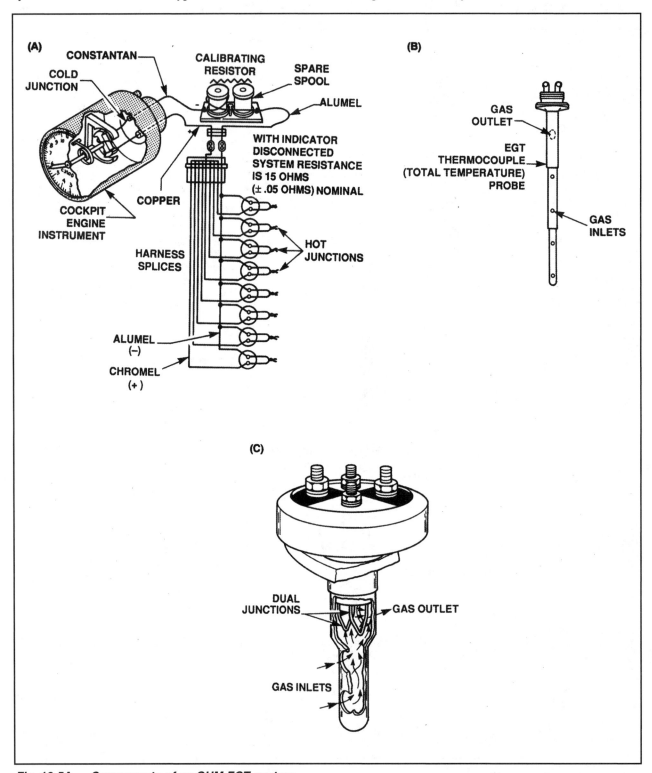

Fig. 12-5A — Components of an OHM EGT system.
Fig. 12-5B — Single hot junction thermocouple probe.
Fig. 12-5C — Dual hot junction thermocouple probe.

The single type (Figure 12-5B) powers only a temperature indicator. The dual type provides an additional identical hot junction which can give a signal to an electronic fuel control for scheduling purposes, or it can be used as a test connection for calibrating the exhaust gas temperature circuit.

In both types, hot gases impact on the outer surface of the thermocouples with some gas entering the inlet holes. The gas then passes over the hot junction(s) on its way to outlet and back to the gas path. In this way, a total temperature of the exhaust gases is measured. This idea is explained further in the following paragraphs.

2. System Operation

Each hot junction is a pair of dissimilar metallic electrical conductors which become a small power source similar to a battery. When connected in a closed loop parallel circuit, the conductors change resistance at a known rate when heated and produce an average current flow which is proportional to the heat applied. Each thermocouple, when heated to 1,000°C higher temperature than the cold junction, will produce approximately 0.004 volts. The chromel lead contains a deficiency of free electrons. The alumel lead has an excess of free electrons.

When heated, the free electrons in the negative lead move from the hot junction, through the cold junction, and back to the positive hot junction lead. The indicator monitors current flow and, if it is a cockpit indicator, reads out in degrees Centigrade (°C). At this time, most temperature calculations for maintenance purposes are accomplished using the Fahrenheit temperature scale.

The function of the cold junction can best be explained in terms of the electron theory. If the same heat were to be applied at the gauge end (the cold junction) as at the thermocouple end (the hot junction), the negative alumel lead at the engine end would try to flow electrons at the same rate as the gauge end. Electron flow is proportional to heat applied, so one flow would cancel out the other. With no current flow, no gauge reading would result.

A reading can normally be observed on an exhaust gas temperature gauge when the engine is not operating and cooled down to ambient temperature. This is because a compensating coil within the gauge is creating an indication of ambient temperature. This in turn provides the operator with an exhaust gas temperature reading that is corrected for ambient temperature.

The thermocouple in use in this example is referred to as a total temperature type because it measures both static temperature and temperature rise due to ram effect. This, of course, represents the actual heat loading on the internal parts of the engine.

The amount of ram effect can be calculated by using the formula for Tt/Ts in Appendix 8.

If the Exhaust Gas Temperature (Tt_7) is 1,600°R and the Mach No. of gas flow is 0.9, what is the Tt/Ts ratio and the temperature due to ram effect?

If:
$$\frac{Tt}{Ts} = 1 + \left[\frac{\gamma - 1}{2} \times M^2\right] \quad \text{also} \quad \frac{Tt}{Ts} = \frac{1,600}{Ts}$$

$$\frac{1,600}{Ts} = 1 + \left[\frac{1.4 - 1}{2} \times 0.9^2\right]$$

And:
$$\frac{1,600}{Ts} = 1 + (0.20 \times 0.81)$$

Then: $Ts = 1,600 \div 1.162$
$Ts = 1,376.9°R$

The amount of heat rise due to ram effect is 1,600 minus 1,376.9, or 223.1°F.

3. EGT Limits

Every engine has strict internal temperature limits. The temperatures shown make no allowance for instrument error. A set of typical EGT limits is shown in Figure 12-6A and Figure 12-6B, and also as follows:

Starting Overtemperature	Action Required
Up to 525°C (normal)	none
526 to 595°C, any time	Inspection A
595 to 630°C, 5 secs. or less	Inspection A
595 to 630°C, more than 5 secs.	Inspection B
630 to 700°C, 5 secs. or less	Inspection B
630 to 700°C, more than 5 secs.	Inspection C
700 to 800°C, any time	Inspection C
More than 800°C, any time	Inspection D
Operating Overtemperature	**Action Required**
Up to 677°C (normal)	none
678 to 690°C, any time	Inspection A
678 to 720°C, 5 secs. or less	Inspection A
691 to 720°C, 5 secs. to 2 min.	Inspection B
721 to 730°C, 5 secs. or less	Inspection B
691 to 720°C, over 2 min.	Inspection C
721 to 730°C, more than 5 secs.	Inspection C
731 to 775°C, any time	Inspection C
More than 775°C, any time	Inspection D

a. Inspection A. Determine and correct cause of over-temperature.

b. Inspection B. Perform visual inspection of all hot section parts:

1) Inspect exhaust duct for foreign particles.

2) Inspect rear of turbine for apparent damage.

3) Inspect burner section and turbine vanes.

c. Inspection C. Perform teardown inspection of all hot section parts:

1) Fluorescent penetrant inspection turbine blades.

2) Inspect turbine vanes for bow, bend and twist.

3) Inspect turbine blades for stretch.

4) Inspect turbine disks for growth and hardness Rockwell A66.

d. Inspection D. Perform complete overhaul inspection of all hot section parts.

In the above table of starting and operating over-temperature limits, the normal operating mode temperature limits are more lenient than the starting

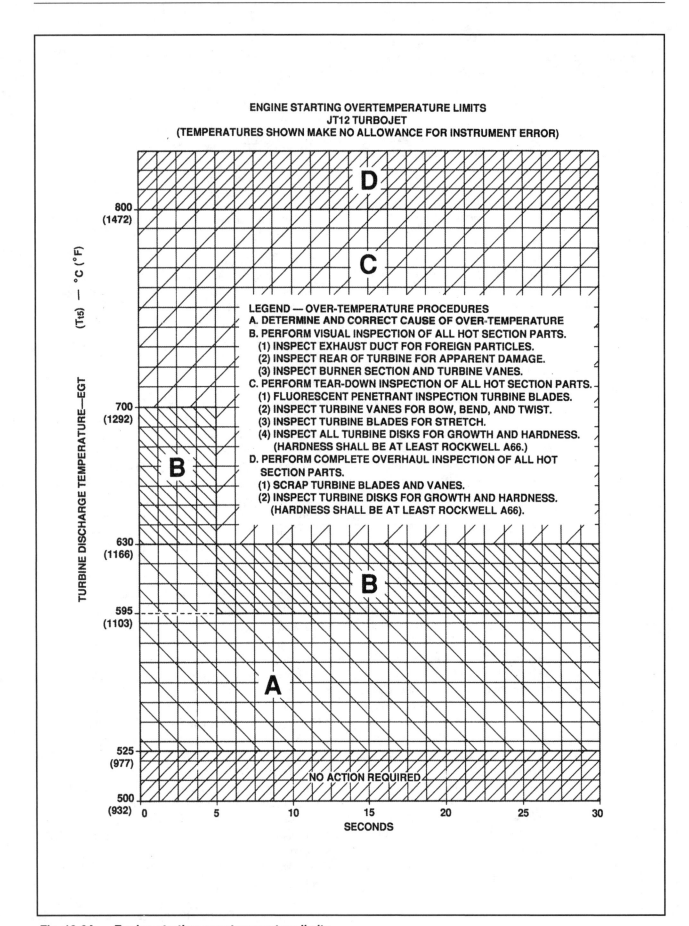

Fig. 12-6A — Engine starting over-temperature limits.

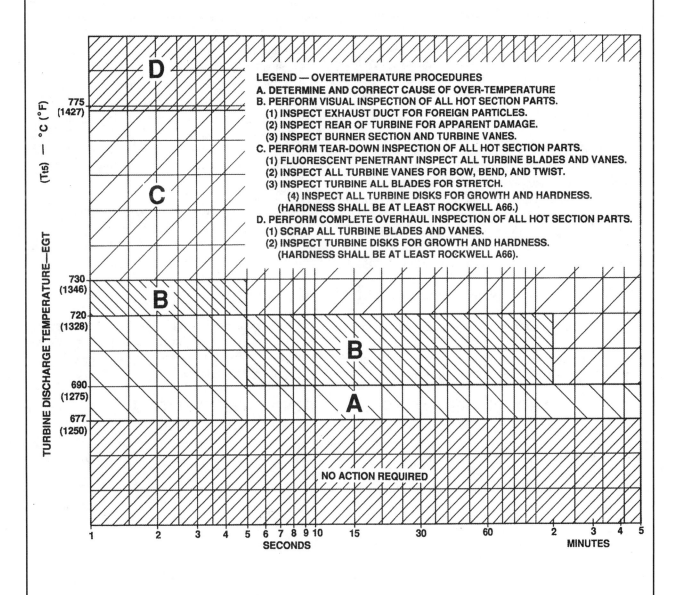

Fig. 12-6B — Engine operating over-temperature limits.

mode limits. This is a design feature of the more modern engine. Because it has been learned that engine service life is greatly reduced by high starting temperatures, newer engines are designed to start and maintain the lowest possible temperatures during the starting cycle. On many older engines, lack of cooling air caused starting temperatures to be very high and this in turn adversely affected hot end service life.

Note that the time limits in the table are very short. Again, extended temperature overshoots precipitate premature failure of hot end parts, which can become a serious flight safety hazard. During the construction process, turbine disks with a Rockwell hardness of A66 are sudden-quench hardened after being heated to their critical temperature. During an engine over-temperature condition, the unit cools slowly to ambient temperature, leaving it in a lower state of hardness.

4. Jetcal Analyzer (Figure 12-7A, B, C, D)

Before maintenance personnel perform engine inspections for over-temperature, they must first establish that the cockpit instrument is indicating accurately. One device which can be used to determine the reliability of the Exhaust Temperature indicating system is the Jetcal Analyzer. Jetcal is a commercial trade name for an EGT and RPM testing device, which has the following capabilities:

1) Check the aircraft EGT system without running the engine.

2) Check the aircraft EGT system during engine run-up.

3) Check continuity and resistance of the EGT circuit. For example, the typical circuit tolerance might be 8 ohms (±) 0.05 ohms.

4) Check individual thermocouple output with the engine static or operating.

5) Check the aircraft percent RPM system during engine run-up.

Figure 12-7A shows a maintenance technician reaching in the tailpipe, installing Jetcal heaters on the thermocouples. This unit heats the thermocouples and accurately registers the temperature on both the Jetcal indicator panel and the cockpit exhaust gas temperature indicator. The cockpit indicator can then be checked against the standard temperature on the Jetcal.

6) Other Checks

If a thermocouple bulb or harness is suspect and special equipment is not available, the system can still be checked out with a multimeter of good quality or a wheatstone bridge, as follows:

a) Check the resistance of each thermocouple bulb as per manufacturer's specifications, typically 0.10 ohm (±) 0.01 ohm.

b) Instrument a known good bulb and a suspect bulb and place both in bake oven to compare readings.

c) Check resistance of bulb and harness together when bulbs are not detachable, typically 3.0 ohms (±) 0.02 ohms.

d) Check for breakdown between the hot junction and outer harness covering, typically 50,000 ohms resistance minimum.

Other systems such as TIT and ITT also have special test units for system checkout. These units are usually supplied as special test equipment by the manufacturer of the engine or the airplane.

TROUBLESHOOTING EGT/ITT INDICATING SYSTEM

NOTE: Refer to Chapter VI for general troubleshooting procedures.

PROBLEM/POSSIBLE CAUSE	CHECK FOR	REMEDY
1. False low EGT/ITT indication at all power settings.		
(other indications appear normal)		
a. Thermocouple Leads	1. Shorting together outside the engine and averaging in a low reading	Relocate leads
	2. Broken thermocouple lead	Repair as necessary
b. Thermocouple	Hot junction burned off (open), causing total circuit resistance to increase	Replace thermocouple
c. Circuit Resistance (high)	1. High circuit resistance from corroded terminals	Clean or repair as necessary
	2. Added wire length during repair	Replace as necessary
	3. System calibration (Jetcal)	Adjust

NOTE: Changing the wire length in the calibrating, spool side of the EGT circuit will raise or lower the circuit resistance which in turn results in a false high or low Egt indication in the cockpit.

PROBLEM/POSSIBLE CAUSE	**CHECK FOR**	**REMEDY**
2. False high EGT/ITT reading at all power settings		
a. Circuit resistance (low)	Shortened wire length during repair. Check resistance with an accurate ohmmeter, Wheatstone bridge, Jetcal or similar unit	Re-calibrate circuit
3. Fluctuating EGT/ITT.		
a. Circuit Leads	Loose connections	Tighten
b. Indicator	Indicator malfunction, (exchange indicator connections or slave in another indicator)	Replace indicator

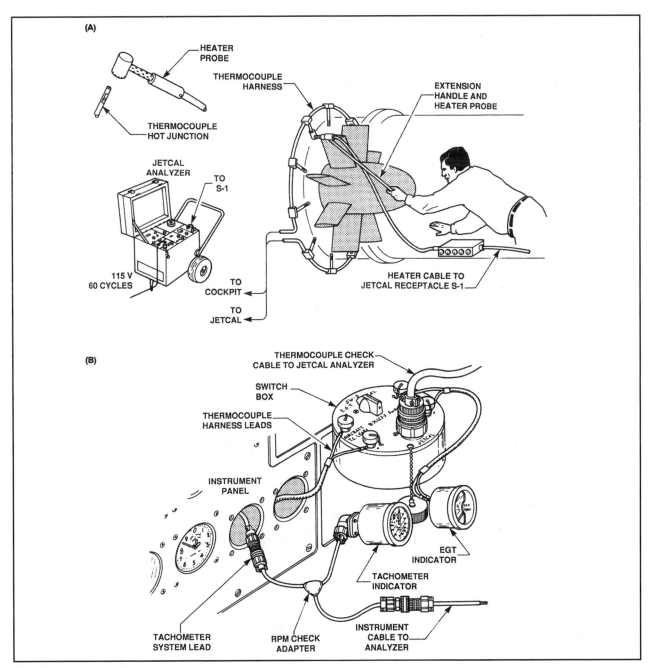

Fig. 12-7A — Jetcal heater probe installation.
Fig. 12-7B — Switch box and rpm check adapter connections.

TROUBLESHOOTING THE ENGINE WITH EGT/ITT INDICATOR

PROBLEM/POSSIBLE CAUSE	CHECK FOR	REMEDY
1. High EGT/ITT throughout engine power lever range.		
a. Turbine Wheel Distress	Check visually through tailpipe or with borescope	Possible engine teardown
b. Turbine Vanes	Same as (a)	
c. Compressor	Contamination or FOD, causing fuel flow increase	Field clean or repair as necessary
d. Engine Bleeds Open	Anti-stall, anti-ice, customer bleed air, etc. causing fuel flow increase	Correct as necessary
e. Fuel Control Sensors (Ps4 or Pb) (P.L. more forward than other engine)	1. Loose connections	Tighten
f. EPR Indicating System reading false low	1. EPR system out of calibration 2. Loose pressure lines to transmitter	Calibrate system Tighten

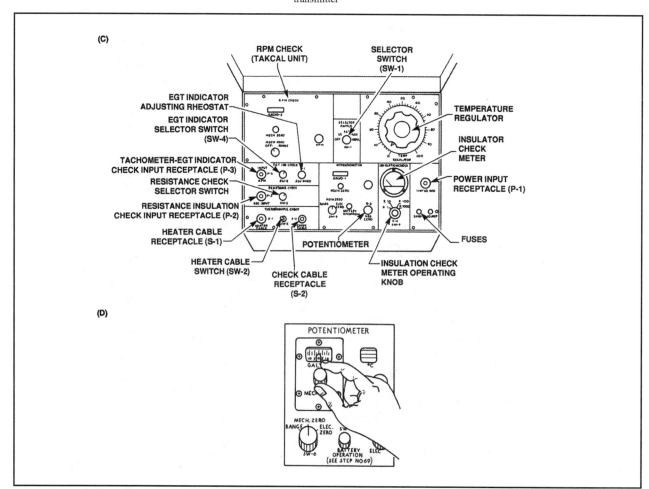

Fig. 12-7C — Jetcal analyzer control panel.
Fig. 12-7D — Setting heater probe temperature.

B. Tachometer Percent RPM Indicating System

Gas turbine engine speed is measured in percent of compressor RPM. The number of compressors generally determines the number of percent rpm indicators present in the cockpit. All aircraft cockpits are required by FAR Part 33 to have a tachometer indicating system.

Because no two engines and no two compressors N_1 and N_2 operate at the same speed, percent RPM is used to simplify the cockpit indication for the operator.

1. The Percent RPM Indicator

The percent RPM indicator is utilized for the following purposes:

a. Monitor RPM during starting sequence. N_1 speed in a single-spool engine, N_2 in a dual spool engine, N_3 in a triple spool engine.

b. Monitor RPM in case of over-speeding. Applies to all tach indicators installed.

c. Indicate both compressor speed and thrust on centrifugal flow engines and some single spool axial flow engines. Refers to N_1 speed.

d. Indicate both compressor speed and thrust on some turbofan engines. Refers to N_1 fan speed.

e. Check operating schedules of engine support systems such as bleed valve, variable vane, etc.

f. Check engine speed during in-flight shutdown and windmilling.

2. Three-Phase Generator, Percent RPM System

The tachometer is an independent electrical system, consisting of an engine driven three phase AC generator and a synchronous motor driven indicator. Most manufacturers set the gearbox tachometer drive ratio to compressor speed, such that at 100% compressor speed the tachometer drive output is 4,200 RPM. This allows for interchangeability of system components, such that the tach generator from one engine could possibly be used on a different engine (Figure 12-8).

Referring to Figure 12-9, the tachometer generator sends a low voltage signal in the range of 20V AC to the synchronous motor field in the indicator. However, frequency in cycles per second is the important factor, not voltage, because the motor magnet is designed to remain in synchronization with the generator magnet. There is no physical connection between the pointer yoke and the flux coupler magnet. The pointer yoke turns the pointer on the indicator dial through induced eddy current.

3. Magnetic Pickup Percent RPM System

One newer system for measuring fan percent RPM employs a sensor mounted in the fan case which places a magnet adjacent to the path of fan blade rotation. The sensor counts the number of blades passing by and converts this to a signal which causes the indicator on the flight deck to show percent RPM.

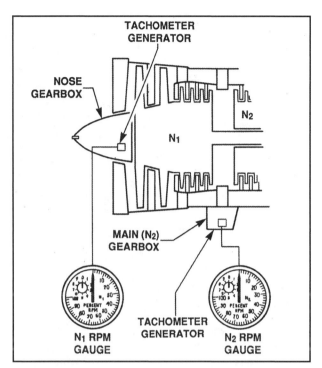

Fig. 12-8 — Location of tachometer generators for low and high pressure compressors.

4. Example System (General Electric CF-6)

The fan tips cut through the magnetic field of the sensor head creating an eddy current. The conditioner unit, a rectifier changing AC to DC, acts to amplify the signal to the percent tachometer indicator. On this installation, the fan has a direct relationship to thrust and the manufacturer has chosen the N_1 tach as the primary thrust indicator. This engine also employs an Engine Pressure Ratio System (EPR) as a backup thrust indicator (Figure 12-10A).

5. Electronic Gearbox Mounted N_2 Speed Sensor

Another system for measuring N_2 percent utilizes a sensor mounted in the main accessory gearbox. The sensor head is fitted very closely to a rotating gear, which has a special ferrous material on one of its teeth. As the lines of flux are broken by the ferrous tooth, the sensor unit electronically counts the tooth rotation as it passes by (Figure 12-10B).

6. N_1 Indication And Speed Sense For FADEC System

Figure 12-11A shows a glass flight deck display of the N_1 tach indicator. This is the same indicator shown in the overall display in Figure 12-3, and is part of the engine indication for a FADEC (full authority digital engine control) equipped system. The information shown on this indicator, from top right in a CCW direction, is as follows:

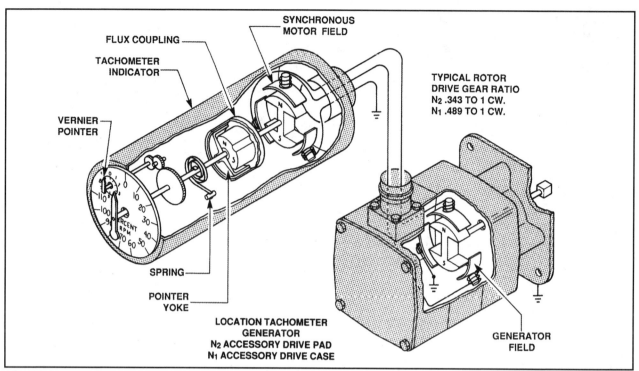

Fig. 12-9 — Engine tachometer indicating system for low pressure compressor (N_1) and high pressure compressor (N_2).

- The 87.0 number indicates the current RPM, in percent, of the N_1 system.
- The 96.0 number indicates the N_1% which has been called for by the auto throttle system or by the N1 set controls on the flight deck. The N_1 reference can be manually set by the pilot by looking at an engine performance chart. It will be set automatically in the auto throttle mode.
- The N_1 redline is the maximum RPM allowed.
- The N_1 reference bug corresponds to the 96% which has been set by the auto throttle system or by the pilot.
- The N_1 command is what the current throttle position is asking for.
- The N_1 command sector shows the difference between the commanded thrust and the actual thrust.
- The N_1 pointer is the analog representation of the

current percent of RPM, and it matches the 87% digital readout.

Figure 12-11B shows the N_1 speed sensor which would provide the signal for the indication shown in Figure 12-11A. As can be seen in the figure, this sensor is mounted on the side of the fan case and has three sensing elements at its tip. The three sensing elements provide the output signals shown at the end of the sensor. One of the outputs goes to the Display Electronics Unit (DEU) and the Airborne Vibration Monitoring (AVM), and the other two go to the two separate channels of the Electronic Engine Control (EEC).

7. Typical RPM Limits

As with exhaust gas temperature, a set of RPM operating parameters is prescribed by the manufacturer. A typical set of percent RPM limits is as follows:

RPM LIMITS

PERCENT RPM LIMITS	INDICATED PERCENT RPM	ACTION REQUIRED
1) 104.2 to 106.2%	105%	Special inspection: Inspect compressor and turbine section for rubbing after shutdown.
2) 106.3% and over	106.3%	Send engine to overhaul.

NOTE: Sometimes a "time limit" is also present for over-speed conditions. The significance of RPM limits can be seen in the fact that centrifugal loading on rotating components varies with the square of the speed. For example, an overspeed from the normal 104.1% limit to 110.1%, a 6% increase in speed, results in a 36% increase in centrifugal loading.

TROUBLESHOOTING THE TACHOMETER INDICATING SYSTEM

PROBLEM/POSSIBLE CAUSE	CHECK FOR	REMEDY
1. No percent RPM indication or fluctuating indication.		
a. Tach indicator	Proper operation by interchanging indicators	Replace indicator
b. Circuit Wiring	Loose leads, connections, continuity.	Tighten or repair as necessary
c. Tach Generator	Proper output voltage with meter or slave in another generator	Replace tach generator

TROUBLESHOOTING THE ENGINE WITH THE TACHOMETER INDICATOR SYSTEM

PROBLEM/POSSIBLE CAUSE	CHECK FOR	REMEDY
1. No percent RPM indication on start.		
a. Starter	Proper operation	Correct as necessary
b. Compressor	Compressor seizing. Turn by Hand. Wait for cool down and check. Attempt a restart	Possible engine teardown
c. Accessories	Accessory seizing. Remove one at a time and turn engine over through the drive pad	Repair as necessary
2. RPM at limit before target EPR is reached.		
a. Internal engine	Distress of gas path components	Possible engine tear down

C. Engine Pressure Ratio System

The engine pressure ratio (EPR) system has for years been the most widely used thrust indicating system for aircraft cockpits. As mentioned in the fuel chapter, the arithmetic value of engine pressure ratio is used as a performance (thrust) setting instrument on many flight decks and is also used as a condition monitoring instrument on some fan speed rated engines which use N_1 speed as their performance instrument.

1. The EPR Formula (in absolute values)

EPR is a ratio of two engine pressures: Turbine discharge total pressure and compressor inlet total pressure. Each manufacturer uses a slightly different engine station numbering system, and engine stations are a means of identifying engine pressure ratio tap-off points.

For example, the Pratt & Whitney Company uses Station (2), Pt_2, and Station (5), Pt_5, to identify the engine

pressure ratio tap-off points of single-spool engines. They also use Stations Two and Seven, Pt_2 and Pt_7, to identify the engine pressure ratio tap-off points of dual-spool engines. The following example is of a Pratt & Whitney JT12 engine pressure ratio cockpit indication. When turbine discharge pressure is 28.52 pounds per square inch - absolute and compressor inlet pressure is 14.7 pounds per square inch - absolute, the EPR would be as follows:

If: $\quad EPR = \dfrac{Pt_5}{Pt_2}$

Where: $\quad Pt_2 = 14.7$ psia
$\quad\quad\quad Pt_5 = 28.52$ psia

Then: $\quad EPR = \dfrac{28.52}{14.7} = 1.94$

For an understanding of the concept of engine pressure ratio being a measure of thrust, recall that a gas turbine engine is a device which increases potential energy in the

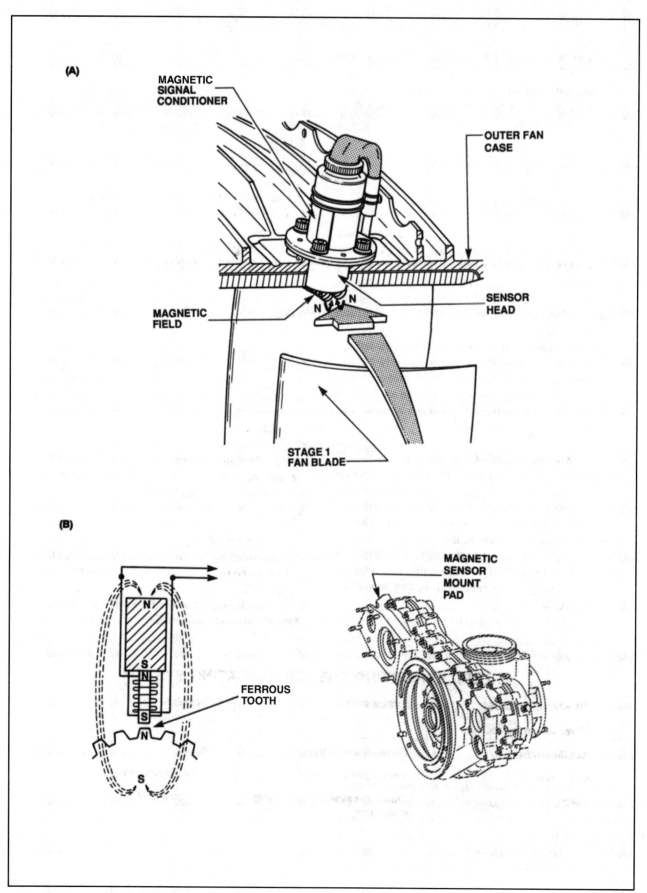

Fig. 12-10A — Electronic fan speed sensor, General Electric CF6 turbofan.
Fig. 12-10B — Electronic gearbox mounted N$_2$ speed sensor.

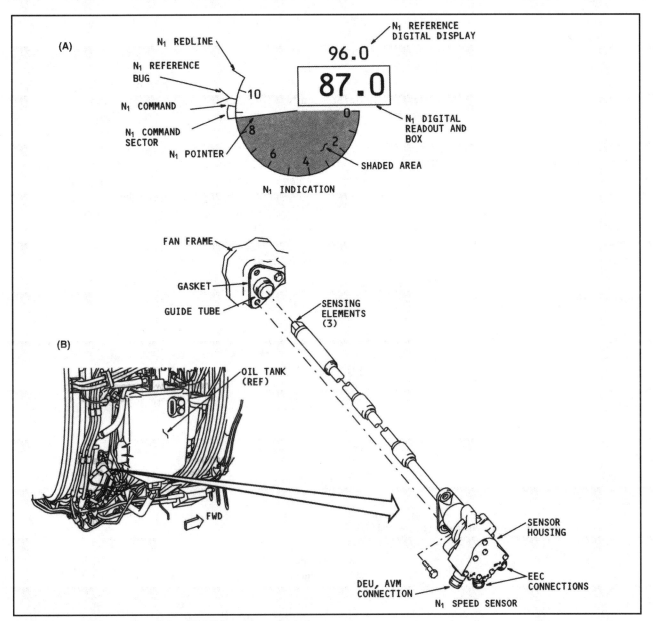

Fig. 12-11A — N₁ Indicator for FADEC equipped engine
Fig. 12-11B — N₁ speed sensor for FADEC equipped engine.

form of high pressure gas and then converts this pressure to kinetic energy in the form of a high velocity jet of gases. The gases exiting the engine tailpipe create a reacting force referred to as thrust.

Recall from Chapter II that total pressure in the tailpipe represents the force it would take to completely stop the flow of gases. With the large exit flow area and high velocities present in the tailpipe, it is easy to see how gas under relatively low pressure (1.94 times ambient) can have a large force (thrust) value.

2. The Cockpit EPR Gauge

The gauge in Figure 12-12A shows that after the operator determined from the performance charts that the takeoff engine pressure ratio was 1.94, the engine pressure ratio reminder was set to display that value.

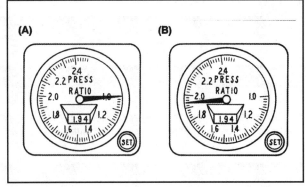

Fig. 12-12A — Take-off EPR set at 1.94 engine not running.
Fig. 12-12B — Engine running at take-off power (1.94 EPR).

Then, in Figure 12-12B, the operator started the engine and accelerated to 1.94 engine pressure ratio for takeoff. The display is later reset for climb engine pressure ratio and for cruise engine pressure ratio, and the engine speed is adjusted accordingly. This is necessary because the EPR value changes (decreases) during flight conditions due to the rise in Pt_2 pressure (ram compression).

3. Example EPR System (Pratt & Whitney Dual-Spool Engine)

The EPR indicating system shown in Figure 12-13 consists of a set of Pt_7 probes, a Pt_2 probe, a manifold, an Autosyn transmitter, and a cockpit indicator.

The single Pt_2 probe senses compressor inlet pressure, either suction at high ground level compressor speeds or pressure above ambient in flight, and sends a signal to the Autosyn transmitter. The several Pt_7 probes, via the manifold, send a signal of turbine discharge pressure to the transmitter. The two signals combine to provide a pressure ratio indication in the cockpit.

The indication of 2.4 engine pressure ratio means that turbine discharge pressure (Pt_7) is 2.4 times greater than compressor inlet pressure (Pt_2). There is no set of over-limits values for engine pressure ratio as there is for exhaust gas temperature and RPM. The target takeoff value of 2.4, once arrived at, is not exceeded except in emergencies and then the engine gas temperature and/or RPM limits prevail for operating the engine.

Engine power management is discussed in detail in Chapter VII.

For an explanation of the Pt_2 vent in Figure 12-13, see Anti-Ice System, Chapter IX.

TROUBLESHOOTING THE EPR INDICATING SYSTEM

PROBLEM/POSSIBLE CAUSE	CHECK FOR	REMEDY
1. No EPR reading in the cockpit.		
a. Circuit Breaker(s)	Circuit breaker(s) tripped	Reset
b. Circuit Power	Voltage and continuity	Repair as necessary
c. Indicator	Proper operation by interchanging instruments	Replace indicator
d. Transmitter	Proper operation by slaving in another unit	Replace transmitter
2. False low EPR at takeoff power lever setting (ground and flight).		
a. Turbine Discharge Pressure	Loose connections or obstructions to flow	Tighten or clean pressure line or probes.
b. Same as 1c or 1d.		
c. Refer to fuel system troubleshooting.		
3. False high cockpit indication (flight).		
a. Pt2 Probe or Line.	Loose connections or obstructions	Tighten or clean
b. Indicator or Transmitter	Leakage or loose connections	Tighten
4. EPR normal but EGT, RPM, and Wf all high indications (ground and flight).		
a. Loose/Leaking Lines in EPR System	Loose turbine discharge pressure lines	Tighten
5. EPR false high when EGT, RPM, Wf all low indications (flight).		
a. Icing in EPR System	Ice in inlet pressure lines	Deice

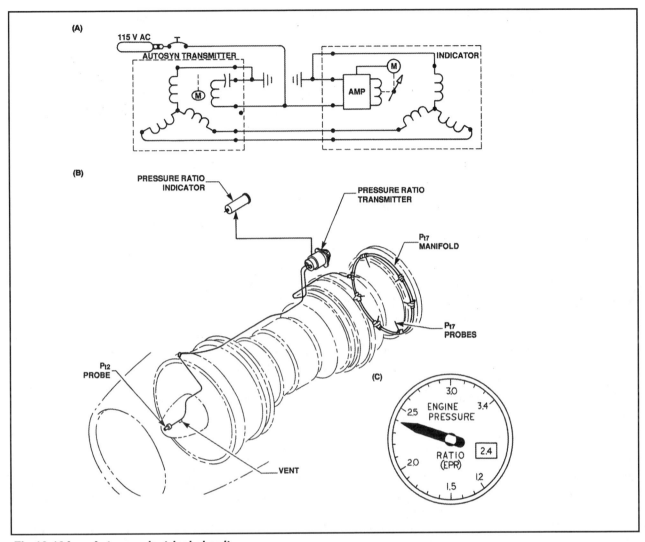

Fig.12-13A — Autosyn electrical circuit.
Fig.12-13B — Typical EPR system arrangement.
Fig.12-13C — Cockpit instrument displaying take-off EPR.

TROUBLESHOOTING THE ENGINE WITH THE EPR SYSTEM

PROBLEM/POSSIBLE CAUSE	CHECK FOR	REMEDY
1. EPR normal at all power settings but EGT, Wf, RPM all high indications.		
a. Internal Engine Problems	1. Contaminated or damaged compressor	Clean or repair
	2. Damaged hot section parts	Repair
	3. Compression loss due to external leaks	Repair
	4. Air bleeds open (anti-ice, bleed band, customer service air, etc.)	
2. EPR high when power lever is aligned with another engine.		
a. Fuel Control Trim	Fuel control out of adjustment	Retrim
b. Rigging Problem	Linkage out of rig	Rerig

PROBLEM/POSSIBLE CAUSE	CHECK FOR	REMEDY
3. EPR low when power lever is aligned with another engine.		
a. Fuel Control Trim	Fuel control out of adjustment	Retrim
b. Rigging Problem	Linkage out of rig	Rerig
4. EPR high or low when power lever is at part power stop.		
a. Engine out of trim. Fuel control out of adjustment.	Correct trim	Perform trim run

5. Unable to attain takeoff power (EPR) before EGT or RPM reaches its limit.

Same as 1. above.

D. Torque Indicating System

Torque indicating systems are required by Federal Aviation Regulations on all torque producing engines, such as turboprops and turboshafts. It is the primary performance instrument in the cockpit.

The torque indicator receives its input from the torque sensing system on the engine. With the benefit of the cockpit torque reading, the operator has, in effect, a continuous indication of the horsepower output of the engine.

Torque is displayed in various ways in the cockpit. The most common are: Torque oil pressure (psi), torque oil pressure (ft. lbs.), torque percent, and sometimes a direct horsepower read-out.

The two torque sensing systems most widely used are the "balanced oil piston" hydro-mechanical system, which converts engine oil pressure to a torque signal, and an electronic "phase shift" system which converts the twist of the power output shaft into a torque signal.

1. Hydro-Mechanical Torque Indicating System

The torque sensing system in Figure 12-14 includes a cockpit gauge, electrical transmitter, hydro-mechanical sensor mechanism, and main and torsion drive gears. The illustration includes both the fixed turbine design and the free turbine design. Recall that in a fixed turbine, the turbine(s) and compressor are mechanically coupled and rotate as one unit and that the free turbine rotates independently of the compressor system.

In the systems shown, both the main and the torsion shafts rotate at the same speed as the turbine(s) that drives them. However, the torsion shaft is subjected to the majority of the load on the turbine(s) from the output shaft. The main shaft is used as a reference point.

The Torque Sensing Mechanism is a hydro-mechanical unit, Figure 12-15. It contains a pilot valve which is under very little tension at zero torque. Engine oil pressure at that time will act on both oil lines

to the differential pressure gauge with the same force and a canceling out action results in a zero gauge reading.

When the output shaft places a load on the torsion gear and forces the outer helical gear to the right, adding tension to the pilot valve spring, a reduced case pressure results and a torque pressure gauge rise occurs. The pressure drop between calibrated engine oil pressure and case oil pressure is proportional to the torque load applied. The torque oil pressure signal to the gauge is proportional to engine torque produced.

A step by step description of the operation of this system is as follows:

a. With an increase in torque on the system, by way of RPM increase or prop pitch increase, the torque sensor (Figure 12-14 and 12-15) would respond in the following way.

1) The main shaft and drive gear is rotating clockwise.

2) The torsion shaft and drive gear is rotating clockwise.

3) The power output gear moves clockwise, overcoming the resistance of the output shaft and propeller drag.

4) The output shaft moves counter clockwise.

5) The outer and inner helical gears move counter clockwise. The inner gear turns slightly more than the outer gear and screws inward (left hand thread pulling the outer gear laterally and to the right) toward the inner gear. That is, when the torsion shaft moves under a load, its gear lags in angular movement because its drive shaft is less rigid. If the angular difference did not occur, the outer gear would not move to the right and the torque oil pressure would not change.

6) When the outer helical gear is pulled to the right by the inner helical gear (acting as a threaded nut), it pushes the pilot valve along with it and to the right. This overcomes the opposing oil force acting on the surface of the pilot valve.

7) When the pilot valve moves to the right compressing the pilot valve spring, the valve moves towards its seat restricting oil flow.

8) This causes the case pressure to decrease.

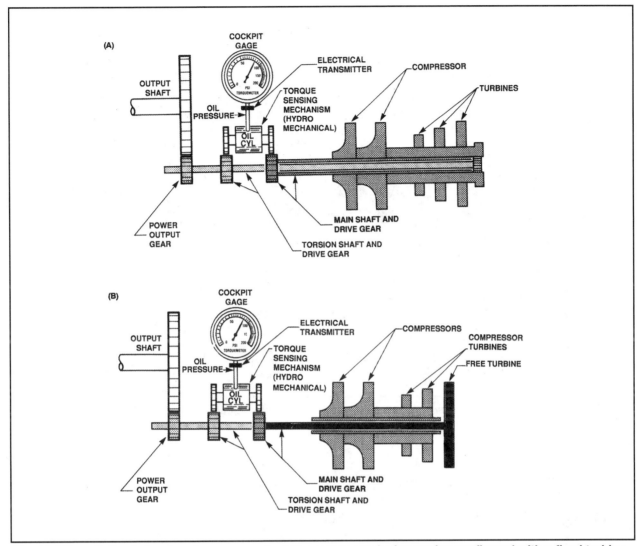

Fig. 12-14A — Method of measuring power output in a torque producing engine configured with a fixed turbine design.

Fig. 12-14B — Method of measuring power output in a torque producing engine configured with a free power turbine design.

9) The torque gauge pressure increases.

10) When the torque load on the system decreases, the helical gear set moves the pilot valve back to the left, increasing case pressure and decreasing the torque oil pressure reading.

2. Electronic Torque Indicating System

The electronic torque indicating system, Figure 12-16, includes a cockpit indicator, torque signal transmitter or pickup, and an inner and outer drive shaft.

Both the inner and outer shafts rotate at the same speed as the engine turbine wheel(s) that are mechanically coupled to them. However, only the inner shaft is subjected to the majority of the load on the turbines from the power output shaft. The outer shaft is used as a reference point.

The teeth machined on the front end of both shafts are aligned when a zero torque condition exists. When a load

is applied to the inner shaft, the machined teeth move out of alignment with the teeth on the outer shaft. The deflection or twist, when applied to the torque sensor circuit, converts this angular deflection to a voltage output which powers the cockpit gauge.

3. Torque Limits

The torque load that can be applied to the power reduction gearbox is limited and overtorque is prevented by the operator who closely monitors the torque gauge during engine operation.

In Figure 12-17, note that the torque limits are influenced by time. For example, the engine can operate to 5,900 foot pounds of torque for 15 seconds maximum with no maintenance action required. If either the torque limit or the 15 second limit is exceeded, the engine power output reduction gearbox must be removed for overhaul.

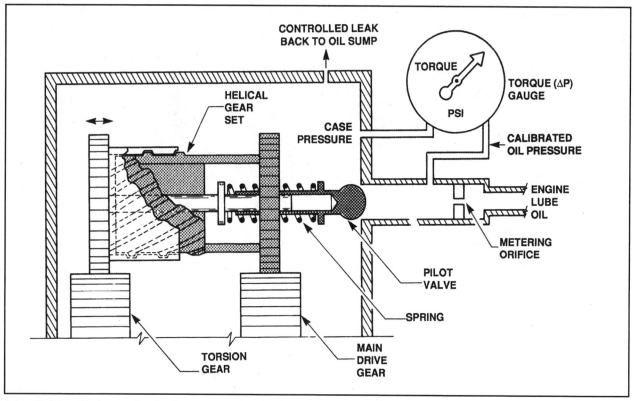

Fig. 12-15 — Hydromechanical torque sensor (main drive shaft moves clockwise with the RPM increase).

TROUBLESHOOTING THE TORQUE INDICATING SYSTEM

PROBLEM/POSSIBLE CAUSE	CHECK FOR	REMEDY
1. No torque reading in the cockpit.		
a. Circuit Breaker(s)	Circuit breaker(s) tripped	Reset
b. Circuit Power	Voltage and continuity	Repair as necessary
c. Indicator	Proper operation by interchanging indicators	Replace indicator
d. Transmitter	Proper operation by slaving in another unit	Replace transmitter
2. Low torque indication at all settings.		
a. Indicator	Indicator malfunction, interchange indicators or slave in another indicator	Replace indicator
b. Transmitter	Transmitter malfunction by slaving in another unit	Replace transmitter
c. Torque Pressure Lines	Loose connections or obstructions to flow	Tighten or clean/flush

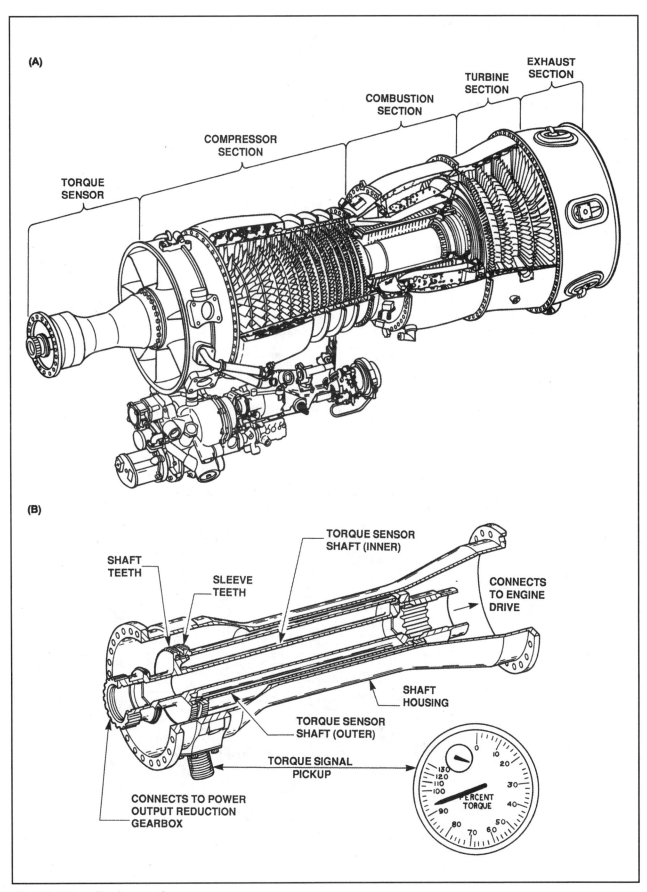

(A)

EXHAUST SECTION

TURBINE SECTION

COMBUSTION SECTION

COMPRESSOR SECTION

TORQUE SENSOR

(B)

SHAFT TEETH

SLEEVE TEETH

TORQUE SENSOR SHAFT (INNER)

CONNECTS TO ENGINE DRIVE

SHAFT HOUSING

TORQUE SENSOR SHAFT (OUTER)

TORQUE SIGNAL PICKUP

CONNECTS TO POWER OUTPUT REDUCTION GEARBOX

PERCENT TORQUE

Fig. 12-16A — Engine sections.
Fig. 12-16B — Torque sensor shaft.

TROUBLESHOOTING THE ENGINE WITH THE TORQUE INDICATING SYSTEM

PROBLEM/POSSIBLE CAUSE	CHECK FOR	REMEDY
1. Torque low or normal but EGT, RPM and Wf all high indications.		
a. Torque Sensing System	Correct torque output signal at engine	Repair as necessary
b. Fuel Control Linkage to Prop Governor	Linkage out of adjustment causing low blade angle	Rerig as necessary
c. Fuel Control or Fuel Governor	Internal malfunction causing low blade angle	Replace faulty units
d. Propeller or Rotor	Blade angle too low	Adjust angle
e. Engine Bleeds	Open bleeds, anti-stall, anti-ice, Customer Service Air	Adjust or repair
f. Internal Engine	1. Contaminated or damaged compressor	Clean or repair
	2. Damaged hot section	Repair as necessary
2. Unable to attain take-off power before EGT or RPM reach their limits.		
a. Same as 1. above		

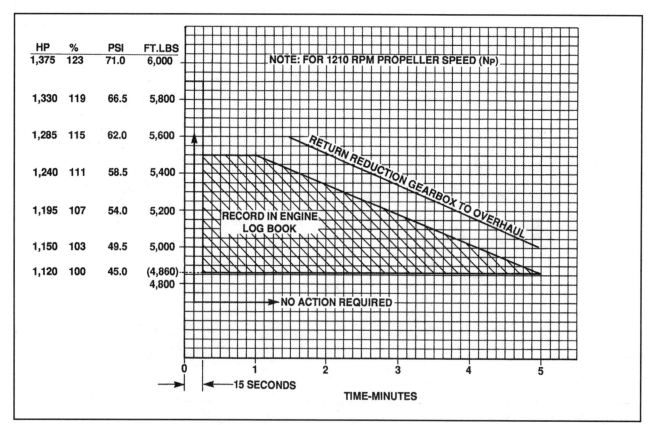

Fig. 12-17 — Typical torque limits (All conditions of engine operation).

E. Fuel Flow Indicating System

The fuel flow indicating system for turbine engines measures fuel consumption in pounds per hour (PPH). Generally, this indicating system is an electrical type, powered by either 26V AC or 115V AC from the aircraft bus.

1. Vane-type Flow Meter System

The vane type flow meter is an older type system and is designed to measure volume of flow. The system consists of a flow meter transmitter generally located in the engine fuel line to the combustor and an indicator located in the cockpit.

In Figure 12-18 the circuit arrangement can be seen. The loop circuit contains the delta windings of both the transmitter and indicator, connected in parallel. The transmitter and indicator magnets are in a 26V AC, 400 cycle circuit. As the vane is moved against its restraining spring by volume of flow, the transmitter magnet moves along with the vane. The magnet in the indicator to which the pointer is attached tracks along with the transmitter magnet, giving a fuel flow reading to the pilot. The gauge in the illustration indicates in pounds per hour.

2. Synchronous Mass Flow

This system, more recently developed than the vane type, is said to have greater accuracy in that it measures mass flow rather than volume. In this way, it compensates for fuel temperature in its readout.

The system in Figure 12-19 also measures in pounds per hour, and its components' locations are similar to the vane type system. Fuel enters the transmitter impeller, which is rotated at a constant 60 revolutions per minute by the synchronous impeller motor. The temperature of the fuel will determine its volume and the amount of force to be created by the action of the impeller. The turbine is twisted against its restraining spring by the mass flow force created by impeller movement. The mass

flow electrical transmitter arrangement is similar to the vane type system.

3. Motorless Mass Flow Meter System

The Motorless flow meter represents the latest in electronic solid-state fuel measuring systems. It is small in size and accounts for variables such as fuel temperatures and specific gravity with an accuracy of ±1% as opposed to approximately 2% for motor driven flow meters. Almost all of the large turbine powered aircraft are configured with the motorless type, pound per hour fuel flow meter system. The readout is on a digital display rather than the traditional gauge and pointer.

The flow meter transmitter converts flow rate into two electronic signals. The signals are created as the flowing fuel gives an angular displacement to two continuously rotating magnets. The magnets induce electronic impulses into stationary coils and the time difference is used as a measure of mass flow rate.

In Figure 12-20, fuel enters from the drive end and rotates the drum containing Magnet No. 1 and the drive shaft. The spring connects the drive shaft to the impeller containing Magnet No. 2. As the magnets rotate, the pick-off coils receive current pulses, the first pulse occurring at Pick-off Coil No. 1. Then as the spring deflects in proportion to fuel flow, No. 2 magnet turns with the impeller and induces a current pulse with a time lag into Pick-off Coil No. 2.

The greater the mass flow, the greater the spring deflection and angular difference between the magnets. That is, the higher the fuel flow the greater the deflection of the impeller relative to the drum shown. The time displacement which results is directly proportional to mass flow rate in this motorless transmitter design.

The 26V AC cockpit indicator contains electronics which convert the time difference to a pound per hour (PPH) readout.

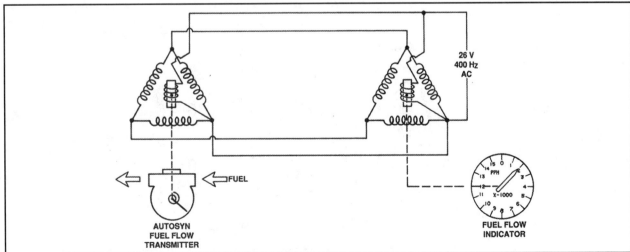

Fig. 12-18 — Vane type fuel flowmeter indicating system.

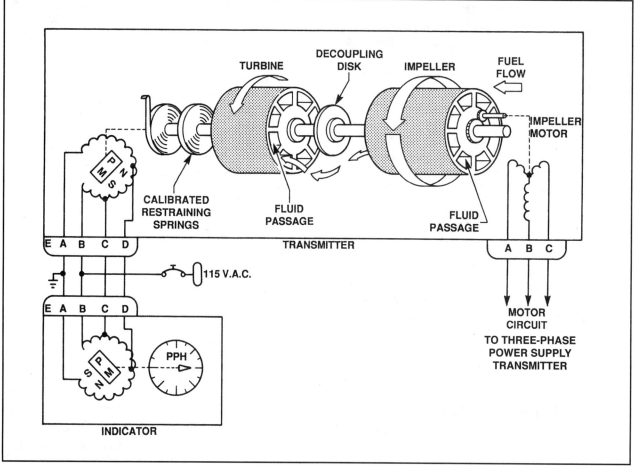

Fig. 12-19 — *Synchronous mass flow type, fuel flowmeter system.*

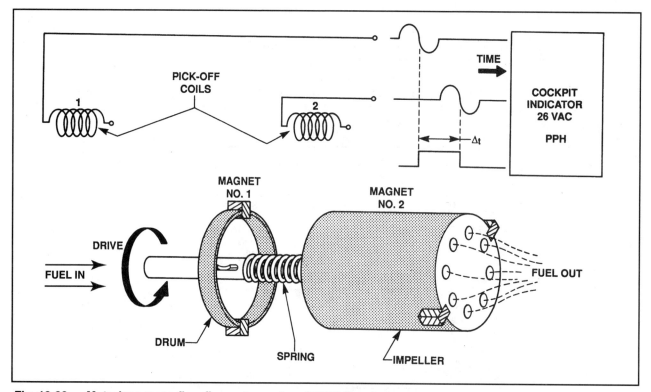

Fig. 12-20 — *Motorless mass flow flowmeter system (EDEC Corp).*

TROUBLESHOOTING THE FUEL FLOW METER SYSTEM

PROBLEM/POSSIBLE CAUSE	CHECK FOR	REMEDY
1. No fuel flow indication or fluctuating indication.		
a. Circuit Wiring	Loose connections and continuity	Tighten or repair as necessary
b. Fuel Flow Indicator	Proper indication by interchanging indicators	Replace indicator
c. Fuel Flow Transmitter	Correct input voltage. Proper operation by slaving in another transmitter	Correct circuit problem or replace transmitter

TROUBLESHOOTING THE ENGINE WITH THE FLOWMETER INDICATOR

PROBLEM/POSSIBLE CAUSE	CHECK FOR	REMEDY
1. High fuel flow indication at all power settings.		
a. Fuel System Malfunction: Refer to fuel system troubleshooting		
b. Turbine Wheel or Stator Vanes	1. Damaged components using a borescope or visually through the tailpipe with a strong light 2. Other high cockpit indications - high fuel flow usually occurs along with other abnormal indicator readings	Possible engine teardown
c. Compressor	1. FOD 2. Contamination	Possible engine teardown Field clean

F. Oil System Indicators (Figure 12-21)

Oil system indicators generally consist of oil temperature, oil pressure, and oil quantity. Also, many cockpits include warning lights for low oil pressure and for filter bypass. Only oil temperature and pressure are discussed here. The other oil system indicating systems are explained in detail in Chapter VI.

1. Oil Temperature Indicating Systems

The location of the temperature sensor in the lubrication system seems to be of little significance. Manufacturers place the sensor in either the pressure subsystem or the scavenge subsystem. This is possible because gas turbine engine oil systems have a high flow rate, circulating at the rate of two to five times the oil tank capacity per minute, causing temperatures to stabilize throughout the entire lube system very rapidly. This gives the cockpit a quick and reliable oil temperature indication.

However, some manufacturers state that placing the sensor in the scavenge subsystem is preferable because it gives a slightly quicker indication of high friction heat buildup from failing parts such as bearings and gears. The more common of the two locations, however, is in the pressure subsystem to show the temperature of the oil entering the engine.

a. Resistance Bulb

The resistance bulb oil temperature indicating system consists of a resistance bulb and an indicator in a 28V DC powered circuit. The bulb contains a temperature-sensitive pure-nickel wire wound around a mica core contained in a steel outer casing. The bulb is installed in an oil line with the tip of the bulb protruding into the oil stream (Figure 12-22).

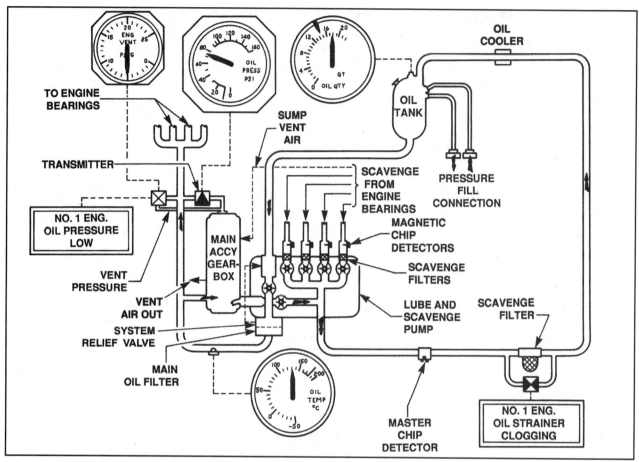

Fig. 12-21 — Engine oil system indicators (Positive sump vent system).

The circuit below shows the resistance bulb as the variable resistor in a wheatstone bridge-type circuit. Bulb resistance increases when heated and, as this occurs, more and more current flows from A to B. This milliampere circuit flow gives an indication of oil temperature in the cockpit (Figure 12-23).

b. Thermocouple

The thermocouple oil temperature indicating system is not powered by the aircraft bus. It is a self-contained and self-generating circuit. It derives its power from a pair of dissimilar metals, iron and constantan, which when heated at the hot junction produce a millivoltage and cause a current flow through a cockpit indicator. This circuit is similar to the exhaust temperature indicating system except that the hot junction in this thermocouple system is in the oil stream and the hot junction of the exhaust gas temperature system is in the exhaust stream (Figure 12-24).

2. Oil Pressure Indicating System

The oil pressure indicating system is an Autosyn design, powered by either 26V AC or 115V AC from the aircraft bus (Figure 12-25).

In the example system, the transmitter receives two input pressure signals, engine vent subsystem pressure and engine oil pressure subsystem pressure. The signals

apply pressure to a pair of opposing bourdon tubes which are linked mechanically to an electro-magnet in a coil. When the magnet rotates within its electrical field, the indicator magnet also rotates because it is in a similar coil connected in parallel with the transmitter coil.

By utilizing two pressure inputs, this system algebraically subtracts vent pressure from the pressure subsystem fluid pressure, giving a differential oil pressure indication in the cockpit. This is required on many engines to give an accurate cockpit indication of the actual oil flow through to the engine.

Two different conditions can occur in bearing sumps in the area of the oil jets. In some engines, pressure will build up from gas path air bleeding inward through bearing seals. On other engines, very tight sealing arrangements will allow the scavenge pumps to create a negative pressure in the sumps. In either case, the vent pressure influence at the oil jet will affect oil flow.

If higher than normal positive pressure is present, it can retard the normal oil flow to a point where insufficient lubrication takes place. The same conditions can take place in a negative sump system. Negative vent pressures are generally in the range of two to six pounds per square inch—gauge below ambient at cruise power, and this vent pressure is designed to generate a designated oil flow in conjunction with the oil pumping

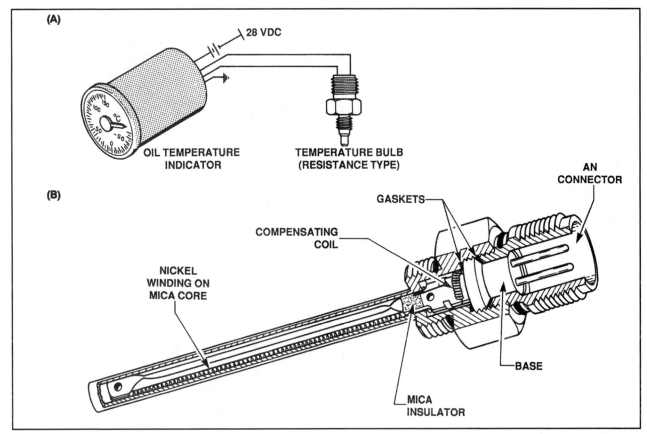

Fig. 12-22A — Resistance bulb and gauge.
Fig. 12-22B — Cutaway view of resistance bulb.

system. If bearing seals leak excessive amounts of air into the sumps, the pressure becomes less negative, moving toward zero gauge pressure or ambient. The back pressure which occurs will retard normal oil flow from the oil jets.

Negative sump systems are stabilized by connecting some part of the system to ambient pressure or by allowing engine bleed air to enter the system at some point to pressurize the return of vent air and contaminants to the atmosphere.

An example of this concept follows for both a negative sump pressure and a positive sump pressure. Negative sump pressure occurs from scavenge pump suction being greater than the seal leakage air entering the bearing sump.

Positive sump example:

    80 psig oil pressure
    -(+5) psig vent pressure
    _____
    75 psig corrected oil pressure (cockpit indicator)

Negative sump example:

    80 psig oil pressure
    -(-5) psig vent pressure
    _____
    85 psig corrected oil pressure (cockpit indicator)

In the positive sump example, five pounds per square inch—gauge back pressure at the oil jet results in a net differential 75 pounds per square inch—gauge actual oil pressure, which in effect represents a calibrated amount of oil flow in gallons per minute.

In the negative sump example, a negative condition is present at the oil jet allowing more oil to flow. The negative five pounds per square inch—gauge, when subtracted algebraically, results in an 85 pounds per square inch—gauge corrected oil pressure, which will naturally flow more oil than if the sump were of positive pressure.

Maintenance personnel need to realize this situation exists when troubleshooting with a direct oil pressure test gauge for low or high oil pressure indication. Two gauges must be used to measure both the oil pressure and the vent pressure to calculate the corrected (differential) oil pressure.

For example, high vent pressure from a damaged carbon seal at a main bearing location could be the cause of a low cockpit pressure indication. Careful troubleshooting and knowledge of system design will reveal the source of this problem to be within the engine itself rather than in the indicating system or in the oil pressure subsystem (Figure 12-26).

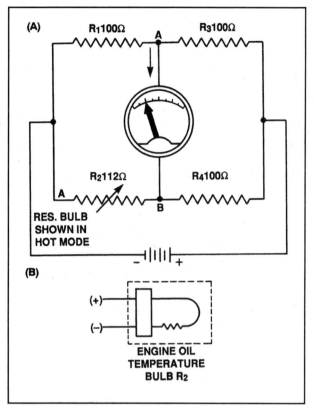

Fig. 12-23A — *Resistance bulb oil temperature indicating bridge circuit.*

Fig. 12-23B — *Resistance bulb shown as a variable resistor.*

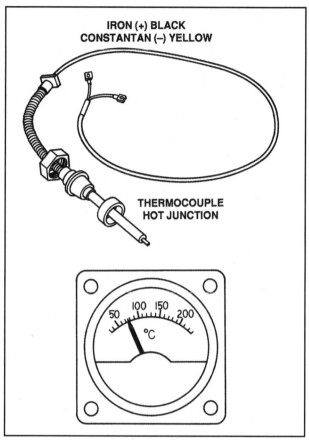

Fig. 12-24 — *Temperature thermocouple and gauge.*

TROUBLESHOOTING THE OIL SYSTEM INDICATOR

PROBLEM/POSSIBLE CAUSE	CHECK FOR	REMEDY
1. No oil temperature indication in the cockpit.		
a. Resistance Bulb		
1) Circuit Breaker	Circuit breaker in	Reset
2) Continuity and Power	Loose connections or open circuit	Tighten or repair as necessary
3) Indicator	Defective indicator by interchanging indicators	Replace indicator
4) Resistance Bulb	Defective bulb by slaving in another bulb	Replace bulb
b. Thermocouple Bulb Circuit		
1) Continuity	Loose connections or open circuit	Tighten or repair as necessary
2) Bulb	Defective bulb by slaving in another bulb	Replace bulb

PROBLEM/POSSIBLE CAUSE	CHECK FOR	REMEDY

2. Oil temperature fluctuates in either the resistance bulb or the thermocouple bulb circuit.

a. Connecting Points	Loose connections	Tighten
b. Indicator	Defective indicator by interchanging indicators	Replace indicator
c. Bulb	Defective bulb by slaving in another bulb	Replace bulb

3. High oil temperature indication.

| a. Indicator | Same as item 2b | |

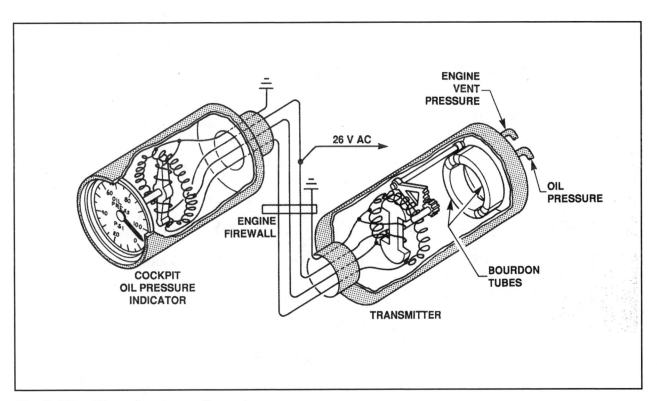

Fig. 12-25 — Oil pressure transmitter and gauge.

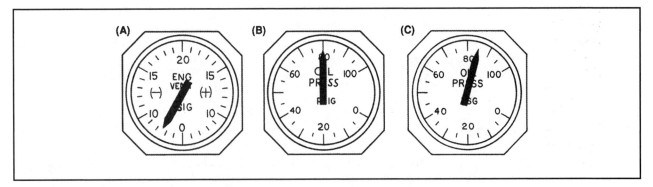

Fig. 12-26A — Vent pressure, test gauge reading.
Fig. 12-26B — Oil pressure, test gauge reading.
Fig. 12-26C — Cockpit gauge reading in corrected units.

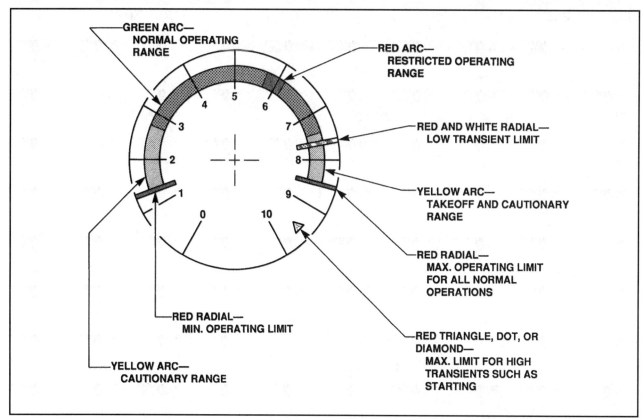

Fig. 12-27A — Typical engine dial type instrument markings.

TROUBLESHOOTING THE ENGINE WITH OIL SYSTEM INDICATORS

PROBLEM/POSSIBLE CAUSE	CHECK FOR	REMEDY
1. High oil temperature indication.		
a. Oil servicing	Low oil level	Add oil
b. Fuel-Oil Cooler	Thermo-valve sticking open, by checking by-pass valve pressure drop across the cooler with direct gages	Replace cooler
c. Main Engine Bearing	Metal contamination at chip detectors and filters	Possible engine teardown
2. Oil pressure high, low or fluctuating.		
a. Refer to oil system troubleshooting.		

G. Marking of Powerplant Instruments (Figures 12-27A and 12-27B)

The following guidelines from Federal Aviation Administration circular AC 20-88 offer acceptable, but not exclusive, methods of compliance with gas turbine powerplant instrument dial face markings:

1. Fuel Pressure

Red Radial at maximum and/or minimum permissible pressures established as engine operating limitations;

Green Arc at normal operating range;

Yellow/Amber Arc at cautionary ranges indicating any potential hazard in the fuel system such as malfunctions, icing, etc.

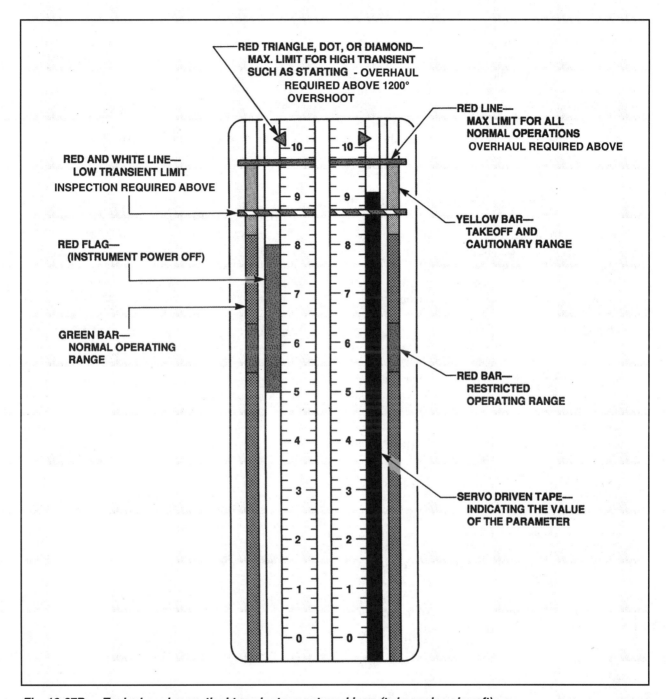

Fig. 12-27B — Typical engine vertical type instrument markings (twin engine aircraft).

2. Oil Pressure

Red Radial at maximum and/or minimum permissible pressures established as engine operating limitations;

Green Arc at normal operating range;

Yellow Arc at cautionary ranges indicating any potential hazard due to over-pressure during cold start, low pressure during idle, etc.

3. Oil Temperature

Red Radial at maximum and/or minimum permissible temperatures established as engine operating limitations;

Green Arc at normal operating range;

Yellow/Amber Arc at cautionary ranges indicating any potential hazard due to overheating, high viscosity at low temperature, etc.

4. Torque Indicator

Red Radial at maximum permissible torque pressure for dry or wet operation, whichever is greater;

Green Arc from maximum torque pressure for continuous operation to minimum torque pressure recommended;

Yellow Arc from maximum torque pressure for continuous operation to maximum permissible torque pressure.

5. Exhaust Gas Temperature

Red Radial at maximum permissible gas temperature for wet or dry operation, whichever is greater;

Green Arc from maximum permissible temperature for continuous operation to minimum recommended by the engine manufacturer;

Yellow/Amber Arc from maximum temperature for continuous operation to maximum permissible gas temperature.

6. Tachometer

Red Radial at maximum permissible rotational speed (RPM);

Green Arc from maximum rotational speed for continuous operation to minimum rotational speed recommended for continuous operation;

Yellow/Amber Arc from maximum rotational speed for continuous operation to maximum rotational speed.

7. Dual Tachometer (Helicopter)

Red Radial on a dual tachometer (Engine) at maximum permissible rotational speed (RPM);

Dual Tachometer (Rotor) at maximum and minimum rotor speed (RPM) for power "OFF" operational condition;

Green Arc on a dual tachometer (engine) from maximum rotational speed for continuous operation to minimum recommended for continuous operating power (except in the restricted ranges, if any);

Dual Tachometer (rotor) from maximum to minimum normal operating range;

Yellow/Amber Arc, dual tachometer (engine) precautionary ranges, such as altitude limits.

8. Gas Producer (N1) Tachometer (Turboshaft Helicopter)

Red Radial at maximum permissible rotational speed (RPM).

9. Thrust Indicator (Turbojet, Turbofan)

This indicator has no markings because values vary considerably with temperature and altitude operating conditions. Limiting gauge markings cannot be established for all such conditions. It is necessary to refer to thrust setting charts (EPR or Pt7) for the proper values.

10. FAA Suggested Methods Of Marking Powerplant Instruments

To satisfy the requirement for clearly visible markings for low light level conditions at a viewing distance of 28 inches, a hypothetical instrument dial and vertical tape instrument are shown. These markings are intended as a guide only. Some instruments need but a few of these markings.

QUESTIONS:

1. Temperature taken forward of the turbine wheel(s) is known by what name?

2. Which cockpit indicator is most likely to show an elevated reading if the turbine wheel becomes damaged?

3. What is the name of the exhaust temperature analyzer unit that is used on gas turbine engines?

4. What are two of the main functions of a tachometer indicator on an EPR rated, axial flow engine?

5. If the aircraft loses its electrical generating power, will the tachometer system continue to function?

6. Does an indication of 100% engine speed on a single-spool turbojet engine mean that 100% thrust is also available?

7. Is there both an EPR indicator and a thrust indicator in the cockpit of a typical turbine engine powered aircraft?

8. Does a Speed-Rated fan engine use an EPR system as a primary thrust indicator?

9. Is the fuel-flow indicating system powered by the AC or the DC aircraft bus?

10. Turbine engine fuel-flow is measured in what units?

11. Where is the flow-meter transmitter usually located?

12. Which of the two oil temperature systems shown is an independent electrical circuit?

13. Which oil system transmitter is vented to the engine gearbox?

CHAPTER XIII
Fire/Overheat Detection And Extinguishing Systems For Turbine Engines

The turbine engine, or cowlings adjacent to the engine, contain fire detection devices which illuminate a warning light in the cockpit if a fire or serious overheat condition occurs. Quite often the engine hot and cold sections are divided into two distinct fire zones. The detection devices are set according to the operating temperature of that zone. Where the cold section might alarm at 200-300°F, the hot section might alarm as high as 300-1200°F.

Several varieties of fire surveillance systems are available for fire detection purposes. The more common types are the single-wire thermal switch, the two-wire thermal switch, the continuous loop, and the pneumatic loop.

A. Single-Wire Thermal Switch

This system is configured with several heat sensitive thermal switches which contain a pair of contacts that are normally open and which close at a preset heat value. In Figure 13-1A, as the switch heats up, the heat sensitive arms to which the contacts are attached expand in the direction opposite the electrical terminal. This completes an electrical circuit to a warning indicator in the cockpit. This system automatically resets itself when cool.

In Figure 13-1B, 28V DC is applied to both paths of the thermal switch loop. If an overheat to alarm temperature or a fire occurs which closes any of the switches, a path to ground is completed through the closed switch. With this loop arrangement, one open circuit can occur and the system will still provide protection at all of the fire surveillance points. The test switch tests the entire loop and will show the operator whether an open circuit is present in the power input lead of the loop. A short circuit in the loop will cause a false fire warning indication. The dimming relay shown provides low voltage to the light for night operation.

B. Two-Wire Thermal Switch

The two-wire thermal switch is designed so that the circuit can withstand either an open or a short and still remain functional. In the circuit, in Figure 13-2, the following sequence of events occurs during operation and testing:

1. Normal Operation

With the trip-over relay in the normal position as shown, 28V DC is supplied to Loop A from both ends. If

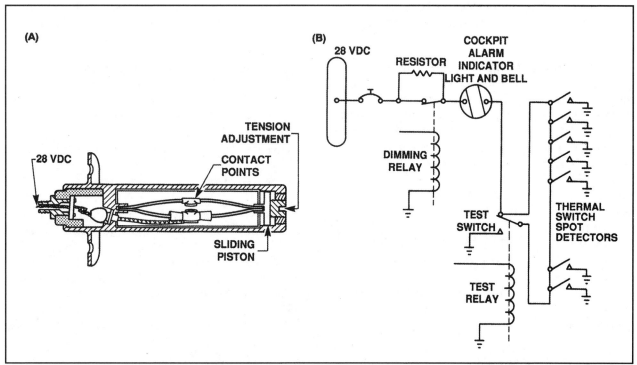

Fig. 13-1A — Fenwall bimetallic thermal switch.
Fig. 13-1B — Single-wire, thermal switch fire (overheat) detector circuit.

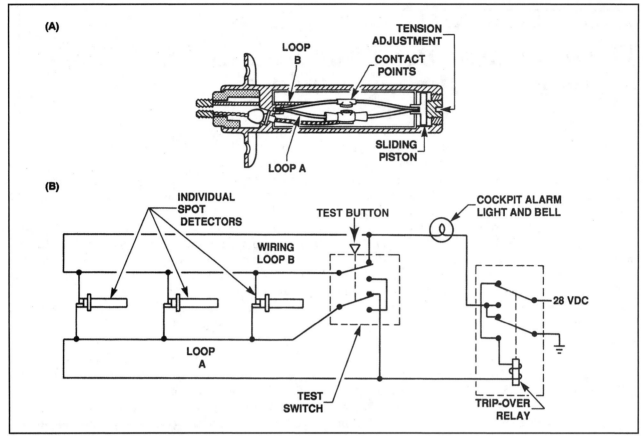

Fig. 13-2A — Bi-metallic thermal switch.
Fig. 13-2B — Two-wire, thermal switch (overheat and fire) detector circuit.

an overheat/fire occurs or the test button is pressed, current will flow through Loop B and illuminate the warning light. The trip-over relay will remain in this position due to the low current draw present in the normal mode of operation.

2. Operation With A Short In Loop A

A high current draw with a short in this loop will be sufficient to cause the trip-over relay to actuate. A reset button on the relay casing will pop out and will remain out until reset by hand. Loop B will now receive the 28V DC power to protect the engine and Loop-A will provide the ground circuit. If a serious overheat or fire occurs or if the test button is pressed, the warning light will illuminate. A short in Loop A is only detectable by observing the popped reset button.

3. Operation With A Short In Loop B

If an overheat/ fire occurs or if the test button is pressed, a high current draw sufficient to cause trip-over will be present. After trip-over, the alarm light will illuminate and remain on, giving an indication that Loop B is shorted.

4. Operation With An Open In Loop A

This loop is powered from both ends and provides protection similar to the single-wire system. If an open is

present in the loop, power is still available to each thermal switch. Pressing the test button will reveal this condition because for current to flow and the light to illuminate, the entire loop has to be secure. With an open circuit in this loop the light will not show.

5. Operation With An Open In Loop B

The system will still provide fire protection with an open circuit in this loop. Pressing the test button will reveal this fault. The alarm light will not illuminate.

As in the single-wire system, after cooling this system automatically resets itself and is ready for reuse.

C. Continuous Loop System

There are two types of electrical continuous loop fire/overheat detection systems in common use today, the single-wire system and the two-wire system. Both are designed for use on larger engines. These systems are discrete in that they are independent of surrounding engine bay temperatures. They alarm only when a temperature rise occurs above the average engine bay temperature.

In the single-wire system, the Inconel outer case provides the ground potential. In the two-wire system, the second wire performs this function. In each case, the hot lead is insulated from ground. One uses ceramic beads coated with a substance called eutectic salt. The other uses a thermistor type material. Each has the property of losing its electrical resistance as melting occurs when heated. The composition of the insulator material determines the alarm temperature.

In addition to being available in single or two-wire cores (Figure 13-3), continuous loop systems are also available in single and dual loop configuration (Figure 13-4B). The dual loop offers a back up capability should one loop fail.

Normally, both loops are set at the same alarm temperature. In the Fenwal system, if different alarm temperatures are required, sensing loop segments set at different alarm temperatures can be connected in series in one continuous loop. Each segment will alarm at its own preset temperature without an averaging effect. The older Kidde systems cannot connect different temperature loops in series, but a newer type of Kidde system can.

In the circuit diagram shown in Figure 13-3, 28V DC is supplied to the hot lead through an alarm relay coil. When cool, the insulation material does not allow current to flow between ground and the hot lead; however, when a fire occurs, the insulator material heats and loses resistance sufficiently to complete a path to ground. The relay coil is energized by this current flow and the alarm light is illuminated in the cockpit.

This system, like the thermal switch systems, will automatically reset itself when cooled.

The continuous loop installation drawing in Figure 13-4 shows two separate loops being utilized, one for the cold section and one for the hot section. It also shows the fire extinguishing system components which are completely independent of the detection circuit. The loop system illustrated incorporates control circuits which automatically compensate for operational heat in the engine compartment.

Figure 13-5 shows a continuous loop testing device, the Jetcal Analyzer unit, which was described in Chapter XII for calibrating the Exhaust Gas Temperature (EGT) system.

The heater probe is used to apply a known heat value to the continuous loop. The heat value displays on the potentiometer of the Jetcal control panel. When the alarm temperature is reached, the cockpit warning light will illuminate. If the light illuminates before its prescribed temperature setting, the entire loop should be inspected for dents, kinks or other damage that could reduce the normal spacing between the power lead and ground potential of the loop.

D. Pneumatic System

The pneumatic fire protection system is another type of fire or overheat surveillance system. It is produced in various sensor tube lengths and with a choice of alarm temperatures.

The tube contains a gas which expands greatly when heated. When trigger temperature is reached, the gas pressure is sufficient to overcome the responder check valve and gas flows to the right side of the diaphragm (Figure 13-6). This in turn forces the diaphragm contacts to the left onto the alarm contacts and energizes the alarm circuit.

The check valve arrangement is such that, after the heat source is removed, the gas returns to a low pressure and the diaphragm forces the gas back into the tube, ready for another operation.

If the hot and cold sections of the engine have separate systems, the cold section would be set to trigger at a lower value than the hot section. If an overheat of perhaps 300°F occurs, it could trigger the cold section alarm. However, in the hot section the combustor could radiate heat normally at the 300 degree level so the alarm

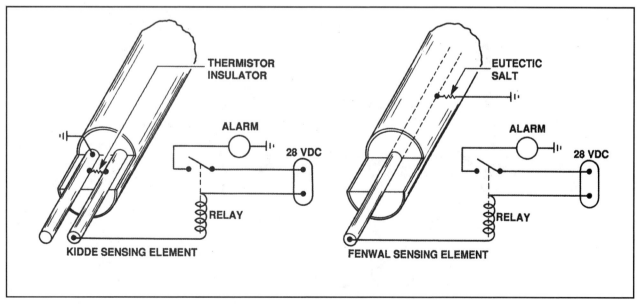

Fig.13-3 — Continuous-loop detector fire (overheat) detector system.

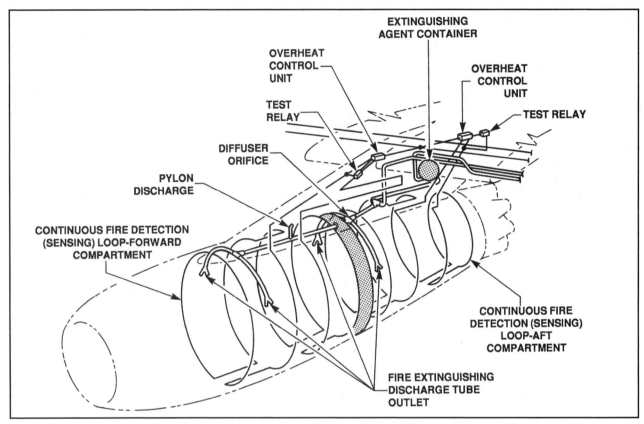

Fig. 13-4A — Typical pod and pylon continuous loop fire (overheat) detection installation.

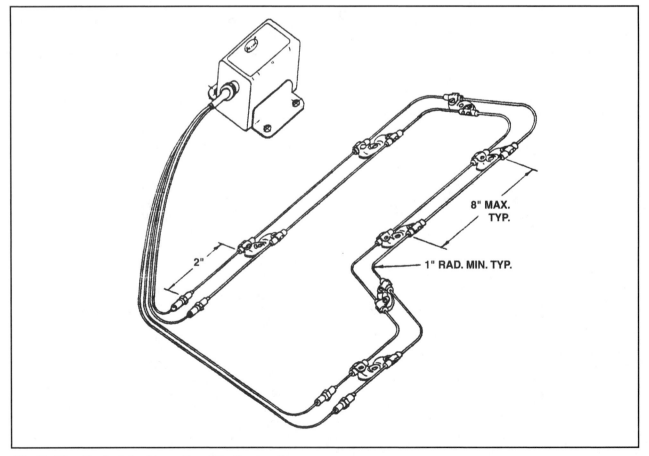

Fig.13-4B — Typical dual loop fire detection system.

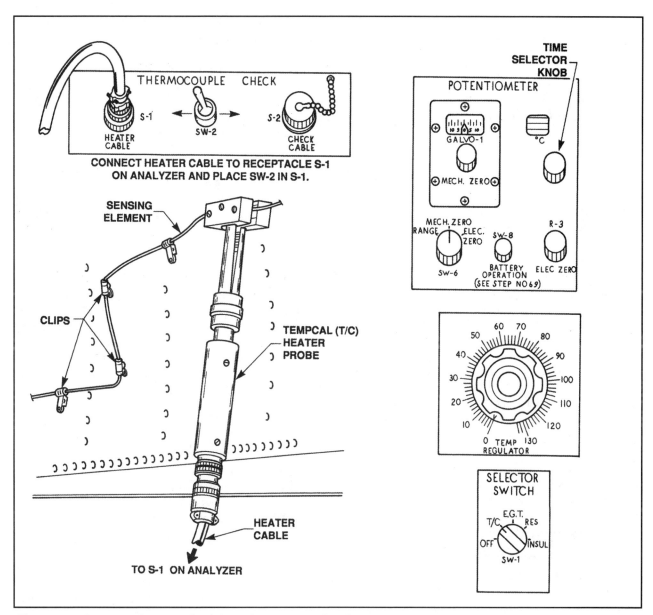

Fig. 13-5 — Jetcal analyzer testing of continuous loop fire detector.

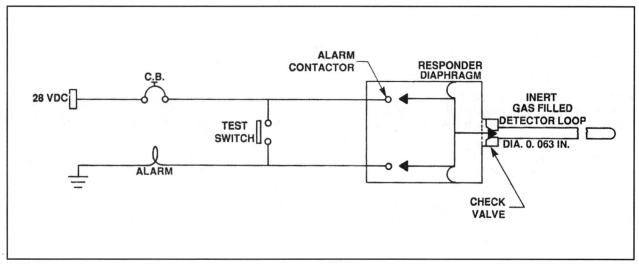

FIG. 13-6 — Pneumatic fire (overheat) system.

temperature would be set to a value of perhaps 500°F. The set temperatures are made at the factory and generally cannot be changed in the field.

To provide "spot" protection as well as area protection, the loop also contains a small core of special material (not shown) which when heated will release a secondary gas. This secondary gas will pressurize the main loop and actuate the responder.

E. Other Fire Detection Systems

A system which gives fire protection without being an overheat detector is the flame detector system. It utilizes infrared detectors to receive direct or reflected rays from a flame source. The detectors are located in the engine nacelle and send a signal to an amplifier which powers an alarm circuit in the cockpit.

Another similar circuit is the smoke detector. It also uses photoelectric cells with a light directed toward them. If smoke is present in sufficient quantity, the reference beam refracts light to the photoelectric cells and the alarm is powered.

Both of these circuits are self resetting to the stand-by state as are the overheat detectors. The photoelectric sensor is not widely used for turbine engine application, because it cannot detect hot air leaks. Such leaks are a common malfunction of the gas turbine engine that can cause a fire if hot air is directed toward an oil or fuel line. This system has a discreet function in that it can distinguish between an overheat condition from a hot air leak and an actual fire. Details of this circuitry are beyond the scope of this text.

F. Fire Extinguishing

1. Fire Extinguishing Methods (Engine Nacelle)

The fire extinguishing system includes a cockpit control switch, fire extinguishing agent containers, and an agent distribution system.

Figure 13-7a shows a typical container which houses the extinguishing agent. An engine can be protected with one bottle only or a cross-feed system with two or more bottles.

The bottle is pressurized in the range of 500 to 600 pounds per square inch—gauge with the agent. The gauge indicates the correct charge. The relief valve is a fusible disk which will rupture if the bottle were to overheat. To discharge the bottle from the cockpit, an electrical current is applied to the contactor which detonates an explosive cartridge (commonly called a squib). This shatters a disk located in the bottle outlet. From there the agent flows to the engine.

Figure 13-7B illustrates a twin engine extinguisher system with a cross-feed. A number one engine fire can be extinguished with a number one fire bottle and also number two fire bottle. The same is true for number two engine through the distribution system.

2. Common Extinguishing Agents, Aircraft and Non-Aircraft Use

a. Carbon Dioxide (CO_2)—The oldest type agent used in aviation. It is noncorrosive to metal parts but can cause shock to hot running parts of the engine if used in great quantity. Extinguishes by dissipating oxygen. CO_2 is considered toxic.

b. Halogenated Hydrocarbons (Freon Products)

1) Carbon Tetrachloride (Halon 104) (CCl_4) —It is poisonous and toxic. Hydrochloric acid vapor, chlorine and phosgene gas are produced whenever carbon tatrachloride is used on ordinary fires. The amount of phosgene gas is increased whenever carbon tatrachloride is brought in direct contact with hot metal, certain chemicals, or continuing electrical arcs. It is no longer approved for any fire extinguishing use.

2) Methyl Bromide (Halon 1001) (CH_3Br) —Lighter in weight than carbon dioxide but more toxic and highly corrosive to non-ferrous alloys. Immediate wash down of contaminated areas is required as per manufacturer's instructions. Not generally recommended for aircraft use.

3) Chlorobromomethane (Halon 1011) (CH_2ClBr) — CB, as it is called, is a more effective agent than CO_2 or CH_3Br, and it is less toxic. It is corrosive to both ferrous and nonferrous metals, and contaminated parts need an immediate wash down. Not recommended for aircraft use.

4) Dibromodifloromethane (Halon 1202) (CBr_2F_2) — An expensive nontoxic, noncorrosive agent. Not recommended for aircraft use.

5) Bromochlorodifluoromethane (Halon 1211) ($CBrClF_2$) —It is colorless, noncorrosive and evaporates rapidly leaving no residue whatever. It does not freeze or cause cold burns and will not harm fabrics, metals, or other materials it contacts. Halon 1211 acts rapidly on fires by producing a heavy blanketing mist that eliminates air from the fire source, but more importantly interferes chemically with the combustion process. It has outstanding properties in preventing reflash after the fire has been extinguished. Approved for aircraft fires.

6) Bromotrifloromethane (Halon 1301) (CF_3Br) —An expensive nontoxic, noncorrosive agent which is very effective on engine fires. Also considered one of the safest agents from the standpoint of toxicity and corrosion. Halon 1301 has all the characteristics of Halon 1211, and it is less toxic. Approved for aircraft fires.

3. Fire Extinguishing (Engine Gaspath)

If a fire occurs on start-up and a dry chemical powder type fire extinguishing agent is used, the compressor should continue to be motored by the starter in order that the observed engine gas temperature can be lowered as rapidly as possible to below 500°C.

After the fire is out and the engine has cooled sufficiently to reduce the likelihood of thermal shock to hot section parts, a good first step would be to wash the engine gas path down by introducing wash solution

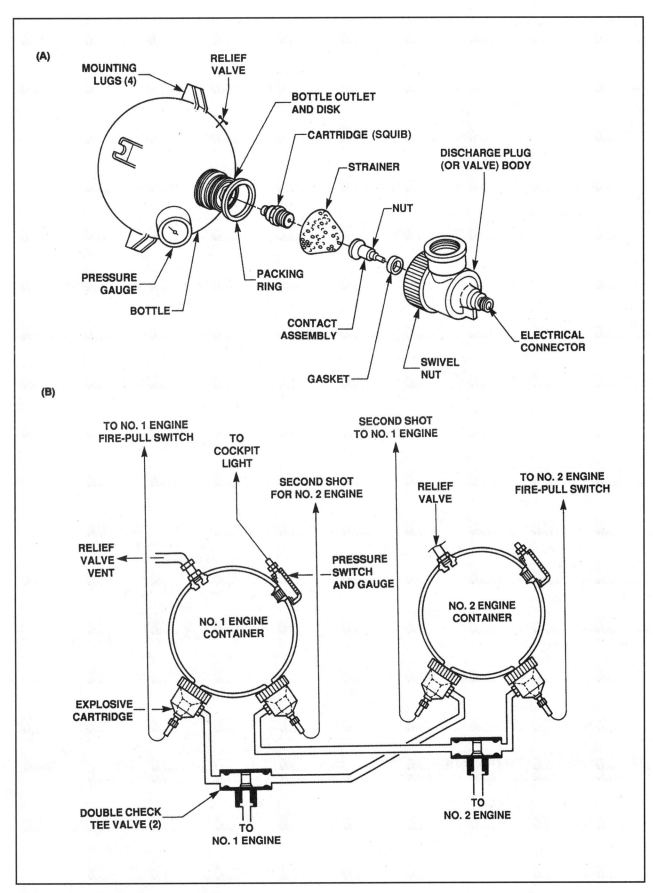

Fig. 13-7A — Fire bottle components.
Fig. 13-7B — Fire extinguishing system for twin engine aircraft.

through the inlet and through the exhaust section. Hot water is more effective, if available, and the washing operation should be done while the engine is being "motored over" if the situation permits this procedure to be accomplished.

Immediately thereafter, it is beneficial to dry the engine either by operation at idle speeds or by the introduction of heat from an external source. This should be followed by spraying a preservative into the gas path, preferably while the engine is being motored.

4. Cleaning the Engine After Use of Extinguishing Agents

The use of chemical fire extinguishing agents in gas turbine engines can be harmful to the engine. The following is a general procedure to apply after extinguishing agents have been used.

When corrosive fire extinguishing agents are introduced into the exterior of the engine or into the engine gas path, such agents may cause severe corrosive damage to engine compressor section and turbine area parts, and they may also cause possible engine oil system contamination. In view of the above, it is extremely important that such dry chemical agents be neutralized and completely removed from all engine parts with the least possible delay. This is necessary because many dry chemical powder fire-extinguishing agents contain a sodium or potassium bicarbonate base that is particularly corrosive to most engine metal parts. The wash solution typically includes a water and chloride mixture to properly remove contaminants.

Such exposure can cause extreme corrosion damage, especially in the rear portions of the gas turbine engine. When internal engine parts are exposed to sodium or potassium bicarbonate-based agents in temperature environments exceeding 500°C, corrosion can occur in a matter of a few hours.

As soon as possible, the engine should be processed through normal shop cleaning. Close attention should be paid to inspection of all parts exposed to the fire extinguishing chemicals to detect and evaluate evidence of possible corrosive attack. Particular attention should be paid to parts with protective coatings to assure that they have not been adversely affected. Refer to the manufacturer's manual for all prescribed procedures to follow.

G. Typical Twin Engine Commercial Airplane System

Figure 13-8 shows a fire detection system, including the flight deck panels, which would be typical of a modern twin engine commercial airplane. The following text will describe what is shown in the figure, breaking it down into four sections (top and bottom right, top and bottom left).

1. Top Right — The top right portion of the figure shows the overheat and fire detector loop system. It is a gas filled type, with four detectors being incorporated into each of the two loops (eight total). The gas pressure in the continuous loop acts on the detectors, causing three switches to be activated or not activated. If the gas is at normal pressure, one of the three switches is activated, to allow a test to confirm a good system. If an engine overheat occurs, the gas pressure rises and activates a second switch which turns on the engine overheat light. If an engine fire occurs, the pressure rises even higher and activates the third switch, turning on the fire warning light.

2. Bottom Right — The bottom right portion of the figure shows the Fire Detection Control Module. This component monitors the detectors in the two loops, and sends out the appropriate signal to the Overheat/Fire Protection Panel in the event of an overheat, a fire, or a fault. This module incorporates built in test equipment (BITE), which allows the operator to evaluate and troubleshoot system faults.

3. Bottom Left — The bottom left portion of the figure shows the Overheat/Fire Protection Panel. This panel would be located right behind the throttle quadrant. The layout of the panel, from left to right, is as follows:

- The switch labeled "OVHT DET" allows the "A" or "B" loop to be separately selected, or in the normal position to have both selected.
- The "ENG 1 OVERHEAT" is the advisory light to show engine #1 is experiencing an overheat condition. It is amber in color.
- The "TEST" switch allows the checking of two circuits, the fault detection circuit and the overheat/fire circuit.
- The number "1" engine discharge T-handle incorporates the red fire light. In the event of a fire, the T-handle would be pulled out, shutting off the flow of fluids, and then rotated left or right to discharge a fire bottle.
- Next to the T-handle are four advisory lights. The top light when red, is for a wheel well fire. The second light is amber and indicates an engine detector fault. The third light is amber and indicates an inoperative detector at the APU. The fourth light is amber and is used to identify a discharged APU fire bottle.
- Next to the four advisory lights is the T-handle for the APU.
- On the far right side of the panel, there is a test switch for checking the squibs at each of the three fire bottles. Below the test switch are three green lights which show the results of the test. The squib, an explosive charge, releases the fire extinguishing agent. (Figure 13-7A)
- Above the test switch for the fire bottle squibs are two amber advisory lights. These lights indicate when the left or right fire bottles have been discharged.

4. Top Left — The top left portion of the figure shows the glareshield panel, where the master caution and fire warning lights are located. This panel is in the line of sight for the flight crew. If an engine fire were to occur,

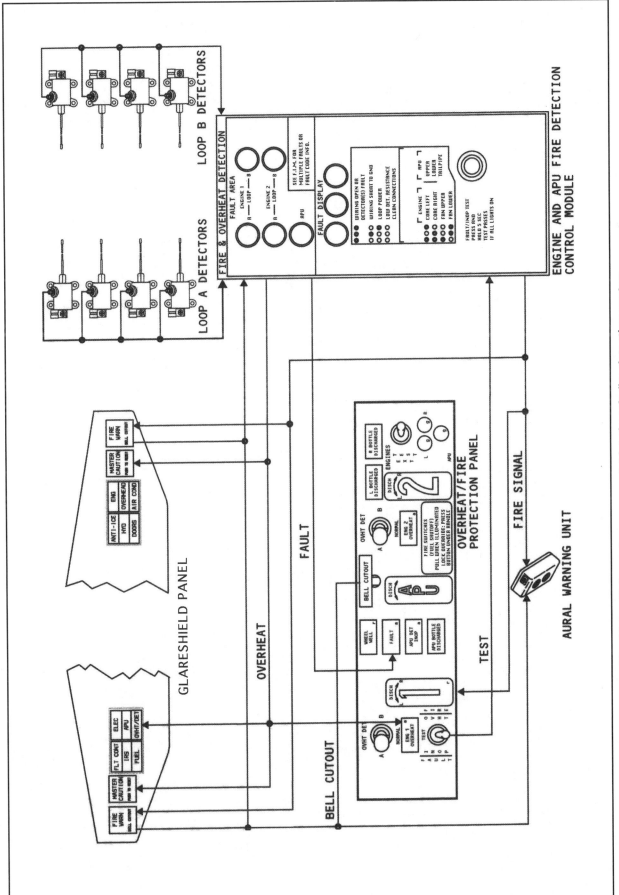

Fig. 13-8 — Twin engine commercial jet aircraft, fire detection system.

the master caution and fire warning lights would both illuminate. The flight crew would then observe the Overheat/Fire Protection Panel to determine the location and extent of the problem.

QUESTIONS:

1. Do any of the fire detector circuits mentioned need power from the aircraft bus?

2. Which of the circuits mentioned contains a switching circuit to provide fire protection to the engine if a short appears in one of its loops?

CHAPTER XIV
Engine Operation

There are many instances when ground personnel other than pilots are required to operate a gas turbine engine. Some of these instances are as follows:

1. To duplicate a flight crew-reported discrepancy for troubleshooting;

2. To perform a basic engine or engine system checkout after maintenance;

3. To move an aircraft from one maintenance location to another;

4. To taxi-check an aircraft system.

A. Safety Precautions

The engine operator must be thoroughly familiar with the flight line safety precautions previously mentioned for engine trimming. This includes the use of ear defenders for hearing protection, awareness of inlet and exhaust area hazards for protection of both personnel and equipment, and knowledge of adverse weather restrictions which, if neglected, could result in poor engine performance or possible engine damage. Complete familiarity with the manufacturer's checklists and maintenance manuals is a must for safe and accurate performance testing.

B. Engine Runup Of Turbojet And Turbofan Engines

Each particular aircraft will have a very specific checklist provided by the manufacturer. The general procedures for operating a turbine engine include, but are not necessarily limited to, the following items:

1. Normal Operating Procedures
a. Prior To Engine Operation

1) Remove Inlet and Exhaust covers, clear the inlet and exhaust areas of personnel and equipment, and clear the ramp of debris which could cause foreign object damage to the engine;

2) Perform a walk-around Inspection of the aircraft to ensure complete security of necessary aircraft and engine systems;

3) Ensure servicing of fuel and oil is adequate for the run-up intended;

4) Connect Ground Power Unit to aircraft if required.

b. When First Entering The Aircraft, Ensure The Following

1) Engine Master Switch — OFF;

2) Landing Gear Handle position — WHEELS DOWN;

3) Seat and Brake Pedals — ADJUSTED;

4) Generator switches — OFF;

5) Power lever — OFF, or Fuel Control shutoff — OFF (Engines with thrust reversers require use of a separate shutoff control);

6) Starter and Ignition — OFF;

7) Aircraft Systems — SAFE FOR ENGINE OPERATION.

c. To Start Engine

1) Master Switch — ON;

2) Select Battery or External Power — ON;

3) Fuel Valves — ON (Aircraft system);

4) Fuel Boost — ON (Aircraft system);

5) Starter — ON (Starter, ignition, and fuel are often time-sequenced);

6) Ignition — ON (Usually between 5 and 10% RPM);

7) Power Lever — OPEN (To approximate idle position) or fuel shutoff — OPEN. (Allow 10 to 20 seconds to light-off, then abort start);

8) Ignition and Starter — OFF (Below idle);

9) Generator — Normally on at this time.

d. Instrument Checks On Start Cycle

1) Exhaust Temperature — WITHIN LIMITS (Starting peak and stabilized);

2) Engine Oil Pressure — WITHIN LIMITS;

3) Dual-Compressor Engines — Ensure a positive N_1 indication by 20% N_2 speed.

e. Instrument Checks Stabilized At Idle

1) Percent RPM (Generally between 40% to 60%);

2) Exhaust Temperature (EGT, TIT, or ITT);

3) Fuel Flow;

4) Fuel Manifold Pressure;

5) Oil Temperature;

6) Fuel Temperature;

7) Oil Pressure;

8) Vibration Amplitude (Large aircraft);

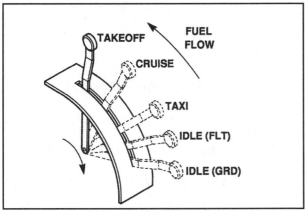

Fig. 14-1 — Power lever (throttle) connects to fuel control.

f. Typical High Power Checks

1) Engine Trim Check (EPR, Fan Speed or Engine Torque);

2) Acceleration and Deceleration time Check;

3) Compressor Bleed Valve and Variable Vane Schedule Checks.

g. Taxi Procedure

Release brakes and move power lever forward as required for RPM, thrust, and ground speed. Communication with the airport control tower is often required before taxiing.

h. Normal Shutdown Procedure

1) Operate engine at prescribed speed for recommended time interval, usually idle or slightly above for 20-30 seconds. This is done to stabilize component temperatures, to prevent engine distortion, to prevent coking of oil on extremely hot surfaces, and to scavenge the oil properly back to the oil tank.

2) Power Lever and/or Fuel Lever — OFF (with a quick motion to the stop).

3) Fuel Boost — OFF.

4) Fuel Valves — OFF.

5) Generator, Battery, External Power — OFF.

6) Master Switch — OFF.

2. Emergency Operating Procedures

a. Procedure For Engine Tailpipe Fire During Ground Start

1) Power Lever and/or Fuel Lever — OFF.

2) Starter — Continue to crank to attempt to blow fire out.

3) Fire Extinguisher — ON (if needed) — A freon based or carbon dioxide extinguisher is preferred to avoid engine contamination.

4) Master Switch OFF, all other switches — OFF.

5) Troubleshoot Cause.

b. Procedure For Hot Start

1) Power Lever and/or Fuel Lever — OFF (if temperature attempts to exceed the red line limit).

2) Master Switch — OFF.

3) Troubleshoot Cause.

c. Procedure For Failure To Start

1) Power Lever and/or Fuel Lever OFF (if engine does not ignite within the required time period, usually 10-20 seconds after fuel is introduced to the engine).

2) Troubleshoot Cause.

NOTE: If the engine fails to start because fuel flow is terminated inadvertently, DO NOT reopen fuel lever because a hot start will more than likely result. Allow 30-60 seconds for fuel to drain from the combustor. If necessary, perform an engine purging procedure to clear the engine of trapped fuel vapors.

d. Engine Purging Procedure

1) Power — ON.

2) Power Lever and/or Fuel Lever — OFF.

3) Ignition — OFF (pull circuit breaker if necessary).

4) Starter — ON (usually 15-20 seconds).

e. Emergency Shutdown Procedure

If engine continues to operate when the power lever or fuel lever is moved to OFF, turn off fuel boost and aircraft fuel valves. The engine will shut down from fuel starvation within 30-60 seconds. This is an emergency procedure only because lubrication of the fuel wetted components will cease and repeated shut downs in this fashion will reduce fuel system service life.

f. Flight RAM-Air Starting Procedure

If an in-flight flameout occurs, the starter switch is placed in the FLT START position. This bypasses the engine starter and allows ignition only to occur. The engine (except at low airspeeds) motors over sufficiently from ram air entering the engine inlet and electrical ignition relights the mixture when fuel is reintroduced into the combustor.

C. Engine Runup of Turboprop Engines (Fixed Turbine Engine)

Turboprop engine powered aircraft are generally configured with at least two engine control on the flight deck. One of the levers controls the engine and the other controls the propeller. The function of these control levers is often integrated, with one or the other controlling both the propeller and the engine fuel scheduling at different power settings.

The Garrett TPE-331 engine a fixed turbine design, with a Hartzell Propeller. The power lever controls both the fuel control and the propeller pitch setting in the low speed beta range. The second lever, referred to as the Condition Lever, controls the propeller at higher speeds in the alpha range (Figure 14-2).

The following sequences of operation are typical of the TPE-331 turboprop engine:

1. Ground Starting Procedure

a. Pre-start checks — COMPLETED (similar to turbojet/turbofan checks).

b. Aircraft electrical power — ON.

c. Aircraft fuel valve and Boost pump — ON.

d. Power Lever — START GROUND IDLE POSITION (beta range).

e. Condition Lever — LOW RPM.

f. Battery or External Power Selector — ON.

g. Starter — ON.

h. Ignition and Fuel — AUTOMATICALLY ON AT 10% RPM.

i. Ignition and Starter — AUTOMATICALLY OFF AT 50% RPM.

j. Engine Instruments — MONITOR CLOSELY (as per manual).

k. Idle — AUTOMATIC ACCELERATION TO 65% RPM.

l. Condition Lever — HIGH RPM (to reset an under-speed governor).

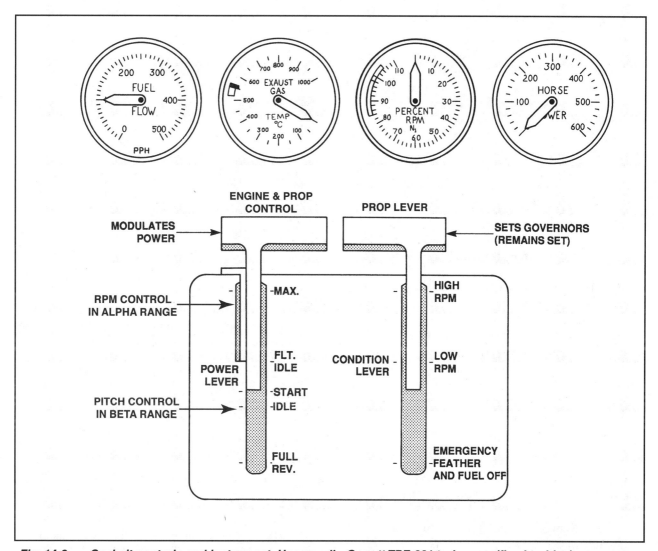

Fig. 14-2 — Cockpit controls and instrument, Honeywell - Garrett TPE-331 turboprop (fixed turbine).

2. Taxi Procedure

a. Condition Lever — HIGH RPM (low blade angle position).

b. Power Lever — FORWARD (toward or past flight idle position, alpha range, as necessary for required thrust and ground speed).

NOTE: For takeoff and flight the engine power is set at a predetermined horsepower or torque value by movement of the power lever. The condition lever sets engine speed by changing the propeller blade angle. During flight this lever usually remains at its set position with the engine running at a constant speed. When power changes are required the Power Lever position is adjusted. Procedures for Pneumatic (air turbine) starting are discussed in detail in Chapter X.

D. PT6 Engine Operation (Free Turbine)

The Pratt & Whitney of Canada PT6 turboprop engine is a free turbine design, configured with four engine control levers in the cockpit. A description of the controls and engine operation is as follows (Figure 14-3):

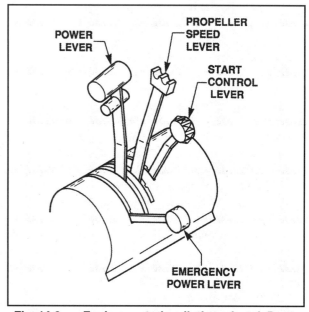

Fig. 14-3 — Engine controls, pilot's pedestal, Pratt & Whitney PT6 Turboprop (Free Turbine).

1. Description Of Controls

a. Power Control Lever — Attaches to the fuel control. Serves to moderate engine power (torque) from full reverse thrust and idle speed to take-off.

b.Propeller Control Lever — Attaches to the propeller governor to request blade angle and maintain RPM. In maximum decrease position feathers the propeller.

c. Start Control Lever — Attaches to the starting fuel control. It has three positions: cut-off, run and high idle.

d. Emergency Power Lever — Used to directly control engine power if the pneumatic side of the fuel control fails.

2. Ground Operations

The aircraft manufacturer should adapt the following procedure to the aircraft Flight Manual in the manner best suited to the technique required to operate a particular type of aircraft. This procedure covers the typical requirements of a fixed-wing installation.

a. Engine Starting

The recommended pre-start operations are:

1) Power Control Lever — IDLE

2) Propeller Control Lever — Anywhere in operating range

3) Starting Control Lever — CUT-OFF

4) Engine Master Switch — ON

5) Fuel System Shutoff Valve — OPEN

6) Fuel Boost Pump Switch — ON

b. The Recommended Start Procedure Is:

1) Engine Ignition Switch and Starter Switch — ON. The minimum speed to obtain a satisfactory light is 4,500 RPM (12%);

2) After attaining stabilized gas generator speed, move the Starting Control Lever to the RUN position;

3) Observe that the engine accelerates normally to Idle RPM and that the maximum allowable inter-turbine temperature starting limit is not exceeded.

CAUTION: Whenever the gas generator fails to light up within ten seconds after moving the starting control lever to the RUN position, cut off fuel, starter, and ignition. Allow a 30-second fuel draining period followed by a 15-second dry motoring run before attempting another start. If, for any reason, a starting attempt is discontinued, allow the engine to come to a complete stop and then accomplish a dry motoring run. Repeat the complete starting sequence, observing the starter limits. (Refer to the applicable Starter Manufacturer's Manual.)

When the engine attains Idle RPM.

4) Engine Starter and Ignition Switches — OFF.

c. Ground Run-Up

Before proceeding with a ground run-up, ensure that the propeller control system is purged by feathering the propeller once or twice with the power control lever in the Idle position.

d. Aircraft Ground Handling

The low range of the power control lever may be utilized for taxiing.

e. Dry Motoring Run

The following procedure is used to clear an engine at any time when it is deemed necessary to remove internally trapped fuel and vapor, or if there is evidence of a fire within the engine. Air passing through the engine serves to purge fuel, vapor or fire from the combustion section, gas generator turbine, power turbine and exhaust system.

1) Starting Control Lever — CUT-OFF.

2) Ignition Switch — OFF.

3) Engine Master Switch — ON (to supply current for engine starter switch).

4) Fuel System Shutoff Valve — OPEN.

5) Fuel Boost Pump Switch — ON (to provide lubrication for the engine driven fuel pumping elements).

6) Engine Starter Switch — ON.

WARNING: Should the fire persist, as indicated by sustained inter-turbine temperature, close the fuel system shutoff valve at this point and continue motoring.

7) Maintain starter operation for the desired duration. Observe the starter limits. (Refer to the applicable Starter Manufacturer's Manual).

8) Engine Starter Switch — OFF.

9) Fuel Boost Pump Switch — OFF.

10) Fuel System Shutoff Valve — CLOSED.

11) Engine Master Switch — OFF.

12) Allow the required cooling period for the starter before any further starting operation is attempted.

f. Engine Shutdown

The following procedure is to be used to shut down an engine:

1) Power Control Lever — IDLE.

NOTE: Allow the engine to stabilize for a minimum of one minute at minimum obtainable ITT.

2) Propeller Control Lever — FEATHER.

3) Starting Control Lever — CUT-OFF.

4) Fuel Boost Pump Switch — OFF.

5) Fuel System Shutoff Switch — CLOSED.

6) Engine Master Switch — OFF.

NOTE: During the shut-down, ensure that the compressor decelerates freely.

WARNING: If there is any evidence of fire within the engine after shutdown, proceed immediately as described under "dry motoring run".

g. Propeller Windmilling

While the aircraft is unattended, ensure that the propeller is tied down to prevent windmilling with zero oil pressure.

3. Flight Operations

a. Takeoff Power Setting

1) Before setting takeoff power:

a) Read corrected O.A.T;

b) Read Barometric Pressure;

c) Enter the applicable takeoff power-setting torque curve (or torque computer) with the above readings and note the takeoff torque value required;

d) If not already done during the run-up, purge the propeller control system as described under "Ground Run-up", Ground Operations.

2) To set takeoff power:

a) Move the propeller control lever to the applicable RPM position;

b) Advance the power control lever to give the required torque pressure;

c) Observe the Inter-turbine Temperature Limits;

d) Note any increase in Ng and Np speeds above the maximum limits.

NOTE: As airspeed is gained during takeoff, an increase in torque pressure at a fixed power control lever position is normal and should be retained provided limiting torque pressure is not exceeded.

b. Climb Setting

Because of the rapidly varying conditions during climb, power may be set by indicated ITT, using the Nominal Climb ITT value.

Should it be desired to execute the climb using a lower rating, power may be set to a lower indicated ITT or by means of the torque setting method.

c. Cruise Setting

The setting of cruise power must be accomplished through the use of the torque indicating system since it is the only parameter that is common to both aircraft performance and engine operating condition. Reference at regular intervals to the torquemeter pressure required for a particular flight condition will also aid in trouble-shooting instrument or engine malfunctions and may be used to identify increased aircraft drag.

4. Emergencies

a. Ground Engine Fire

See "Dry Motoring Run" under Ground Operation, Paragraph 2. e.

b. In-Flight Engine Fire

In case of an in-flight engine fire, the following procedure should be used:

1) Propeller Control Lever — FEATHER.

2) Staring Control Lever — CUT-OFF.

3) Fuel Boost Pump Switch — OFF.

4) Fuel System Shutoff Valve — CLOSED.

5) Engine Master Switch — OFF.

6) Power Control Lever — IDLE.

7) Shut off all equipment operated by engine bleed air.

8) Carry out the procedure recommended in the aircraft Flight Manual.

c. Engine Failure

The following procedure is to be used in case of an engine failure:

1) Propeller Control Lever — FEATHER.

2) Starting Control Lever — CUT OFF.

3) Fuel Boost Pump Switch — OFF.

4) Fuel System Shutoff Valve — CLOSED.

5) Engine Master Switch — OFF.

6) Power Control Lever — IDLE.

WARNING: Caution is mandatory during a suspected engine failure on takeoff or landing in order to avoid shutting down an engine unnecessarily. Do not attempt to restart an engine which is definitely known to have failed.

d. Engine Flameout

The symptoms of an engine flameout will be the same as those of an engine failure. A flameout will be noticed by a drop in inter-turbine temperature, torquemeter pressure, and RPM. The flameout may result from the engine running out of fuel or, possibly, may be caused by unstable engine operation. Once the fuel supply has been restored to the engine or cause of unstable operations eliminated, the engine may be restarted in the manner described under Air Starts, following.

CAUTION: Do not attempt a relight if Ng tachometer indicates zero RPM.

e. Air Starts

The most common air start technique is to initiate the relight procedure immediately after a flameout occurs, provided the pilot is certain that the flameout was not the result of some malfunction which might make it dangerous to attempt a relight. Successful air starts may be achieved at all altitudes and airspeeds normally flown. However, above 14,000 feet, or with gas generator RPM below 10%, starting temperatures tend to be higher and caution is required.

f. Immediate Relights

There is always the chance that the engine may light up successfully just as soon as the ignition is turned on. In an emergency, turn on the ignition just as soon as possible after flameout, provided the gas generator speed has not dropped below 50%. Under these circumstances, it is not necessary to cut off the fuel or feather the propeller. The power control lever, however, should be retarded to IDLE.

NOTE: Propeller feathering is dependent on circumstances and is at the discretion of the pilot. However, a minimum engine oil pressure of 15 pounds per square inch—gauge should be registered if propeller is windmilling.

g. Emergency Air Starts (Below 10% Ng)

The following emergency air start procedure may be utilized:

1) Propeller Control Lever — Anywhere in operating range.

2) Power Control Lever — IDLE.

3) Starting Control Lever — CUT OFF.

4) Fuel Boost Pump Switch — ON.

5) Ignition Switch — ON.

6) Advance starting control lever to RUN and monitor ITT. If over-temperature tendencies are encountered, the starting control lever should be moved to the OFF position periodically during acceleration to Idle.

7) Ensure 50% gas generator RPM has been attained before advancing the power control lever to the desired power setting.

h. Normal Air Starts

1) The recommended pre-air-start check procedure is:

a) Propeller Control Lever — Anywhere in operating range

NOTE: Propeller feathering is dependent on circumstances and is at the pilot's discretion. Fine pitch selection will provide increased gas generator windmilling speed for emergency starts in the remote event of starter failure.

b) Power Control Lever — IDLE.

c) Engine Master Switch — ON.

d) Fuel System Shutoff Valve — OPEN.

e) Starting Control Lever — CUT OFF.

f) Fuel Boost Pump Switch — ON.

g) Fuel Inlet Pressure Indicator — 5 PSIG (MIN.)

2) The recommended air start procedure is:

a) Engine Ignition Switch and Engine Starter Switch — ON. The minimum gas generator RPM to obtain a satisfactory light is 4,500 (12%Ng). A windmill air re-start without electrical starter assist is not possible on many free turbine engines.

b) Starting Control Lever to RUN, after approximately five seconds of stabilized gas generator speed;

NOTE: A re-light normally should be obtained within ten seconds and will be evidenced first by a rise in gas generator RPM. A rise in inter-turbine temperature will also be noted.

When engine attains idle RPM:

c) Engine Starter and Ignition Switch — OFF (If no automatic cut off is provided);

d) Propeller Control Lever — Into operating range;

e) Power Control Lever — Adjust to desired position;

g) Check that the engine operating limits are not exceeded. If a satisfactory start is not obtained, discontinue the air start. Repeat the engine air start procedure if another starting attempt is to be made.

E. FAA Engine Power Ratings

Turbine engines, both turbojet and turbofan, are thrust rated in terms of either engine pressure ratio or fan speed and turboshaft/turboprop engines are SHP rated in the following categories: Takeoff, maximum continuous, maximum climb, maximum cruise, and idle. For certification purposes, the manufacturer demonstrates to the Federal Aviation Administration (FAA) that the engine will perform at certain thrust or shaft horsepower levels for specified time intervals and still maintain its airworthiness and service life for the user.

These ratings can usually be found on the engine Type Certificate Data Sheets. The ratings are classified as follows:

Takeoff Wet Thrust/SHP — This rating represents the maximum power available while in water injection and is time limited. It is used only during takeoff operation. Engines are trimmed to this rating.

Takeoff Dry Thrust/SHP — Limits on this rating are the same as takeoff wet but without water injection. Engines are trimmed to this rating.

Maximum Continuous Thrust/SHP — This rating has no time limit but is to be used only during emergency situations at the discretion of the pilot, for example, during one engine-out cruise operation.

Maximum Climb Thrust/SHP — Maximum climb power settings are not time limited and are to be used for normal climb, to cruising altitude, or when changing altitudes. This rating is sometimes the same as maximum continuous.

Maximum Cruise Thrust/SHP — This rating is designed to be used for any time period during normal cruise at the discretion of the pilot.

Idle Speed — This power setting is not actually a power rating but, rather, the lowest usable thrust setting for either ground or flight operations.

Figure 14-4 shows an airliner flight envelope with its ceiling at 45,000 feet. It also shows limits of airspeed and altitude between which the pilot must remain during climb, at maximum climb, or maximum continuous power ratings.

F. Typical Operating Cautions For All Turbine Powered Aircraft, Ground And Flight

1. Starting

There is no doubt that poor starting technique contributes to hot end deterioration. Good starting requires an adequate power supply to the starter and correct fuel flow to the engine. Ensure that the power source (APU, GPU, Battery Truck, or Aircraft Battery) is well maintained and the output meets the requirements of the aircraft manual.

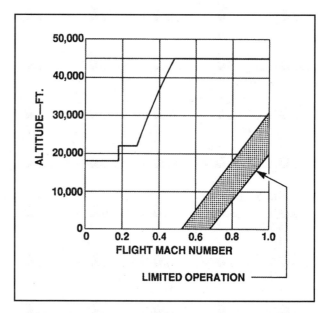

Fig. 14-4 — Airliner flight envelope.

Monitor the exhaust gas temperature during the start cycle and, in the event of a rapid rise of exhaust gas temperature, reduce the fuel flow by retarding the power lever or shutoff lever, whichever is applicable. The aim here is to minimize peak exhaust gas temperatures without reducing the acceleration time of the engine.

Do not increase the fuel too early in the start cycle and do not open the power lever (throttle) to taxi until idle RPM has stabilized. This will ensure that thermal gradients within the engine are kept to a minimum.

2. Takeoff

Prior to takeoff, obtain accurate pressure altitude and outside air temperature figures to ensure the correct takeoff power setting of engine torque, pressure ratio (EPR), or fan speed. Open the throttles to the takeoff position smoothly. Where conditions permit, carry out a rolling takeoff. Rapid power lever movements will lead to accelerated deterioration of the hot end components.

When a choice is available between a dry or a wet takeoff, use dry takeoff. This will give savings on water mixtures and possibly lower parts replacement costs in the future.

On either wet or dry takeoff, reduce RPM to the climb setting as soon as possible, compatible with aircraft safety requirements.

3. Maximum Continuous Rating

This rating is used when an engine has failed in flight or has been shutdown in flight.

The remaining engine(s) can be held at this power setting at the discretion of the pilot.

4. Maximum Cruise Rating

This rating can be used when conditions require more than normal Climb and Cruise Power but less than Maximum Continuous. Occasions when this rating may be used are:

a. When severe turbulence exists at the normal flight altitude and additional altitude is required;

b. When additional power is required for high terrain clearance;

c. When A.T.C. requirements dictate a faster rate of climb;

d. After an engine failure, when use of Maximum Continuous power is not required.

5. Climb And Cruise

After takeoff, select climb power (EPR, Torque, or Fan Speed) as soon as possible. Where possible, use the alternate (lower) power setting for climb. It is necessary to monitor exhaust gas temperature during climb and adjust the power lever as required. Most fuel controls are designed with sensors which reduce fuel flow to maintain a constant engine gas temperature with increasing altitude. Variations from the standard lapse rate and tolerances on fuel control calibration and trimming may cause changes in exhaust gas temperature to which the operator might have to react.

6. Descent And Approach

Ensure power lever is set no lower than flight idle position.

7. Landing

Move the power lever to ground idle position. Apply brakes and thrust reverse as applicable to runway conditions, normally 75% N_2 maximum, 100% N_2 in emergencies.

8. Shutdown

When shutting down the engine, ensure the power lever is in the manufacturer's recommended shutdown position, wait until the RPM has stabilized, then move the fuel shutoff to the closed position. Failure to observe this procedure will result in uneven cooling of the engine hot section, and can cause turbine seal rub. In addition, a rapid shutdown can lead to incorrect oil consumption figures due to variable oil tank levels that result from poor scavenging.

Appendix 1

DEPARTMENT OF TRANSPORTATION
FEDERAL AVIATION ADMINISTRATION

E1GL
ALLISON
250-C28

April 28, 1976

TYPE CERTIFICATE DATA SHEET NO. E1GL

Engines of models described herein conforming with this data sheet (which is part of type certificate No. E1GL) and other approved data on file with the Federal Aviation Administration, meet the minimum standards for use in certificated aircraft in accordance with pertinent aircraft data sheets and applicable portions of the Federal Aviation Regulations provided they are installed, operated and maintained as prescribed by the FAA approved manufacturer's manuals and other FAA approved instructions.

Type Certificate Holder	Detroit Diesel Allison Division of General Motors Corporation Indianapolis, Indiana 46206
Model	250-C28
Type	Free turbine turboshaft 1 stage centrifugal flow gas producer compressor 2 stage gas producer turbine 2 stage power turbine Single combustion chamber with pre-chamber
Shaft ratio	5.55:1

Ratings (see NOTE 3)
Max. continuous

s. hp. at sea level	478
Gas producer r.p.m.	50193
Output shaft r.p.m.	6016
Measured rated gas temp.	1392° F (755° C)

Takeoff s. hp.

5 min. at sea level	500
Gas producer r.p.m.	51005
Output shaft r.p.m.	6016
Measured rated gas temp.	1430° F (777° C)

30 Minute power,

s. hp. at sea level	500
Gas producer r.p.m.	51005
Output shaft r.p.m.	6016
Measured rated gas temp.	1430° F (777° C)

Output shaft	Internal spline
Control system	Bendix gas producer fuel control DP-T1 Bendix power turbine governor AL-AC1 Pneumatic accumulators and check valves or orifices (see NOTE 10)
Electronic Power Turbine Overspeed Control System	N2 Overspeed Control, P/N 6893-63 Overspeed Solenoid Valve, Valcor V5000-125 Power Turbine Speed Pickup P/N 6894602

Fuel pump	Single element fuel pump Sundstrand Model 500950 or TRW model 388100
Fuel	MIL-T-5624, Grade JP-4 or JP-5; Aviation Turbine Fuels ASTM-D1655 Jet A or A-1 or Jet B; (for other fuel and limitations see NOTE 9).
Lubricating oil	MIL-L-23699 and subsequent revisions

Principal dimensions:
Length overall, in.	43.000
Width, in.	21.940
Height, in.	25.130
C.G. location, aft of side mount pad centerline, in.	5.73
C.G. location, above side mount pad, centerline, in.	3.23
C.G. location, left side of engine cenerline looking forward, in.	.02
Weight (dry), lb. Includes basic engine, fuel pump, ignition and fuel control systems	219

Ignition system (see NOTE 12)	Low tension capacitor discharge exciter. Simmonds Precision P/N 43754 or Bendix Scintilla P/N 10-387150-1 Shunted surface gap spark igniter. Champion P/N CH34078 or AC P/N 8990157
Certification basis	Part 33 of the Federal Aviation Regulations effective February 1, 1965, and Amendments 33-2, 33-3, and 33-4, and Exemption No. 2087 from FAR 33.69, Regulatory Docket No. 13294 issued February 24, 1975. Application for Type Certificate dated October 2, 1973.
Production basis	Production Certificate No. 310

NOTE 1.   Maximum permissible temperatures:

Measured gas temperature

Takeoff and 30 minute power	1450° F (787° C)
Maximum continuous	1430° F (777° C)
Maximum transients (not to exceed 6 seconds)	1450° F (787° C) to 1600° F (872° C)
Starting (not to exceed 10 seconds)	1450° F (787° C) to 1600° F (872° C)
Oil inlet temperatures	Minus 65° F (-55° C) to 225° F (107° C)

E1GL

NOTE 2. Fuel inlet and oil pressure limits:

Fuel: Applicable to MIL-T-5624 and ASTM-D1655 Jet A or A-1 minimum at fuel connection
to engine: not less than ambient pressure minus 9 in. Hg at sea level; ambient
minus 5.5 in. Hg at 6000 ft.; ambient minus 3.5 in. Hg at 10,000 ft.; ambient
minus 1.0 in. Hg at 15,000 ft.; and ambient plus 1.5 in. Hg at 20,000 ft. altitude.
Maximum pressure 25 p.s.i.g No inlet depression permitted with MIL-G-5572 fuel.

Oil: Operating gauge pressures:

48,000 rpm (94.2 percent) gas generator speed and above	115 to 130 p.s.i.g.
40,000 rmp (78.5 percent) to 48,000 rpm (94.2 percent)	90 to 130 p.s.i.g.
Below 40,000 rpm (78.5 percent)	50 to 130 p.s.i.g.
Oil pump inlet pressure:	5 in. Hg absolute minimum.

NOTE 3. The engine ratings, unless otherwise specified, are based on static sea level standard
conditions. Compressor inlet air (dry) 59° F, 29.92 in. Hg. Compressor inlet bell attached
to provide suitable air approach conditions. No external accessory loads and no air bleed.

Measured rated gas temperature as indicated by average of the 4 gas temperature thermocouples.

NOTE 4. The following accessory drive mounting provisions are available:

	*Direction of Rotation	Speed Ratio To turbine	Max. Torque (in-1b) Continuous Static		Max. Overhung Moment (in-1b)
Driven by Gas Producer Turbine					
Tachometer	CC	0.0825	7	50	4
Starter-Generator	C	0.2351	**550	1100	150
Driven by Power Turbine					
Tachometer	CC	0.1257	7	50	4
Power Take-off	C	0.180	***5556	10,000	100
Spare	C	0.3600	79	395	150

*   C - Clockwise viewing drive pad: CC - Counterclockwise

**   The maximum generator load is 12 horsepower.

*** The sum of the torques extracted in any combination from the front and rear power output drives
shall not exceed the torque values specified in NOTE 7. The value given in the above table
represents the 30 minute limited maximum total torque.

NOTE 5. External air bleed may not exceed 4.5 percent.

NOTE 6. There are no engine equipment items which are aircraft mounted.

NOTE 7. The maximum allowable torque as measured by the torquemeter for below standard inlet air temperature and/or ram conditions is 463 lb-ft for takeoff and 30 minute power, 417 lb-ft for maximum continuous and 480 lb-ft for 10 seconds.

NOTE 8. The maximum output shaft speed for momentary transients (up to 15 seconds) varies linearly from 113 percent at flight autorotation to 105 percent at takeoff. The maximum output shaft speed limit for sustained periods varies linearly from 108% at flight autorotation to 103 percent at takeoff. Gas producer speeds are permissible up to 105 percent for 10 seconds and up to 104 percent for sustained periods. 100 percent output shaft speed is defined as 6016 r.p.m. and 100 percent gas producer speed is defined as 50940 r.p.m.

NOTE 9. Emergency use of aviation gasoline MIL-G-5572, all grades, is limited to the amount of fuel required to operate the engine for not over 6 hours during any overhaul period except that a mixture consisting of 1/3 by volume of aviation gasoline MIL-G-5572, grade 80/87 and 2/3 by volume MIL-T-5624, grade JP-5, or aviation turbine fuels ASTM-D1655, Jet A or A-1 may be used for unrestricted periods of time. A mixture consisting of 1/3 by volume of aviation gasoline MIL-G-5572, grade 100/130 with a maximum of 2.0 mi./gal. lead content and 2/3 by volume of MIL-T-5624, grade J-5, or aviation turbine fuels ASTM-D1655 Jet A or A-1 may be used for not over 300 hours during any overhaul period. It is not necessary to purge the unused fuel from the system before refueling with different type fuels. No fuel control adjustment is required when switching these type fuels. Fuels containing Tri-Cresyl-Phosphate additives shall not be used. Anti-icing additives conforming to MIL-I-27686 are approved for use in fuels in amounts not to exceed 0.15 percent by volume. Shell anti-static additive is approved for use at a concentration that will not exceed fuel conductivity of 300 picomhos per meter.

NOTE 10. A pneumatic accumulator(s), double check valve(s) or other attentuating devices can be incorporated for compatability with the rotor system of the particular model helicopter in which the engine is to be installed.

NOTE 11. A magnetic oil drain plug indicator lamp is an installation requirement.

NOTE 12. Engines produced under the terms of this type certificate having single ignition systems, are limited to installation in rotorcraft certificated in accordance with FAR 27 or FAR 29 Category B. The engine is not eligible for installation in transport Category A rotorcraft certificated under FAR 29.

NOTE 13. Life limits established for critical rotating components are published in Detroit Diesel Allison Commercial Service Letter No. 250-C28 2005.

NOTE 14. Engine produced under this type certificate require inlet protection, not having been tested by ingestion of Group II foreign objects.

Appendix 2

E23EA-4

GENERAL ELECTRIC
CF6-6D
CF6-6D1
CF6-6H
CF6-50A
CF6-50C
CF6-50D
CF6-50E
CF6-50H

December 15, 1974

DEPARTMENT OF TRANSPORTATION

FEDERAL AVIATION ADMINISTRATION

TYPE CERTIFICATE DATA SHEET NO. E23EA

PART B - CF6 - SERIES

Engines of models described herein conforming with this data sheet (which is part of type certificate No. E23EA) and other approved data on file with the Federal Aviation Administration, meet the minimum standards for use in certificated aircraft in accordance with pertinent aircraft data sheets and applicable portions of the Federal Aviation Regulations provided they are installed, operated and maintained as prescribed by the approved manufacturer's manuals and other approved instructions.

Type Certificate Holder: General Electric Company, Aircraft Engine Group, Cincinnati, Ohio 45215

	CF6-50A	CF6-50C	CF6-50D	CF6-50E	CF6-50H
Model					
Type	High bypass turbofan: Coaxial front fan driven by multi-stage low pressure turbine, multi-stage compressor with two stage turbine and annular combustor	--	--	--	--
Rating					
Maximum continuous at sea level, static thrust, lb.	46,300	--	--	--	--
Takeoff (5 min.) at sea level, static thrust, lb.	48,400	50,400	--	51,800	50,400
Alternate takeoff (5 min.) at sea level, static thrust, lb.	--	--	--	--	48,400
Flat rating ambient temperature					
Takeoff	87°F (30.5°C)	86°F (30.0°C)	77°F (25°C)	78°F (25.5°C)	86°F (30.0°C)
Alternate takeoff	86°F (30.0°C)	=	=	87°F (30.5°C)	87°F (30.5°C)
Maximum continuous		=	=	=	=

"--" indicates "same as preceding model"
"=" indicates "does not apply"

	CF6-50A	CF6-50C	CF6-50D	CF6-50E	CF6-50H
Fuel					
Fuel control, Woodward, GE P/N	9070M55	--	9148M33	--	9070M55
CIT sensor, Woodward, GE P/N	9069M91	--	--	--	--
Fuel pump, GE P/N	9039M45 single-element gear type pump	--	--	--	--
Fuel	Conforming to GE Specification D50TF2 (see Note 7)	--	--	--	--
Oil	Synthetic type conforming to GE Specification D50TF1, Classes A or B. GE Service Bulletin 79-1 lists approved brand oils.				
Ignition System	Two ignition units, GE P/N 9101M52; Two igniter plugs, GE P/N 9101M37	--	--	--	--
Starting					
Starter	AiResearch Model ATS100-350, GE P/N 9014M18	--	--	--	--
Starter valve	AiResearch, GE P/N 9033M46	--	--	--	--
Principle dimensions:					
Length, in. (fan spinner to LPT aft flange fact)	183	--	--	--	--
Width, in. (maximum envelope)	94	--	--	--	--
Height, in. (maximum envelope)	105	--	--	--	--
Weight (dry), lb. (includes basic engine accessories and optional equipment as listed in Manufacturer's engine specification, including condition monitoring instrumentation sensors per GE Specification, GEK 9251	8560	--	8625	--	--
Center of Gravity Location:					
Station, in. (engine only)	223.0 ± 2.0	--	--	--	--
Waterline, in. (engine only)	98.1 ± 1.0	--	--	--	--
Notes	1 through 12	--	--	--	--

E23EA-4
Part B
CF6-50 Series

Certification basis:

FAR33 effective February 1, 1965 as amended by 33-1, 33-2, 33-3, and Special Conditions No. 33-36-EA-9

	CF6-50A	CF6-50C	CF6-50D	CF6-50E	CF6-50H
Date of Application	5 Sept 1969	9 July 1971	--	2 April 1973	21 Aug 1973
Date T.C. E23EA issued/revised	23 Mar 1972	20 Nov 1973	27 Nov 1972	20 Nov 1973	7 Sept 1973

Production Basis:

Production Certificate No. 108

	CF6-50A	CF6-50C	CF6-50D	CF6-50E	CF6-50H
	--	--	--	--	--

Import Requirements:

Licensing agreement dated 2 December 1970, revised 8 January 1971, effective 17 June 1971 between General Electric, Cincinnati, Ohio and SNECMA, France, identified as "Production Agreement for CF6-50 Engine for A300B Airbus between General Electric Technical Services Co. Inc. and Societe Nationale d'Etude et de Construction de moteurs d'Aviation" and Licensing agreement dated 20 January 1971, revised 29 January 1971, effective 17 June 1971 between General Electric, Cincinnati, Ohio and M.T.U., Germany, identified as "Production Agreement for CF6-50 Engine for A300B Airbus between General Electric Technical Services Co. Inc. and Motoren and Turbinen Union, Munchen, GMBH" for the production of the General Electric model CF6-50 series turbofan engines and parts in Europe. The engines produced in accordance with these agreements conform to type certificate E23EA, are in condition for safe operation, and have been subjected to a final operational check.

Engine identification plates shall be marked as follows:

1. Manufactured by SNECMA, France.
2. Model CF6-50A or CF6-50C
3. Serial Numbers 455-701 and up
4. Type Certificate Number E23EA
5. Established Rating

CF6-50A		CF6-50C
48,400 TO		50,400 TO
46,300 MC		46,300 MC

For parts, assemblies, or modules produced by SNECMA, France and/or MTU, Germany for use in certificated aircraft, they must be accompanied by a French (if produced by SNECMA) or German (if produced by MTU) certificate containing the following statement and signatures.

This certifies that engine (parts, assemblies, modules, etc.) manufactured by (name and address) and listed here are made to Type Certificate E23EA type design and quality control data accepted by the United States Federal Aviation Administration.

(List articles and serial numbers covered and affix thereto the dated signature of responsible employee of supplier for Director of Quality Control and that of the authorized representative of Airworthiness Authority of Country of Manufacture.)

		CF6-50A	CF6-50C	CF6-50D	CF6-50E	CF6-50H
NOTE 1.	Maximum permissible engine rotor speeds:					
	Low pressure rotor (N_1), r.p.m.	3982 (116%)	--	--	3999 (116.5%)	3982 (116%)
	High pressure rotor (N_2), r.p.m.	10,613 (108%)	--	--	--	--
NOTE 2.	Maximum permissible temperatures: Turbine exhaust gas temperatures (T5.4);					
	Takeoff (5 min.)	1679°F (915°C)	1715°F (935°C)	1679°F (915°C)	1715°F (935°C)	1679°F (915°C)
	Maximum continuous	1607°F (875°C)	--	--	--	--
	Maximum for acceleration (2 min.)	1706°F (930°C)	1742°F (950°C)	1706°F (930°C)	1742°F (950°C)	1706°F (930°C)
	Starting (max. transient for 10 sec.)	1598°F (870°C)	--	--	--	--
	(Additional 10 sec. or total of 20)	1382°F (750°C)	--	--	--	--
	(Additional 20 sec. or total of 40)	1247°F (675°C)	--	--	--	--
	Refer to CF6 Operating Instructions for time temperature envelope	GEK 28467	--	--	--	--
	Oil outlet: Continuous operation	320°F (160°C)	--	--	--	--
	Transient operation (Transient operation is limited to 15 minutes)	347°F (175°C)	--	--	--	--

E23EA-4
Part B
CF6-50 Series

	CF6-50A	CF6-50C	CF6-50D	CF6-50E	CF6-50H

NOTE 3. Fuel and oil pressure limits:

Fuel: Minimum at engine pump inlet; 3.5 p.s.i. above absolute fuel vapor pressure, with maximum of 50 p.s.i. above absolute ambient atmospheric pressure.

Oil: At idle, 10 p.s.i.g. minimum. Operating range, 30 to 90 p.s.i.g.

Operating Instruc-
tions
range
limits   GEK 28467   ---   ---   ---   ---

NOTE 4. Accessory drive provisions:

Drive Pad	Rotation	Gear Ratio to Core Speed CF6-50 Series	Torque (in.-lb.) Cont.	Static	Static Overhung Moment (in.-lb.)
Starter	CC	0.956	10,800	19,200	400
CSD	CC	0.832	(250 h.p.)	17,400	900
Alternator*	C	-----	------	------	1,000
Tachometer (core)**	C	0.409	7	540	3
Hydraulic pump	CC	0.350	(85 h.p.)	7,400	500
Hydraulic pump	CC	0.350	(85 h.p.)	7,400	500

C = Clockwise; CC = Counter-clockwise
* = Alternator DRiven by CSD
** = Tachometer Mounted on and Driven Through Main Lube & Scavenge Pump

NOTE 5. Engine ratings are based on calibrated stand performance under the following conditions:
Fan inlet air at 59°F and 29.92 in. Hg.
GE bellmouth air inlet per GE Drawing 4013106-124, or 4013070-409 (light weight)
No external air bleed or accessory drive power for aircraft accessories.
Fan nozzle configuration defined by GE Drawing 4013157-495.
Jet nozzle configuration defined by GE drawing 4013156-186.
Turbine temperature and engine rotor speed limits not exceeded.
Core engine acceptance test cowling defined by GE Drawing 4013124-021.
Pylon configuration acceptance test cowling defined by GE Drawing 4013124-091.
Stand thrust adjusted for scrubbing drag per Figure A-11 of CF6 Installation Manual GEK 9286.
Engine performance deck R71AEG135 is the prime source of engine performance data throughout the flight envelope.

NOTE 6. Maximum permissible air bleed extraction is as follows:

Bleed location	CF6-50A	CF6-50C	CF6-50D	CF6-50E	CF6-50H
Stage 8, Compressor airflow % (normal)	5	--	--	--	--
Stage 8, compressor airflow % (intermittent)*	5.75	--	--	--	--
Compressor discharge					
Steady state at takeoff rating	5	--	--	--	--
Steady state between 80% N_2 and maximum continuous	10	--	--	--	--
During acceleration above 80% N_2	7	--	--	--	--
Operation at 80% N_2 or below	12.5	--	--	--	--
Stage 10	2	--	--	--	--

*The engine manufacturer is to be consulted regarding conditions, number of occurrences and duration of each occurrence within the limitations of: average of 2×10^{-3} occurrences per engine operating hour and a maximum of .5 hour duration per occurrence (cumulative total of 50 hours). Intermittent operation is defined as "dispatch with a bleed system inoperative, or bleed system or engine failure in flight" and should be confined to the physical core speed (N_2) range of 81.5 to 98.5 r.p.m.

NOTE 7. a) Approved fuel conforming to GE Specification D50TF2. MIL-T-5624H, Grades JP-4 or JP-5, ASTM D 1655-65T, Jet A, A1 and B, and ASTM ES-2-74 are consistent with this General Electric Specification. Primary fuel is Jet A, with other fuels listed being acceptable alternates. No fuel control adjustment is required when changing from primary to alternate fuels. A fuel control specific gravity adjustment is required when operating with Avgas to provide proper engine starting characteristics. Consult the Operating Manual for other restrictions when using Avgas.

b) Use of aviation gasoline under emergency conditions is restricted to 3 hours continuous operation at any one time, not to exceed 10 hours total cumulative time during any one hot section inspection period.

NOTE 8. Life limits established for critical rotating components are published in the CF6 Shop Manual, Inspection Section.

```
E23EA-4
PART B
CF6-50 SERIES
```

NOTE 9. Power setting, power checks and control of engine thrust output in all operations is to be based on GE engine charts referring to Fan Speed (N_1). Speed sensors are included in the engine assembly for this purpose.

NOTE 10. The following thrust reverser models are approved in accordance with FAR 33.97 for incorporation on CF6 engine models:

	CF6-50A	CF6-50C	CF6-50D	CF6-50E	CF6-50H
Fan Reverser Model No.	TR-CF6-F3	--	TR-CF6-F6	--	TR-CF6-F3
Turbine Reverser Model No.	TR-CF6-5	--	TR-CF6-7	--	TR-CF6-5

NOTE 11: British Civil Aviation Authority validation of FAA type certification of engine model CF6-50A as detailed herein granted 31 May 1972.

NOTE 12: The following models incorporate the following general characteristics:

CF6-50 Series	Characteristics
-50A	Basic model
-50C	Same as -50A except takeoff rating increased to 50,400 lbs, flat rated to 86°F ambient temperature sea level static and with improved engine parts.
-50D	Same as -50A except the engine is operated to an increased takeoff thrust of 50,400 lbs at a lower flat rated ambient temperature of 77°F sea level static.
-50E	Same as -50C except the engine is operated to increased thrust of 51,800 lbs. at a lower flat rated ambient temperature of 78°F sea level static.
-50H	Same as -50A except takeoff rating increased to 50,400 lbs flat rated to 86°F ambient temperature sea level static with an alternate takeoff rating of 48,400 lbs at a flat rated ambient temperature of 87°F with improved engine parts.

...END...

Appendix 3

Decimal Equivalents

Inch Fraction	Decimal	mm	Inch Fraction	Decimal	mm	Inch Fraction	Decimal	mm
1/64	0.0156	0.397	23/64	0.3594	9.128	45/64	0.7301	17.859
1/32	0.0312	0.794	3/8	0.3750	9.525	23/32	0.7187	18.256
3/64	0.0469	1.191	25/64	0.3906	9.922	47/64	0.7344	18.653
1/16	0.0625	1.587	13/32	0.4062	10.319	3/4	0.7500	19.050
5/64	0.0781	1.984	27/64	0.4219	10.716	49/64	0.7656	19.447
3/32	0.0937	2.381	7/16	0.4375	11.112	25/32	0.7812	19.844
7/64	0.1094	2.778	29/64	0.4531	11.509	51/64	0.7969	20.241
1/8	0.1250	3.175	15/32	0.4687	11.906	13/16	0.8125	20.637
9/64	0.1406	3.572	31/64	0.4844	12.303	53/64	0.8281	21.034
5/32	0.1562	3.969	1/2	0.5000	12.700	27/32	0.8437	21.431
11/64	0.1719	4.366	33/64	0.5156	13.097	55/64	0.8594	21.828
3/16	0.1875	4.762	17/32	0.5312	13.494	7/8	0.8750	22.225
13/64	0.2031	5.159	35/64	0.5469	13.891	57/64	0.8906	22.622
7/32	0.2187	5.556	9/16	0.5625	14.288	29/32	0.9062	23.019
15/64	0.2344	5.953	37/64	0.5781	14.686	59/64	0.9219	23.416
1/4	0.2500	6.350	19/32	0.5937	15.081	15/16	0.9375	23.812
17/64	0.2656	6.747	39/64	0.6094	15.478	61/64	0.9531	24.209
9/32	0.2812	7.144	5/8	0.6250	15.875	31/32	0.9687	24.606
19/64	0.2969	7.540	41/64	0.6406	16.272	63/64	0.9844	25.003
5/16	0.3125	7.937	21/32	0.6562	16.669	1	1.0000	25.400
21/64	0.3281	8.334	43/64	0.6719	17.065			
11/32	0.3437	8.731	11/16	0.6875	17.462			

Drill Sizes/Decimal Equivalents

Drill No.	Dia. in.	Drill No.	Dia. in.	Drill No.	Dia. in.	Drill No.	Dia. in.	Drill No.	Dia. in.	Drill No.	Dia. in.
A	0.234	G	0.261	L	0.290	Q	0.332	V	0.377		
B	0.238	H	0.266	M	0.295	R	0.339	W	0.386		
C	0.242	I	0.272	N	0.302	S	0.348	X	0.397		
D	0.246	J	0.277	O	0.316	T	0.358	Y	0.404		
E	0.250	K	0.281	P	0.323	U	0.368	Z	0.413		
F	0.257										

Drill No.	Dia. in.	Drill No.	Dia. in.	Drill No.	Dia. in.	Drill No.	Dia. in.	Drill No.	Dia. in.
1	0.2280	17	0.1730	33	0.1130	49	0.0730	65	0.0350
2	0.2210	18	0.1695	34	0.1110	50	0.0700	66	0.0330
3	0.2130	19	0.1660	35	0.1100	51	0.0670	67	0.0320
4	0.2090	20	0.1610	36	0.1065	52	0.0635	68	0.0310
5	0.2055	21	0.1590	37	0.1040	53	0.0595	69	0.0292
6	0.2040	22	0.1570	38	0.1015	54	0.0550	70	0.0280
7	0.2010	23	0.1540	39	0.0995	55	0.0520	71	0.0260
8	0.1990	24	0.1520	40	0.0980	56	0.0465	72	0.0250
9	0.1960	25	0.1495	41	0.0960	57	0.0430	73	0.0240
10	0.1935	26	0.1470	42	0.0935	58	0.0420	74	0.0225
11	0.1910	27	0.1440	43	0.0890	59	0.0410	75	0.0210
12	0.1890	28	0.1405	44	0.0860	60	0.0400	76	0.0200
13	0.1850	29	0.1360	45	0.0820	61	0.0390	77	0.0180
14	0.1820	30	0.1285	46	0.0810	62	0.0380	78	0.0160
15	0.1800	31	0.1200	47	0.0785	63	0.0370	79	0.0145
16	0.1770	32	0.1160	48	0.0760	64	0.0360	80	0.0135

Screw Dia. = (Screw No. × 0.013) + 0.060

Temperature Conversions — Fahrenheit to Centigrade

Degrees Fahrenheit to Degrees Centigrade* $^{\circ}C = [\tfrac{5}{9} (^{\circ}F + 40)] - 40$

Values for Interpolation in the Following Table

Degrees Fahrenheit —	1	2	3	4	5	6	7	8	9
Degrees Centigrade —	0.56	1.11	1.67	2.22	2.78	3.33	3.89	4.44	5.00

*All decimals in the tables are repeating decimals — 37.78 is actually 37.777 . . .

°F	°C	°F	°C	°F	°C	°F	°C	°F	°C	°F	°C	°F	°C
−40	−40.00	25	−3.89	70	21.11	175	79.44	400	204.44	650	343.33	1,500	815.56
−38	−38.89	26	−3.33	71	21.67	180	82.22	405	207.22	660	348.89	1,550	843.33
−36	−37.78	27	−2.78	72	22.22	185	85.00	410	210.00	670	354.44	1,600	871.11
−34	−36.67	28	−2.22	73	22.78	190	87.78	415	212.78	680	360.00	1,650	898.89
−32	−35.56	29	−1.67	74	23.33	195	90.55	420	215.56	690	365.56	1,700	926.67
−30	−34.44	30	−1.11	75	23.89	200	93.33	425	218.33	700	371.11	1,750	954.44
−28	−33.33	31	−0.56	76	24.44	205	96.11	430	221.11	710	376.67	1,800	982.22
−26	−32.22	32	0.00	77	25.00	210	98.89	435	223.89	720	382.22	1,850	1,010.00
−24	−31.11	33	+0.56	78	25.56	215	101.67	440	226.67	730	387.78	1,900	1,037.78
−22	−30.00	34	1.11	79	26.11	220	104.44	445	229.44	740	393.33	1,950	1,065.56
−20	−28.89	35	1.67	80	26.67	225	107.22	450	232.22	750	398.89	2,000	1,093.33
−18	−27.78	36	2.22	81	27.22	230	110.00	455	235.00	760	404.44	2,050	1,121.11
−16	−26.67	37	2.78	82	27.78	235	112.78	460	237.78	770	410.00	2,100	1,148.89
−14	−25.56	38	3.33	83	28.33	240	115.56	465	240.55	780	415.56	2,150	1,176.67
−12	−24.44	39	3.89	84	28.89	245	118.33	470	243.33	790	421.11	2,200	1,204.44
−10	−23.33	40	4.44	85	29.44	250	121.11	475	246.11	800	426.67	2,250	1,232.22
−8	−22.22	41	5.00	86	30.00	255	123.89	480	248.89	810	432.22	2,300	1,260.00
−6	−21.11	42	5.56	87	30.56	260	126.67	485	251.67	820	437.78	2,350	1,287.78
−4	−20.00	43	6.11	88	31.11	265	129.44	490	254.44	830	443.33	2,400	1,315.56
−2	−18.89	44	6.67	89	31.67	270	132.22	495	257.22	840	448.89	2,450	1,343.33
0	−17.78	45	7.22	90	32.22	275	135.00	500	260.00	850	454.44	2,500	1,371.11
+1	−17.22	46	7.78	91	32.78	280	137.78	505	262.78	860	460.00	2,550	1,398.89
2	−16.67	47	8.33	92	33.33	285	140.55	510	265.56	870	465.56	2,600	1,426.67
3	−16.11	48	8.89	93	33.89	290	143.33	515	268.33	880	471.11	2,650	1,454.44
4	−15.56	49	9.44	94	34.44	295	146.11	520	271.11	890	476.67	2,700	1,482.22
5	−15.00	50	10.00	95	35.00	300	148.89	525	273.89	900	482.22	2,750	1,510.00
6	−14.44	51	10.56	96	35.56	305	151.67	530	276.67	910	487.78	2,800	1,537.78
7	−13.89	52	11.11	97	36.11	310	154.44	535	279.44	920	493.33	2,850	1,565.59
8	−13.33	53	11.67	98	36.67	315	157.22	540	282.22	930	498.89	2,900	1,593.33
9	−12.78	54	12.22	99	37.22	320	160.00	545	285.00	940	504.44	2,950	1,621.11
10	−12.22	55	12.78	100	37.78	325	162.78	550	287.78	905	510.00		
11	−11.67	56	13.33	105	40.55	330	165.56	555	290.55	960	516.56		
12	−11.11	57	13.89	110	43.33	335	168.33	560	293.33	970	521.11		
13	−10.56	58	14.44	115	46.11	340	171.11	565	296.11	980	526.67		
14	−10.00	59	15.00	120	48.89	345	173.89	570	298.89	990	532.22		
15	−9.44	60	15.56	125	51.67	350	176.67	575	301.67	1,000	537.78		
16	−8.89	61	16.11	130	54.44	355	179.44	580	304.44	1,050	565.56		
17	−8.33	62	16.67	135	57.22	360	182.22	585	307.22	1,100	593.33		
18	−7.78	63	17.22	140	60.00	365	185.00	590	310.00	1,150	621.11		
19	−7.22	64	17.78	145	62.78	370	187.78	595	312.78	1,200	648.89		
20	−6.67	65	18.33	150	65.56	375	190.55	600	315.56	1,250	676.67		
21	−6.11	66	18.89	155	68.33	380	193.33	610	321.11	1,300	704.44		
22	−5.56	67	19.44	160	71.11	385	196.11	620	326.67	1,350	732.22		
23	−5.00	68	20.00	165	73.89	390	198.89	630	332.22	1,400	760.00		
24	−4.44	69	20.56	170	76.67	395	201.67	640	337.78	1,450	787.78		

Temperature Conversions — Centigrade to Fahrenheit

	Degrees Centigrade to Degrees Fahrenheit						°F = [9/5 (°C + 40)] – 40						
	Values for Interpolation in the Following Table												
	Degrees Centigrade —		1	2	3	4	5	6	7	8	9		
	Degrees Fahrenheit —		1.8	3.6	5.4	7.2	9.0	10.8	12.6	14.4	16.2		

°C	°F	°C	°F	°C	°F	°C	°F	°C	°F	°C	°F	°C	°F
−40	−40.0	0	32.0	30	86.0	100	212	250	482	400	752	1,000	1,832
−38	−36.4	+1	33.8	31	87.8	105	221	255	491	405	761	1,050	1,922
−36	−32.8	2	35.6	32	89.6	110	230	260	500	410	770	1,100	2,012
−34	−29.2	3	37.4	33	91.4	115	239	265	509	415	779	1,150	2,101
−32	−25.6	4	39.2	34	93.2	120	248	270	518	420	788	1,200	2,192
−30	−22.0	5	41.0	35	95.0	125	257	275	527	425	797	1,250	2,282
−28	−18.4	6	42.8	36	96.8	130	266	280	536	430	806	1,300	2,373
−26	−14.8	7	44.6	37	98.6	135	275	285	545	435	815	1,350	2,462
−24	−11.2	8	46.4	38	100.4	140	284	290	554	440	824	1,400	2,552
−22	−7.6	9	48.2	39	102.2	145	293	295	563	445	833	1,450	2,642
−20	−4.0	10	50.0	40	104.0	150	302	300	572	450	842	1,500	2,732
−19	−2.2	11	51.8	41	105.8	155	311	305	581	455	851	1,550	2,822
−18	−0.4	12	53.6	42	107.6	160	320	310	590	460	860	1,600	2,912
−17	+1.4	13	55.4	43	109.4	165	329	315	599	465	869	1,650	3,002
−16	3.2	14	57.2	44	111.2	170	338	320	608	470	878	1,700	3,092
−15	5.0	15	59.0	45	113.0	175	347	325	617	475	887	1,750	3,182
−14	6.8	16	60.8	46	114.8	180	356	330	626	480	896	1,800	3,272
−13	8.6	17	62.6	47	116.6	185	365	335	635	485	905	1,850	3,362
−12	10.4	18	64.4	48	118.4	190	374	340	644	490	914	1,900	3,452
−11	12.2	19	66.2	49	120.2	195	383	345	653	495	923	1,950	3,542
−10	14.0	20	68.0	50	122.0	200	392	350	662	500	932	2,000	3,632
−9	15.8	21	69.8	55	131.0	205	401	355	671	550	1,022	2,050	3,722
−8	17.6	22	71.6	60	140.0	210	410	360	680	600	1,112	2,100	3,812
−7	19.4	23	73.4	65	149.0	215	419	365	689	650	1,202	2,150	3,902
−6	21.2	24	75.2	70	158.0	220	428	370	698	700	1,292	2,200	3,992
−5	23.0	25	77.0	75	167.0	225	437	375	707	750	1,382	2,250	4,082
−4	24.8	26	78.8	80	176.0	230	446	380	716	800	1,472	2,300	4,172
−3	26.6	27	80.6	85	185.0	235	455	385	725	850	1,562	2,350	4,262
−2	28.4	28	82.4	90	194.0	240	464	390	734	900	1,652	2,400	4,352
−1	30.2	29	84.2	95	203.0	245	473	395	743	950	1,742	2,450	4,442

Conversion Factors

Multiply	By	To Obtain	Multiply	By	To Obtain
Amperes	1.04×10^{-5}	Faradays/Sec.	Grams/Liter	0.122	Ounces/Gallon (Troy)
Amperes/Sq. Ft.	0.00108	Amperes/Sq. Cm.	Grams/Liter	0.134	Ounces/Gallon (Avdp)
Ampere-hours	3,600	Coulombs	Grams/Liter	1,000	Parts Per Million
Amperes/Sq. Cm.	929	Amperes/Sq. Ft.	Grams/Liter	2.44	Pennyweights/Gallon
Angstrom Units	3.94×10^{-9}	Inches	Inches	2.54	Centimeters
Angstrom Units	1×10^{-10}	Meters	Inches	1/12	Feet
Angstrom Units	1×10^{-4}	Microns	Inches	1,000	Mils
Centimeters	0.394	Inches	Kilograms	15,432.4	Grains
Centimeters	393.7	Mils	Kilograms	1,000	Grams
Centimeters	0.0328	Feet	Kilograms	35.27	Ounces (Avdp)
Circular Mils	5.07×10^{-6}	Sq. Centimeters	Kilograms	32.15	Ounces (Troy)
Circular Mils	7.85×10^{-7}	Sq. Inches	Kilograms	643.01	Pennyweights
Cubic Centimeters	3.53×10^{-5}	Cubic Feet	Kilograms	2.205	Pounds (Avdp)
Cubic Centimeters	0.061	Cubic Inches	Kilograms	2.679	Pounds (Troy)
Cubic Centimeters	2.64×10^{-4}	Gallons	Liters	1,000.027	Cubic Centimeters
Cubic Centimeters	9.9997×10^{-4}	Liters	Liters	0.035	Cubic Feet
Cubic Centimeters	0.0338	Ounces (Fluid)	Liters	61.025	Cubic Inches
Cubic Centimeters	0.0021	Pints	Liters	0.264	Gallons
Cubic Centimeters	0.0011	Quarts (Liquid)	Liters	33.81	Ounces (Fluid)
Cubic Feet	28.317	Cubic Centimeters	Liters	2.11	Pints
Cubic Feet	1.728	Cubic Inches	Liters	1.057	Quarts (Liquid)
Cubic Feet	7.48	Gallons	Meters	100	Centimeters
Cubic Feet	28.32	Liters	Meters	3.281	Feet
Cubic Feet	29.92	Quarts	Meters	39.37	Inches
Cubic Feet of Water			Meters	0.001	Kilometers
60°F (16°C)	62.37	Pounds	Meters	1.094	Yards
Cubic Inches	16.39	Cubic Centimeters	Microhms	1×10^{-12}	Megohms
Cubic Inches	0.0043	Ounces (Fluid)	Microhms	1×10^{-6}	Ohms
Cubic Inches	0.0173	Quarts (Liquid)	Microns	3.9×10^{-5}	Inches
Faradays	9.65×10^{-4}	Coulombs	Microns	0.001	Millimeters
Faradays/Second	96,500	Amperes	Mile	1.15	Knots
Feet	30.48	Centimeters	Miles per hour (mph)	1.467	Feet/Second
Feet	12	Inches	Milligrams	0.0154	Grains
Feet	0.3048	Meters	Milligrams	0.001	Grams
Feet/Second	0.6817	Miles Per Hour	Milligrams	1×10^{-6}	Kilograms
Gallons	4	Quarts (Liquid)	Milligrams	3.5×10^{-5}	Ounces (Avdp)
Gallons	3,785.4	Cubic Centimeters	Milligrams	3.215×10^{-5}	Ounces (Troy)
Gallons	0.1337	Cubic Feet	Milligrams	6.43×10^{-4}	Pennyweights
Gallons	231	Cubic Inches	Milligrams	2.21×10^{-6}	Pounds (Avdp)
Gallons	3,785	Liters	Milligrams	2.68×10^{-6}	Pounds (Troy)
Gallons	128	Ounces (Fluid)	Milligrams/Liter	1.0	Parts Per Million
Gallons (Imperial)	1.201	Gallons	Milliliters	1.000027	Cubic Centimeters
Gallons	0.8327	Gallons (Imperial)	Milliliters	0.061	Cubic Inches
Gallons	8	Pints	Milliliters	0.001	Liters
Gallons	8.31	Pounds (Avdp of Water at 62°F (17°C))	Milliliters	0.034	Ounces (Fluid)
			Millimeters	.0.1	Centimeters
Grains	0.0648	Grams	Millimeters	0.039	Inches
Grains	0.0023	Ounces (Avdp)	Millimeters	0.001	Meters
Grains	0.0021	Ounces (Troy)	Millimeters	1,000	Microns
Grains	0.0417	Pennyweights (Troy)	Mils	0.0025	Centimeters
Grains	1/7,000	Pounds (Avdp)	Mils	0.001	Inches
Grains	1/5,760	Pounds (Troy)	Mils	25.4	Microns
Grams	15.43	Grains	Ounces (Avdp)	437.5	Grains
Grams	1,000	Milligrams	Ounces (Avdp)	28.35	Grams
Grams	0.0353	Ounces (Avdp)	Ounces (Avdp)	0.911	Ounces (Troy)
Grams	0.0321	Ounces (Troy)	Ounces (Avdp)	18.23	Pennyweights
Grams	0.643	Pennyweights	Ounces (Avdp)	1/16	Pounds (Avdp)
Grams	0.0022	Pounds (Avdp)	Ounces (Avdp)	0.076	Pounds (Troy)
Grams	0.0027	Pounds (Troy)	Ounces/Gallon (Avdp)	7.5	Grams/Liter

Conversion Factors, cont'd.

Multiply	By	To Obtain	Multiply	By	To Obtain
Ounces (Troy)	480	Grains	Pounds (Avdp)	14.58	Ounces (Troy)
Ounces (Troy)	31.1	Grams	Pounds (Avdp)	291.67	Pennyweights
Ounces (Troy)	31,103.5	Milligrams	Pounds (Avdp)	1.215	Pounds (Troy)
Ounces (Troy)	1.097	Ounces (Avdp)	Pounds (Troy)	5,760	Grains
Ounces (Troy)	20	Pennyweights	Pounds (Troy)	373.24	Grams
Ounces (Troy)	0.069	Pounds (Avdp)	Pounds (Troy)	0.373	Kilograms
Ounces (Troy)	1/12	Pounds (Troy)	Pounds (Troy)	13.17	Ounces (Avdp)
Ounces/Gallon (Troy)	8.2	Grams/Liter	Pounds (Troy)	12	Ounces (Troy)
Ounces (Fluid)	29.57	Cubic Centimeters	Pounds (Troy)	240	Pennyweights
Ounces (Fluid)	1.80	Cubic Inches	Pounds (Troy)	0.823	Pounds (Avdp)
Ounces (Fluid)	1/128	Gallons	Pounds of Water 62°F (17°C)	0.016	Cubic Feet
Ounces (Fluid)	0.0296	Liters			
Ounces (Fluid)	29.57	Milliliters	Pounds of Water 62°F (17°C)	27.68	Cubic Inches
Ounces (Fluid)	1/16	Pints			
Ounces (Fluid)	0.031	Quarts	Pounds of Water 62°F (17°)	0.1198	Gallons
Ounces/Gallon (Fluid)	7.7	CC/Liter			
Pennyweights	24	Grains	Quarts (Liquid)	946.4	Cubic Centimeters
Pennyweights	1.56	Grams	Quarts (Liquid)	57.75	Cubic Inches
Pennyweights	1,555	Milligrams	Quarts (Liquid)	0.033	Cubic Feet
Pennyweights	0.0549	Ounces (Avdp)	Quarts (Liquid)	0.25	Gallons
Pennyweights	0.05	Ounces (Troy)	Quarts (Liquid)	0.946	Liters
Pennyweights	0.0034	Pounds (Avdp)	Quarts (Liquid)	32	Ounces (Fluid)
Pennyweights	0.0042	Pounds (Troy)	Quarts (Liquid)	2	Pints
Pennyweights/Gallon	0.41	Grams/Liter	Square Centimeters	127.32	Circular Millimeters
Pints	473.2	Cubic Centimeters	Square Centimeters	197,350	Circular Mils
Pints	0.017	Cubic Feet	Square Centimeters	0.001	Square Feet
Pints	28.88	Cubic Inches	Square Centimeters	0.155	Square Inches
Pints	0.125	Gallons	Square Centimeters	100	Square Millimeters
Pints	0.473	Liters	Square Feet	929.03	Square Centimeters
Pints	16	Ounces (Fluid)	Square Feet	144	Square Inches
Pints	0.5	Quarts	Square Inches	1.2732	Circular Mils
Pounds (Avdp)	7,000	Grains	Square Inches	6.45	Square Centimeters
Pounds (Avdp)	453.6	Grams	Square Inches	1/144	Square Feet
Pounds (Avdp)	0.454	Kilograms	Square Inches	1×10^{-6}	Square Mils
Pounds (Avdp)	16	Ounces (Avdp)	Square Inches	1/1,296	Square Yards

Appendix 4

Gas Turbine Powered Aircraft Familiarization

The civil aircraft included in this Appendix have been selected because they are the most common in commercial and general aviation. Many aircraft receive newer engine models over time. For a complete listing, including aircraft and engine dash models of civil, military and foreign aircraft, refer to the Jeppesen publication 'Encyclopedia of Jet Aircraft and Engines'. Explanation of abbreviations appears at the end of this listing.

A. Fixed Wing Aircraft of the World

AIRCRAFT MANUFACTURER	ENGINE MANUFACTURER	DESIGNATION	ENGINES NUMBER/TYPE
Airbus Industries, EADS*			
A-300	General Electric	CF6	(2) TF
	Pratt & Whitney	PW4000	(2) TF
A-310	General Electric	CF6	(2) TF
	Pratt & Whitney	PW4000	(2) TF
A-318	CFM International	CFM56	(2) TF
A-319	International Aero Engines	V2500	(2) TF
A-320/321	CFM International	CFM56	(2) TF
	International Aero Engines	V2500	(2) TF
A-330	General Electric	CF6	(2) TF
	Pratt & Whitney	PW4000	(2) TF
	Rolls-Royce	Trent 500	(2) TF
A-340	CFM International	CFM56	(4) TF
	Rolls-Royce	Trent 500	(2) TF
A-380	General Electric, P&W	GP7000	(2) TF
	Rolls-Royce	Trent 900	(2) TF
Antonov Aero Corporation, Russia			
An-70	Progressive	D-27	(4) PF
An-218	Progressive	D-18	(2) TF
An-225	Progressive	D-18T	(6) TF
Avions de Transport Regional (ATR), France			
ATR-42, -52	Pratt & Whitney (Can.)	PW121/127	(2) TP
ATR-72	Pratt & Whitney (Can.)	PW1204/127	(2) TP
ATR-82	Allison, R-R*	AE2100	(2) TP
Boeing Company, USA			
707 early models	Pratt & Whitney	JT3C & JT4C	(4) TJ

AIRCRAFT MANUFACTURER	ENGINE MANUFACTURER	DESIGNATION	ENGINES NUMBER/TYPE
707	Pratt & Whitney	JT3D	(4) TF
717	Rolls-Royce/BMW	BR715	(2) TF
727	Pratt & Whitney	JT8D	(3) TF
737	Pratt & Whitney	JT8D	(2) TF
	CFM International	CFM56	(2) TF
747	Pratt & Whitney	JT9D/PW4000	(4) TF
	General Electric	CF6	(4) TF
	Rolls-Royce	RB-211/Trent	(4) TF
757	Pratt & Whitney	PW2000	(2) TF
	Rolls-Royce	RB-211	(2) TF
767	Pratt & Whitney	JT9D/PW4000	(2) TF
	General Electric	CF6	(2) TF
	Rolls-Royce	RB-211/Trent	(2) TF
777	Pratt & Whitney	PW4000	(2) TF
	Rolls-Royce	Trent 800	(2) TF
	General Electric	GE-90	(2) TF
BBJ (Boeing Business Jet)	CFM International	CFM56	(2) TF

Boeing (McDonnell) Corporation, USA

DC-8	Pratt & Whitney	JT3D	(4) TF
	CFM International	CFM56	(4) TF
DC-9	Pratt & Whitney	JT8D	(2) TF
DC-10	General Electric	CF-6	(3) TF
	Pratt & Whitney	JT9D	(3) TF
MD-11	Pratt & Whitney	PW4000	(3) TF
	General Electric	CF6	(3) TF
MD-80 to MD-88	Pratt & Whitney	JT8D	(2) TF
MD-90	Int'l Aero Engines	V2500	(2) TF

Bombardier (Canadair) Corporation (Canada)

Challenger -600	Honeywell	ALF-502	(2) TF
Challenger -601	General Electric	CF-34	(2) TF
Challenger -604	General Electric	CF-34	(2) TF
Corporate Jetliner	General Electric	CF-34	(2) TF
CRJ200, 700	General Electric	CF-34	(2) TF
CRJ900	General Electric	CF-34	(2) TF

AIRCRAFT MANUFACTURER	ENGINE MANUFACTURER	DESIGNATION	ENGINES NUMBER/TYPE
Bombardier (DeHavilland) Corporation, Canada			
Dash-6	Pratt & Whitney (Can.)	PT6	(2) TP
Dash-7	Pratt & Whitney (Can.)	PT6	(4) TP
Dash-8 (Q100, 200, 300)	Pratt & Whitney (Can.)	PW120	(4) TP
Dash-8 (Q400)	Pratt & Whitney (Can.)	PW150	(4) TP
Bombardier Corporation, (Learjet-Gates) Canada			
Learjet 24 to 29	General Electric	CJ-610	(2) TJ
Learjet 35 to56	Honeywell	TFE-731	(2) TF
Learjet 60	Pratt & Whitney (Can.)	PW305	(2) TF
British Aerospace Corporation (GT. Britain)			
Avro RJ 70	Honeywell	ALF502/LF507	(4) TF
Avro RJ 85	Honeywell	ALF502/LF507	(4) TF
Avro RJ 100	Honeywell	ALF502LF507	(4) TF
Avro RJX 70	Honeywell	AS977	(4) TF
Avro RJX 85	Honeywell	AS977	(4) TF
Avro RJX 100	Honeywell	AS977	(4) TF
BAC-111	Rolls-Royce	Spey	(2) TF
BAe-ATP	Pratt & Whitney (Can.)	PW120	(2) TP
BAe-125	Honeywell	TFE-731	(2) TF
BAe-146	Honeywell	ALF-502/LF507	(4) TF
Concorde	Rolls-Royce	Olympus 593	(4) TJ
Hs-748	Rolls-Royce	Dart	(2) TP
Jetstream	Honeywell	TPE331	(2) TP
CASA Corporation, EADS*			
C212	Honeywell	TPE-331	(2) TP
CN235	General Electric	CT7	(2) TP
Cessna Corporation, USA			
Citation I, II, and V	Pratt & Whitney (Can.)	JT15D	(2) TF

A4-4

AIRCRAFT MANUFACTURER	ENGINE MANUFACTURER	DESIGNATION	ENGINES NUMBER/TYPE
Citation III, IV	Honeywell	TFE-731	(2) TF
Citation X	Allison, R/R*	AE3007	(2) TF
Citation Bravo	Pratt & Whitney (Can.)	PW530	(2) TF
Citation Encore	Pratt & Whitney (Can.)	PW535	(2) TF
Citation Excell	Pratt & Whitney (Can.)	PW545	(2) TF
Citation Jet(CJ1,CJ2)	Williams Int'l.	FJ44	(2) TF
Citation Ultra	Pratt & Whitney (Can.)	JT15D	(2) TF
Citation Sovereign	Pratt & Whitney (Can.)	PW306	(2) TF
Conquest	Honeywell	TPE-331	(2) TP
Caravan	Pratt & Whitney (Can.)	PT6	(1) TP

Convair Corporation

Convair 540	Allison, R/R*	501D	(2) TP

Dassault Corporation, France

Falcon 10	Honeywell	TFE-731	(2) TF
Falcon 20F	General Electric	CF-700	(2) TF
Falcon 50 /100	Honeywell	TFE-731	(2) TF
Falcon 900	Honeywell	TFE-731	(3) TF
Falcon 2000	LHTEC*	CFE-738	(2) TF
	Pratt & Whitney (Can.)	PW308	(2) TF

Daimler-Chrysler Corporation, Germany

D0 128	Pratt & Whitney (Can.)	PT6	(2) TP
D0 228	Honeywell	TPE-331	(2) TP
D0 328	Pratt & Whitney (Can.)	PW119	(2) TP

Embraer Corporation, Brazil

EMB-110/111/121	& Whitney (Can.)	PT6	(2) TP
EMB-120	Pratt & Whitney (Can.)	PW118	(2) TP
EMB-135/140/145	Allison, R/R*	AE3007	(2) TF
EMB-170/190	General Electric	CF34	(2) TF

AIRCRAFT MANUFACTURER	ENGINE MANUFACTURER	DESIGNATION	ENGINES NUMBER/TYPE
Fairchild Industries, USA			
328 Jet	Pratt & Whitney (Can.)	PW306	(2) TF
528 Jet	General Electric	CF-34	(2) TF
Envoy-3	Pratt & Whitney (Can.)	PW306	(2) TF
Envoy-7	General Electric	CF-34	(2) TF
FH-227	Rolls-Royce	Dart	(2) TP
Fairchild Dornier Industries, USA			
Merlin	Honeywell	TPE331	(2) TP
Metro	Honeywell	TPE331	(2) TP
Fooker Corporation, Netherlends			
Fokker F27	Rolls-Royce	Dart	(2) TP
Fokker F50	Pratt & Whitney (Can.)	PW125/127	(2) TP
Fokker F60	Pratt & Whitney (Can.)	PW127	(2) TP
Fokker 70	Rolls-Royce	TAY	(2) TF
Fokker 100	Rolls-Royce	TAY	(2) TF
Gulfstream American Corporation, USA			
Gulfstream I	Rolls-Royce	Dart	(2) TP
Gulfstream II, III	Rolls-Royce	Spey	(2) TF
Gulfstream IV	Rolls-Royce	TAY	(2) TF
Gulfstream V	Rolls-Royce/BMW	BR710	(2) TF
Ilyushin Corporation, Russia			
IL-96	Perm	PS-90	(4) TF
	Pratt & Whitney	PW2000	(4) TF
IL-114	Klimov	TV117	(2) TP
Lockheed Corporation, USA			
Jetstar I	Pratt & Whitney	JT12	(4) TJ
Jetstar II	Honeywell	TFE-731	(4) TF
Hercules (C-130)	Allison, R/R*	T-56	(4) TP
Hercules II	Allison, R/R*	AE2100	(4) TP

AIRCRAFT MANUFACTURER	ENGINE MANUFACTURER	DESIGNATION	ENGINES NUMBER/TYPE
Tristar L1011	Rolls-Royce	RB-211	(3) TF
Mitsubishi Corporation, Japan			
MU-2	Honeywell	TPE-331	(2) TP
Pilatus Corporation, Switzerland			
PC-6	Pratt & Whitney (Can.)	PT6	(2) TP
Piaggio Aero Industries, Italy			
P.166	Pratt & Whitney (Can.)	PT6	(2) TP
P.180	Pratt & Whitney (Can.)	PT6	(2) TP
Piper Corporation, USA			
Cheyenne I, II, III	Pratt & Whitney (Can.)	PT6	(2) TP
Cheyenne 400	Honeywell	TPE-331	(2) TP
Turbine Malibu	Pratt & Whitney (Can.)	PT6	(2) TP
Raytheon (Beechcraft) Corporation, USA			
Beech 1900	Pratt & Whitney (Can.)	PT6	(2) TP
B-99	Pratt & Whitney (Can.)	PT6	(2) TP
KingAir C-90	Pratt & Whitney (Can.)	PT6	(2) TP
KingAir 350	Pratt & Whitney (Can.)	PT6	(2) TP
KingAir B-200	Pratt & Whitney (Can.)	PT6	(2) TP
Super King 300	Pratt & Whitney (Can.)	PT6	(2) TP
Starship-1	Pratt & Whitney (Can.)	PT6	(2) TP
Beechjet-400	Pratt & Whitney (Can.)	JT15	(2) TF
Hawker-800	Honeywell	TFE731	(2) TF
Hawker Horizon	Pratt & Whitney (Can.)	PW305	(2) TF
Hawker 1000	Pratt & Whitney (Can.)	PW305	(2) TF
Premier-1	Williams Int'l.	FJ44	(2) TF
Precision Airmotive Corporation, USA (Formerly Rockwell and Gulfstream)			
Commander series	Honeywell	TPE-331	(2) TP
Aero Commander	Pratt & Whitney (Can.)	PT6	(2) TP

AIRCRAFT MANUFACTURER	ENGINE MANUFACTURER	DESIGNATION	ENGINES NUMBER/TYP
Saab Corporation, Sweden			
Saab 340	General Electric	CT7	(2) TP
Saab 2000	Allison, R/R*	AE2100	(2) TP
Sabreliner Corporation, USA			
Sabreliner 40 /65	Honeywell	TFE-731	(2) TF
Sabreliner 60	Pratt & Whitney (Can.)	JT12	(2) TJ
Sabreliner 75/85	General Electric	CF-700	(2) TF
Tupolev Corporation, Russia			
TU-204	Perm	PS90	(2) TF
TU-334	Progress	D-436	(2) TF
Yakovlev Corporation, Russia			
Yak-40	Saturn	AI-25	(3) TF
Yak-242	Saturn	PS90	(2) TF

B. Rotary Wing Aircraft of the World

Augusta Corporation, (Italy)

AIRCRAFT MANUFACTURER	ENGINE MANUFACTURER	DESIGNATION	ENGINES NUMBER/TYP
A 109	Allison, R/R*	250	(2) TS
	Pratt & Whitney (Can.)	PT6T	(2) TS
A 119	Pratt & Whitney (Can.)	PT6T	(1) TS
A129	Rolls-Royce	GEM	(2) TS
AB 205	Honeywell	T-53	(1) TS
AB 206	Allison, R/R*	250	(1) TS
AB 212	Pratt & Whitney (Can.)	PT6T	(2) TS
AB 412	Pratt & Whitney (Can.)	PT6T	(2) TS
Bell Corporation, USA			
Bell 205	Honeywell	T53	(1) TS
Bell 206	Allison, R/R*	250	(2) TS
Bell 209	General Electric	T700	(2) TS
Bell 212	Pratt & Whitney (Can.)	PT6T	(2) TS

AIRCRAFT MANUFACTURER	ENGINE MANUFACTURER	DESIGNATION	ENGINES NUMBER/TYPE
Bell 214	Honeywell	T53	(2) TS
Bell 230	Allison, R/R*	250	(2) TS
Bell 406/407	Allison, R/R*	250	(2) TS
Bell 412	Pratt & Whitney (Can.)	PT6T	(2) TS
Bell 430	Allison, R/R*	250	(2) TS
V-22 (Bell/Boeing)	Allison, R/R*	T-406	(2) TS
Boeing Company, USA			
234	Honeywell	AL5512	(2) TS
414	Honeywell	T-55	(2) TS
CH-46	General Electric	T-58	(2) TS
CH-47	Honeywell	T-55	(2) TS
Boeing (McDonnell) Helicopter Company			
MD 500	Allison, R/R*	250	(1) TS
MD 520, 530	Allison, R/R*	250	(1) TS
MD 600	Allison, R/R*	250	(1) TS
MD 900/901/902	Pratt & Whitney (Can.)	PW206	(2) TS
EH Industries LTD (Great Britain)			
EH 101	Turbomeca	RTM 322	(3) TS
	General Electric	CT-7	(3) TS
Eurocopter Company, EADS*			
AS 330 (Puma)	Turbomeca	Turmo	(2) TS
AS 332 (Super Puma)	Turbomeca	Makila	(2) TS
AS 350 (Ecureuil)	Allison, R/R*	250	(1) TS
AS 355	Allison, R/R*	250	(2) TS
SA 365 (Dauphin)	Turbomeca	Arriel	(2) TS
BO.105	Allison, R/R*	250	(2) TS
BK.117	Honeywell	LTS101	(2) TS
EA 135	Pratt & Whitney (Can.)	PW206	(2) TS
EA 145	Turbomeca	Arrius	(2) TS

AIRCRAFT MANUFACTURER	ENGINE MANUFACTURER	DESIGNATION	ENGINES NUMBER/TYPE
EA 145	Turbomeca	Arrius	(2) TS
NH-90	Turbomeca	RTM322	(2) TS
SA 315, 318 (Lama)	Turbomeca	Artouse	(1) TS
Rogerson Helicopter Co.			
H-1100	Allison, R/R*	250	(1) TS
Sikorsky (United Technologies), USA			
S-61, S-62	General Electric	CT-58	(2) TS
S-64	General Electric	CT-64	(2) TS
S-65 (H-53)	General Electric	CT-64	(2) TS
S-70	General Electric	CT7	(2) TS
S-76	Allison, R/R*	250	(2) TS
S-80	General Electric	CT64	(3) TS
S-92	General Electric	CT7	(2) TS
Sweizer Helicopter Co.			
Model 330, 333	Allison, R/R*	250	(1) TS
Westland Helicopters LTD (Great Britain)			
Lynx	Rolls-Royce	GEM	(2) TS
Lynx 800	LHTEC*	CTS-800	(2) TS
W30	Rolls-Royce	GEM	(2) TS
W30-200, 300	General Electric	CT7	(2) TS
Wessex	Rolls-Royce	Gazelle	(2) TS

Engine Type Abbreviations:

TJ = Turbojet

TF = Turbofan

TP = Turboprop

TS = Turboshaft

PF = Propfan

Abbreviations: (*) Can. – Canada; CASA – Constructiones Aeronauticas, Spain; EADS – European Aeronautic Defense and Space Co. (France, Germany, Spain); LHTEC - Light Helicopter Turbine Engine Co., USA; R/R – Rolls-Royce, G.B

Appendix 5
Common Hand Signals

EMERGENCY SIGNALS

PERSONNEL IN DANGER (for any reason) REDUCE THRUST AND SHUT DOWN ENGINE(S).
(A) Draw right forefinger across throat. When necessary for multi-engine aircraft. Use a numerical finger signal (or point) with the left hand to designate which engine should be shut down.
(B) As soon as the signal is observed, cross both arms high above the face. The sequence of signals may be reversed, if more expedient.

FIRE IN TAILPIPE. TURN ENGINE OVER WITH STARTER.
(A) With the fingers of both hands curled and both thumbs extended up, make a gesture pointing upward.
(B) As soon as the signal is observed, use circular motion with right hand and arm extended over the head (as for an engine start). When necessary for multi-engine aircraft, use a numerical finger signal (or point) with the left hand to designate the affected engine.

FIRE IN ACCESSORY SECTION. SHUT DOWN ENGINE AND EVACUATE AIRCRAFT.
(A) Draw right forefinger across throat. When necessary for multi-engine aircraft, use a numerical finger signal (or point) with the left hand to designate which engine should be shut down.
(B) As soon as the signal is observed, extend both thumbs upward, then out. Repeat, if necessary.

GENERAL SIGNALS

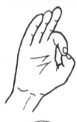
AFFIRMATIVE CONDITION SATISFACTORY OK, TRIM GOOD, ETC.
Hold up thumb and forefinger, touching at the tips to form the letter "O"

NEGATIVE CONDITION UNSATISFACTORY NO GOOD, ETC.
With the finger curled and thumb extended, point thumb downward toward the ground.

ADJUST UP (higher)
With the fingers extended and plam facing up, move hand up (and down), vertically, as if coaxing upward.

ADJUST DOWN (lower)
With the fingers extended and plam facing down, move hand down (and up), vertically, as if coaxing downward.

SLIGHT ADJUSTMENT
Hold up thumb and forefinger, slightly apart (either simultaneously) with the other hand when calling for an up or down adjustment, or with the same hand, immediately following the adjustment signal.)

SHORTEN ADJUSTMENT (as when adjusting linkage)
Hold up thumb and forefinger somewhat apart (other fingers curled), then bring thumb and forefinger together in a slow, closing motion.

LENGTHEN ADJUSTMENT (as when adjusting a linkage)
Hold up thumb and forefinger pressed together (other fingers curled), then separate thumb and forefinger in a slow, opening motion.

NUMERICAL READING (of any instrument or to report a numerical value of any type)
Hold up appropriate number of fingers of either one or both hands, as necessary, in numerical sequence (i.e., 5, then 7 = 57).

ENGINE OPERATING SIGNALS

CONNECT EXTERNAL POWER SOURCE.
Insert extended forefinger of right hand into cupped fist of left hand.

DISCONNECT EXTERNAL POWER SOURCE
Withdraw extended forefinger of right hand from cupped fist of left hand.

START ENGINE
Circular motion with right hand and arm extended over the head. When necessary for multi-engine aircraft, use a numerical finger signal (or point) with the left hand to designate which engine should be started.*

*NOTE: To use as an "ALL CLEAR TO START" signal, pilot, or engine operator initiates the signal from the aircraft cockpit. Ground crewman repeats the signal to indicate "ALL CLEAR TO START ENGINE."

Appendix 6

Local Speed Of Sound (Cs) Chart

°F	200	180	160	140	120	100	80	60	40	20	0	−20	−40	−60	−80	−100
ft/sec	1260	1240	1220	1200	1180	1160	1140	1120	1100	1075	1051	1028	1004	980	955	930
mph	860	845	830	818	804	790	776	762	747	732	716	700	684	668	650	635

1. C_S = THE TERMINAL VELOCITY °F SOUND WAVES IN AIR AT A SPECIFIED TEMPERATURE.

2. C_S = 1116.8 FPS AT SEA LEVEL, STANDARD TEMPERATURE 59° F, WITH A CHANGE OF 1.1 FPS FOR EACH DEGREE FAHRENHEIT INCREASE.

3. $C_S = 49.022 \sqrt{°R}$ and $°R = °F + 460$

4. MACH NO. = VELOCITY (FPS) ÷ C_S (FPS)

Appendix 7

U.S. Standard Atmosphere, 1962 (Geopotential Altitude)

Altitude feet	Temperature			British Units Pressure		Sonic Velocity		ft.³/lb.	lb./ft³
	°F	°R	°C	psia	in. Hg	ft./sec.	kts.		
-2000	66.1	525.8	19.0	15.79	32.15	1124.	666.0		
-1000	62.5	522.2	17.0	15.23	31.02	1120.2	663.7		
0	59.0	518.7	15.0	14.70	29.92	1116.8	661.5	13.1	.076474
1000	55.4	515.1	13.0	14.17	28.86	1112.6	659.2		
2000	51.9	511.6	11.0	13.66	27.82	1108.7	656.9		
3000	48.3	508.0	9.1	13.17	26.82	1104.9	654.6		
4000	44.7	504.4	7.1	12.69	25.84	1101.0	652.3		
5000	41.2	500.9	5.1	12.23	24.90	1097.1	650.0	15.2	.065896
6000	37.6	497.3	3.1	11.78	23.98	1093.2	647.7		
7000	34.0	493.7	1.1	11.34	23.09	1089.2	645.4		
8000	30.5	490.2	-0.8	10.92	22.23	1085.3	643.0		
9000	26.9	486.6	-2.8	10.50	21.39	1081.3	640.7		
10000	23.3	483.0	-4.8	10.11	20.58	1077.4	638.3	17.7	.056475
11000	19.8	479.5	-6.8	9.720	19.79	1073.4	636.0		
12000	16.2	475.9	-8.8	9.346	19.03	1069.4	633.6		
13000	12.6	472.3	-10.7	8.984	18.29	1065.4	631.2		
14000	91.0	468.8	-12.7	8.633	17.58	1061.3	628.8		
15000	5.5	465.2	-14.7	8.294	16.89	1057.3	626.4	20.8	.048117
16000	1.9	461.6	-16.7	7.965	16.22	1053.2	624.0		
17000	-1.6	458.1	-18.7	7.647	15.57	1049.2	621.6		
18000	-5.2	454.5	-20.7	7.339	14.94	1045.1	619.2		
19000	-8.8	450.9	-22.6	7.041	14.34	1041.0	616.7		
20000	-12.3	447.4	-24.6	6.754	13.75	1036.8	614.3	24.5	.040745
21000	-15.9	443.8	-26.6	6.475	13.18	1032.7	611.9		
22000	-19.5	440.2	-28.6	6.207	12.64	1028.5	609.4		
23000	-23.0	436.7	-30.6	5.947	12.11	1024.4	606.9		
24000	-26.6	433.1	-32.5	5.696	11.60	1020.2	604.4		
25000	-30.2	429.5	-34.5	5.454	11.10	1016.0	601.9	29.2	.034267
26000	-33.7	426.0	-36.5	5.220	10.63	1011.7	599.4		
27000	-37.3	422.4	-38.5	4.994	10.17	1007.5	596.9		
28000	-40.9	418.8	-40.5	4.777	9.725	1003.2	594.4		
29000	-44.4	415.3	-42.4	4.567	9.298	988.9	591.9		
30000	-48.0	411.7	-44.4	4.364	8.886	994.6	589.3	35.0	.028608
31000	-51.6	408.1	-46.4	4.169	8.489	990.3	586.8		
32000	-55.1	404.6	-48.4	3.981	8.106	986.0	584.2		
33000	-58.7	401.0	-50.4	3.800	7.737	981.6	581.6		
34000	-62.3	397.4	-52.4	3.626	7.383	977.3	579.0		
35000	-65.8	393.9	-54.3	3.458	7.041	972.9	576.4	42.2	.023699
36000	-69.4	390.3	-56.3	3.297	6.712	968.5	573.8		
*36089	-69.7	390.0	-56.5	3.282	6.683	968.1	573.6	44.0	.022798
37000	-69.7	390.0	-56.5	3.142	6.397	968.1	573.6		
38000	-69.7	390.0	-56.5	2.994	6.097	968.1	573.6		
39000	-69.7	390.0	-56.5	2.854	5.811	968.1	573.6	50.7	.019735
40000	-69.7	390.0	-56.5	2.720	5.538	968.1	573.6		
41000	-69.7	390.0	-56.5	2.592	5.278	968.1	573.6		
42000	-69.7	390.0	-56.5	2.471	5.030	968.1	573.6		
43000	-69.7	390.0	-56.5	2.335	4.794	968.1	573.6		
44000	-69.7	390.0	-56.5	2.244	4.569	968.1	573.6	64.4	.015531
45000	-69.7	390.0	-56.5	2.139	4.335	968.1	573.6		
46000	-69.7	390.0	-56.5	2.039	4.151	968.1	573.6		
47000	-69.7	390.0	-56.5	1.943	3.956	968.1	573.6		
48000	-69.7	390.0	-56.5	1.852	3.770	968.1	573.6		
49000	-69.7	390.0	-56.5	1.75	3.953	968.1	573.6	81.8	.012213
50000	-67.9	390.0	-56.5	1.682	3.425	968.1	573.6		
51000	-69.7	390.0	-56.5	1.603	3.264	968.1	573.6		

Altitude feet	Temperature			British Units Pressure		Sonic Velocity		ft.³/lb.	lb./ft.³
	°F	°R	°C	psia	In. Hg	ft./sec.	kts.		
52000	-69.7	390.0	-56.5	1.528	3.111	968.1	573.6		
53000	-69.7	390.0	-56.5	1.456	2.965	968.1	573.6		
54000	-69.7	390.0	-56.5	1.388	2.826	968.1	573.6	104.1	.009605
55000	-69.7	390.0	-56.5	1.323	2.693	968.1	573.6		
56000	-69.7	390.0	-56.5	1.261	2.567	968.1	573.6		
57000	-69.7	390.0	-56.5	1.201	2.446	968.1	573.6		
58000	-69.7	380.0	-56.5	1.145	2.321	968.1	573.6		
59000	-69.7	390.0	-56.5	1.091	2.222	968.1	573.6	132.4	.007553
60000	-69.7	390.0	-56.5	1.040	2.118	968.1	573.6		
61000	-69.7	390.0	-56.5	.9913	2.018	968.1	573.6		
62000	-69.7	390.0	-56.5	.9448	1.924	968.1	573.6		
63000	-69.7	390.0	-56.5	.9005	1.833	968.1	573.6		
64000	-69.7	390.0	-56.5	.8582	1.747	968.1	573.6		
65000	-69.7	390.0	-56.5	.8179	1.665	968.1	573.6	176.7	.005660
*65617	-69.7	390.0	-56.5	.7941	1.617	968.1	573.6		
70000	-67.3	392.4	-55.2	.6437	1.311	971.0	575.3		
75000	-64.6	395.1	-53.6	.5073	1.0333	974.4	577.3		
80000	-61.8	397.9	-52.1	.4005	.8155	977.8	579.3		
85000	-59.1	400.6	-50.6	.3167	.6449	981.2	581.3		
90000	-56.3	403.4	-49.1	.2509	.5108	984.5	583.3		
95000	-53.6	406.1	-47.5	.1990	.4052	987.9	585.3		
100000	-50.8	408.9	-46.0	.1581	.3220	991.2	587.3		
*104987	-48.1	411.6	-44.5	.1259	.2563	994.5	589.2		
150000	21.0	480.7	-6.1	.01893	.03854	1074.8	636.8		
*154199	27.5	487.2	-2.5	.01609	.03275	1082.0	641.1		
*170604	27.5	487.2	-2.5	.00557	.01742	1082.0	641.1		
200000	-5.1	454.9	-20.4	.02655	.005406	1045.5	619.5		
*200131	-5.2	454.8	-20.5	.02641	.005377	1045.4	619.4		

*Boundary between atmosphere layers of constant thermal gradient.

Note: The ICAO atmosphere is identical to the U.S. Standard Atmosphere for altitudes below 65,617 ft.

Adiabatic Lapse Rates: 1. Temperature 3.57°F per 1,000 ft.
2. Pressure 0.934 In. Hg. per 1,000 ft.

Appendix 8
Other Useful Formulae And Standard Information

1. Specific heat at Constant Volume C_v = 0.1715 Btu/lb. °F

2. Specific heat at Constant Pressure C_p = 0.24 Btu/lb. °F

3. 1 Btu = 778 ft. lbs.

4. Ratio of specific heat (C_p/C_v) γ = 1.4

5. 778 × ($C_p - C_v$) = 53.3 ft. lb.

6. F_g Afterburning vs. Non–afterburning = $\sqrt{T_a}$

   Where: Temperature Ratio $(T_a) = \dfrac{°R \text{ with A/B}}{°R \text{ without A/B}}$

7. To calculate T_S if T_T and M are known: $T_T/T_S = 1 + \left[\dfrac{\gamma-1}{2}\right] \times M^2$

   Where: T = °R
   M = Mach number

8. C_S (mph) = 33.42 $\sqrt{°R}$

9. C_S (kts) = 29.04 $\sqrt{°R}$

10. $\text{ESHP}_{(FLT)} = \text{SHP} + \dfrac{F_n \times V_1 \text{ (fps)}}{550 \times \text{propeller eff. (\%)}}$ $\text{ESHP}_{(GROUND)} = \text{SHP} + \text{JET HP}$

11. Horsepower to drive the compressor

   $hp = \dfrac{.24 \times T_r \times m_s \times 778}{550}$

   Where: T_r= Temperature rise above ambient at compressor discharge(°F)
   m_s= lb./sec. mass airflow
   .24= C_p (Btu/lb.°F)
   550= conversion to hp

12. Weight of air at 59°F (std. day) = 0.07647 lb./ft.^{3}
    or = 13.1 ft.^{3}/lbs.

13. Specific Weight and Density Explained:
    Specific Weight = lb./ft.^{3}
    Density = lb./ft.^{3}/g or lb. sec.^{2}/ft.^{4}

14. To calculate Total Pressure if Density and Velocity are known:
    $P_t = (½\rho V^2) + P$
    P_t = lb. sec.^{2}/ft.^{4} × ft.^{2}/sec.^{2} + P
    Where: P_t = Kinetic + Static
    ρ = Density
    P = Static Pressure

15. To calculate Ram Pressure if P_t and M are known:

    $\dfrac{Q}{P_t} = ½\,\gamma\,M^2\left[1 + \dfrac{\gamma-1}{2} \times M^2\right]^{\frac{\gamma}{1-\gamma}}$
    Where: Q = Ram pressure
    P_t = Total Pressure
    M = Any Subsonic Velocity

16. To calculate Total Pressure (P_t) or Static Pressure (P_s) if Mach number (M) is known:

    $\dfrac{P_t}{P_s} = \left[1 + \left(\dfrac{\gamma-1}{2} \times M^2\right)\right]^{\frac{\gamma}{\gamma-1}}$

Appendix 9

Table 1 — Pressure Correction Factors

$$\text{DELTA}(\delta) = \frac{P}{Po} = \frac{P}{29.92}$$

P IN. HG. ABS	δ	P IN. HG. ABS	δ	P IN. HG. ABS	δ	P IN. HG. ABS	δ
39.9	1.334	35.4	1.183	30.9	1.033	26.4	0.8823
39.8	1.330	35.3	1.180	30.8	1.029	26.3	0.8790
39.7	1.327	35.2	1.176	30.7	1.026	26.2	0.8757
39.6	1.324	35.1	1.173	30.6	1.023	26.1	0.8723
39.5	1.320	35.0	1.170	30.5	1.019	26.0	0.8690
39.4	1.317	34.9	1.166	30.4	1.016	25.9	0.8656
39.3	1.313	34.8	1.163	30.3	1.013	25.8	0.8623
39.2	1.310	34.7	1.160	30.2	1.009	25.7	0.8586
39.1	1.307	34.6	1.156	30.1	1.006	25.6	0.8556
39.0	1.303	34.5	1.153	30.0	1.003	25.5	0.8523
38.9	1.300	34.4	1.150	29.9	0.9993	25.4	0.8489
38.8	1.297	34.3	1.146	29.8	0.9960	25.3	0.8456
38.7	1.293	34.2	1.143	29.7	0.9926	25.2	0.8422
38.6	1.290	34.1	1.140	29.6	0.9893	25.1	0.8389
38.5	1.287	34.0	1.136	29.5	0.9859	25.0	0.8356
38.4	1.283	33.9	1.133	29.4	0.9826	24.9	0.8322
38.3	1.280	33.8	1.130	29.3	0.9793	24.8	0.8289
38.2	1.277	33.7	1.126	29.2	0.9759	24.7	0.8255
38.1	1.273	33.6	1.123	29.1	0.9726	24.6	0.8222
38.0	1.270	33.5	1.120	29.0	0.9692	24.5	0.8188
37.9	1.267	33.4	1.116	28.9	0.9659	24.4	0.8155
37.8	1.263	33.3	1.113	28.8	0.9626	24.3	0.8122
37.7	1.260	33.2	1.110	28.7	0.9592	24.2	0.8088
37.6	1.257	33.1	1.106	28.6	0.9559	24.1	0.8055
37.5	1.253	33.0	1.103	28.5	0.9525	24.0	0.8021
37.4	1.250	32.9	1.100	28.4	0.9492	23.9	0.7988
37.3	1.247	32.8	1.096	28.3	0.9458	23.8	0.7954
37.2	1.243	32.7	1.093	28.2	0.9425	23.7	0.7921
37.1	1.240	32.6	1.090	28.1	0.9392	23.6	0.7888
37.0	1.237	32.5	1.086	28.0	0.9358	23.5	0.7854
36.9	1.233	32.4	1.083	27.9	0.9325	23.4	0.7821
36.8	1.230	32.3	1.080	27.8	0.9291	23.3	0.7787
36.7	1.227	32.2	1.076	27.7	0.9258	23.2	0.7754
36.6	1.223	32.1	1.073	27.6	0.9224	23.1	0.7720
36.5	1.220	32.0	1.070	27.5	0.9191	23.0	0.7687
36.4	1.217	31.9	1.066	27.4	0.9158	22.9	0.7654
36.3	1.213	31.8	1.063	27.3	0.9124	22.8	0.7620
36.2	1.210	31.7	1.059	27.2	0.9091	22.7	0.7587
36.1	1.207	31.6	1.056	27.1	0.9057	22.6	0.7553
36.0	1.203	31.5	1.053	27.0	0.9024	22.5	0.7520
35.9	1.200	31.4	1.049	26.9	0.8990	22.4	0.7487
35.8	1.196	31.3	1.046	26.8	0.8957	22.3	0.7453
35.7	1.193	31.2	1.043	26.7	0.8924	22.2	0.7420
35.6	1.190	31.1	1.039	26.6	0.8890	22.1	0.7386
35.5	1.186	31.0	1.036	26.5	0.8857	22.0	0.7353

P IN. HG. ABS	δ	P IN. HG. ABS	δ	P IN. HG. ABS	δ	P IN. HG. ABS	δ
21.9	0.7319	19.4	0.64684	16.9	0.5648	14.4	0.4813
21.8	0.7286	19.3	0.6450	16.8	0.5615	14.3	0.4779
21.7	0.7253	19.2	0.6417	16.7	0.5581	14.2	0.4746
21.6	0.7219	19.1	0.6384	16.6	0.5548	14.1	0.4713
21.5	0.7186	19.0	0.6350	16.5	0.5515	14.0	0.4679
21.4	0.7152	18.9	0.6317	16.4	0.5481	13.9	0.4646
21.3	0.7119	18.8	0.6283	16.3	0.5448	13.8	0.4612
21.2	0.7085	18.7	0.6250	16.2	0.5415	13.7	0.4579
21.1	0.7052	18.6	0.6216	16.1	0.5381	13.6	0.4545
21.0	0.7019	18.5	0.6183	16.0	0.5348	13.5	0.4512
20.9	0.6985	18.4	0.6150	15.9	0.5314	13.4	0.4479
20.8	0.6952	18.3	0.6116	15.8	0.5281	13.3	0.4445
20.7	0.6918	18.2	0.6083	15.7	0.5147	13.2	0.4412
20.6	0.6885	18.1	0.6050	15.6	0.5214	13.1	0.4378
20.5	0.6852	18.0	0.6016	15.5	0.5180	13.0	0.4345
20.4	0.6818	17.9	0.5983	15.4	0.5147	12.9	0.4311
20.3	0.6785	17.8	0.5949	15.3	0.5114	12.8	0.4278
20.2	0.6751	17.7	0.5916	15.2	0.5080	12.7	0.4245
20.1	0.6718	17.6	0.5882	15.1	0.5047	12.6	0.4211
20.0	0.6684	17.5	0.5849	15.0	0.5013	12.5	0.4178
19.9	0.6651	17.4	0.5815	14.9	0.4780	12.4	0.4144
19.8	0.6618	17.3	0.5782	14.8	0.4946	12.3	0.4111
19.7	0.6584	17.2	0.5749	14.7	0.4913	12.2	0.4077
19.6	0.6551	17.1	0.5715	14.6	0.4880	12.1	0.4044
19.5	0.6517	17.0	0.5682	14.5	0.4846	12.0	0.4011

Temperature Correction Factors

$°F = \dfrac{9}{5}(°C + 32)$

$°F = °R + 460$

$°C = \dfrac{5}{9}(°F - 32)$

$C = °K + 273$

$THETA\ (\theta) = \dfrac{T}{T_O} = \dfrac{T}{519}$

FOR INTERPOLATION, 1° C = 1.8° F

T (°F)	θ	√θ	T (°F)	θ	√θ	T (°F)	θ	√θ	T (°F)	θ	√θ
200	1.272	1.128	160	1.195	1.093	120	1.118	1.057	80	1.041	1.020
199	1.270	1.127	159	1.193	1.092	119	1.116	1.0566	79	1.039	1.019
198	1.269	1.126	158	1.191	1.091	118	1.114	1.055	78	1.037	1.018
197	1.267	1.125	157	1.189	1.090	117	1.112	1.054	77	1.035	1.017
196	1.265	1.124	156	1.187	1.089	116	1.110	1.054	76	1.033	1.016
195	1.263	1.123	155	1.185	1.089	115	1.108	1.053	75	1.031	1.015
194	1.261	1.123	154	1.183	1.088	114	1.106	1.052	74	1.029	1.014
193	1.259	1.122	153	1.181	1.087	113	1.104	1.051	73	1.028	1.013
192	1.257	1.121	152	1.179	1.086	112	1.102	1.050	72	1.026	1.012
191	1.255	1.120	151	1.177	1.085	111	1.100	1.049	71	1.024	1.012
190	1.253	1.119	150	1.176	1.084	110	1.098	1.048	70	1.022	1.011
189	1.251	1.118	149	1.174	1.083	109	1.096	1.047	69	1.020	1.010
188	1.249	1.117	148	1.172	1.082	108	1.095	1.046	68	1.018	1.009
187	1.247	1.117	147	1.170	1.082	107	1.093	1.045	67	1.016	1.008
186	1.245	1.116	146	1.168	1.081	106	1.191	1.044	66	1.014	1.007
185	1.243	1.115	145	1.166	1.080	105	1.089	1.043	65	1.012	1.006
184	1.242	1.114	144	1.164	1.079	104	1.187	1.042	64	1.010	1.005
183	1.240	1.113	143	1.162	1.078	103	1.085	1.041	63	1.008	1.004
182	1.238	1.112	142	1.160	1.077	102	1.083	1.041	62	1.006	1.003
181	1.236	1.111	141	1.158	1.076	101	1.082	1.040	61	1.004	1.002
180	1.234	1.111	140	1.156	1.075	100	1.080	1.039	60	1.002	1.001
179	1.232	1.110	139	1.154	1.074	99	1.078	1.038	59	1.000	1.000
178	1.230	1.109	138	1.152	1.073	98	1.076	1.037	58	0.999	0.999
177	1.228	1.108	137	1.150	1.073	97	1.074	1.036	57	0.997	0.998
176	1.226	1.107	136	1.149	1.072	96	1.072	1.035	56	0.995	0.997
175	1.224	1.106	135	1.147	1.071	95	1.070	1.034	55	0.993	0.996
174	1.222	1.105	134	1.145	1.070	94	1.068	1.033	54	0.991	0.995
173	1.220	1.104	133	1.143	1.069	93	1.066	1.032	53	0.989	0.994
172	1.218	1.104	132	1.141	1.068	92	1.064	1.031	52	0.988	0.993
171	1.216	1.103	131	1.139	1.067	91	1.062	1.030	51	0.986	0.992
170	1.214	1.102	130	1.137	1.066	90	1.060	1.029	50	0.984	0.991
169	1.212	1.101	129	1.135	1.065	89	1.058	1.029	49	0.982	0.990
168	1.210	1.100	128	1.133	1.064	88	1.056	1.028	48	0.980	0.989
167	1.208	1.099	127	1.131	1.064	87	1.055	1.027	47	0.978	0.988
166	1.206	1.098	126	1.129	1.063	86	1.053	1.026	46	0.976	0.987
165	1.204	1.097	125	1.127	1.062	85	1.051	1.025	45	0.974	0.986
164	1.202	1.096	124	1.125	1.061	84	1.049	1.024	44	0.972	0.985
163	1.200	1.095	123	1.123	1.060	83	1.047	1.023	43	0.970	0.984
162	1.199	1.095	122	1.122	1.059	82	1.045	1.022	42	0.968	0.984
161	1.197	1.094	121	1.120	1.058	81	1.043	1.021	41	0.966	0.983

T (°F)	θ	√θ	T (°F)	θ	√θ	T (°F)	θ	√θ	T (°F)	θ	√θ
40	0.964	0.982	10	0.907	0.952	−20	0.848	0.921	−50	0.790	0.889
39	0.962	0.981	9	0.905	0.951	−21	0.846	0.920	−51	0.788	0.888
38	0.960	0.980	8	0.903	0.950	−22	0.844	0.919	−52	0.786	0.887
37	0.959	0.979	7	0.901	0.949	−23	0.842	0.918	−53	0.784	0.886
36	0.957	0.978	6	0.899	0.948	−24	0.840	0.917	−54	0.782	0.885
35	0.955	0.977	5	0.897	0.947	−25	0.838	0.916	−55	0.780	0.883
34	0.953	0.976	4	0.895	0.946	−26	0.836	0.914	−56	0.778	0.882
33	0.951	0.975	3	0.893	0.945	−27	0.834	0.913	−57	0.777	0.881
32	0.949	0.974	2	0.891	0.944	−28	0.832	0.912	−58	0.775	0.880
31	0.947	0.973	1	0.889	0.943	−29	0.831	0.911	−59	0.773	0.879
30	0.945	0.972	0	0.887	0.942	−30	0.829	0.910	−60	0.771	0.878
29	0.943	0.971	−1	0.884	0.940	−31	0.827	0.909	−61	0.769	0.877
28	0.941	0.970	−2	0.883	0.939	−32	0.825	0.908	−62	0.767	0.876
27	0.939	0.969	−3	0.881	0.938	−33	0.823	0.907	−63	0.765	0.875
26	0.937	0.968	−4	0.879	0.937	−34	0.821	0.906	−64	0.763	0.874
25	0.935	0.967	−5	0.877	0.936	−35	0.819	0.905	−65	0.761	0.872
24	0.934	0.966	−6	0.875	0.935	−36	0.817	0.904	−66	0.759	0.871
23	0.932	0.965	−7	0.873	0.934	−37	0.815	0.903	−67	0.757	0.870
22	0.930	0.964	−8	0.871	0.933	−38	0.813	0.902	−68	0.755	0.869
21	0.928	0.963	−9	0.869	0.932	−39	0.811	0.901	−69	0.753	0.868
20	0.926	0.962	−10	0.867	0.931	−40	0.809	0.900	−70	0.751	0.867
19	0.924	0.961	−11	0.865	0.930	−41	0.807	0.899	−71	0.750	0.866
18	0.922	0.960	−12	0.863	0.929	−42	0.805	0.897	−72	0.748	0.865
17	0.920	0.959	−13	0.861	0.928	−43	0.804	0.896	−73	0.746	0.864
16	0.918	0.958	−14	0.859	0.927	−44	0.802	0.895	−74	0.744	0.862
15	0.916	0.957	−15	0.857	0.926	−45	0.800	0.894	−75	0.742	0.861
14	0.914	0.956	−16	0.856	0.925	−46	0.798	0.893	−76	0.740	0.860
13	0.912	0.955	−17	0.854	0.924	−47	0.796	0.892	−77	0.738	0.859
12	0.910	0.954	−18	0.852	0.923	−48	0.794	0.891	−78	0.736	0.858
11	0.908	0.953	−19	0.850	0.922	−49	0.792	0.890	−79	0.734	0.857

Appendix 10

Ground Vs. Flight Performance Data

	Operation at Sea Level	Operation at Mach 0.8 at 36,089 feet	Data Source
1. Ambient Pressure (P_{am})	30.0 in. Hg	6.7 in. Hg	measured
2. Ambient Temperature (T_{am})	535 °R	390 °R	measured
3. Ram Pressure Ratio ($\frac{P_{t2}}{P_{am}}$)	1.0	1.524	measured
4. Ram Temperature Ratio ($\frac{T_{t2}}{T_{am}}$)	1.0	1.135	measured
5. Engine Inlet Total Pressure (P_{t2})	30.0 in. Hg	10.2 in. Hg	1 × 3
6. Engine Inlet Total Temperature (T_{t2})	535 °R	443 °R	2 × 4
7. Pressure Correction Factor (δ_{t2})	1.003	0.341	$\frac{5}{29.92}$
8. Temperature Correction Factor (θ_{t2})	1.031	0.854	$\frac{6}{519}$
9. Square Root of θ_{t2}	1.015	0.924	$\sqrt{8}$
10. Net Thrust (F_n)	7,000 lbs.	3,000 lbs.	measured
11. Corrected Net Thrust ($\frac{F_n}{\delta_{t2}}$)	6,979 lbs.	8,798 lbs.	$\frac{10}{7}$
12. Fuel Flow (W_t)	4,600 pph	3,100 pph	measured
13. Corrected Fuel Flow ($\frac{W_t}{\delta_{t1}\sqrt{\theta_{t2}}\,0.5}$)	4,569 pph	9,272 pph	$\frac{12}{7 \times 9}$
14. Exhaust Gas Temperature (T_{t5})	1,400 °R	1,500 °R	measured
15. Corrected EGT ($\frac{T_{t5}}{\theta_{t2}}$)	1,358 °R	1,756 °R	$\frac{14}{8}$
16. Compressor Speed (rpm)	9,000	9,100	measured
17. Corrected Compressor Speed ($\frac{rpm}{\sqrt{\theta_{t2}}}$)	8,867	9,848	$\frac{16}{9}$

Glossary

This glossary is provided as a ready reference of terms as used in this text. These definitions may differ from those of standard dictionaries, but are more common in reference to the gas turbine engine.

Aborted start   Termination of the engine starting cycle when combustion (light-off) does not occur within a prescribed time limit.

Acceleration due to gravity   The acceleration of a freely falling body due to the attraction of gravity, expressed as the rate of increase of velocity per unit of time. In a vacuum the rate is 32.2 feet per second per second near sea level.

Absolute pressure   Pressure above zero pressure as read on a barometer type instrument. e.g. Standard Day, 14.7 PSI-A.

Accessory drive gearbox   Also called Main Gearbox. Provides mounting space for engine accessories.

Afterburner   A tubular combustion chamber with a variable-size exhaust outlet attached to the rear of a gas turbine engine into which fuel is injected through a set of spray bars. An example is the Concorde SST aircraft. Burning of fuel in the exhaust supplements the normal thrust of the engine by increasing the acceleration of the air mass through an additional temperature rise.

Airfoil   Any surface designed to obtain a useful reaction upon its surfaces from the air through which it moves. Velocity increases over the cambered side producing lift on the underside.

Air, ambient   The atmospheric air surrounding all sides of the aircraft or engine. Expressed in units of lbs./sq. inch or in. Hg.

Annular combustor   A cylindrical one piece combustion chamber, sometimes referred to as a single basket type combustor.

Auxiliary power unit   A type of gas turbine, usually located in the aircraft fuselage, whose purpose is to provide either electrical power, air pressure for starting main engines, or both. Similar in design to ground power units.

Axial   Motion along a real or imaginary straight line which an object supposedly or actually rotates. The engine centerline.

Axial flow compressor   Compressor with airflow parallel to the axis of the engine. The numerous compressor stages raise pressure of air but essentially make no change in direction of airflow.

Bernoulli's Theorem   Principle which states static pressure and velocity (RAM) pressure of a gas or fluid passing through a duct (at constant subsonic flow rate) are inversely proportional, i.e. total pressure does not change.

Blade   A rotating airfoil utilized in a compressor as a means of compressing air or in a turbine for extracting energy from the flowing gases.

Brayton Cycle   A thermodynamic cycle of operation that may be used to explain the operating principles of the gas turbine engine. It is sometimes referred to as the continuous combustion, or constant pressure cycle.

British Thermal Unit (BTU)   A unit of heat. One BTU equals the heat energy required to raise one pound of water one degree Fahrenheit (e.g. one pound of jet fuel contains approximately 18,600 BTU).

Bucket   Accepted jargon for turbine blade.

Can-annular combustor   A set, generally of 6 to 10 liners within one outer annulus (combustor outer case).

Centrifugal flow compressor   An impeller shaped device which receives air at its center and slings air outward at high velocity into a diffuser to increase pressure. Sometimes referred to as a radial outflow compressor.

Choked airflow   An airflow condition from a convergent shaped nozzle, where the gas is traveling at the speed of sound and cannot be further accelerated. Any increase in internal pressure will pass out the nozzle in the form of pressure.

Combustor   The section of the engine into which fuel is injected and burned to create expansion of the gases.

Compressor   An impeller or a mufti-bladed rotor assembly. A component which is driven by a turbine rotor for the purpose of compressing incoming air.

Compressor pressure ratio   The result of compressor discharge pressure divided by compressor inlet pressure. e.g. a large turbofan may have a compressor pressure ratio of 40:1.

Compressor stage   A rotor blade set followed by a stator vane set. Simply stated the rotating airfoils create air velocity which then changes to pressure in the numerous diverging ducts formed by the stator vanes.

Compressor stall   A condition in an axial-flow compressor in which one or more stages of rotor blades fail to pass air smoothly to the succeeding stages. A stall condition is caused by a pressure ratio that is incompatible with the engine rpm. Compressor stall will be indicated by a rise in exhaust temperature or rpm fluctuation, and if allowed to continue, may result in flame out and physical damage to the engine.

Convergent duct   A cone-shaped passage or channel in which a gas may be made to flow from its largest area to its smallest area, resulting in an increase in velocity and a decrease in pressure. Referred to as nozzle shaped. With this relationship present, the weight of airflow will remain constant.

Diffuser   The divergent section of the engine which is used to convert the velocity energy in the compressor discharge air to pressure energy. Aircraft inlet ducts and compressor stator vanes are also described as diffusers due to their effect on air in raising pressure.

Directional reference   An industry standard to describe engine locations. The orientation is to look from the rear towards the front of the engine and use standard twelve hour clock reference points. Right Side and Left Side are also determined in this manner.

Divergent duct   A cone-shaped passage or channel in which a gas may be made to flow from its smallest to its largest area resulting in an increase in pressure and a decrease in velocity. With this relationship present, the weight of airflow remains constant, e.g. the engine diffuser.

Dual-Spool compressor   A design utilizing two independently rotating axial flow compressors. The front compressor is referred to as the Low Pressure (LP) Compressor while the rear is referred to as the High Pressure (HP) compressor.

Energy   Inherent power or the capacity for performing work. When a portion of matter is stationary, it often has engine energy due to its position in relation to other portions of matter. This is called potential energy. If the matter is moving, it is said to have kinetic energy, or energy due to motion.

Engine cycle   Cycles are recorded as one takeoff and landing, and are used to compute time between overhaul of engines and components where operating hours are not used.

Engine pressure ratio (EPR)   The ratio of turbine discharge pressure divided by compressor inlet pressure. Displayed in the cockpit as an indication of engine thrust.

Engine stations   Numbered locations along the engine length, or along the gas path used for the purpose of identifying pressure and temperature points, component locations and the like.

Exhaust gas temperature (EGT)   Temperature taken at the turbine exit. Often referred to as Tt_7.

Exhaust nozzle   Also referred to as the jet nozzle, this is the rear-most part of the engine.

Flame out   An unintentional extinction of combustion due to a blowout (too much fuel) or die-out (too little fuel).

Foreign object damage (FOD)   Mainly compressor damage from ingestion of foreign objects into the engine inlet. Also damage resulting from objects being dropped into the compressor or other internal engine parts.

Free power turbine   A turbine wheel which drives a power output gearbox rather than a compressor. Found in Turboprop and Turboshaft engines.

Fuel control unit   The main fuel scheduling device which receives a mechanical input signal from the power lever and various other signals, such as Pt_2, Tt_2, etc. These signals provide for automatic scheduling of fuel at all ambient conditions of ground and flight operation.

Fuel flow   Rate at which fuel is consumed by the engine in pounds per hour (pph).

Fuel nozzle   A device used to spray fuel into a combustion liner. The two most common types are the Atomizing Nozzle and the Vaporizing Nozzle.

Gas generator turbine   High pressure turbine wheels) which drive the compressor of a turboshaft or turboprop

Gas turbine   Engine consisting of a compressor, combustor and turbine, using a gaseous fluid as a working medium and producing either shaft horsepower, jet thrust, or both. The four common types of Gas Turbine Engines are Turbojet, Turbofan, Turboprop and Turboshaft.

Ground power unit   A type of small gas turbine whose purpose is to provide either electrical power, air pressure for starting aircraft engines, or both. A ground unit is connected to the aircraft when needed. Similar to an aircraft installed auxiliary power unit.

High pressure turbine   The turbine rotor which drives the high pressure compressor in a dual or triple spool axial flow gas turbine engine.

Horsepower   Unit of power equal to 33,000 foot pounds of work per minute, 550 foot pounds per second, or 375 mile pounds per hour.

Hot start   A start which occurs with normal engine rotation, but exhaust temperature exceeds prescribed limits. This is usually caused by an excessively rich mixture in the combustor. The fuel to the engine must be terminated immediately to prevent engine damage.

Hung start   A condition of normal lightoff but with rpm remaining at some low value rather than increasing to the normal idle rpm. This is often the result of insufficient power to the engine from the starter. In the event of a hung start, the engine should be shut down.

Idle   A percent rpm setting, the value of which changes from engine to engine. It is the lowest engine operating speed authorized.

Igniter plug   An electrical sparking device used to start the burning of the fuel-air mixture in a combustor.

Impeller   Name given to the centrifugal flow compressor rotor.

Inlet duct   The ambient air entrance duct which directs air into the engine.

Inlet guide vane   Stationary airfoil which preceeds the first stage compressor rotor blades. These guide vanes form straight through passages and are present to direct air onto the blades at the optimum angle.

Jet engine   A reaction engine which derives its thrust from the acceleration of an air mass through an orifice. There are four common types: rocket, ramjet, pulsejet, and turbojet.

Kinetic energy   Energy due to motion.

Low pressure turbine   The turbine rotor which drives the low pressure compressor in a dual or triple spool axial flow gas turbine engine.

Mach number   The ratio of the speed of the airplane to the speed of sound (at the temperature in which the airplane is operating.)

Mass   A basic property of matter. Mass is referred to as weight when in the field of gravity such as that of the earth.

Overtemperature   Any time exhaust gas temperature exceeds the maximum allowable limits.

Potential energy   Energy due to position.

Power lever   The cockpit lever which connects to the fuel control unit for scheduling fuel flow to the combustor. Also called power control lever or throttle.

Power turbine   A turbine rotor connected to an output reduction gearbox. Also referred to as free power turbine.

Pressure, static   The pressure measured in a duct containing air, a gas or a liquid in which no velocity (ram) pressure is allowed to enter the measuring device. Symbol (Ps).

Pressure, total   Static pressure plus ram pressure. Total pressure can be measured by use of a specially shaped probe which stops a small portion of the gas or liquid flowing in a duct thereby changing velocity (ram) energy to pressure energy. Symbol (Pt).

Probe   A sensing device that extends into the airstream or gas stream for measuring pressure, velocity or temperature. In the case of pressure, it is used to measure total pressure. For temperature it measures total temperature.

Propulsive efficiency   External efficiency of an engine expressed as a percentage.

Ram pressure rise   Pressure rise in the inlet due to the forward speed of the aircraft, e.g. at M = .85 a pressure of 1.6 times above ambient will typically occur.

Rotor   Either compressor or turbine. A rotating disk or drum to which a series of blades are attached.

SA.E.   Society of Automotive Engineers.

Shock stall   Turbulent airflow on an airfoil which occurs when the speed of sound is reached. The shock wave distorts the aerodynamic airflow, causing a stall and loss of lift.

Shroud   A cover or housing used to aid in confining an air or gas flow to a desired path.

Single-Spool Compressor   A single axial flow compressor design, typically with eight or more stages.

Speed of sound   The terminal velocity of sound waves in air at a specific air temperature. Referred to as Mach one. Symbol (M).

Symbols

A	—	Acceleration
A_j	—	Area of jet nozzle
C_p	—	specific heat
C_s	—	local speed of sound
F_g	—	static or gross thrust
Fn	—	net thrust
g	—	gravity
Ke	—	Kinetic energy
m	—	mass airflow
M	—	mach number
N_c	—	speed, single compressor
N_1	—	speed, low pressure compressor
N_2	—	speed, high pressure compressor
N_f	—	speed, free turbine
N_g	—	speed, gas producer turbine
P_{am}	—	pressure, ambient
P_b	—	pressure, burner
P_j	—	pressure at jet nozzle
P_s	—	pressure, static
P_t	—	pressure, total
T_c	—	temperature, total
V_1	—	velocity of aircraft
V_2	—	velocity, jet nozzle
W_f	—	weight of fuel
γ	—	Gamma, ratio of specific heats (Cp/Cv)
η	—	Eta, efficiency
ρ	—	Rho, density

Thermal efficiency   Internal engine efficiency or fuel energy available versus work produced, expressed as a percentage.

Thrust   A pushing force exerted by one mass against another, which tends to produce motion in the masses. In jet propulsion, thrust is the forward force in the direction of motion caused by the pressure forces acting on the inner surfaces of the engine. Or, in other words, it is the reaction to the exhaust gases exiting the nozzle. Thrust force is generally measured in pounds or kilograms.

Thrust, gross   The force which the engine exerts against its mounts while it is operating but not moving. Also called static thrust. Symbol (Fg).

Thrust, net   The effective thrust developed by the engine during flight, taking into consideration the initial momentum of the air mass prior to entering the influence of the engine. Symbol (Fn).

Thrust reverser   A device attached to a turbine engine tailpipe to reverse the exhaust gas flow. Reversers assist aircraft brakes and provide aircraft control during landing and during rejected takeoffs.

Thrust specific fuel consumption (TSFC)   An equation: TSFC = Wf /Fg where: Wf is fuel flow in pounds per hour, and Fn is net thrust in pounds; used to calculate fuel consumed and as a means of comparison between engines.

Time between overhaul (TBO)   The time in hours or engine cycles the manufacturer recommends as the engine, or engine component, service life from new to overhaul, or from one overhaul to the next.

Torque   A force multiplied by its lever arm, acting at right angles to an axis.

Torquemeter indicator   A turboprop or turboshaft cockpit instrument used to indicate engine power output. The propeller or rotor inputs a twisting force to an electronic or oil operated torquemeter which sends a signal to the indicator.

Turbine stage   A stage consists of a turbine stator vane set followed by a turbine rotor blade set.

Turbine wheel   A rotating device actuated by either reaction, impulse or a combination of both, and used to transform some of the kinetic energy of the exhaust gases into shaft horsepower to drive the compressors and accessories.

Vector   A line which, by scaled length, indicates magnitude, and whose arrow point represents direction of action.

Velocity   The actual change of distance with respect to time. The average velocity is equal to total distance divided by total time. Usually expressed in mph or fps.

Answers to Study Questions

CHAPTER I

1. Hero's aeolipile, 100-200 BC.
2. Sir Frank Whittle.
3. The German Heinkel 178.
4. The Boeing 707.
5. The Anglo-French Concorde.

CHAPTER II

1. Turbofan.
2. Turboshaft.
3. Centrifugal impeller.
4. Turboprop
5. Kinetic energy.
6. Power, velocity, acceleration.
7. Newton's third law.
8. Continuous combustion cycle.
9. An inverse proportion.
10. Net.
11. Thrust.
12. Ambient temperature, altitude and airspeed.
13. E.S.H.P.
14. Tip, shock stall.
15. Compression ratio

CHAPTER III

1. Divergent.
2. To increase static pressure.
3. Turboshaft.
4. Control the direction of the air to each stage.
5. A profile or squeeler.
6. High peak efficiency and pressure ratio.
7. The diffuser section.
8. 25% to 35%.
9. Cooling of the liner and gases.
10. Its shorter length and lighter weight.
11. The shrouded tip.
12. At the base.
13. Nickel alloy.

14. Exhaust or jet nozzle.
15. Mechanical and aerodynamic blockage.
16. It has lower exhaust velocity.

CHAPTER V

1. Field cleaning.
2. No, overhaul.
3. Thermal cracking.
4. Across the leading and trailing edges of turbine blades.
5. To maintain turbine wheel balance.
6. It is thinner and converging cracks will more easily cause loss of material.
7. Malfunctioning fuel nozzle.
8. Both axial and radial loads.
9. They offer little rotational resistance.

CHAPTER VI

1. Little change in viscosity.
2. Higher.
3. The word "oil".
4. Turbine oils have a naturally low pour point.
5. Pressurization check valve.
6. Located between the pump and the internal system.
7. To compensate for entrained air in the oil.
8. Fuel cooled and air cooled types.
9. Pressure subsystem.

CHAPTER VII

1. Fuel control.
2. Power lever or throttle lever.
3. No, this is a reciprocating engine control lever.
4. Burner can pressure:
5. Demineralized or distilled water (sometimes a water/alcohol mixture).
6. Takeoff.
7. Trimming.
8. Assure maximum rated thrust is being developed.
9. Engine thrust.
10. No wind and low humidity.

11. Only the gear type.

12. At the filter screens.

13. Engine starting and idle speed.

14. Act as a flow divider and dump fuel from the manifold on shutdown.

15. Combustor gas pressure.

CHAPTER VIII

1. To reduce the engine's tendency to stall on acceleration or deceleration at low or intermediate speed.

2. All.

3. RPM effect on airflow.

4. Yes.

5. Overboard.

6. Maladjustment of system.

CHAPTER IX

1. No, to prevent ice formation.

2. No, bi-metallic spring controlled.

3. Airflow is blocked or distorted into the compressor.

CHAPTER X

1. On the engine accessory gearbox.

2. The overrunning clutch assembly.

3. The starter-generator.

4. Starter pressure regulating and shutoff valve.

5. APU, GPU, or engine cross bleed air.

CHAPTER XI

1. To change AC to DC.

2. The turbine has a much higher intensity spark.

3. Secondary.

4. Nickel-chromium alloy.

CHAPTER XII

1. Turbine Inlet Temperature (TIT).

2. EGT or ITT indicator.

3. Jetcal analyzer.

4. Monitor engine speed during start and for over-speed.

5. Yes, this is an independent electrical system.

6. No, on a very warm day thrust is necessarily well below 100%.

7. No, EPR is the thrust indicator on an EPR rated engine.

8. No, the tachometer indicator is the thrust indicator on a speed rated turbofan engine.

9. The AC bus.

10. Pounds per hour (pph).

11. In the engine fuel line to the combustor.

12. The thermocouple.

13. The oil pressure transmitter.

CHAPTER XIII

1. Yes, all do.

2. The two-wire thermal switch.

Index

A

Abrasion 5-39, 5-56
Absolute pressure 7-14
AC versus DC input, ignition 11-3
Acceleration 2-13, 7-14
Acceleration check 7-28`
Acceleration limiter 7-25
Acceleration thermostat 7-25
Acceleration, axial 3-40
Accessory case 3-62
Accessory gearbox 3-8, 6-7, 10-1
Accessory gearbox, Allison-250 4-34
Accessory gearbox, PT6 4-34
Accessory section, engine 3-8
Active clearance control 3-29, 3-45
Active tip clearance 3-43
Actuating, pneumatic 3-51
Adjustment, fuel flow 7-14
Adjustment, specific gravity 7-26
Adjustments, fuel control 7-27
Aeolipile 1-1
Aerodynamic blockage, reverser 3-51
Aerodynamic efficiency 3-5
Aero-thermodynamic duct 2-1
Afterburner 3-50
Afterburner fuel 3-50
Aft-fan 2-8
Agent, microbiocidal 7-2
Air balance chamber 5-35
Air blast fuel nozzle 7-54
Air conditioning system 3-10
Air density 2-37, 7-14
Air elasticity 2-37
Air flow, laminar 3-10
Air leakage 3-38, 6-5
Air manifold, starting 10-10
Air seal, turbine 3-39
Air start 14-2
Air starter 10-12
Air starting, manifold 10-12
Air temperature, anti-icer 9-2
Air temperature, VRS/speed of sound 2-36
Air turbulence, blade tips 3-18
Air valve, starting 10-12
Air, bleed 3-10
Air, compressor bleed 3-10, 9-2
Air, compressor discharge 3-7
Air, primary 3-31, 7-5
Air, ram (ventilating) 3-60
Air, secondary 3-31
Airacomet, Bell 1-6
Aircraft familiarization Appendix 4
Aircraft speed (V_1) 2-25
Airflow capacity 5-56
Airflow density 7-6
Airflow separation 3-13
Airflow, axial 3-18
Airflow, mass 2-8, 3-2, 5-49, 7-9, 8-2
Airflow, primary combustor 7-6
Airflow, radial 3-11
Airflow, total 7-6
Airflow, velocity 3-2
Airfoil, compressor 3-14
Airfoil, materials 3-62
Airfoil, supersonic 3-4
Airfoil, transonic flow 3-4

Air-fuel mixture 7-6
Air-fuel ratio 7-6
Air-oil cooler 6-26
Air-oil separator 6-29
Airspeed 2-4, 2-33
Airspeed, effect on thrust 2-35
Airspeed, effect on TSFC 7-4
Air-water ratio 7-41
Airworthiness directive (AD) 5-7
Allison-250 turboshaft 4-17
Alloy, nickel-base 3-62
Alloy, super 3-62
Alternating current, ignition 11-5
Alternator, ignition 11-5
Altitude compensation 7-14
Altitude, effect on thrust 2-34
Altitude, effect on TSFC 7-4
Altitude, geopotential Appendix 7
Alumel lead 12-4
Alumel material 12-4
Aluminum cases 3-62
Ambient pressure 2-18, 2-22, 3-2
Ambient temperature 2-34, 7-41, 7-16, 8-2, 12-7
American Society of Testing Materials (ASTM) 6-2
Amplifier, electronic control 7-16
Analysis, Instrument 5-53
Analysis, spectrometric oil 6-12
Analysis, trend 5-53
Analyzer, Jetcal 12-10, 13-5
Angle of attack (AOA) 3-24, 7-5, 8-1, 8-12
Angle, propeller blade 7-6
Angle, stagger 3-16
Angular velocity, turbine 3-38
Annular combustor 3-30
Annular reverse-flow combustor 3-30
Annulus, gearbox 6-16
Annulus, tapered (compressor) 3-24
Anti-foaming, oils 6-1
Anti-friction bearing 5-34
Anti-icing 7-2, 9-1
Anti-microbiocidal agent 7-2
Anti-stall systems 8-2
Arnold, H.H. "Hap" 1-6
"As new" performance 7-31
Aspect ratio, blades 3-16
Assembly, clutch (starter) 10-3
Assembly, fuel bellows 7-10
Assembly, oil filter 6-12
Athodyd 2-1
Atmosphere, US. standard Appendix 7
Atmospheric pressure 2-15
Atomization 7-51
Attachment, turbine blades 3-42
Attenuating, noise 3-56
Augmentation, thrust 5-56, 7-39
Auto-ignition 11-2
Autosyn transmitter 12-18
Auto-throttle system 7-24
Auxiliary power unit (APU) 7-24, 10-4, 11-8
Avco Lycoming T-53/55 3-33
Axial acceleration, turbine 3-40
Axial airflow 2-9, 3-18, 7-29
Axial flow compressor 1-5, 2-36, 3-14
Axial velocity 2-24, 3-21, 8-1
Axial-centrifugal compressor 3-21, 8-6

B

Back pressure, combustor 3-26
Back pressure, gasflow 3-38, 7-32
Balance, turbine wheel 5-28
Balanced oil piston 12-20
Balanced piston torquemeter 7-35
Ball bearings 5-33
Band, bleed 8-7
Barometric pressure (P_{am}) 2-34, 7-30
Beam welding 5-17
Bearing distress 5-39
Bearing failure 3-62, 6-26
Bearing handling 5-38
Bearing housing 5-34
Bearing installation 5-39
Bearing magnetism 5-39
Bearing seals 3-10, 5-36, 12-28
Bearing sump 5-37, 12-28
Bearing, JT8D main 4-3
Bearings, Allison-250 4-34
Bearings, main 5-33
Bell Airacomet 1-6
Bell Aircraft Company 1-6
Bell XP-59 1-6
Bellmouth inlet 3-5
Bellows assembly, fuel 7-10
Bellows, dual (fuel) 7-16
Bendix DP-L2 7-14
Bendix fuel control 7-9
Bernoulli's principle 2-14, 3-11
Blade angle, propeller 7-39, 12-24
Blade chord 3-23
Blade efficiency 3-39
Blade inlet pressure 3-40
Blade radial loading 5-19
Blade replacement 15-19
Blade reverse, pitch 3-56
Blade root galling 3-18
Blade tip 3-17
Blade twist 3-19
Blade, compressor 3-17
Blade, fan 3-17, 7-5, 12-13
Blade, G-Force 3-38
Blade, high aspect ratio 3-20
Blade, impulse-reaction 3-40
Blade, low aspect ratio 3-20
Blade, profile 3-17
Blade, rotor 3-17
Blade, transonic 3-29
Blade, turbine 3-37
Blade, twist 3-16, 3-40
Blade, wide chord 3-20
Bleed air 3-10
Bleed air, compressor 9-1
Bleed air, customer 3-10
Bleed air, engine 3-10, 9-1, 12-12
Bleed band 8-7
Bleed resistor, ignition 11-5
Bleed system, CFM-56 8-12
Bleed system, JT8D 8-7
Bleed, compressor 8-5
Blending 5-16
Blister 5-56
Blockage, aerodynamic (reverser) 3-51
Blockage, mechanical (reverser) 3-51
Blocker panel 3-56

Blocking diode, ignition 11-4
Blow-away jet 3-7
Blowout, rich 7-1
BMW Company 1-5
Boeing 2707 1-7
Boeing 707 1-7
Boeing 727 4-1
Boeing 737 4-1
Boeing 747 1-7, 2-5, 10-7
Boeing 7J7 1-8
Boeing Company 1-7
Booster pump 7-9
Borescope 7-54
Bourdon tube 12-28
Bowing 5-56
Brake horsepower (bhp) 2-4
Braking, thrust 3-52
Branca, Giovanni 1-1
Brayton cycle 2-18
Brayton, George 2-18
Brinelling (false) 5-39
Brinelling (true) 5-39
Bucket, turbine 3-38
Buckling 5-56
Bulb, resistance 12-30
Bulb, thermocouple 12-30
Burner-can pressure (P_b) 7-9
Burner-can shift 5-24
Burnishing 5-39
Burn-through damage 5-30
Burst speed 10-8
Bypass condition, oil filter 6-15
Bypass ratio 2-8, 3-20, 7-5
Bypass valve, oil filter 6-15
Bypass warning light, oil filter 6-19
Bypass, fan ratio 3-20
Bypass, fuel 7-8
Bypass, impending (oil filter) 6-19

C

Cabin pressurization 3-10
Calibration, torque wrench 5-41
Campini, Secundo 3-30
Can-annular combustor 11-5
Capacitor, doubler (ignition) 11-4
Capacitor, ignition 11-5
Capacitor, storage (ignition) 11-5
Capacity, airflow 5-56
Caproni Company 1-6
Caproni-Campini jet 1-6
Carboblast 5-6
Carbon buildup, combustor 3-64
Carbon dioxide (CO_2) 13-6
Carbon enrichment cracks 5-31
Carbon seal 5-37
Carburetor heat 9-1
Cartridge-pneumatic starter 10-12
Cascade effect 3-23
Cascade reverser 3-51
Case deflection 3-62
Case distortion 5-19
Case, accessory 3-62
Case, compressor 3-62, 5-22
Case, exhaust 5-31
Case, fan 3-62
Case, inlet 3-62
Case, JT8D turbine exhaust 4-11
Case, turbine 3-64, 5-30
Casting, single crystal 3-63
Cathode ray tube (CRT) 12-1

Cavitation, oil pump 6-5
Center of gravity, turbine blade 3-38
Centistoke value 6-2
Centrifugal compressor 2-36, 3-10
Centrifugal impeller 3-62
Centrifugal loading 3-38
Ceramic coating 3-63
Chafing 5-39
Chamber, air balance 5-35
Chamber, combustion 3-30
Chamber, oil tank dwell 6-10
Chamber, precombustor 3-34
Check, acceleration 7-28
Check, data plate speed 7-31
Check, engine performance 7-28
Check, full power 7-30, 14-2
Check, performance 7-28
Check, throttle cushion 7-28
Check, trim 7-28
Checks, instrument 14-1
Chinese rocket 1-1
Chip detector 6-26
Chlorobromomethane (CH_2ClBr) 13-6
Choked nozzle 2-22, 3-45
Choking 2-22
Chord, blade 3-23
Chromel lead 12-4
Chromel material 12-4
Civil aviation kerosene 7-1
Clamshell reverser 3-51
Classes, turbine vane 3-38
Cleaning, compressor 5-4
Cleaning, engine 13-8
Cleaning, field 7-31
Cleaning, igniter plug 11-10
Cleaning, oil filter 6-16
Cleaning, ultrasonic 6-16
Clearance control, active 3-43
Clearance, shroud 3-43
Clearance, tip 2-33, 3-43, 5-19
Climb 14-7
Climb setting 14-5
Climb-out 7-26
Clutch assembly 10-3
Clutch, friction 10-4
Clutch, overrunning 10-4
Clutch, sprag 10-8
Coating, plasma 5-18, 5-30
Coating, thermal barrier 3-63
Coil, primary (ignition) 4-11
Coil, resistance (ignition) 11-9
Coil, secondary (ignition) 11-4
Coking, oil 2-26
Cold junction, EGT 12-6
Cold section 3-62, 13-1
Cold section inspection 5-15
Cold section repair 5-15
Cold stream reversing 3-56
Cold tank lubrication 6-37
Cold weather start 3-34, 6-15, 6-21
Collector, exhaust 3-45, 3-30
Combustion 9-10, 2-5, 3-10, 7-5, 10-12
Combustion chamber 3-30
Combustion cycle 3-34
Combustion cycle, continuous 2-18
Combustion liner 3-30, 5-22
Combustion pressure 3-32
Combustion section 3-30
Combustion section, Allison-250 4-30
Combustion section, JT8D 4-8
Combustion section, PT6 4-36

Combustion zone 7-5
Combustor 2-6, 3-30
Combustor back pressure 3-26
Combustor cooling 3-50
Combustor efficiency 3-32, 5-24
Combustor instability 3-32
Combustor liner 3-34
Combustor pollutants 3-34
Combustor pressure 3-28
Combustor section malfunction 5-56
Combustor, annular 2-4, 3-32
Combustor, can-annular 3-32
Combustor, multiple-can 3-32
Combustor, reduced smoke 3-31
Combustor, reverse flow 3-22
Comet, DeHavilland 1-6
Compensation, altitude 7-14
Composite material 3-62
Compression 2-8, 3-3, 5-19, 7-3, 9-3
Compression loading, bearings 6-1
Compression ratio (Cr) 3-3
Compression temperature 2-32
Compression, calculation 3-3
Compression, inlet 3-5
Compression, ram 2-7, 3-2
Compression, total 3-3
Compressor 3-10
Compressor airflow 3-10
Compressor airfoil 3-14
Compressor anti-stall systems 8-1
Compressor blade 3-14
Compressor bleed air 3-10, 9-2
Compressor case 4-20, 5-22, 3-29
Compressor contamination 5-54
Compressor disassembly 5-15
Compressor discharge air 3-23
Compressor discharge pressure 3-20
Compressor disk 3-17
Compressor efficiency 3-21, 5-22, 5-54
Compressor field cleaning 5-4
Compressor impeller 1-2, 3-11
Compressor inlet 3-2
Compressor inlet pressure 3-2, 7-29
Compressor inlet screen 3-6
Compressor inlet temperature (CIT) 8-2
Compressor inlet total pressure 3-2, 8-7, 12-15
Compressor inlet, bellmouth 3-4
Compressor interstage airflow 3-22
Compressor JT8D, N2 4-3
Compressor manifold 3-11
Compressor outlet 2-23
Compressor performance 3-10, 5-19
Compressor pressure ratio (Cr) 2-10, 3-18, 5-49, 7-6, 8-2
Compressor revolutions per minute 3-14
Compressor rotor 3-29
Compressor section 3-10
Compressor section contamination 5-54
Compressor section, Allison-250 4-20
Compressor section, PT6 4-36
Compressor speed 2-10
Compressor stall 3-24, 8-2, 9-1, 9-3
Compressor stator vane 3-23
Compressor taper 3-24
Compressor turbine, PT6 4-36
Compressor, air velocity 3-22
Compressor, axial flow 1-5, 2-36, 3-11
Compressor, axial-centrifugal 3-21
Compressor, centrifugal flow 1-5, 2-36, 3-10
Compressor, dual-spool 27, 2-36, 3-14

Compressor, high pressure 3-14
Compressor, impeller 3-11
Compressor, JT8D 4-3
Compressor, low pressure 3-14
Compressor, mixed-flow 3-21
Compressor, multi-spool 3-14
Compressor, N_1 3-14
Compressor, N_2 3-14
Compressor, N_3 3-14
Compressor, radial out-flow 3-10
Compressor, single-spool 3-14
Compressor, triple-spool 3-14
Computing section, fuel 7-8
Computing, pneumatic (fuel control) 7-10
Concorde SST 1-1, 2-14, 7-56
Conductivity, metals (thermal) 3-63
Cone, exhaust 3-45
Cone, tail 3-45
Constant efficiency per stage 3-20
Construction materials 3-62
Contact loading, blades 3-18
Contaminants, airborne 12-29
Contaminants, fuel 7-48
Contaminants, oil 6-3, 6-12
Contamination, compressor 5-54
Contamination, oil 6-12
Contamination, oil filter 6-16
Contamination, silicone 6-5
Contamination, threshold limit 6-4
Contamination, water 5-56
Continuous combustion 2-18
Continuous duty circuit 11-2
Continuous ignition 11-2
Continuous loop fire detection 13-2
Continuous thermodynamic cycle 2-18
Continuous thrust 7-4
Control, active clearance 3-43
Control, fuel 7-1, 7-5
Controllable pitch propeller 2-29
Convection cooling 3-43
Convergent duct 3-45
Convergent nozzle 3-45
Convergent-divergent (C-D) duct 3-49
Convergent-divergent (C-D) nozzle 3-49
Convergent-divergent (C-D) tailpipe 3-49
Conversion factors Appendix 3
Conversion, percent rpm to rpm 7-39
Conversion, temperature Appendix 3
Conversion, torque 7-39
Conversion, torque psi (gauge) to torque ft.lb. 7-39
Cooler, air-oil 6-26
Cooler, fuel-oil 6-26
Cooler, General Electric CJ610 oil 6-25
Cooling air 3-43
Cooling, combustor 3-32
Cooling, convection 3-43
Cooling, internal air flow 3-43
Cooling, surface film 3-43
Cooling, turbine blade 3-43
Cooling, turbine case 3-43
Correction table, pressure Appendix 9
Correction table, temperature Appendix 9
Corrosion 3-62, 5-4, 10-9, 11-8, 13-8
Corrosion resistance, materials 3-62
Corrosion, bearing 5-39
Corrosion, scaling 3-63
Counter, cycle 5-52
Counter-rotating turbine 3-43
Crack, stress rupture 5-28
Cracking pressure, relief valve 6-22

Crazing 5-56
Creep 5-28
Creep resistance 3-63
Cross-bleed starting 10-4
Cruise power 7-4
Cruise setting 14-5
Cruise, engine operation 14-7
Current flow, ignition 11-5
Current, alternating (ignition) 11-5
Current, direct (ignition) 11-4
Customer bleed air 3-10
Cut-off and dump, fuel valve 7-12
Cycle counter 5-52
Cycle, Brayton 2-18
Cycle, combustion 3-34
Cycling, thermal 6-15

D

Damage, burn-through 5-30
Damage, domestic object 5-4
Damage, engine 5-4
Damage, fan blade 5-16
Damage, foreign object 3-62, 5-3, 14-1
Damage, heat 9-3
Damage, impact 5-16, 5-22, 5-30, 9-1
Damage, leading edge 5-17
Damage, stall 3-62
Damped bearing 5-34
Damping, tip vibration 3-17
Danger zone, trim 7-34
d'Arsonval meter 12-5
Dart, Rolls Royce 3-32
Data plate 7-31
Data, engine run 5-47
Data, in-flight 5-53
Data, performance Appendix 10
DC-10 2-25, 7-5
De-aerator, oil tank 6-33
Deceleration 7-14, 8-1
Decibel meter 3-58
Decibel, effective perceived noise 3-56
Decimal equivalents Appendix 3
Decomposition, oil 6-1
Decompression, aircraft 1-6
Deflection, case 3-62
Deformation 5-56
Degausser 5-39
DeHavilland Comet 1-7
Delta-P (Δ-P) oil light 6-19
Delta-p (Δ-p) rating 6-15
Density pressure 2-34
Density, air 2-34, 7-14
Density, definition 2-10
Density, inlet air 2-33
Depressurization, oil tank 6-9
Desalination wash 5-4
Descent, aircraft 14-7
Descent, rate of 3-51
Design, axial turbine 3-37
Design, combustor 3-32
Design, compressor blade 3-28
Design, fir tree 3-28
Detection, fire 13-1
Detection, overheat 13-1
Detection, water 7-3
Detector, chip 6-26
Detector, infrared 13-6
Detector, pulsed chip 6-27
Detector, smoke 13-6
Diaphragm 7-10, 8-7, 8-10

Dibromodifloromethane (CBr_2F_2) 13-6
Die-out, lean 7-1
Diester 6-5
Differential metering head regulator 7-14
Differential pressure 6-15, 7-17
Differential pressure regulator 7-17
Diffuser 3-29
Diffuser case, JT8D 4-3
Diffuser, compressor 3-29
Diffuser, inlet 3-2
Diffuser, supersonic 3-4
Diode, blocking (ignition) 11-4
Diode, light emitting (ignition) 12-1
Direct current, ignition 11-4
Directional reference, engine 3-67
Disassembly, compressor 5-15
Discharge air, compressor 2-8, 3-7
Discharge nozzle, compressor 3-7
Discharge pressure, compressor 3-20
Discoloration, lubricant 6-5
Discrepancy, engine 6-21
Disk, compressor 3-14
Disk, turbine 3-40
Displacement positive 6-10
Disposable filter 6-15
Distortion, case 5-19
Distortion, shock 3-50
Distress, bearing 5-39
Distribution, thrust 2-23, 3-54
Divergent duct 2-24, 3-2
Domestic Object Damage (DOD) 5-4
Drag 1-4, 2-3, 2-29, 10-1
Drag, inlet momentum 2-22
Drag, ram 2-22, 3-51
Drain tank, fuel 7-57
Drill sizes Appendix 3
Drive pad, accessory 3-8
Drive shaft shear point 10-8
Droop 7-9
Dry motoring run 14-4
Dry sump 6-8
Dry sump, integral oil tank 6-31
Dry sump, oil tank 6-31
Dry takeoff 14-7
Dual bellows, fuel schedule 7-16
Dual coaxial turbine shaft 3-42
Dual compressor turbofan 2-19
Dual tachometer marking 12-34
Dual-line duplex fuel nozzle 7-54
Dual-sided impeller 3-11
Dual-spool compressor 2-36, 3-14
Duct loss 3-5
Duct recovery 3-19
Duct, aero-thermodynamic 2-1
Duct, convergent 3-45
Duct, convergent-divergent 2-24, 3-4
Duct, divergent 32, 3-2
Duct, engine entrance 3-2
Duct, exhaust 3-20
Duct, fan 3-20
Duct, inlet 3-1
Duct, outlet 3-32
Duct, PT6 exhaust 4-43
Ducted UHB engine 2-10
Dump valve, fuel 7-56
Dumping, fuel manifold 7-56
Duplex fuel nozzle 7-54
Dwell chamber, off tank 6-9
Dychem 5-31
Dye penetrant inspection 5-12
Dynamometer 2-26, 214

E

Ear protection 7-34
Eddy current 12-13
Eddy current inspection 5-15
Eddy turbulence 3-58
Edge, leading 3-23
Edge, trailing 3-23
Effect, cascade 3-23
Effect, gyroscopic 3-16
Effect, inlet 3-22
Effect, ram 3-4
Effective perceived noise decibels (Epndb) 3-57
Effective thrust horsepower 1-5
Efficiency, aerodynamic 3-5
Efficiency, combustor 3-34, 5-24
Efficiency, component 2-36
Efficiency, compressor 3-10, 5-54
Efficiency, engine fuel 7-3
Efficiency, overall 2-31
Efficiency, propulsive 2-7, 2-29, 3-21, 7-3
Efficiency, thermal 2-31, 3-18
Efficiency, turbine 3-26, 5-56
Efficiency, turbine wheel 3-43
Efficiency, turbofan 7-3
Ejector 3-58
Elasticity, air 2-37
Electric pulsed chip detector 6-27
Electric starters 10-3
Electrical heat strips 9-1
Electro-hydromechanical fuel control 7-6
Electron beam welding 5-17
Electron theory, EGT 12-7
Electronic control amplifier, fuel 7-16
Electronic fuel scheduling 7-16
Electronic torque indicating system 12-21
Emergency operating procedures 14-2
Emergency shutdown 14-2
Emergency, PT6 14-5
Emission, sound 3-57
End-bend Blades 3-17
Energy, heat 3-30
Energy, kinetic 2-14, 3-47
Energy, potential 2-14, 3-47
Engine bleed air 3-39, 9-1, 12-12
Engine compartment ventilation 3-59
Engine compression ratio 3-47
Engine condition indicators 12-1
Engine data sheets 4-60
Engine design 3-1
Engine design, Allison-250 4-17
Engine design, JT8D 4-1
Engine design, PT6 4-34
Engine failure 14-6
Engine fire 14-5
Engine gearbox 10-8
Engine history 1-1
Engine indicator maximum pointer reset 12-2
Engine inlet 3-1
Engine inspection 5-47
Engine instruments 12-1
Engine locator Appendix 4
Engine mounts 3-60
Engine operation 14-1
Engine operation, PT6 14-3
Engine performance 5-47, 7-26, 8-2
Engine performance curve 2-29
Engine power ratings 14-6
Engine pressure ratio (EPR) 3-4, 5-53, 7-31, 8-7, 9-3

Engine pressure ratio system 12-15
Engine pressure ratio trim 7-29
Engine purging 14-2
Engine run data 5-47
Engine sections, Allison-250 4-17
Engine sections, JT8D 4-3
Engine service life 12-10
Engine shutdown 7-14, 14-4
Engine speed (Nc) 3-46, 7-6, 10-4, 12-13
Engine start 7-12, 14-1
Engine stations 3-1, 3-64, 4-17, 12-15
Engine theory 2-1
Engine thrust (F_g) 3-15, 7-3
Engine vibration 3-16, 5-7, 12-1
Engine, lift-fan 3-51
Engine, speed rated 7-29, 12-15
Engine, torque producing 7-35
Enrichment valve, fuel 7-10
Enrichment, fuel 7-16
Entrained water, fuel 7-2
Entrance ducts 3-1
Environmental Protection Agency (EPA) 1-8, 3-34
Epoxy-resin material 3-62
Equivalent shaft horsepower (eshp) 2-27
Equivalents, decimal Appendix 3
Erosion 5-3, 11-17
Erosion, seal 5-56
Exhaust case 5-31
Exhaust case, JT8D turbine 4-11
Exhaust cone 2-24, 3-45
Exhaust duct 3-45
Exhaust duct pressure 3-49
Exhaust duct, PT6 4-36
Exhaust gas temperature (EGT) 3-26, 5-53, 9-3, 10-3, 12-2
Exhaust gas temperature limits 12-7
Exhaust gas temperature marking 12-34
Exhaust mixer 3-49
Exhaust nozzle 3-45
Exhaust nozzle pressure 3-45
Exhaust section 3-45
Exhaust stream 3-50
Exhaust temperature indicating 12-34
Exhaust thrust 2-7
Exhaust velocity 2-8, 2-18, 3-50
Exhaust, fan 3-51
Exhaust, hot 3-51
Exhaust, mixed 3-50
Exit guide vane 3-23
Exit pressure 3-19
Exit velocity 3-21
Expansion, gas 3-49
Expansion, thermal 3-43
Expected service life 5-8
Extended duty ignition 11-1
Extinguishing agent, fire 13-6

F

FAA Form 337 5-8, 5-41
Factors, conversion Appendix 3
FADEC Components 7-17
Failure to start 14-2
Failure, bearing 3-62
Failure, engine 3-26, 14-5
False start 7-59
Familiarization, aircraft Appendix 4
Familiarization, CFM-56 4-46
Fan blade 3-17, 7-5
Fan blade damage 5-16
Fan blade rotation 12-13

Fan bypass ratio 3-20
Fan case 3-62
Fan compression ratio 3-20
Fan discharge 3-2
Fan discharge temperature 8-12
Fan duct 3-20
Fan engine thrust 2-25
Fan exhaust 3-20
Fan pressure ratio 3-20
Fan speed trim 7-31
Fan, bypass 3-17
Fan, high bypass 2-9, 3-21
Fan, ultra high bypass (UHB) 2-10, 3-21
Fatigue cracking 1-6
Fatigue failure, inlet screen 3-6
Fatigue fracture, airfoils 3-18
Fatigue, oil filters 6-14
Federal Aviation Administration (FAA) 1-8
FF gauge 12-1
Field cleaning 7-31
Field cleaning, compressor 5-4
Field detector 5-39
Field temperature, trimming 7-29
Film strength, oil 6-1
Filter bypass warning light, oil 6-19
Filter cleaning 6-16
Filter, fuel 7-48
Filter, last chance oil 6-26
Filter, oil 6-12
Filter, woven wire 6-15
Fine grain turbulence, exhaust 3-58
Fire detection systems 13-1
Fire extinguishing 13-6
Fire seal 3-60
Fire, engine 14-5
Fir-tree design, turbine 3-42
Fixed geometry inlet 3-2
Fixed turbine 2-7, 12-20
Flaking 5-56
Flame detector 13-6
Flame propagation, combustor 3-32
Flame zone, combustor 3-32
Flameholder 3-50
Flameout 7-14, 11-1
Flash point, oil 6-1
Flashover, igniter, 11-5
Flat rating 7-35
Flight thrust 7-4
Flow control, starting 7-12
Flow cycle, continuous 2-20
Flow divider, fuel 7-9
Flow separation, air 3-11
Flow velocity, air 3-29
Flow, axial 2-7, 3-29
Flow, electron (EGT) 12-4
Flow, fuel 3-26, 5-53
Flow, laminar air 3-10
Flow, mass (fuel) 12-25
Flow, oil 12-29
Flow, starting control (fuel) 7-9
Flow, subsonic axial (air) 3-28
Flow, supersonic (air) 3-50
Flow, supersonic 3-4
Flow, synchronous mass (fuel) 12-25
Flow, throat (tailpipe) 3-50
Flow, transonic airfoil 3-28
Flowmeter, fuel (motorless mass) 12-25
Flowmeter, synchronous (fuel) 12-25
Flush patch 3-2
Flux coupler magnet 12-13
Flyweight 7-10

Flyweight force 7-10
Flyweight, fuel control 7-10
Foaming, oil 6-1
Force, definition 2-12
Force, flyweight 7-10
Force, thrust 2-4
Force, twisting 5-41
Force, vector 3-22
Foreign object damage (FOD) 3-62
Forging 3-63
Formula, acceleration 2-13
Formula, compressor horsepower 2-28
Formula, Delta/Theta correction 5-47
Formula, engine pressure ratio 7-29, 12-15
Formula, equivalent shaft horsepower 2-27
Formula, exhaust gas temperature 12-7
Formula, fan engine thrust 2-25
Formula, force 2-12
Formula, fuel consumption 7-3
Formula, G-Force on rotating blade 3-38
Formula, gross thrust 2-21
Formula, horsepower 2-12
Formula, indicated torque 5-43
Formula, inlet compression 3-3
Formula, inlet temperature drop 9-1
Formula, joule rating 11-3
Formula, kinetic energy 2-37
Formula, mass units 2-19
Formula, metered fuel by weight 7-8
Formula, overall efficiency 2-31
Formula, power 2-12
Formula, pressure correction factor 5-47
Formula, propeller thrust 2-26
Formula, propulsive efficiency 2-29
Formula, ram compression 3-3
Formula, reverse thrust 3-56
Formula, speed of sound 2-37
Formula, thrust distribution 2-23
Formula, thrust horsepower 2-25
Formula, thrust specific fuel consumption 7-3
Formula, tip speed 2-36
Formula, torque horsepower 7-37
Formula, torque hp to shp 7-37
Formula, total pressure 7-37
Formula, velocity 2-13
Formula, work 2-12
Formulae, general Appendix 8
Free power turbine 2-6
Free turbine 12-20
Frequency tuning 3-17
Fretting, bearings 5-41
Friction clutch 10-4
Friction loads 6-1
Frosting, materials 5-56
Fuel additive 7-2
Fuel bypass 7-8
Fuel computing section 7-8
Fuel consumption 1-5, 2-2, 5-19, 7-35, 8-12, 12-25
Fuel control 7-37, 8-1
Fuel control adjustments 7-39
Fuel control discharge pressure 8-2
Fuel control governor 3-15
Fuel control sensors 7-22
Fuel control unit (FCU) 7-9
Fuel filter 7-59
Fuel filter warning switch 7-50
Fuel flow 12-25
Fuel flow (W_f) 5-49, 7-4
Fuel flow indicating system 12-25
Fuel governing 7-16

Fuel handling 7-1
Fuel heater 7-45
Fuel metering device 7-5
Fuel metering section 7-8
Fuel nozzle 3-31, 7-51
Fuel pressure (P_2) 7-9, 8-2, 8-4, 8-5
Fuel pressure differential (P_1-P_2) 7-9
Fuel pressure gauge marking 12-32
Fuel pressurizing and dump valve 7-56
Fuel pump 7-9
Fuel return 7-10
Fuel scheduling 7-9
Fuel solenoid 7-25
Fuel system accessories 7-43
Fuel system components 7-49
Fuel system, CFM-56 7-62
Fuel system, JT-12 7-59
Fuel system, JT8D 7-59
Fuel systems 7-1
Fuel temperature 7-10, 12-25
Fuel, afterburner 3-50
Fuel, atomization 3-34
Fuel, hydrocarbon 7-1
Fuel, jet 7-1
Fuel, metered 7-8
Fuel, metered pressure 7-9
Fuel, primary 7-53
Fuel, rich 10-3
Fuel, secondary 7-53
Fuel, turbo 5 7-2
Fuel, turbo A1 7-1
Fuel, turbo A 7-1
Fuel, turbo B 7-1
Fuel-air mixture 3-50
Fuel-oil cooler 6-23
Full power check 7-30
Full reversing propeller 3-56
Furnace, casting 3-64

G

Galling 3-18, 5-41, 5-56
Garrett ATF-3 7-17
Garrett Company 1-8
Garrett GTP-30 7-24
Garrett TFE-731 3-14, 7-3
Garrett TPE-331 2-27, 14-2
Gas flow 3-33
Gas generator section 2-6
Gas path 5-4
Gas path erosion 5-4
Gas path, Allison-250 4-17
Gas path, PT6 4-34
Gas producer (N_1) tachometer marking 12-34
Gas velocity 3-38
Gauge tube, manometer 2-16
Gauge, oil pressure 6-19
Gauge, torque 7-39
Gear pump 6-12
Gear reduction 3-8
Gear train, Allison-250 4-28
Gearbox annulus 6-16
Gearbox ratio, fan 3-14
Gearbox sump 6-33
Gearbox, accessory 3-10, 10-1, 12-13
Gearbox, Allison-250 4-28
Gearbox, engine 10-8
Gearbox, external 3-8
Gearbox, JT8D main accessory 4-8
Gearbox, main 3-8

Gearbox, PT6 accessory 4-45
Gearbox, PT6 propeller reduction 4-43
Gearbox, reduction 2-7, 7-37
General Electric CF-6 5-52, 7-4
General Electric CF-6 variable vane system 8-1
General Electric CFM-56 bleed system 8-12
General Electric CJ610 5-8
General Electric CJ610 lubrication 6-22
General Electric Company 1-2
General Motors-Allison Company 1-8, 4-1
Generator, three-phase (tachometer) 12-13
Geopotential altitude Appendix 7
Gerotor oil pump 6-10
G-Force 3-38, 5-33
Gloster E28/39 1-2
Gloster Meteor 1-3
Glow plug Igniter 11-9
Governor bellows pressure (P_x, P_y) 7-10
Governor valve, fuel 7-10
Governor, fuel control 3-15
Governor, high rotor fuel control 7-16
Governor, propeller 7-12
Governor, turbine 7-9
Gravensade 1-2
Gravity, center of 3-38
Gravity, specific 7-10, 12-25
Green-Dye inspection 5-12
Grooving 5-41
Gross thrust 3-51
Ground idle speed 3-53
Ground performance 7-31
Ground power unit (GPU) 7-24, 10-10, 14-1
Ground run-up 3-46, 14-1
Ground start 11-1, 14-1
Ground test 3-5
Ground troubleshooting 5-53
Ground use, reverser 3-51
Guide vane, exit 3-23
Guide vane, inlet 3-18
Guide vane, variable 3-18
Guttering 5-4
Gyroscopic effect 5-33
Gyroscopic load 5-34

H

Half-life hot section inspection 5-50
Half-wave rectifier, ignition 11-4
Hand signals Appendix 5
Harmonics 5-31
Heat damage, inlet 9-3
Heat energy 3-30
Heat of evaporation principle 7-41
Heat strips, electrical 9-1
Heat, carburetor 9-1
Heat, conductivity 3-62
Heater, fuel 7-45
Heavy maintenance 5-8
Heavy repairs 5-8
Heinkel Company 1-5
Heinkel He-178 1-5
Hero 1-1
Heron 1-1
High aspect ratio blade 3-20
High bypass fan 2-10, 10-3
High bypass turbofan 2-9, 2-38, 3-21
High pressure compressor 3-14
High pressure discharge pressure (P_{S4}) 8-7
High pressure turbine 3-42
High rotor governor, fuel 7-16

High tension ignition 11-5
High-low pressure pneumatic starter 10-12
High-pressure compressor, JT8D 4-34
History, turbine development 2-1
Horsepower 2-12, 12-20
Horsepower, brake 2-4
Horsepower, effective thrust 1-5
Horsepower, equivalent shaft 2-27
Horsepower, isentropic gas 2-28
Horsepower, ram shaft 2-29
Horsepower, shaft 2-27
Horsepower, thermodynamic 2-28
Horsepower, thrust 2-26
Hot exhaust 3-51
Hot junction (thermocouple) 12-4
Hot section 1-6, 3-60, 7-32, 13-1
Hot section inspection 5-22
Hot section repair 5-22
Hot start 10-1, 14-2
Hot streaking, fuel nozzle 5-26, 7-51
Hot stream reverser 3-56
Hot tank lubrication 6-36
Hot thrust 2-7
Housing, bearing 5-34
Humidity factor, thrust 2-25
Hung stall 3-26
Hung start 10-1
Hush kit 3-58
Hydraulic starter 10-12
Hydrocarbon fuel 7-1
HYDROKIT® 7-3
Hydro-mechanical torque indicating system 12-20
Hydro-pneumatic fuel control 7-9

I

Ice probe 9-3
Ice separator 3-6
Icing 7-34, 9-1, 10-9, 11-2
Idle speed 7-12, 10-1
Igniter plug 3-39, 11-1, 11-8
Igniter, spark 11-8
Ignition system, CFM-56 11-14
Ignition systems 11-1
Ignition temperature 3-30
Ignition, continuous 11-2
Ignition, extended duty 11-6
Ignition, high tension 11-5, 11-8
Ignition, intermittent 11-4
Ignition, low tension 11-4
Ignition, main 11-1
Imbalance, rotor 3-62
Impact damage 5-16, 5-22, 5-30, 9-1
Impact tube, manometer 2-16
Impeller 3-11
Impeller compressor 2-6
Impeller, centrifugal 3-10
Impeller, compressor 1-2, 3-11
Impeller, dual sided 3-11
Impeller, single sided 3-11
Impending bypass, oil filter 6-19, 7-50
Impulse position, turbine blade 3-40
Impulse reaction blade, turbine 3-40
Impulse wheel 1-1
In cascade, airflow 3-23
Inclusion 5-41, 5-56
Inconel 3-64
Index, viscosity 6-2
Indicated torque 5-43
Indicating system, exhaust temperature 12-2

Indicating system, fuel flow 12-25
Indicating system, oil pressure 12-28
Indicating system, oil temperature 12-27
Indicating system, tachometer 12-13
Indicating system, torque 12-20
Indicator, engine condition 12-1
Indicator, performance 12-1
Indicator, thrust 12-34
Indicator, torque 12-20
Indicators, oil system 12-27
In-flight data 5-53
Infrared detector, fire detector 13-6
Ingestion, foreign object 5-3
Inlet air density 2-33
Inlet air pressure 10-9
Inlet air velocity 3-19
Inlet case 3-62
Inlet compression 3-3
Inlet compression ratio 3-3
Inlet diffuser 3-2
Inlet duct 3-2
Inlet effect, vector 3-22
Inlet guide vane 3-18, 8-1
Inlet momentum drag 2-22
Inlet pressure (Pt_2) 3-3, 7-9
Inlet pressure, turbine blade 3-40
Inlet ram pressure 3-49
Inlet screen, compressor 3-6
Inlet shock wave 3-4
Inlet temperature (Tt_2) 7-6
Inlet velocity, centrifugal compressor 3-21
Inlet vortex dissipator 3-7
Inlet, Bellmouth compressor 3-4
Inlet, compressor 2-23
Inlet, diffuser 3-29
Inlet, engine 3-2
Inlet, fixed geometry 3-4
Inlet, flight cowling 3-64
Inlet, fuel 7-14
Inlet, subsonic 3-2
Inlet, supersonic 3-4
Inlet, turbine nozzle 3-32
Inlet, variable geometry 3-4
Inner race bearing 5-33
Input, AC vs. DC (ignition) 11-8
Inspection, bearing seals 5-36
Inspection, cold section 5-15
Inspection, combustion section 5-22
Inspection, dye penetrant 5-12
Inspection, engines 5-3
Inspection, fuel filter 7-48
Inspection, half-life hot section 5-50
Inspection, hot section 5-22
Inspection, igniter plug 11-11
Inspection, magnetic particle 5-12
Inspection, main bearings 5-38
Inspection, nondestructive 5-10
Inspection, overtemperature 12-7
Inspection, radiographic 5-14
Inspection, turbine general 5-1
Inspection, turbine section 5-26
Inspection, turbine wheel 5-26
Inspection, ultrasonic 5-15
Instability, combustor 3-32
Installation, bearing 5-38
Instrument analysis 5-53
Instrument checks 14-1
Instrument marking 12-32
Instrument, engine 12-1
Integral oil tank 6-31
Integrity check, engine 5-45

Intergranular stress 5-31
Intermittent duty ignition 11-1, 11-4
International Standard Day (ISD) 5-49
Inter-stage airflow 3-22
Interval, oil change 6-7
Isentropic gas horsepower 2-28
ITT gauge 12-10

J

Jet engine, types 2-1
Jet fuels 7-1
Jet nozzle 2-14, 3-45
Jet pipe 3-45
Jet propulsion theory 1-2, 2-1
Jet, blow-away 3-7
Jet, General Electric CJ610 oil 6-22
Jet-A 7-1
Jet-B 7-1
Jetcal analyzer 12-10, 13-5
Joule rating 11-3
JT8D engine design 4-1
JT8D lubrication 6-31
JT8D pressure subsystem 6-33
JT8D scavenge subsystem 6-31
JT8D turbofan 4-1
JT8D vent subsystem 6-33
Junker Company 1-5

K

Kerosene, civil aviation 7-1
Kinematic viscosimeter 6-2
Kinematic Viscosity Rating 6-2
Kinetic energy 2-14
Knife-edged seal 3-18

L

Labyrinth seal 5-36, 6-15
Lacquer, oil system 6-1
Laminar air flow 3-10
Landing, aircraft 14-7
Lead, alumel 12-4
Lead, chromel 12-4
Leading edge damage, compressor 5-17
Leak test, engine run 5-47
Leakage, air 3-38, 6-5
Leakage, compressor blade tip 3-17
Leakage, magnetic particle test 5-12
Lean die-out 7-1
Lever, power 7-1, 14-1
Lift-fan engine 3-51
Light emitting diode (LED) 12-1
Light-off, engine 7-52
Limit, temperature 3-64
Limited heavy maintenance 5-8
Limiter, acceleration 7-25
Limiting, power turbine 7-14
Limits, exhaust gas temperature 12-7
Limits, revolutions per minute 12-14
Limits, starting 12-7
Limits, torque 12-21
Line maintenance 5-6
Liner inspection 3-32
Liner, combustion 3-63, 7-6
Liner, machined ring 3-34
Linkage, multiplying (fuel) 7-8
Load, temperature 3-60
Load, centrifugal 3-38
Load, thermal 3-38
Load, torque on engine mounts 3-38
Loading, bearings 5-33

Loading, blade radial 5-19
Loading, centrifugal 3-38, 5-30, 7-10
Loading, compression 5-33
Loading, gyroscopic (bearings) 5-33
Loading, heat 12-7
Loading, primary (bearings) 5-33
Loading, radial (bearings) 5-33
Loading, tension 5-33
Loading, thrust 5-33
Loading, tip (turbine) 3-42
Locator, engine Appendix 4
Lock tab 5-45
Lock wire 5-44
Lock wiring 5-44
Lock, vapor 7-1
Locking methods 5-44
Lockout temperature, filter pop-out 6-21
Lockwasher 5-45
Loop, continuous (fire detector) 13-2
Loop, thermal switch (fire detector) 13-1
Loss, energy-of-flow 3-35
Lost wax method, casting 3-64
Low aspect ratio blade 3-20
Low bypass turbofan 2-8
Low frequency noise 3-57
Low pressure compressor 3-14
Low pressure turbine 3-42
Low pressure warning light, fuel 3-42
Low pressure warning light, oil 6-19
Low tension ignition 11-4
Low-pressure compressor, JT8D 4-3
Low-pressure turbine, JT8D 4-8
Lubricant discoloration 6-5
Lubricant, Type-1 6-5
Lubricant, Type-2 6-5
Lubricants, synthetic 6-4
Lubrication systems 6-1
Lubrication, Allison-250 4-34
Lubrication, CFM-56 6-33
Lubrication, cold tank 6-36
Lubrication, dry sump 6-8
Lubrication, FAA requirements 6-1
Lubrication, General Electric CJ610 6-22
Lubrication, hot tank 6-36
Lubrication, JT8D 6-30
Lubrication, troubleshooting 6-37
Lubrication, under-race (bearings) 6-26
Lubrication, wet sump 6-7
Lycoming T-53 7-56

M

Magnesium zirconate 3-64
Magnet, flux coupler (tachometer) 12-13
Magnetic field leakage check 5-12
Magnetic particle inspection 5-12
Magnetic pickup percent RPM system 12-13
Magnetism check, bearings 5-39
Main accessory gearbox, JT8D 4-8
Main bearings 4-8, 5-33
Main fuel pump 7-43
Main gearbox 3-8
Main ignition system 11-1
Maintenance, fuel control 7-26
Maintenance, limited heavy 5-8
Maintenance, line 5-1
Maintenance, modular 5-41
Maintenance, shop 5-8
Maintenance, test cell 5-45
Maintenance, turbine general 5-1
Maintenance, unlimited heavy 5-8

Malfunction, combustor section 5-56
Malfunction, compressor section 5-54
Malfunction, engine 9-2
Malfunction, fuel scheduling 7-16
Malfunction, turbine section 5-56
Maneuverability, flight 3-51
Manifold dumping, fuel 7-56
Manifold, compressor 3-11
Manometer 2-16
Margin, stall 3-28
Marking, instrument 12-32
Marking, parts for repair 5-31
Mass airflow 2-1, 3-26, 5-49, 7-98, 8-2
Mass flow, deflection (combustor) 3-37
Mass flow, flowmeter 12-25
Mass flow, velocity (combustor) 3-37
Mass units 2-19
Mass, definition 2-12
Materials, construction 3-62
Maximum climb thrust/SHP 14-7
Maximum continuous rating 14-7
Maximum continuous thrust/SHP 14-7
Maximum cruise rating 14-7
Maximum cruise thrust/SHP 14-7
Maximum flow stop adjustment, fuel 7-14
Maximum thrust 2-37, 7-28
McDonnell-Douglas DC-10 7-4
McDonnell-Douglas DC-9 4-1
Mechanical blockage, reverser 3-51
Mechanical monitoring, engine 5-53
Mechanical pressure, material stress 3-62
Medium bypass turbofan 2-9
Mesh number, filters 7-50
Messerschmitt Me-262 1-6
Metallization 5-56
Metallurgy, powder 3-63
Meter, d'Arsonval 12-5
Meter, flow 12-25
Metered fuel 7-8
Metered fuel pressure (P2) 7-9
Metering valve 7-9
Metering, fuel 7-5
Methyl bromide (CH3Br) 13-6
Metric viscosity measurement 6-2
Microbiocidal agent 7-2
Micron 300, 6-13
Micron rating 6-13
Micron rating versus mesh size 7-48
Military fuel JP-4 7-1
Military fuel JP-5 7-1
Minimum flow adjustment, fuel 7-14
Mixed exhaust 3-50
Mixed-flow compressor 3-29
Mixer, exhaust 3-49
Mixing, exhaust 3-57
Mixture, air-fuel 357
Modular maintenance 5-41
Molecular motion, air 2-10
Moment arm, torque 7-37
Moment-weight 5-22
Monitoring, mechanical 5-53
Monitoring, performance 5-53
Moss, Dr. Sanford 1-2
Motion, first law of 2-19, 7-39
Motion, molecular 2-10
Motion, second law of 2-19, 3-40
Motion, third law of 1-2, 2-20, 3-40
Motorless mass flow meter system 12-25
Mount, engine 3-60

Multimeter 12-10
Multiple-can combustor 3-32
Multiplying linkage 7-8
Multi-spool compressor 3-14
Multi-viscosity oils 6-2

N

N_1 compressor 3-15
N_1 compressor, JT8D 4-3
N_1 speed 5-53
N_1 tach 12-1
N_1 turbine 3-15
N_1 turbine, Allison 4-30
N_1 turbine, JT8D 4-8
N_1 turbine, PT6 4-36
N_2 compressor 3-15
N_2 compressor, JT8D 4-3
N_2 speed 5-53
N_2 tach 12-1
N_2 turbine 3-42
N_2 turbine rotor, JT8D 4-8
N_2 turbine, Allison-250 4-30
N_2 turbine, PT6 4-39
N_3 compressor 3-15
Nat'l Advisory Comm. of Aeronautics
     (NACA) 2-25
Natural frequency vibration 5-31
Negative sump, oil 12-28
Net thrust 2-22, 3-51
Newton, Isaac 1-2
Newton's first law 2-19, 7-39
Newton's second law 2-19
Newton's third law 1-2, 2-20
Nickel-base alloy 3-62
Nickel-chromium alloy 3-62
Noise attenuation 3-56
Noise suppression 3-56
Noise, low frequency 3-57
Nomograph, oil 6-2
Nondestructive inspection (NDI) 5-10
Nondestructive testing (NDT) 5-10
Nozzle pressure ratio 3-46
Nozzle vane, JT8D 4-8
Nozzle, air blast (fuel) 7-55
Nozzle, choked (exhaust) 3-45
Nozzle, choked 2-22
Nozzle, choked exhaust 2-22
Nozzle, convergent-divergent (exhaust) 3-49
Nozzle, divergent (exhaust) 3-49
Nozzle, duplex fuel 7-56
Nozzle, exhaust 3-45
Nozzle, fuel 3-31, 7-51
Nozzle, Jet 2-22, 3-45
Nozzle, simplex (fuel) 7-52
Nozzle, turbine 3-38
Nozzle, vectoring exhaust 3-51
Number, station 3-64

O

Occupational Safety and Health
     Administration 7-34
Oil analysis, spectrometric 6-2
Oil change intervals 6-7
Oil consumption 6-7
Oil cooler, GE CJ610 6-23
Oil decomposition 6-12
Oil discoloration 6-5
Oil filter 6-12
Oil filter assembly 6-15

Oil flow 12-28
Oil foaming 6-5
Oil jet, General Electric CJ610 6-26
Oil mixing 6-7
Oil overflow 6-9
Oil oxidation 6-13
Oil pressure 6-17, 12-1, 12-28
Oil pressure indicating system 12-28
Oil pressure marking 12-33
Oil pressure, GE CJ610 6-22
Oil pressure, torque 12-20
Oil pump 6-9
Oil pump cavitation 6-5
Oil quantity 12-1
Oil sampling 6-2
Oil spectrometer 6-3
Oil system indicators 12-27
Oil system servicing 6-5
Oil systems 6-1
Oil tank 6-8
Oil temperature 6-25, 7-48, 12-1, 12-27
Oil temperature indicating systems 12-27
Oil temperature marking 12-33
Oil trend analysis 6-3
Oil, low pressure procedures 6-20
Oil, petroleum 6-1
Oil, scavenge 2-10, 5-37, 6-26, 6-35
Oil, turbine 6-5
Oils, synthetic 6-4
Olympus, Rolls Royce 1-8
On/off, anti-Ice 9-3
On-speed condition 7-9
Operation, auxiliary power unit 7-25
Operation, engine 14-1
Operation, hydro-pneumatic fuel control 7-10
Operation, PT6 engine 14-3
O-Rings 5-45
Outlet duct 3-32
Outlet, compressor 2-23
Outlet, diffuser 3-30
Outlet, turbine 3-67
Output, power 2-4
Outside air temperature (OAT) 2-33, 7-29
Overall efficiency 2-31
Overhaul, JT8D 4-3
Overhaul, time between 5-50
Overheat detection systems 13-1
Overload thermostat 7-25
Over-rich mixture 3-32
Overrunning clutch 10-4
Over-speed condition 7-25, 10-9
Over-temperature condition 7-6
Overtorque 12-21
Oxidation inhibitor 6-5
Oxidation resistance 3-63
Oxidation, oil 6-13
Oxidizer 2-1
Ozone 1-7

P

P and D valve, fuel 7-56
Panel, blocker 3-56
Part power trim 7-30
Patch, flush (inlet) 3-2
Path, gas 3-64
Pawl cage, starter 10-4
Peening 5-41, 5-59
Percent RPM, conversion to actual RPM 7-39

Perforated liner, combustor 3-30
Performance check, turboprop 7-35
Performance check, turboshaft 7-35
Performance checks, engine 7-28
Performance curves, engine 2-29
Performance data, ground vs. flight Appendix 10
Performance indicators, engine 12-1
Performance monitoring, engine 5-53
Performance recovery wash, engine 5-4
Performance, as new 7-31
Performance, compressor 3-1
Performance, engine 5-47, 9-2
Performance, engine thrust 5-47
Performance, ground 7-4
Performance, turbine vs. piston 2-5
Phase shift torquemeter 12-20
Physics 2-10
Pipe, jet 3-45
Piston vs. turbine performance 2-5
Piston, balanced oil (torquemeter) 12-20
Piston, servo 10-8
Pitting 5-41, 5-59
Plain bearings 5-33
Plasma coating 3-63, 5-18
Plasma spray 3-63
Plating 3-63
Plenum chamber 3-11
Plug fouling, igniter 11-10
Plug, exhaust 3-45
Plug, igniter 3-32, 11-1, 11-8
Plug, shunted-gap (igniter) 11-5, 11-7
Pneumatic actuating, reverser 3-51
Pneumatic computing, fuel control 7-10
Pneumatic fire protection 13-3
Pneumatic start 3-10, 10-4
Pointer yoke, RPM indicator 12-13
Pollutants, combustion 3-34
Positive displacement pump 7-43
Positive sump (oil system) 12-28
Post-exit position, reverser 3-52
Potential energy 2-14, 3-10
Pour point, oil 6-1
Powder metallurgy 3-64
Power back procedure 3-51
Power check, engine 14-2
Power gearbox, Allison-250 4-34
Power Jets, Ltd. 1-3
Power lever 7-1, 8-2, 14-1
Power management system 7-23
Power output comparisons 2-5
Power setting, takeoff 7-39
Power to weight ratio 2-6, 3-64
Power turbine (N_2) governor 7-12
Power turbine 7-12
Power turbine limiting 7-14
Power turbine section 2-6
Power turbine, Allison-250 4-30
Power turbine, PT6 4-39
Power unit, auxiliary 7-24, 10-10
Power unit, ground 7-24, 10-4, 14-3
Power, cruise 7-4
Power, definition 2-12
Power, reactive 2-20, 3-35
Power, shaft 3-35
Power, takeoff 7-29, Appendix 6
Power, total 2-7
Pratt & Whitney Company 7-8, 3-29, 4-1
Pratt & Whitney JT-12 7-59
Pratt & Whitney JT-12 fuel system 7-59
Pratt & Whitney JT-15D 3-33

Pratt & Whitney JT8D bleed system 8-7, 8-12
Pratt & Whitney JT8D engine design 4-1
Pratt & Whitney JT8D fuel system 7-59
Pratt & Whitney JT8D lubrication 6-30
Pratt & Whitney PT6 engine operation 14-3
Pratt & Whitney PT6 lubrication 6-29
Pratt & Whitney PT6 turboprop 4-34, 11-9
Pratt & Whitney PW-4000 2-9
Precombustor chamber 3-34
Pre-exit position, reverser 3-52
Pressure correction factor, run checks 5-47
Pressure correction, tables Appendix 9
Pressure cycle, constant 2-18
Pressure differential, fuel 7-8
Pressure ratio 2-8, 3-3
Pressure ratio bleed control 8-7
Pressure ratio per stage 3-3
Pressure subsystem, JT8D (oil) 6-31
Pressure subsystem, PT6 oil 6-30
Pressure thrust 2-22, 3-50, 2-22
Pressure, absolute 3-14
Pressure, ambient 2-18, 3-2
Pressure, atmospheric 2-16
Pressure, back (trimming) 7-32
Pressure, back 3-26
Pressure, barometric 7-29
Pressure, bearing compartment 5-37
Pressure, burner 7-6
Pressure, combustion 3-32
Pressure, compressor discharge 3-51
Pressure, compressor inlet 3-19, 7-29
Pressure, compressor inlet total 3-19, 12-15
Pressure, compressor ratio 3-19, 7-6, 8-2
Pressure, cracking (oil) 6-22
Pressure, definition 2-16
Pressure, differential 6-22
Pressure, downstream (turbine) 3-38
Pressure, engine ratio 7-28
Pressure, exhaust duct 3-49
Pressure, exhaust nozzle 3-47
Pressure, exit (turbine) 3-20
Pressure, fuel 7-10, 8-2
Pressure, fuel control discharge 8-2
Pressure, governor bellows (fuel) 7-10
Pressure, inlet 3-2, 7-6
Pressure, low compressor discharge 8-12
Pressure, low fuel 7-50
Pressure, metered fuel 7-9
Pressure, oil 6-17, 12-28
Pressure, pump 6-9, 7-14, 12-1
Pressure, ram 2-16, 3-2
Pressure, stagnation 3-4
Pressure, static 2-1, 3-2
Pressure, torque 12-20
Pressure, torque oil 12-20
Pressure, total 2-16, 3-3, 7-19, 12-15
Pressure, turbine discharge 3-46, 7-29
Pressure, turbine discharge total 12-15
Pressure, vent system (oil) 6-29
Pressure-atomizing nozzle, fuel 7-51
Pressurization, cabin 3-10
Pressurized air 7-24
Pressurizing and dump valve 7-56
Primary air 3-31, 7-5
Primary airfoil 3-62
Primary coil, ignition 11-4
Primary combustor airflow 7-6
Primary creep, blades 5-30
Primary fuel 7-53
Primary load, bearings 5-33

PRIST® 7-2
Probe, icing 9-3
Probe, temperature 12-2
Procedures, low oil pressure 6-37
Profile blade 3-18
Profiling 3-18
Propeller efficiency 2-27
Propeller governor 7-12
Propeller reduction gearbox, PT6 4-43
Propeller thrust 2-19
Propeller, full reversing 3-56
Propfan 2-7
Propfan, ultrahigh bypass 3-21
Propulsion, jet 9-45
Propulsive efficiency 2-29, 3-21, 7-3
Propulsive efficiency formula 2-29
Propulsive power 3-50
Protection, ear 7-34
P_{S3} pressure 8-10
P_{S4} pressure 8-2, 8-10
Pt_2 pressure 8-10
Pt_2 probe 9-3
PT6 engine design 4-34
PT6 fuel control 7-9
PT6 lubrication 6-29
Pulsed chip detector 6-27
Pulse-jet 2-1
Pump output pressure 6-18
Pump pressure (P1) 7-9
Pump, booster 7-9
Pump, constant displacement 6-10
Pump, fuel 7-9
Pump, gear 6-12
Pump, gerotor 6-10
Pump, oil 6-9
Pump, positive displacement 6-10, 7-9
Pump, scavenge 6-30
Pump, vane 6-10

R

Radial airflow, compressor 3-31
Radial inflow turbine 3-45
Radial loading, bearings 5-33
Radial out-flow compressor 3-10
Radiographic inspection 5-14
Ram air, ventilation 3-60
Ram compression 2-35, 3-3
Ram drag (Fd) 2-22, 3-51
Ram effect 1-2, 3-4, 12-7
Ram pressure 2-6, 3-19
Ram pressure ratio 3-3
Ram pressure recovery 3-2
Ram pressure, inlet 3-49
Ram shaft horsepower 2-29
Ramjet 2-1
Rate of descent 3-51
Rate, leakage 3-10
Rate, spark (ignition) 11-6
Rated power 11-3
Rated speed 7-24
Rated thrust 2-23, 3-5, 5-5, 7-28
Rating, delta-p (oil bypass) 6-15
Rating, engine power 14-6
Rating, flat (engine) 7-35
Rating, flat 7-35
Rating, maximum continuous 14-7
Rating, maximum cruise 14-7
Rating, micron 6-13
Rating, thrust 7-3
Ratio, air-fuel 7-9

Ratio, air-water (water injection) 7-41
Ratio, aspect (blades) 3-16
Ratio, compression 2-32, 3-18
Ratio, compressor pressure 2-8, 3-18, 8-2
Ratio, engine compression 3-47
Ratio, engine pressure 3-47, 5-53, 7-29, 8-7, 9-3
Ratio, fan bypass 2-7, 3-20
Ratio, fan compression 3-20
Ratio, fan pressure 3-20
Ratio, fuel consumption 7-35
Ratio, inlet compression 3-3
Ratio, power-to-weight 3-64
Ratio, pressure 3-3
Ratio, pressure per stage 3-3
Ratio, ram pressure 3-3
Ratio, specific heat 2-28
Ratio, thrust 2-9
Ratio, variable-bypass 2-10
Ratio, weight-to-power 2-2
Reaction principle 1-1
Reactive power 2-20
Reactive thrust 2-1, 2-31
Rearward thrust 3-52
Rearward velocity 3-54
Recovery, ram pressure 3-2
Rectifier, half-wave (ignition) 11-4
Rectifier, ignition 11-4
Red-Dye inspection 5-12
Reduced smoke combustor 3-31
Reduction gearbox 2-7, 7-39
Reduction gearing 2-2
Reference, directional 3-67
Regulator valve, anti-ice 9-3
Regulator, differential metering 7-14
Regulator, differential pressure 7-17
Re-light 14-5
Remanufacturing facility 5-8
Repair, cold section 5-15
Repair, hot section 5-22
Resistance bulb 12-27
Resistance coil, ignition 11-5
Resistance, corrosion 3-62
Resistor, bleed (ignition) 11-5
Resonance 5-31
Restart 7-1
Restrictions, trim 7-32
Return fuel (P_O) 7-10
Reverse flow annular combustor 3-30
Reverse thrust 3-52
Reverse, blade 3-56
Reverse-idle 3-53
Reverser, cascade 3-52
Reverser, clamshell 3-52
Reverser, cold stream 3-56
Reverser, hot stream 3-56
Reverser, thrust 3-52
Reverse-throttle 3-56
Reversing propeller 3-56
Revolutions per minute, compressor 3-14
Revolutions per minute, effect on thrust 2-33
Revolutions per minute, thrust limits 2-36
Rich blowout 7-1
Rich flame-out 3-32
Rich fuel mix 10-3
Rim, rotating 3-39
Ring liner 3-34
Ring, shock 3-50
Ring, shroud 3-62
Rippling 5-28
Rocket 1-1, 2-1

Rockwell Sabreliner 7-59
Roller bearings 5-33
Rolls Royce Company 1-8
Rolls Royce Dart 3-32
Rolls Royce Olympus 1-7, 2-28, 7-56
Rolls Royce RB-211 7-16
Rotary air-oil separator 6-29
Rotating rim 3-39
Rotor blade 3-23, 8-1
Rotor, compressor 3-11
Rotor, thermatic compressor 3-29
Rotor, turbine 3-35
Run, dry motoring 14-4
Run, starting control 7-12
Rundown, engine 7-12
Run-up 7-26, 14-1
Run-up, ground 14-4

S

Safety wiring 5-44
Safety, engine operation 14-1
Safety, fuel 7-2
Safety, ignition system 11-3
Sampling, oil 6-2
Sand separator 3-6
Saybolt Universal Seconds (S.U.S.) Viscosimeter 6-2
Saybolt Universal Viscosity 6-2
Saybolt viscosimeter 6-2
Scaling 3-63
Scavenge oil 3-10, 5-37, 6-35
Scavenge pump 6-35
Scavenge subsystem 6-33
Scavenge subsystem, General Electric CJ610 6-26
Scavenge subsystem, JT8D 6-33
Scavenge subsystem, PT6 6-30
Schematic, fuel control 7-6
Scoring 5-41, 5-59
Scram-jet 2-1
Seal erosion, turbine 5-56
Seal race, oil seal 5-37
Seal, bearing 5-36, 12-28
Seal, knife-edged 3-18
Seal, labyrinth 6-15
Secondary air 3-31
Secondary coil, ignition 11-5
Secondary creep, blades 5-30
Secondary fuel 7-59
Seizure 5-59
Sensing, torque 12-20
Sensor, speed 10-1
Sensor, temperature (fuel scheduling) 7-6
Separation, airflow (compressor) 6-29
Separator, air-oil 6-21
Separator, ice 3-6
Separator, sand 3-6
Sermetal® 5-19
Service interval, oil 6-7
Service life, engine components 5-50
Servicing, oil system 6-5
Setting, climb 14-5
Setting, cruise 14-5
Shaft horsepower (shp) 2-28, 7-37
Shaft, dual coaxial 3-41
Shaft, splined (turbine) 3-41
Shaft, torsion (torquemeter) 12-20
Shear point, drive shaft (starter) 10-8
Shift, burner-can 5-24
Shift, phase (torquemeter) 12-20

Shock distortion, airflow 3-50
Shock formation, impellers 3-4
Shock ring, afterburner 3-50
Shock stall, blade tips 2-36, 3-29
Shock wave, airflow 3-50
Shock, sonic 3-23
Shock, thermal 13-6
Shop maintenance 5-8
Shroud ring, turbine 3-38
Shroud seal, turbine 3-43
Shroud strip, compressor 3-18
Shroud, support (fan blades) 3-20
Shrouded tip, blades 3-42
Shunted-gap plug, igniter 11-5
Shutdown, engine 14-2
Sieve number, filters 7-50
Signals, hand Appendix 5
Silicon, in oil 6-3
Silicone contamination 6-5
Simplex fuel nozzle 7-51
Single crystal casting 3-63
Single sided impeller 3-11
Single-line duplex fuel nozzle 7-53
Single-spool compressor 3-14
Single-wire thermal switch 13-1
Size, drill Appendix 3
Slip torque, starter 10-4
Smoke detector 13-6
Sodium, protection against 3-63
Solenoid, fuel 7-25
Solid state ignition systems 11-16
Sonic shock 3-23
Sonic velocity, exhaust 3-49
Sound emission 3-57
Sound, frequency 3-57
Sound, speed of 2-37
Space shuttle 2-1
Spalling 5-41, 5-59
Span-shroud 3-17
Spark igniter 11-8
Spark rate 11-6
Specific gravity 7-10, 12-25
Specific gravity adjustment 7-26
Specific heat ratio (C_p) 2-28
Specific total resistance 12-2
Spectrometer, oil 6-3
Spectrometric oil analysis 6-3
Speed check, data plate 7-31
Speed of sound 2-37, Appendix 6
Speed rated engine 12-15
Speed scheduling 7-10
Speed sensor 10-1
Speed trim 7-29
Speed, aircraft 2-25, 3-51
Speed, blade tip 3-14
Speed, burst 10-8
Speed, definition 2-13
Speed, engine 7-6, 12-15
Speed, ground idle 3-53
Speed, idle 7-12, 10-12
Speed, N_1 5-53, 12-13
Speed, N_2 3-56, 5-53, 12-13
Speed, rated 7-24
Speed, tachometer 12-13
Speed, tip 3-11
Speed-rated engine 7-31
Spill valve, inlet 3-4
Splined shaft, turbine 3-41
Split inner race, bearing 5-34
Spoiler, thrust 3-56
Sprague clutch, starter 10-8

Spray bars, fuel 3-50
Spray, plasma 3-63
Spring-back, power lever 7-28
Stagger angle, blading 3-16
Stagger torquing, bolts 5-44
Stagnation pressure, inlet 3-4
Stainless steel 3-62
Stall curve, variable vane 8-2
Stall margin, compressor 3-26
Stall, compressor (bleed systems) 9-1
Stall, compressor 3-28, 9-3
Stall, hung 3-26
Stall, shock 2-36, 3-29
Stall, tip shock 2-29
Stall, transient 3-26
Standard Day Condition 2-21, 5-47
Start engine 14-1
Start, air 14-2
Start, cold weather 6-15
Start, engine 7-12, 14-4
Start, failure 14-2
Start, ground 11-1, 14-2
Start, hot 10-1, 14-2
Start, hung 10-1
Starter systems 10-1
Starter, air 10-12
Starter, cartridge-pneumatic 10-12
Starter, electric 10-3
Starter, fuel-air combustion 10-12
Starter, high-low pressure pneumatic 10-12
Starter, hydraulic 10-12
Starter, pneumatic 10-8
Starter-generator 10-6
Starting flow control 7-12
Starting limits 12-7
Starting procedure 10-10
Starting sequence 10-2
Starting, cross-bleed 10-12
Starting, pneumatic 3-10, 10-10
Starting, turbine impingement 10-12
Static pressure (P_S) 3-19
Static pressure 2-16, 3-19
Static tube 2-16
Station number 3-64
Station, engine 3-64, 4-17, 12-15
Stator vane 3-16, 3-17
Stator, turbine 3-35
Steel, stainless 3-62
Storage capacitor, ignition 11-5
Stream, exhaust 3-56
Strength, film (oil) 6-1
Stress rupture crack 5-28
Stress, intergranular 5-31
Stress, tensile 3-62
Stress, thermal 3-62, 5-30
Stress, vibratory 3-62
Subsonic axial flow 3-28
Subsonic inlet 3-2
Sulfidation, turbine 5-5
Sulfur, protection against 3-62
Sump, bearing 5-37, 12-28
Sump, dry 6-8
Sump, gearbox 6-9
Sump, integral dry 6-31
Sump, negative 12-28
Sump, oil 3-53
Sump, positive 12-28
Sump, wet 6-7, 10-12
Super alloy 3-62
Supersonic diffuser 3-4
Supersonic flow 3-50

Support strut, tail cone 3-47
Suppression, noise 3-56
Surface erosion 3-62
Surface film cooling, turbine 3-43
Surge-stall zone 3-26
Swirl vane, combustion liner 3-31
Switch, thermal 13-1
Synchronous mass flow flowmeter 12-25
Synthetic lubricants 6-4

T

Tab, lock 5-47
Tachometer indicator 9-3
Tachometer marking 12-34
Tachometer percent rpm indicating system 12-13
Tachometer, dual 12-34
Tachometer, gas producer 12-34
Tail cone 3-45
Tailpipe 3-45
Tailpipe outlet 2-25
Tailpipe, convergent-divergent 3-49
Takeoff 14-7
Takeoff dry thrust/SHP 14-6
Takeoff power 7-29, 14-4
Takeoff power setting 7-39
Takeoff thrust 1-5
Takeoff wet thrust/SHP 14-6
Takeoff, dry 14-6
Tangential velocity (turbine) 3-37
Tank, oil 6-8
Taper, compressor design 3-24
Tapered annulus, compressor 3-24
Tapered roll bearings 5-33
Taxi procedure 14-2
Temperature conversion Appendix 3
Temperature correction Appendix 9
Temperature correction factor 5-47
Temperature limit, materials 3-62
Temperature lockout, oil filter 6-21
Temperature probe (EGT) 12-4
Temperature rise (Tr), compressor 2-28
Temperature sensor, fuel control 7-6
Temperature, air 2-33, 9-1
Temperature, ambient 2-34, 3-15, 7-41, 8-2, 12-7
Temperature, combustor 2-18
Temperature, compression 2-32
Temperature, compressor inlet 8-2
Temperature, conversion Appendix 3
Temperature, correction Appendix 9
Temperature, definition 2-10
Temperature, exhaust 12-7
Temperature, exhaust gas 3-26, 5-53, 10-12, 12-2
Temperature, fan discharge 8-12
Temperature, fuel 7-10, 12-25
Temperature, ignition 3-30
Temperature, interstage turbine 12-1
Temperature, oil 6-23, 12-1, 12-27
Temperature, outside air 2-33
Temperature, total 12-2
Temperature, turbine inlet 2-32, 3-43, 7-3, 12-2
Temperature, turbine outlet 12-2
Tension loading 5-26
Tertiary creep 15-30
Test bed 5-45
Test cell maintenance 5-45
Test, ground 3-5

Testing, nondestructive 5-10
T-handle start 10-9
Theory, jet propulsion 9-45
Thermal barrier coating 3-63
Thermal conductivity, materials 3-62
Thermal cycling, oil filters 6-15
Thermal efficiency 2-32, 3-18
Thermal expansion 3-43
Thermal lockout, oil filter 6-21
Thermal shock, during cleaning 13-8
Thermal stress, turbine 5-30
Thermal switch loop 13-1
Thermal switch, single-wire 13-1
Thermal switch, two-wire 13-2
Thermatic Compressor Rotor® 3-29
Thermistor, fire detector 3-29
Thermocouple 12-2
Thermodynamic cycle, continuous 2-18
Thermodynamic horsepower 2-28
Thermostat, acceleration 7-25
Thermostat, overload 7-25
Theta (Θ) 5-47
Three-phase generator, percent RPM 12-13
Throat flow, C-D nozzle 3-49
Throttle cushion check 7-28
Through-flow combustor 3-30
Thrust 2-1
Thrust augmentation 3-50, 7-39
Thrust braking, reverser 3-51
Thrust calculations 2-21
Thrust distribution 2-23, 3-54
Thrust force 2-4
Thrust horsepower (THP) 2-25
Thrust indicator marking 12-34
Thrust loading, bearings 5-33
Thrust performance 5-47
Thrust ratio 2-9
Thrust reverser 3-51
Thrust setting, examples 7-4
Thrust specific fuel consumption (TSFC) 7-3
Thrust spoiler 3-56
Thrust, afterburner 3-50
Thrust, continuous 7-4
Thrust, engine 3-50, 7-17
Thrust, exhaust 2-7
Thrust, factors affecting 2-33
Thrust, fan engine 2-25
Thrust, flight 7-4
Thrust, gross 2-21, 3-51
Thrust, hot 2-28
Thrust, humidity factor 2-25
Thrust, maximum 2-37, 7-28
Thrust, maximum climb 14-6
Thrust, maximum continuous 14-6
Thrust, maximum cruise 14-6
Thrust, net 2-22, 3-51
Thrust, pressure 2-12, 3-50
Thrust, propeller 2-19
Thrust, rated 2-23, 5-49, 7-28
Thrust, reactive 2-31
Thrust, reverse 3-51
Thrust, reverse 3-51
Thrust, static 2-21
Thrust, takeoff 1-6, 14-6
Thrust, total 2-22
Thrust, turbine 2-20
Thrust, water injection 7-39
Time between overhaul (TBO) 5-50
Time since overhaul (TSO) 5-50
Tip clearance 3-43
Tip leakage 3-18

Tip loading 3-42
Tip loss 3-42
Tip shock 3-18
Tip speed 2-36, 3-14
Tip vibration 3-18
Tip, fan 3-18
Tip, flat-machine 3-17
Tip, profile 3-17
Tip, shrouded 3-18
Tip, squeeler 3-17
Tip, vortex 3-18
Titanium 3-62
Torque arm force 3-40
Torque gauge 2-26, 7-39
Torque indicating system 12-20
Torque indicator 7-39
Torque indicator marking 12-33
Torque limits 12-21
Torque load, engine mounts 3-60
Torque oil pressure 12-21
Torque percent 12-20
Torque pounds per square inch–gauge 7-39
Torque pressure 12-20
Torque procedure 5-41
Torque producing engine 7-35
Torque sensing mechanism 12-20
Torque tube 7-10
Torque wrench 5-41
Torque, electronic 12-21
Torque, hydro-mechanical 12-20
Torque, indicated 5-43
Torque, slip 10-4
Torquemeter 7-35
Torsion shaft 12-20
Total airflow 7-6
Total compression 3-20
Total power 2-7
Total pressure (Pt) 2-15, 3-30, 7-19, 12-15
Total temperature 12-2
Total thrust 2-22, 7-3
Transducer, vibration 5-47
Transformer, ignition 11-1
Transient stall, compressor 3-26
Transistor, ignition 11-6
Transmitter, Autosyn (EPR) 12-18
Transmitter, fuel flow 12-25
Transonic velocity, compressor 3-28
Trend analysis, flight data 5-50, 6-3
Trend analysis, oil 6-3
Triflorobromomethane (CF₃Br) 13-6
Trim check 7-28
Trim danger zone 7-34
Trim procedure 7-28
Trim restrictions 7-32
Trim, engine pressure ratio 7-29
Trim, fan speed 7-29
Trim, full power 7-30
Trim, part power 7-30
Trim, speed 7-31
Trim, speed rated engine 7-29
Trimming 7-30, 14-1
Triple-spool compressor 3-16
Trip-over, fire detector 13-2
Troubleshooting sequence 5-53
Troubleshooting, anti-ice system 9-5
Troubleshooting, compressor bleed 8-12
Troubleshooting, EGT/ITT indicators 12-10
Troubleshooting, EPR indicator 12-18
Troubleshooting, fuel flowmeter 12-27
Troubleshooting, fuel systems 7-63
Troubleshooting, ground 5-53

Troubleshooting, ignition systems 11-17
Troubleshooting, in-flight data 5-53
Troubleshooting, lubrication 6-37
Troubleshooting, oil system 12-32
Troubleshooting, starter systems 10-16
Troubleshooting, tachometer indicator 12-15
Troubleshooting, torque indicating 12-22
Troubleshooting, variable vane 8-5
True air temperature 9-2
Tt₂ sensor 8-2
Tube, bourdon 12-28
Tube, cathode ray 12-1
Tube, flame propagation 3-32
Tube, torque 7-10
Tuning, blade frequency 3-17
Turbine case 3-43, 5-30
Turbine discharge pressure 3-46, 7-29
Turbine discharge total pressure 12-1
Turbine disk 3-64
Turbine efficiency 3-26, 5-56
Turbine engine development 1-1
Turbine governor 7-9
Turbine impingement starting 10-12
Turbine inlet temperature (T1T) 2-32
Turbine inspection 5-1
Turbine maintenance 5-1
Turbine oils 6-1
Turbine outlet temperature (TOT) 12-2
Turbine rotor 3-35
Turbine section 3-35, 5-26
Turbine section malfunction 5-56
Turbine sulfidation 5-5
Turbine vs. piston performance 2-2
Turbine wheel 3-35, 5-26, 7-3
Turbine wheel balance 5-26
Turbine wheel efficiency 3-43
Turbine, axial 3-41
Turbine, case 5-30
Turbine, counter-rotating 3-43
Turbine, fixed 2-7, 12-20
Turbine, free 2-7, 12-20
Turbine, N₁ 3-42
Turbine, N₂ 3-42
Turbine, power 7-30
Turbine, radial inflow 3-43
Turbine-airscrew 1-4
Turbo fuel 5 7-1
Turbo fuel A 7-1
Turbo fuel A-1 7-1
Turbo fuel B 7-2
Turbofan 1-4, 2-8, 3-2, 7-3, 14-1
Turbofan efficiency 7-3
Turbofan, dual compressor 2-19
Turbofan, dual spool 2-28
Turbofan, fully ducted 3-2
Turbofan, high bypass 2-9, 3-2
Turbofan, replacing turbojet 2-37
Turbofan, ultra high bypass 2-10, 3-2
Turbojet 1-5, 2-37, 3-2, 7-3, 14-1
Turbojet, turbofan replacement 2-6
Turboprop 1-4, 2-7, 7-3, 14-2
Turboshaft 2-6, 3-11
Turbulence, air 3-18
Turbulence, eddy (exhaust) 3-58
Turbulence, fine grain (exhaust) 3-58
Turbulence, vortex 3-32
Turning vane, reverser 3-52
Two-wire thermal switch 13-1
Type Certificate Data Sheet 14-6
Type-1 lubricant 6-5
Type-2 lubricant 6-5
Type-3 lubricants 6-33

U

UDF engine 1-8
Ultra high bypass fan (UHB) 2-10, 3-21
Ultrasonic cleaning 6-16
Ultrasonic inspection 5-15
Under speed condition, flyweights 7-8
Under-race lubrication, bearings 6-26
Unducted fan engine (UDF) 1-8
Units, mass 2-19
Unlimited heavy maintenance 5-8
Untwist, blades 5-28
U.S. standard atmosphere Appendix 7

V

V1 pulsejet 1-4
V-1 pulsejet 1-4
V-1 rocket 2-1
V-2 rocket 2-1
Value, centistoke 6-2
Valve, combustor drain 7-59
Valve, enrichment (fuel) 7-10
Valve, fuel dump 7-56
Valve, fuel enrichment 7-10
Valve, fuel pressurizing and dump 7-56
Valve, governor (fuel) 7-10
Valve, metering (fuel) 7-14
Valve, oil bypass 6-14
Valve, regulator (anti-ice) 9-2
Valve, relief (fuel) 7-10
Valve, spill (air inlet) 3-4
Valve, vent pressurizing (oil system) 6-29
Vane pump, oil 6-10
Vane, inlet guide 3-18, 8-1
Vane, stator 3-18, 5-22, 8-1
Vane, swirl (combustor) 3-31
Vane, turning (reverser) 3-52
Vane, variable (compressor) 8-1
Vane-type flow meter system 12-25
Vapor lock, fuel system 7-1
Vaporizing fuel nozzle 7-55

Variable vane actuating system,
    compressor 8-1
Variable vane schedule, compressor 8-2
Variable vane, compressor 8-1
Variable-bypass ratio 2-10
Variable-geometry inlet 3-4
Vector force, airflow 3-56
Vector, analysis of air flow 3-56
Vector, velocity (airflow) 3-56
Vector, velocity 3-56
Vectoring exhaust nozzle 3-51
Velocity of mass flow 3-35
Velocity vector 3-56
Velocity vector, airflow 3-56
Velocity, angular (turbine) 3-38
Velocity, axial 2-16, 3-38, 8-1
Velocity, definition 2-13
Velocity, exhaust 2-18, 3-50, 7-3
Velocity, exit (compressor) 3-21
Velocity, gas (exhaust) 3-49
Velocity, inlet 3-21
Velocity, sonic 3-49
Velocity, tangential (turbine) 3-37
Velocity, transonic (compressor) 3-28
Vent pressurizing valve, oil 6-29
Vent subsystem, GE CJ610 6-28
Vent subsystem, JT8D 6-33
Vent subsystem, PT6 6-30
Vibrating load, ceramics 3-64
Vibration 2-5
Vibration damping, blade tips 3-17
Vibration transducer 5-47
Vibration, compressor blade tip 3-17
Vibration, engine 5-31, 12-1
Vickers Viscount 1-6
Viscosimeter 6-2
Viscosity, oil 6-2
Viscount, Vickers 1-6
Volatility, oil 6-1
Von Ohain, Hans 1-5
Vortex tip, compressor blades 3-18
Vortex turbulence, combustor 3-32
V-STOL 3-51

W

Warning light, delta-p (oil) 6-19
Warning light, filter bypass (oil) 6-19
Warning light, metallic chip (oil) 6-26
Warning light, oil pressure 6-20
Wash, desalination 5-5
Wash, performance recovery 5-5
Washer, lock 5-47
Water contamination, compressor 5-54
Water detection, fuel 7-1
Water injection fluids 7-41
Water injection thrust 7-40
Water, entrained (fuel) 7-1
Wave, shock 3-50
Wear metals, oil 6-4
Weight, definition 2-10
Weight-to-power ratio, engine 2-2
Welding, electron beam 5-17
Westinghouse J-34 7-3
Wet sump 6-7
Wet sump, oil system 6-7, 10-12
Wheatstone bridge, EGT check 12-10
Wheel, turbine 3-35
Whittle turbojet 2-6
Whittle, Frank 1-2, 2-6
Windmilling 11-2
Wiring, lock 5-44
Wiring, safety 5-44
Work, definition 2-12
Woven wire filter, oil 6-15
Wrench, torque 5-41

Y

Yoke, pointer (percent RPM) 12-14

Z

Zone, combustion 7-5
Zone, flame 3-30
Zone, surge-stall 3-26

Aviation Maintenance Training

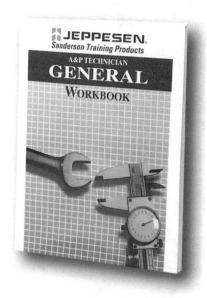

A&P Technician General Workbook

Contains questions covering the general section of aviation technician training. It is designed to be used with the A&P technician general textbook. Answer key bound into back of workbook. ISBN# 0-88487-212-2. 204 pages.

Item Number JS322710 $12.95

A&P Technician General Test Guide

An excellent, self-contained study program. Provides coverage of key points required to answer the FAA's computerized test questions. Also includes: a reprint of the FAA's computerized test questions, answers, explanations and references. Each question is page referenced for easy study. ISBN# 0-88487-204-1.

168 pages.

Item Number JS312691 $12.95

FAR Handbook For Aviation Maintenance Technicians

Contains the most current and easy-to-use FAR information available. Updated annually to include all changes published by the FAA in the previous year, the changes are identified to make them easy to find. The handbook contains only those FAR parts which are pertinent to an aviation maintenance technician: 1, 13, 21, 23, 27, 33, 34, 35, 39, 43, 45, 47, 65, 91, 119, 125, 135, 145, 147, 183 as well as applicable SFARS.

As an added bonus, each book contains a copy of applicable Advisory Circulars including: AC 20-62, AC 20-109, AC 21-12, AC 39-7, AC 43-9, AC 43.9-1, AC 65-11, and AC 65-19G, Inspection Authorization Study Guide. ISBN# 0-88487-200-9.

Item Number JS312616 $19.95

Visit your Jeppesen Dealer or Call 1-800-621-JEPP

Prices subject to change

Special Interest Reference Books

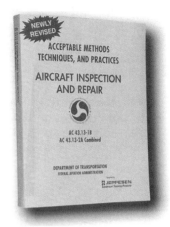

Acceptable Methods, Techniques and Practices/Aircraft Alterations

A newly revised FAA reprint, this is the "bible" of aircraft maintenance. It is a combined edition of both the AC 43.13-1B and -2A series handbooks that establish the standards for inspection, repair and alterations. ISBN# 0-89100-306-1. 768 pages.

Item Number JS312617 $19.95

Best Of AMJ Maintenance Tips

The best of the Aviation Mechanics Journal's popular "Maintenance Tips". These "tips" from the "pros" in the field will help you to do things better, faster and easier. ISBN# 0-89100-341-X. 184 pages.

Item Number JS312629 $13.95

Standard Aviation Maintenance Handbook

Hundreds of the most commonly-used charts, diagrams, scales and measurements for aviation maintenance personnel in a "tool box"-sized, spiral-bound reference guide. ISBN# 0000-89100-282-0. 240 pages.

Item Number JS312624 $13.95

Aircraft Technical Dictionary (3rd Edition)

Updated and expanded. The best way to learn the aviation maintenance language. ISBN# 0-89100-410-6.
504 pages.

Item Number JS312625 $14.95

JEPPESEN REFERENCE MATERIALS

AVIATION WEATHER 2ND EDITION

The most comprehensive, award-winning aviation weather book just got better. New 480-page hard cover edition is extensively updated with the latest METAR, TAF, and Graphic Weather Products from AC00-45E, Aviation Weather Services. Full-color illustrations and photographs present detailed material in an uncomplicated way. International weather considerations are included as well as accident/incident information to add relevance to the weather data. Expanded coverage of icing, weather hazards, and flight planning. Review questions with answers at the end of the book. All new expanded appendices cover common conversions, weather reports, forecasts, and charts, as well as domestic and international METAR, TAF and graphic weather products. Completely revised Instructor's Guide available on CD-ROM (for flight school use only.)

ITEM NUMBER JS319010 $54.95
INSTRUCTORS GUIDE ON CD-ROM   ITEM NUMBER JS285320 $29.95

JEPPPREP

Now students can prepare for their FAA knowledge exams on the internet. With the purchase of JeppPrep, you will receive a 60-day period of unlimited study for a particular FAA knowledge exam. A renewal can be purchased for each additional 30-day period for an additional charge. JeppPrep contains the latest FAA questions taken from the FAA database, so it is always current. Pilots can take practice FAA exams and review their performance once the exams are scored

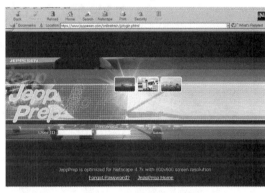

ITEM NUMBER WB100500 JeppPrep Initial Order $29.95
ITEM NUMBER WB100543 JeppPrep 30-day Renewal $19.95

AIRCRAFT SYSTEMS FOR PILOTS

The most comprehensive book available on aircraft systems as they relate to pilots and pilot training. All systems types are covered in detail. Contains excellent descriptions of aircraft systems for all pilots. ISBN#0-8487-214-9. 450 pages.

ITEM NUMBER JS312686 $28.95

TRANSPORT CATEGORY AIRCRAFT SYSTEMS

The only text available that covers FAR part 121 aircraft. A system-by-system approach to understanding jet transports. Includes systems coverage on the B-777 aircraft. Necessary for A&P students and pilots seeking at ATP license. ISBN#0-88487-232-7. 396 pages.

ITEM NUMBER JS312631 $31.95

INDIVIDUAL TRAINING BOOKS

AVIATION HISTORY BY JEPPESEN

Announcing an exciting new full-color book that gives both new and experienced pilots a unique perspective on international aviation history. Each of the ten chapters is packed with information, containing over 950 photographs and color illustrations to guide you through the birth of aviation in the 1700s to the recent record-setting flight of the Breitling Orbiter 3.

ITEM NUMBER JS319008 $69.95

FAR'S EXPLAINED

Jeppesen *FAR's Explained* has quickly become an industry standard. It helps answer the question, " I know what it says, but what does it mean?" Includes FAR Parts 1, 61, 91, 141, and NTSB 830. Recently updated and expanded.

ITEM NUMBER JS319012 $30.95

FAA REFERENCE HANDBOOKS

AVIATION INSTRUCTOR'S HANDBOOK

Supercedes AC 60-14. Contains fundamentals of instructing and extensive details on how to pass along aeronautical knowledge and skills to students.

ITEM NUMBER JS312802 $17.95

AIRPLANE FLYING HANDBOOK

Supercedes AC 61-21A. Introduces basic pilot skills and aeronautical knowledge to student pilots. It is beneficial for students and flight instructors who wish to improve their flying proficiency and aeronautical knowledge.

ITEM NUMBER JS312801 $9.95

ROTORCRAFT FLYING HANDBOOK

Supercedes AC 60-13B. Includes complete illustrated coverage of how to fly helicopters and gyroplanes. It provides authoritative technical information for applicants preparing for private, commercial and flight instructor pilot certificates with helicopter or gyroplane class ratings.

ITEM NUMBER JS312806 $16.95

AIRCRAFT WEIGHT & BALANCE HANDBOOK

Supercedes AC 91-23A. Provides AMT's with a method of determining the empty weight and empty-weight center of gravity (EWCG) of an aircraft and to furnish the basic crew with information on loading the aircraft within allowable limits.

ITEM NUMBER JS312800 $12.95

PILOT SUPPLIES

TECHSTAR PRO AND DATALINK

JEPPESEN'S "NEXT GENERATION" AVIATION COMPUTER

Jeppesen's innovative TechStar Pro is the first handheld flight computer and personal organizer. Combining the latest technology and ease of use, TechStar Pro gives you a 7-function aviation computer and an 8-function personal organizer. All-in-one compact handheld unit. Students to Airline Transport Pilots, use it in the cockpit, home, office or classroom.

TECHSTAR PRO
ITEM NUMBER JS505000 $89.95

Datalink sold separately.

TECHSTAR PRO DATALINK SOFTWARE AND CABLE

- Simple to use - Windows 3.1 or higher
- Backup data on your Techstar Pro
- Edit, add and delete records from your PC and then download the records
- Save time when inputting data

FUEL TESTER

The last fuel tester you'll ever need! Strong, clear butyrate plastic resists cracking, breaking and yellowing. Works with both pin and petcock actuators. Removable splash guard prevents fuel spillage and attaches to side for flat, slimline storage. Solid bronze rod actuator prevents breaking and pushing down. Measures 8.25" x 3.25" x 1".

FUEL TESTER ITEM NUMBER JS628855 $13.95

JEPPSHADES

IFR FLIP-UP TRAINING GLASSES

- Replaces bulky, hard-to-use instrument training hoods
- Improved design allows better student/instructor interaction
- Cockpit proven design works conveniently under headsets
- Universal adjusting strap reduces pressure on ears and temple
- Velcro™ strap fits comfortably under headsets • Flip-Up lens allows convenient IFR/VFR flight transition • High quality polycarbonate lens is impact resistant

JEPPSHADES ITEM NUMBER JS404311 $24.95

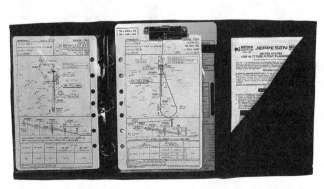

THREE-RING TRIFOLD KNEEBOARD

- Great for holding approach charts • Valuable IFR flight information on clipboard (also available separately) • Includes three approach chart pockets • Features collapsible rings • Elastic, pen/pencil and penlight holder • Includes Free U.S. Low Flight Planning Chart!
- Measures 10" x 20" open

KNEEBOARD/CLIPBOARD
ITEM NUMBER JS626010 $39.95

CLIPBOARD ONLY
ITEM NUMBER JS626011 $15.95

INTRODUCING JEPPESEN FLIGHT BAGS

THE CAPTAIN FLIGHT BAG

The Jeppesen *Captain Flight Bag* is the most versatile bag available. The headset bags can be removed and attached together to form a dual headset bag. The removable Transceiver/GPS bag can be worn on your belt. The flexible design allows you to add or subtract components to match your flying needs. The roomy interior has a 4-way custom divider that can hold four Jeppesen binders. An exterior zippered pocket provides a convenient storage space to help pilots organize their supplies. Two large zippered storage pockets can hold glasses, charts, pilot operating handbooks and other miscellaneous accessories. Carry your supplies in comfort with a wide cushioned shoulder strap. 12″x22¹/₂″x8″

THE CAPTAIN FLIGHT BAG (BLACK OR BLUE)
ITEM NUMBER JS621214 (BLACK) **$139.95**
ITEM NUMBER JS621251 (BLUE) **$139.95**

THE NAVIGATOR FLIGHT BAG

The *Navigator Flight Bag* includes all of the features and benefits of the Captain Flight Bag, except the removable Transceiver/GPS bag and the two zippered exterior storage pockets. Instead, it includes two exterior pockets for easy access to sectional and world aeronautical charts. 12″x22¹/₂″x8″

THE NAVIGATOR FLIGHT BAG (BLACK OR BLUE)
ITEM NUMBER JS621213 (BLACK) **$99.95**
ITEM NUMBER JS621250 (BLUE) **$99.95**

THE PROTECTOR HEADSET BAGS

The *Protector Headset Bags* are constructed of fully padded 600 denier poly for extra protection. Each bag comes with its own snap-on handle grip for comfort. Large enough to fit the ANR headsets (12″x2³/₄″x8″). Offered in both a single and dual configuration. Designed to fit the Core Captain Flight Bag.

THE PROTECTOR HEADSET BAGS (BLACK)
SINGLE JS621220 $17.95
DUAL JS621219 $35.95

THE STUDENT PILOT FLIGHT BAG

The *Student Pilot Flight Bag* is designed for new student pilots. Numerous outside pockets will organize charts, flight computer, fuel tester, plotter, pens and pencils, flashlight and much more. Additional features include a wide removable shoulder strap for comfort and a reinforced bottom. 10″x5¹/₂″x17″

THE STUDENT PILOT FLIGHT BAG (BLACK)
ITEM NUMBER JS621212 $41.95

NEW! THE AVIATOR BAG

The Aviator Bag is constructed of fully padded vynlon for extra durability. Each bag includes one headset bag and one Transceiver/GPS bag. The interior has a 2-way divider that can be used to separate your pilot accessories.

THE AVIATOR BAG (BLACK)
ITEM NUMBER JS621252 $79.95

VISIT YOUR JEPPESEN DEALER OR CALL 1-800-621-5377
MAKE SURE TO CHECK OUT OUR WEB PAGE AT HTTP://WWW.JEPPESEN.COM
PRICES SUBJECT TO CHANGE.